The Mental Health Act Commission

In Place of Fear?

**Eleventh Biennial Report
2003–2005**

London: **TSO**

Published by TSO (The Stationery Office) and available from:

Online
www.tsoshop.co.uk

Mail, Telephone, Fax & E-mail
TSO
PO Box 29, Norwich, NR3 1GN
Telephone orders/General enquiries: 0870 600 5522
Fax orders: 0870 600 5533
E-mail: book.orders@tso.co.uk
Textphone 0870 240 3701

TSO Shops
123 Kingsway, London, WC2B 6PQ
020 7242 6393 Fax 020 7242 6394
68-69 Bull Street, Birmingham B4 6AD
0121 236 9696 Fax 0121 236 9699
9-21 Princess Street, Manchester M60 8AS
0161 834 7201 Fax 0161 833 0634
16 Arthur Street, Belfast BT1 4GD
028 9023 8451 Fax 028 9023 5401
18-19 High Street, Cardiff CF10 1PT
029 2039 5548 Fax 029 2038 4347
71 Lothian Road, Edinburgh EH3 9AZ
0870 606 5566 Fax 0870 606 5588

TSO Accredited Agents
(see Yellow Pages)

and through good booksellers

Published with the permission of the Mental Health Act Commission on behalf of the Controller of Her Majesty's Stationery Office.

First published 2006

ISBN 0 11 322717 5

Mental Health Act Commission,
Maid Marian House,
56 Hounds Gate,
Nottingham,
NG1 6BG

Tel: 0115 943 7100

Email: chief.executive@mhac.org.uk

Printed in the United Kingdom for The Stationery Office

Acknowledgements

The principal author of this report was Mat Kinton of the MHAC Policy Unit.

We thank everybody who helped with the report's preparation. All responsibility for its content rests, of course, with the MHAC itself.

We are particularly grateful to the legal experts who agreed to act as readers of Chapter One and who kindly gave a day of their time to meet with us to discuss our shared ideas and concerns: Paul Barber (Bevan Brittan), Professor Peter Bartlett (Nottingham University), Christian Dingwall (Bevan Brittan), Prof K W M (Bill) Fulford (Warwick University), David Hewitt (Hempsons), John Horne (University of Northumbria), Andrew Parsons (Radcliffe-le-Brasseur), Robert Robinson, and Lucy Scott-Moncrieff (both Scott-Moncrieff, Harbour & Sinclair).

Prof R D Mackay (De Montfort University) and Dr Martin Humphreys (University of Birmingham) provided valuable comments as readers of Chapter Five of the report.

Inspector Bruce Frenchum, Chief Superintendent Dave Grant and their colleagues in the Metropolitan Police Service helpfully read and commented on parts of Chapter 4 where we discuss police business.

We are also grateful to Janey Antoniou, Prof Len Bowers, Les Carr, Chris Curran (Healthcare Commission), Emma Forrest (Health Service Journal), Lindsay Gee (Capsticks solicitors), Dr Dave Hambridge, Mike Hood, Adam Jones (MHRT), George Kappler (Mental Welfare Commission for Scotland), Simon Lawton-Smith (King's Fund), Yens Marsen-Luther (IMHAP), Dr Kevin Murray (North West London Mental Health NHS Trust), Glenn Palmer and colleagues at the Dept. of Health, Jane Scott, and Rick Tucker (NHS CFSMS).

A number of MHAC secretariat employees, Commissioners and Service User Reference Panel members helped with this report, including Simon Armson, Karen Carder, Elisa Cioffi, Nicola Couch, Dawn Cutler, Barbara Davis, Gul Davis, Suki Desai, Vicki Eley, Katherine Herzberg, Deborah Hickman, Richard Holmes, Trevor Howard, Phil Howes, Yasmin Jackson, Craig Jennings, Margaret Jessop, Steve Klein, Emma Laughton, Stephen Maloyd, Derek McCarthy, Sue McMillan, Abina Parshad-Griffin, Gemma Pearce, Ron Rushbrook, Kay Sheldon, Rose Sibley, Jo Simpson, Paramjit Thamu, Phil Wales, Angela Williams, and Stuart Wooding. A full list of Commissioners serving over this reporting period is at Appendix B: we are grateful for their general contribution.

Nelsons Solicitors, Nottingham, generously provided access to their legal library.

We are grateful to West London Mental Health NHS Trust for permission to use the cover image, which shows patients and staff on the terrace of Broadmoor Hospital in 1908. We chose the image primarily on the basis that we thought it was appropriate to picture detained psychiatric patients on the front of our report. We were also happy to discover an image that does not conform to the sinister clichés about the hospital.

We thank the managers and staff of hospitals and other authorities responsible for operating the 1983 Act, who have been so willing to co-operate with our work over past years, and the patients who meet with us on visits.

This report is dedicated to all patients who have been detained under the 1983 Act, and to the memory of Bob Bamlett (1939–2005) and Neville Lees OBE (1935–2004), Mental Health Act Commissioners, and Dr Stefano Olivieri (1947–2004), SOAD.

Contents

3   Future Directions

4   The Mental Health Act in Practice

9

Appendices

Chairman's Foreword

In Place of Fear?

The Mental Health Act Commission's Eleventh Biennial Report

When Aneurin Bevan wrote about the creation of the National Health Service he recognised that its role went deeper than the simple cure or management of illness, in that it also served to provide reassurance to *everybody* that they would receive appropriate and dignified care were they to fall ill. During this reporting period, recognition of this aspect of the NHS was given by the Secretary of State for Health, as we discuss in the introduction to this report. It may be argued that it is in this respect more than any other that mental health services have generally been the 'Cinderella' service within the NHS: mental health wards and their occupants are still feared by many, and many people with long-term serious mental health problems are not yet secure in the knowledge that the services that they will encounter at moments of acute need will be safe, welcoming or even appropriate places for their care and protection.

It is with this in mind that we have echoed the title of Bevan's 1952 book, *In Place of Fear*, in the title of this report. There are examples of mental health services across all security levels that provide their patients with dignified, humane and effective care, but there are also services where even the best efforts of staff (assuming that staff are motivated to make their best efforts) cannot overcome resource limitations relating to personnel or infrastructure. There are aspects of mental health law (particularly in relation to the rules concerning 'Nearest Relatives') that remain incompatible with human rights requirements several years after being condemned by the judiciary. The focus on 'dangerousness' as a criterion for compulsion in future mental health law threatens to undermine the work undertaken (including by Government itself) challenging the stigma of mental illness. The spectre of preventive detention without clinical justification continues to haunt proposals for 'reform' of mental health law. Black and minority ethnic patients' disproportionate detention within mental health services lead to the 'circles of fear' whereby people are discouraged from approaching services for help with their mental disorder at an early stage. Staff and patients fear violent behaviour in many services. Developments in the criminal law continue to extend mandatory sentencing and threaten to undermine policies of diverting mentally disordered offenders from prison, whilst definitions of legal culpability remain rooted in Victorian approaches to 'insanity'. If we need to look around for areas where we can work to put patient care in place of fear, these are the obvious starting points.

In my foreword to the Tenth Biennial Report, I highlighted the significant shifts in mental health law being established through the courts as a result of challenges largely, although not exclusively, resulting from the 1998 Human Rights Act's incorporation of the European Convention on Human Rights into domestic law. There continues to be a high volume of case-law relating to the Mental Health Act 1983, much of it engaging ECHR principles, and we continue to hear practitioners complain that it is difficult to keep up to date with the current status of the law. This report gives considerable space to discussion of cases in and subsequent to our reporting period (the financial years 2003/04 and 2004/05).

As this report was being prepared for press, two significant decisions of the House of Lord's Appellate Committee were announced that have disappointed some legal and human-rights practitioners. In the *Munjaz* case, the Lords reversed the 2003 ruling which had declared policy-level departures from the Code of Practice unlawful. In the case of *MH*, a declaration of incompatibility regarding rights of appeal against detention for mentally incapacitated patients was struck out. In both cases, which are discussed in this report[1], the Secretary of State intervened in the courts to have decisions which could have increased patient protection overturned.

Our disappointments over the Government's actions in opposing court decisions that could have been of benefit to patients is compounded with some frustration at Government's approach to using its central authority to impose minimum legal standards and enforce human rights based practice (see this report on issues of regulating seclusion practice below). However, this sense of frustration is tempered by evidence that Government is willing to seek to address resource issues and to engage with specific equality issues:

- In common with all other mental health agencies, we are extremely pleased that an extra £130 million investment for the mental health services' estate was announced in October 2005, alongside a pledge to provide all mental health Trusts with an appropriate place of safety[2]. We hope that this is the beginning of a refocus on the problems of inpatient environments and services, of which this report provides significant account.

- We are very grateful to Ministers for their personal support for *Count Me In*, the National Mental Health and Ethnicity Census 2005, the summary report from which is due for publication at roughly the same time as this report. We are especially pleased at the ongoing commitment to continue the census in forthcoming years so as to establish a good baseline of data relating to the use of mental health services, and as a basis of initiatives to address the disproportionate representation of Black and minority ethnic patients in the detained psychiatric population.

I present this report to be laid before Parliament with the following observation. As the MHAC is an arm's length body of the Secretary of State we take our role to be that of a critical friend to the government of the day. Our more fundamental role as a body established to monitor the implementation of the 1983 Act is to visit and meet in private with patients who are detained in psychiatric hospital under the powers of that Act. We leave

---

[1]   See introduction, para xvi and Chapters 1.87, 4.111 below.

[2]   Department of Health Press Release 2005/0354, 20 October 2005.

it to Parliament to determine whether any government requires the sort of critical friendship evidenced in the following pages, but we will continue to argue strenuously that detained patients do need an independent and specialised body to visit them in hospital and to monitor their care. We do not believe that generic health and social care inspections would be an adequate substitute for the focused attention on the patient provided by visiting Commissioners under current arrangements. Whatever new arrangements are proposed for monitoring the use of new mental health law, we hope that Parliamentarians will ensure that patients' visits remain their central and undiluted focus.

Professor Kamlesh Patel

Chairman, Mental Health Act Commission

Summary of this Report

In the English, Gujarati, Hindi, Urdu, Somali and Welsh languages

Overview of this Report

The Mental Health Act Commission is charged with monitoring the implementation of powers and discharge of duties arising from the detention and treatment of patients under the Mental Health Act 1983. This report is based upon our work over the financial years 2003/04 to 2004/05, during which time we have continued to visit all psychiatric facilities that detain patients, and meet with patients in private.

The title of this report echoes the title of the book by Aneurin Bevan, who was the Minister with responsibility for the establishment and running of the National Health Service after the Second World War. In 2003, the then Secretary of State for Health (Dr John Reid MP) evoked Bevan's title – 'In Place of Fear' – to illustrate the responsibilities of his Government post. He said that the role encompassed not only issues of health and illness but also extended to questions of security, care, and a feeling of belonging.

We question whether all inpatient mental health services provide their patients with acceptable levels of security, care, or a sense of being treated as someone who matters. We welcome the Government's announced refocus on inpatient services and call for it to concentrate on building up these aspects, in place of the fear that many patients have of services and that many people have of mentally disordered people. We acknowledge Ministerial support, especially for the importance of breaking such 'circles of fear' for Black and minority ethnic patients.

Some acute services are unable to provide a quality of care that patients will welcome, and this may lead to the problems with compliance that Government seeks to address through an extension of statutory powers of coercion. There is evidence that inpatient services are losing staff and resources to community services, but that pressures on inpatient beds remain high. Over half of all wards are full or have more patients than beds, with staffing shortages and unpleasant ward environments undermining the therapeutic purpose of inpatient admission. We highlight the dangers inherent in devolved service commissioning for ensuring adequate levels of specialist provision, and note the vulnerability of mental health services as Trusts face financial crises. The extension of patient 'choice' across health service provision should not be allowed further to disadvantage or ostracise patients who are unable to exercise choice because of their mental incapacity or because of legal powers of compulsion held over their treatment.

We describe the boundaries of current mental health law under stress, with discussion of about forty cases in court, and a more general observation of legal powers being used in ways that may not have been intended by Parliament, often for pragmatic reasons where professionals are keen to intervene in what they perceive to be a person's best interest or as measures of social order. For these reasons we urge Parliament to ensure that new mental health legislation is carefully defined and limited.

This report discusses aspects of the use of present mental health powers in relation to civil detention and police powers, and we include an extended discussion on the detention of mentally disordered offenders. We provide analysis of deaths of detained patients; seclusion incidents notified to the Commission; and Second Opinion activity during this period.

The 2004 ECtHR judgment *HL v United Kingdom* has cast into doubt the policy commitment towards a preference for informal treatment of mentally disordered people, which has continued since the founding of the NHS. We urge Government to adopt appropriate safeguards against *de facto* detention whilst guarding against the unintentional reintroduction of paternalistic 'Poor Law principles' of care. This requires a strong focus on measures to encourage and support the empowerment of all patients, including those without mental capacity to make certain decisions about their care. Such measures can build upon the great amount of work done in mental health services over human rights awareness in recent years: health services and Government should view decent and empowering healthcare to be a right of mentally disordered people.

Finally we review the proposed future arrangements for monitoring detention of mentally disordered persons and suggest ways in which the forthcoming Mental Health Bill might be improved to ensure acceptability to mentally disordered persons and the effective protection of their rights.

এই বিবরণের সংক্ষিপ্তসার

মেন্টাল হেলথ অ্যাক্ট ১৯৮৩(Mental Health Act 1983) অনুযায়ী রোগীদের আটক ও চিকিৎসার ক্ষেত্রে ক্ষমতা ও দায়িত্বপালন সম্বন্ধে তত্ত্বাবধান করার কাজে মেন্টাল হেলথ অ্যাক্ট কমিশন (Mental Health Act Commission) নিযুক্ত হয়েছে। এই বিবরণ আর্থিক বছর ২০০৩/৪ থেকে ২০০৪/৫ পর্যন্ত আমাদের কাজের ভিত্তিতে তৈরী হয়েছে, যখন আমরা যে সব মানসিক চিকিৎসালয়ে রোগীরা আটক থাকে, সেইসব জায়গায় গিয়ে রোগীদের সাথে একান্তে সাক্ষাৎ করেছি।

এই বিবরণের শিরোনাম অ্যান্যুরিন বেভানের বইয়ের নামেরই প্রতিধ্বনি করে, যিনি দ্বিতীয় বিশ্বযুদ্ধের পরে ন্যাশনাল হেলথ সার্ভিসের স্থাপনা ও পরিচালনার দায়িত্বে আসীন মন্ত্রী ছিলেন। ২০০৩ সালে, তৎকালীন স্বাস্থ্যবিভাগের সেক্রেটারি অফ স্টেট (ডক্টর জন রীড, এমপি) বিভাগের বইয়ের শিরোনাম 'ইন প্লেস অফ ফিয়ার' ব্যবহার করেন – তার সরকারী পদের দায়িত্ব ব্যাখ্যা করতে। তিনি জানান যে তার ভূমিকা শুধুমাত্র স্বাস্থ্য ও অসুখের বিষয়েই সীমাবদ্ধ নয় বরং এর ব্যাপ্তি নিরাপত্তা, যত্ন ও নিজেকে আমাদেরই একজন ভাবার অনুভূতির বিষয়পর্যন্তও বিস্তৃত।

সব অন্তর্বিভাগীয় সেবা সমূহ তাদের রোগীদের মানসিক স্বাস্থ্যসেবা প্রদানে পর্যাপ্ত স্তরে নিরাপত্তা, যত্ন এবং এমন কেউ যার প্রয়োজন আছে সেই মনোভাব দেখায় কিনা সে বিষয়ে আমরা প্রশ্ন করি। আমরা সরকার ঘোষিত অন্তর্বিভাগীয় চিকিৎসা সেবার প্রতি পুনর্দৃষ্টিকে স্বাগত জানাই, এবং যে ভয় অনেক রোগীর এই সেবাগুলির প্রতি আছে, এবং অনেক মানুষের মানসিকভাবে অসুস্থ ব্যক্তিদের প্রতি আছে, তাদের এই দৃষ্টিভঙ্গির পরিবর্তনের উপর জোর দিতে আহ্বান করি। আমরা মন্ত্রনালয়ের সহায়তার কথা স্বীকার করি, বিশেষভাবে কৃষ্ণকায় এবং সংখ্যালঘু সম্প্রদায়ের রোগীদের 'ভীতির চক্র' ভাঙ্গার প্রয়োজনের বিষয়ে।

কিছু কিছু জটিল সেবা রোগীদের সন্তোষজনক যত্ন প্রদান করতে পারে না, এবং তার ফলে তারা সরকারের আইনী ক্ষমতার বাধ্যবাধকতা বিস্তারের চেষ্টার বিষয়ে অসুবিধায় পড়তে পারে। প্রমান আছে যে অন্তর্বিভাগীয় চিকিৎসার সেবাগুলি সম্প্রদায়ের সেবাগুলির কাছে লোকবল ও সম্মতি হারাচ্ছে, কিন্তু ভর্তি করার বেডের উপর চাপ বেশীই থাকছে। অর্ধেকের বেশী ওয়ার্ড ভর্তি বা সেখানে বেডের থেকে রোগী বেশী, এবং লোকবলের অভাব ও ওয়ার্ডের অপ্রীতিকর পরিবেশ রোগীর অন্তর্বিভাগীয় চিকিৎসাসেবার উদ্দেশ্যকে ক্ষতিগ্রস্ত করছে।

আমরা সেবা শুরু করার জন্য কেবলমাত্র প্রয়োজন অনুযায়ী বিশেষজ্ঞ ব্যবস্থাতে সীমিত রাখার বিপদের উপর আলোকপাত করি, এবং ট্রাস্টগুলি আর্থিক সঙ্কটের সম্মুখীন হওয়াতে মানসিক স্বাস্থ্য সেবার ক্ষতিগ্রস্ত হওয়ার সম্ভাবনা স্বীকার করি। যে রোগীরা তাদের মানসিক অক্ষমতা বা তাদের চিকিৎসার বিষয়ে আইনী ক্ষমতা ও বাধ্যবাধকতার জন্য চয়নে অসমর্থ,

স্বাস্থ্য সেবার বিষয়ে রোগীদের "চয়নের" বিস্তারের ফলে তাদের যেন অসুবিধায় ফেলা বা বহিষ্কার করা না হয়।

আমরা সাম্প্রতিক মানসিক স্বাস্থ্যের আইনের সীমা চাপের মধ্যে আছে বলে মনে করি, কারণ প্রায় চল্লিশটি মামলা আদালতে শুনানি চলছে, এবং সাধারনভাবে মনে করি যে আইনি ক্ষমতা এমনভাবে ব্যবহৃত হচ্ছে যা সংসদ নাও চাইতে পারে, অনেকসময় বাস্তবিক কারণে যেখানে পেশাদাররা হস্তক্ষেপ করতে চান এই ভেবে যে তা ব্যক্তির ভালোর জন্যই অথবা তা সমাজের নিয়মের পরিমাপ। এই কারণে আমরা সংসদকে অনুরোধ করি এটি নিশ্চিত করতে যে নূতন মানসিক স্বাস্থ্য আইন সাবধানে নির্ধারিত ও পরিসীমিত হোক।

এই বিবরণে সামাজিক আটকাদেশ ও পুলিশী ক্ষমতার পরিপ্রেক্ষিতে মানসিক স্বাস্থ্যের বিষয়ে ক্ষমতার ব্যবহারের দৃষ্টিকোণ নিয়ে আলোচনা করা হয়েছে, এবং মানসিক ভারসাম্যহীন অপরাধীদের আটক রাখার সম্বন্ধে এক বিস্তারিত আলোচনাও আমরা এতে অন্তর্গত করেছি। আমরা আটক রোগীদের মৃত্যু; কমিশনকে জানানো আলাদা করে রাখার ঘটনা; এবং এই সময় দ্বিতীয় মতামতের কার্যক্রমের বিশ্লেষণ করেছি।

২০০৪ সালে স্ট্র্যাসবার্গ রায় *এইচএল বনাম ইউনাইটেড কিংডম* (Strasbourg judgment HL v United Kingdom) মানসিকভাবে অসুস্থ ব্যক্তিদের অনাড়ম্বরে চিকিৎসার প্রতি অগ্রাধিকার দেওয়ার নীতির সম্বন্ধে দ্বিধা প্রকাশ করেছে, যা এন এইচ এস-এর (NHS) স্থাপনার সময় থেকে চলে আসছে। আমরা সরকারকে আর্জি জানাই প্রকৃতভাবে আটক রাখার বিরুদ্ধে যথাবিহিত ব্যবস্থা নিতে, অথচ সেবাযত্নের 'পুয়র ল প্রিন্সিপলস'-এর ('Poor Law principles') সদাশয় স্বৈরশাসনের অনিচ্ছাকৃত পুনরায় প্রবর্তনের বিরুদ্ধে সজাগ থাকতে। এর জন্য প্রয়োজন *সকল রোগীর সক্ষমতা বাড়াতে উৎসাহ ও সমর্থনের মাপকাঠির প্রতি সুদৃঢ় নজর রাখা, সেইসব রোগী সহ যারা তাদের নিজেদের যত্ন সম্বন্ধে কোন কিছু ঠিক করতে মানসিকভাবে অসমর্থ।* এই মানদণ্ডগুলি মানসিক স্বাস্থ্যের সেবাগুলিতে মানবাধিকার বিষয়ে অবগত করার যে বহু কাজ করা হয়েছে, তার ভিত্তিতে গড়ে তোলা যায়ঃ স্বাস্থ্য সেবা ও সরকারের মনে রাখা উচিত যে মানসিকভাবে অসুস্থ ব্যক্তিদের অধিকার এক উপযুক্ত ও সক্ষম স্বাস্থ্য-ব্যবস্থা।

সবশেষে আমরা মানসিকভাবে অসুস্থ ব্যক্তিদের আটক রাখার ভবিষ্যৎ তত্ত্বাবধানের বিষয়টি নিরীক্ষণ করি এবং পরামর্শ দিই কিভাবে ভবিষ্যৎ মানসিক স্বাস্থ্য আইন উন্নত করা যায় তা মানসিকভাবে অসুস্থ ব্যক্তিদের কাছে বাঞ্ছনীয় করতে এবং তাদের অধিকার কার্যকর ভাবে রক্ষা করতে।

આ અહેવાલની રૂપરેખા

મેન્ટલ હેલ્થ એક્ટ કમીશનને મેન્ટલ હેલ્થ એક્ટ (માનસિક આરોગ્ય અધિનિયમ) 1983 હેઠળના દર્દીઓને રોકી રાખવા અને તેમની સારવારથી ઉદ્ભવતી સત્તાઓ અને ફરજ બજાવણીના અમલીકરણની નોંધ રાખવાની જવાબદારી સોંપાઇ છે. આ અહેવાલ 2003/04 થી 2004/05 નાણાકીય વર્ષ દરમિયાનની અમારી કામગીરી પર આધારિત છે, જે સમય દરમિયાન અમે દર્દીઓને રોકી રાખતી બધી સાઇકિયાટ્રિક સુવિધાઓની મુલાકાત લઇ અને દર્દીઓને ખાનગીમાં મળવાનું ચાલુ રાખ્યું છે.

આ અહેવાલનું મથાળું બીજા વિશ્વ યુદ્ધ પછી નેશનલ હેલ્થ સર્વિસ સ્થાપવા અને તેનું સંચાલન કરવાની જવાબદારી ધરાવતા મંત્રી એન્યૂરિન બેવનના પુસ્તકના શીર્ષકને પ્રતિધ્વનિત કરે છે. 2003માં એ વખતના સેક્રેટરી ઑફ સ્ટેટ ફૉર હેલ્થ (ડૉ જોન રીડ MP) તેમના સરકારી પદની જવાબદારીઓનો દાખલો આપતા બેવનના શીર્ષક 'ઇન પ્લેસ ઑફ ફીયર' ની યાદ અપાવી હતી. એમણે કહ્યું કે એમના કર્તવ્યમાં ફક્ત આરોગ્ય અને બીમારીના મુદ્દાઓનો સમાવેશ નહોતો થતો પરંતુ તેમાં સુરક્ષા, સંભાળ અને સહભાગી હોવાની એક લાગણીના પ્રશ્નોને પણ સમાવી લેવામાં આવ્યા હતા.

અમે બધી ઇનપેશન્ટ માનસિક આરોગ્ય સેવાઓ તેમના દર્દીઓને સ્વીકાર્ય સ્તરની સુરક્ષા, સંભાળ અથવા તેમને એક મહત્ત્વપૂર્ણ વ્યક્તિ માનવામાં આવે એવી લાગણી પૂરી પાડે છે કે કેમ તેની પૂછપરછ કરીએ છીએ. અમે ઇનપેશન્ટ સેવાઓ પર ફરી ધ્યાન કેંદ્રિત કરવા સરકાર કરેલ જાહેરાત અને દર્દીઓની સેવાઓ માટે અને માનસિક બીમારી ધરાવતા લોકો પ્રત્યે રહેલ ઘણા લોકોના ડરને દૂર કરી આ પાસાઓને વધુ વિકસાવવા પર ધ્યાન આપવા કરેલી હાકલને આવકારીએ છીએ. અમે મંત્રાલયનો ટેકો સ્વીકારીએ છીએ, ખાસ કરીને અશ્વેત અને લઘુમતિ વંશીય દર્દીઓના 'ડરના ઘેરા' તોડવાની અગત્યતા માટે.

કેટલીક સંવેદનશીલ સેવાઓ દર્દીઓ આવકારે એવી સંભાળની ગુણવત્તા પૂરી નથી પાડી શકતી અને આથી સપ્તાઈની વૈધાનિક સત્તાઓના વિસ્તાર દ્વારા સરકાર કરેલ અનુપાલનના પ્રયત્નો માટે સમસ્યાઓ ઊભી થઇ શકે છે. આ વાતનો પુરાવો છે કે ઇનપેશન્ટ સેવાઓના કર્મચારીઓ અને સાધનસંપત્તિ સામુદાયિક સેવાઓ તરફ વળી રહ્યા છે, પરંતુ ઇનપેશન્ટ પથારીઓની માંગ ઊંચી રહે છે. બધા વોર્ડમાંના અડધા કરતાં વધુ ભરેલા હોય છે અથવા પથારીઓ કરતાં વધુ દર્દીઓ હોય છે અને સાથે કર્મચારીઓની અછત અને વોર્ડનું અપ્રિય વાતાવરણ ઇનપેશન્ટને દાખલ કરવાના રોગનિવારક હેતુને નબળો પાડે છે.

અમે વિકેંદ્રિત સેવા કમીશનિંગમાં નિષ્ણાત પુરવઠાના પર્યાપ્ત સ્તરોની ખાતરી કરવામાં રહેલા જોખમો પર ધ્યાન દોરીએ છીએ અને ટ્રસ્ટો નાણાકીય કટોકટીનો સામનો કરી રહ્યા હોવાથી માનસિક આરોગ્ય સેવાઓની સંવેદનશીલતાની નોંધ લઇએ છીએ. સમગ્ર આરોગ્ય સેવા પુરવઠામાં દર્દીની 'પસંદગી'ના વિસ્તરણને તેમની માનસિક અક્ષમતાના લીધે અથવા સારવારપર દબાણની કાનૂની સત્તા હોવાના કારણે પસંદગીનો ઉપયોગ ન કરી શકતા હોય તેવા દર્દીઓને વધુ ગેરલાભ પહોંચાડવા કે બાકાત કરવા ન દેવું જોઇએ.

અમે લગભગ ચાલીસ કોર્ટના કેસિસનું વર્ણન કરીએ છીએ અને ઘણીવાર વ્યાવહારિક કારણોસર કોઇ વ્યક્તિનું સર્વોત્તમ હિત જણાય ત્યારે વ્યાવસાયિકો હસ્તક્ષેપ કરવા આતુર હોય ત્યારે અથવા સામાજિક દરજ્જાના પગલાં તરીકે સંસદનો ઇરાદો ન હોય તે રીતે વાપરવામાં આવતી કાનૂની સત્તાઓનું એક વધુ સામાન્ય નિરીક્ષણ સાથે હાલના દબાણ હેઠળના માનસિક આરોગ્ય કાયદાની હદનું વર્ણન કરીએ છીએ. આ કારણોસર અમે સંસદને નવા માનસિક આરોગ્ય કાયદાની સાવચેતીપૂર્વક વ્યાખ્યા કરવા અને તેની મર્યાદા બાંધવાની ખાતરી કરવા વિનંતિ કરીએ છીએ.

આ અહેવાલ સિવિલ અટકાયત અને પોલીસ સત્તાના સંબંધમાં હાલના માનસિક આરોગ્ય સત્તાના ઉપયોગના પાસાઓની ચર્ચા કરે છે અને અમે આમાં માનસિક રીતે બીમાર ગુનેગારોની અટકાયત અંગે એક વિસ્તૃત ચર્ચાનો સમાવેશ કરીએ છીએ. અમે રોકી રાખેલા દર્દીઓના મૃત્યુ, કમીશનને અધિસૂચિત કરેલ એકાંતવાસના બનાવો અને આ અવધિ દરમિયાન બીજા અભિપ્રાયની પ્રવૃત્તિનું પૃથક્કરણ પૂરું પાડીએ છીએ.

2004ના HL વિરુદ્ધ યુનાઇટેડ કિંગ્ડમ સ્ટ્રૅસબોર્ગ ચુકાદાએ NHSની સ્થાપનાથી ચાલી આવતી માનસિક રીતે બીમાર લોકોની અનૌપચારિક સારવાર માટેની પસંદગી પ્રત્યે નીતિ વચનબદ્ધતા તરફ શંકા બતાવી છે. અમે સરકારને સંભાળના પૈતૃક 'ખરાબ કાનૂની સિદ્ધાંતો' ને બિનઇરાદાપૂર્વક ફરીથી લાગુ કરવા સામે રક્ષણ કરવાની સાથે પ્રત્યક્ષ અટકાયત સામે યોગ્ય સંરક્ષણ અપનાવવા વિનંતિ કરીએ છીએ. આના માટે પોતાની સંભાળ અંગે અમુક નિર્ણયો લેવાની માનસિક ક્ષમતા ન હોય તેવા લોકો સહિત બધા દર્દીઓને અધિકાર આપવામાં પ્રોત્સાહન અને ટેકો આપતા પગલાંપર મક્કમતાથી ધ્યાન કેંદ્રિત કરવું જરૂરી છે. એવા પગલાં તાજેતરના વર્ષો દરમિયાન માનવ અધિકારોની જાગૃતિ તરફ માનસિક આરોગ્ય સેવાઓમાં મોટા પાયે થયેલી કામગીરીને આગળ ધપાવી શકે છે: આરોગ્ય સેવાઓ અને સરકાર વાજબી અને અધિકાર આપતી આરોગ્યસંભાળને માનસિક રીતે બીમાર લોકોનો હક્ક સમજવું જોઇએ.

છેવટે અમે માનસિક રીતે બીમાર વ્યક્તિઓની અટકાયતની નોંધ રાખવા માટે ભવિષ્યની પ્રસ્તાવિત વ્યવસ્થાઓની સમીક્ષા કરીએ છીએ અને માનસિક રીતે બીમાર વ્યક્તિઓની સ્વીકાર્યતા અને તેમના હક્કોના અસરકારક રક્ષણની ખાતરી કરવા માટે આવી રહેલા મેન્ટલ હેલ્થ બિલમાં કેવી રીતે સુધારા કરી શકાય તે અંગે સૂચવીએ છીએ.

21

इस रिपोर्ट की समीक्षा

'मानसिक स्वास्थ्य विधान कमीशन' को यह जिम्मेदारी दी गई थी कि वह 'मानसिक स्वास्थ्य कानून 1983' के अंतर्गत मरीज़ों को नज़रबन्द करने तथा उनका इलाज करने से उत्पन्न अधिकारों का प्रयोग करने तथा कर्त्तव्यों का पालन करने पर नज़र रखे। यह रिपोर्ट वित्त वर्ष 2003/04 से 2004/05 के बीच हमारे द्वारा किए गए काम पर आधारित है। इस अवधि के दौरान हम उन सभी मनोचिकित्सक सुविधाओं का दौरा करने रहे हैं जो रोगियों को नज़रबन्द करती हैं तथा उनसे अकेले में मिलती हैं।

इस रिपोर्ट का शीर्षक अनीरिन बैवन (Aneurin Bevan) की पुस्तक के शीर्षक की याद दिलाता है जो दूसरे विश्व युद्ध के बाद मन्त्री थे तथा जिन्हें राष्ट्रीय स्वास्थ्य सेवा की स्थापना करने तथा उसे चलाने की जिम्मेदारी दी गई थी। स्वास्थ्य मंत्रालय के तत्कालीन सेक्रेटरी ऑफ स्टेट (डा. जॉन रीड, एम पी) ने अपने सरकारी पद की जिम्मेदारियों को समझाने के लिए सन् 2003 में बैवन के शीर्षक 'डर के स्थान पर' का उदाहरण दिया। उन्होंने कहा कि उनकी भूमिका केवल स्वास्थ्य तथा बीमारी के मुद्दों तक ही सीमित नहीं थी बल्कि उसमें सुरक्षा और उत्तमभाल के प्रश्न तथा अपनेपन का एहसास होना भी शामिल था।

हमने यह प्रश्न उठाया है कि क्या सभी मानसिक स्वास्थ्य सेवाएं, जिनमें मरीज़ों को दाखिल किया जाता है, मरीज़ों को उस स्तर की सुरक्षा तथा उत्तमभाल प्रदान कर सकती हैं जिसकी उनसे आशा की जानी है, तथा क्या अपने व्यवहार द्वारा वे रोगियों को यह एहसास दिला सकती हैं कि रोगी महत्त्वपूर्ण हैं। हम सरकार द्वारा अपना ध्यान एक बार फिर रोगियों को दाखिल करने वाली सेवाओं पर केन्द्रित करने तथा ऊपर बताए पक्षों को मज़बूत करने की घोषणा का स्वागत करने हैं जिससे उस डर को हटाया जा सकेगा जो कई रोगियों को इन सेवाओं से लगता है तथा जो कई लोगों को मानसिक विकार वाले रोगियों से लगता है। विशेष तौर पर काले तथा अल्पमत जातियों के रोगियों के मन से डर के साये को दूर करने के महत्व को ध्यान में रखते हुए, हम मंत्रालय की सहायता के लिए आभारी हैं।

कुछ कुशाग्र सेवाएं उत्तमभाल का वह स्तर प्रदान नहीं कर पाती हैं जैसा रोगी चाहते हैं, तथा इसके कारण नियमों के पालन में ऐसी समस्याएं हो सकती हैं जिनका निदान सरकार कानूनी दमन की शक्ति बढ़ाकर करना चाहती है। इस बात का सबूत मौजूद है कि रोगियों को दाखिल करने वाली संस्थानों में से कर्मचारी तथा साधन कम करके सामुदायिक सेवाओं को दे दिए जाते हैं, किंतु दाखिल होने वाले रोगियों की संख्या का दबाव बना रहता है। आधे से अधिक वार्ड या तो पूरे भरे हुए हैं या उनमें बिस्तरों की संख्या की अपेक्षा रोगियों की संख्या अधिक है, कर्मचारियों की संख्या कम है तथा वार्ड का वातावरण अपिय है जिसके कारण इलाज की दृष्टि से रोगी को दाखिल करवाने के उद्देश्य को क्षति पहुंचती है।

उपयुक्त स्तर के विशेषज्ञ उपलब्ध कराने की दृष्टि से हमने हस्तांतरित सेवा आदेश व्यवस्था (Devolved Service Commissioning) में छिपे खतरों पर प्रकाश डाला है तथा इस बात की ओर ध्यान दिलाया है कि यदि ट्रस्ट वित्तीय संकटों का सामना करने हैं तो मानसिक स्वास्थ्य सेवाएं असुरक्षित हो सकती हैं। रोगी की 'पसन्द' को पूरी स्वास्थ्य सेवा पर विस्तृत

करने का अर्थ उन रोगियों के अधिकारों का और अधिक हनन अथवा बहिष्कार नहीं होना चाहिए जो अपनी मानसिक असमर्थता के कारण अथवा अपने इलाज पर लगी कानूनी बाध्यता के कारण अपनी पसन्द का चयन करने की स्थिति में नहीं हैं।

अदालतों में चल रहे लगभग चालीस मुकदमों का ब्यौरा देकर हमने मौजूदा स्वास्थ्य कानून की उन सीमाओं का वर्णन किया है जिन पर दबाव है तथा अधिक सामान्य रूप में यह बताया है कि कानूनी शक्ति का प्रयोग कई ऐसे तरीकों से किया जा रहा है जो शायद पार्लियामेंट की मंशा के अनुरूप नहीं हैं। बहुत बार ऐसा व्यावहारिक दृष्टि से किया जाना है जब पेशावर लोग इसलिए उग्रलअंदाज़ी करने के लिए उत्सुक होने हैं क्योंकि उनकी नज़र में इसमें रोगी की भलाई होती है अथवा वे इस उग्रलअंदाज़ी को कोई महत्त्वपूर्ण सामाजिक कारवाई समझते हैं। इन्हीं कारणों से हमने पार्लियामेंट से यह प्रार्थना की है कि नये स्वास्थ्य कानून को बड़े ध्यान से परिभाषित तथा सीमित किया जाए।

इस रिपोर्ट में नागरिक नज़रबंदी तथा पुलिस के अधिकारों के संबंध में मौजूदा मानसिक स्वास्थ्य अधिकारों के प्रयोग के कुछ पक्षों पर चर्चा की गई है तथा हमने मानसिक विकार वाले अपराधियों की नज़रबंदी पर एक विस्तृत चर्चा को इस रिपोर्ट में शामिल किया है। इस रिपोर्ट में हमने नज़रबंद रोगियों की मौतों का, एकांतीकरण वाली घटनाओं का, जिनकी सूचना कमीशन को दी गयी थी, तथा इस अवधि में किए गए "दूसरी राय" कार्यक्रम का विश्लेषण किया है।

वर्ष 2004 में 'HL बनाम यूनाइटिड किंगडम' मामले में स्ट्रासबुर्ग निर्णय ने मानसिक विकार वाले लोगों के अनौपचारिक इलाज को वरीयता देने की कटिबद्ध नीति पर प्रश्न चिन्ह लगा दिया है हालांकि यह नीति NHS के स्थापन के समय से चली आ रही है। हम सरकार से वस्तुत: नज़रबंदी के विरुद्ध सुरक्षा साधन अपनाने, किन्तु साथ ही पितृ व्यवहार वाले उत्तमभाल के "निर्धन लोगों के लिए कानून" के नियमों को अनजाने में दोबारा लागू करने से बचने की अपील करने हैं। इसके लिए ऐसे कदम उठाने पर ध्यान केन्द्रित करना आवश्यक है जिनसे सभी रोगियों को, जिनमें वे रोगी भी शामिल हैं जिनके पास अपनी उत्तमभाल के सम्बंध में कुछ ख्वास निर्णय लेने की मानसिक शक्ति नहीं है, अधिक सशक्त करने की प्रकिया को प्रोत्साहन तथा सहायता मिले। ऐसे कदम उस महान कार्य को आगे बढ़ा सकते हैं जो पिछले कुछ वर्षों में मानसिक स्वास्थ्य सेवाओं के क्षेत्र में मानव अधिकारों के प्रति जागरूकता बढ़ाने के लिए किया गया है: स्वास्थ्य सेवाओं तथा सरकार को यह समझना चाहिए कि एक शालीन तथा सशक्त स्वास्थ्य सेवा मानसिक विकार वाले रोगियों का अधिकार है।

अन्तत: हमने मानसिक विकार वाले रोगियों की नज़रबंदी पर भविष्य में नज़र रखने के लिए प्रस्तावित प्रबंधों पर विचार किया है तथा ऐसे कदम उठाने की सलाह दी है जिनसे आनेवाले 'मानसिक स्वास्थ्य कानून' में सुधार हो सके और वह मानसिक विकार वाले लोगों को मान्य हो सके तथा उनके अधिकारों की प्रभावपूर्ण ढंग से सुरक्षा कर सके।

رپورٹ کا جائزہ

منٹل ہیلتھ ایکٹ کمیشن (Mental Health Act Commission) کو یہ ذمہ داری سونپی گئی ہے کہ وہ منٹل ہیلتھ ایکٹ مجریہ 1983 (Mental Health Act 1983) کے تحت مریضوں کی حراست اور ان کے علاج سے متعلق عائد ہونے والے فرائض کی انجام دہی اور اختیارات کے نفاذ کی نگرانی کرے۔ یہ رپورٹ مالی سال 2003/04 سے 2004/05 کے دوران ہمارے کام پر مبنی ہے، جس میں ہم ان تمام نفسی علاج کی سہولت گاہوں کا معائنہ کرتے رہے ہیں جہاں پر مریض رکھے جاتے ہیں اور مریضوں سے تنہائی میں ملاقات کرتے رہے ہیں۔

اس رپورٹ کا عنوان انیورن بیوان (Aneurin Bevan) کی کتاب کے عنوان کی یاد دلاتا ہے جو دوسری عالمی جنگ کے بعد نیشنل ہیلتھ سروس کو قائم کرنے اور اس کو چلانے کی ذمہ داری سنبھالنے پر مامور وزیر تھے۔ سال 2003 میں، اس وقت کے وزیر مملکت برائے صحت [ڈاکٹر جان ریڈ ایم پی (Dr John Reid MP)] سرکاری عہدے کی اپنی ذمہ داریوں کے لیے بیوان (Bevan) کے رکھے گئے عنوان – 'خوف کی جگہ' ('In Place of Fear') – کو تازہ کیا۔ اس میں انھوں نے کہا کہ ان کا کام صحت اور بیماری کے مسائل کا ہی احاطہ نہیں کرتا تھا بلکہ اس میں حفاظت و سلامتی، نگہداشت اور احساس تعلق کے سوالات بھی شامل تھے۔

ہم یہ سوال کرتے ہیں کہ کیا دماغی صحت کی تمام داخلی خدمات اپنے مریضوں کو قابل قبول سطح کی حفاظت، نگہداشت یا اہمیت رکھنے والے کسی شخص کی حیثیت سے زیر علاج رہنے کا احساس کراتی ہیں۔ ہم داخلی مریضوں کی خدمات کی حکومت کے اعلان شدہ دوبارہ توجہ اور خدمات سے متعلق بہت سے مریضوں کے ذہن میں، اور دماغی ناسازی میں مبتلا لوگوں سے متعلق عام لوگوں کے ذہن میں، چھپے خوف کے بجائے ان پہلوؤں کو ترقی دینے کی طرف متوجہ کرنے کا استقبال کرتے ہیں۔ ہم وزارتی سطح پر ملنے والی مدد کا اعتراف کرتے ہیں خصوصاً سیاہ فام اور اقلیتی نسلی گروپوں سے تعلق رکھنے والے مریضوں کے لیے 'خوف کے حصار' کو توڑنے کی اہمیت کی وجہ سے۔

بعض اہم خدمات اس معیار کی نگہداشت فراہم کرنے سے قاصر ہیں جس کا استقبال مریض کر سکیں اور اس کے نتیجے میں تعمیل سے متعلق مسائل پیدا ہو سکتے ہیں جن کا حل حکومت دستوری جبری اختیارات کی توسیع کے ذریعے نکالنا چاہتی ہے۔ ایسے ثبوت ملے ہیں کہ داخلی مریضوں کی خدمات عملی اور وسائل سے محروم ہو رہی ہے اور وہ کمیونٹی خدمات میں چلے جاتے ہیں، لیکن داخلی مریضوں پر پڑنے والا دباؤ بڑھتا رہتا ہے۔ تقریباً تمام وارڈوں کا آدھا حصہ بھرا رہتا ہے اور ان میں بستروں سے زیادہ مریض ہیں ساتھ ہی عملے کی کمی ہے اور ماحول ناخوشگوار ہے جس سے داخلی مریضوں کے قیام کے معالجاتی مقصد کی اہمیت کم ہو جاتی ہے۔

چونکہ ٹرسٹوں کو مالی بحران کا سامنا ہے ہم ان خطرات کو خاص طور پر نمایاں کرتے ہیں جو تفویض شدہ خدمت میں پوشیدہ ہیں جس کا کام اختصاصی انتظام کی اطمینان بخش سطح کو یقینی بنانا ہے اور دماغی صحت کی خدمات کو لاحق خطرات کا مشاہدہ کرنا ہے۔ خدمات صحت کے انتظامات میں مریضوں کے 'انتخاب' کی سہولت کی توسیع کی اجازت مزید نہیں دی جانی چاہیے کیونکہ اس سے ان

مریضوں کو نقصان ہوتا ہے یا وہ مریض الگ تھلگ ہو کر رہ جاتے ہیں جو اپنی دماغی نقص کی وجہ سے اپنے انتخاب کے حق کو استعمال نہیں کر سکتے۔

ہم موجودہ دماغی صحت کے قانون کی حدود کا بیان کرتے ہیں جو دباؤ میں ہے۔ ہم عدالت میں زیر سماعت تقریباً چالیس معاملات پر گفتگو کریں گے اور ایسے طریقوں سے قانونی اختیارات استعمال کیے جانے کا عام مشاہدہ پیش کریں گے جو کبھی بھی شاید پارلیمنٹ کا منصوبہ نہ رہا ہو اور ایسا اکثر ان عملی اسباب سے ہوگا جہاں پیشہ ور افراد ان معاملات میں مداخلت کے لیے بیتاب رہتے ہیں جسے وہ کسی شخص کے بہترین مفاد سے وابستہ تصور کرتے ہوں یا سماجی نظام کے طریقوں میں ایک طریقہ سمجھتے ہوں۔ یہ وہ اسباب ہیں جن کی بناء پر ہم پارلیمنٹ سے یہ درخواست کرتے ہیں کہ دماغی صحت سے متعلق نئے قانون کی احتیاط کے ساتھ وضاحت کی جائے اور اسے محدود رکھا جائے۔

اس رپورٹ میں دیوانی حراست اور پولس کے اختیارات کے تعلق سے دماغی صحت کے قانون کے موجودہ اختیارات کے استعمال کے پہلوؤں کے بحث کی گئی ہے اور ہم نے دماغی ناسازی میں مبتلا مجرموں کی حراست سے متعلق ایک توسیع شدہ بحث بھی اس میں شامل کی ہے۔ ہم زیر حراست مریضوں کی اموات؛ کمیشن کے علم میں لائے جانے والے مریضوں کو تنہا رکھے جانے کے واقعات؛ اور اس مدت کے دوران سکنڈ اوپینین کے عمل سے متعلق تجزیہ فراہم کرتے ہیں۔

سال 2004 میں اسٹراس بورگ (Strasbourg) کا فیصلہ ایچ ایل (HL) بنام یونائیٹڈ کنگڈم (United Kingdom) کے مقدمے میں دماغی ناسازی میں مبتلا لوگوں کے غیر رسمی علاج سے متعلق پالیسی کی پابندی پر شک کا سایہ ڈال دیا ہے جو NHS کی بنیاد پڑنے سے اب تک جاری رہا ہے۔ ہم حکومت سے چاہیں گے کہ وہ ایسی فرضی حراست کے خلاف احتیاطی تدابیر اختیار کرے اور نگہداشت کے پدریت پسندانہ 'ضرورت مند غریب افراد سے تعلق قانونی اصول' ('Poor Law principles') کے غیر ارادی باز ترویج کی طرف سے ہوشیار رہے۔ اس کے لیے ضرورت ہے کہ ان اقدامات پر خصوصی توجہ دینے کی جو تمام مریضوں کو باختیار بنانے اور انھیں مدد دینے کی حوصلہ افزائی کریں اور ان میں وہ افراد بھی شامل ہیں جو اپنی نگہداشت کے بارے میں بعض فیصلے کرنے کی ذہنی صلاحیت سے محروم ہوں۔ ایسے اقدامات حالیہ برسوں میں حقوق انسانی سے تعلق کیے گئے قابل ذکر کام کو اور بہتر شکل عطا کر سکتے ہیں جو دماغی صحت کی خدمات کے میدان میں کیا گیا ہے؛ خدمات صحت اور حکومت دونوں کو عمدہ اور باختیار بنانے والی نگہداشت کو دماغی ناسازی میں مبتلا افراد کا حق تصور کرنا چاہیے۔

آخر میں، ہم دماغی ناسازی میں مبتلا افراد کی حراست کی نگرانی کے لیے مجوزہ آئندہ انتظامات کا جائزہ لیتے اور ایسے طریقے تجویز کرتے ہیں جن سے متوقع منٹل ہیلتھ بل (Mental Health Bill) کو بہتر بنایا جائے تاکہ ذہنی طور پر مریض افراد کے لیے اس کی قبولیت اور ان کے حقوق کے تحفظ کو یقینی بنایا جاسکے۔

本报告的概述

心理健康法案委员会 (Mental Health Act Commission) 的职责是：依据 1983 年的《心理健康法案》，对因拘留和治疗患者而引起的权力执行及职责履行情况进行监控。本报告基于我们在 2003/04 到 2004/05 财年所做的工作，在这两年中，我们不断拜访所有拘留患者的精神病治疗机构，并私下与患者会谈。

本报告的标题仿效 Aneurin Bevan 的一本著作的书名，他是二战后英国负责建立和运营国家健康中心 (National Health Service) 的卫生大臣。在 2003 年，当时的卫生大臣（议员 John Reid 博士）引用了 Bevan 的书名 "In Place of Fear"（打消恐惧）来描述他担任的政府职务的责任。他说，他的职责不仅包括卫生保健和疾病防治，还涉及到保障、监护和归属感等问题。

我们质疑是否所有的精神病患者收治机构均为患者们提供了可接受的保障和监护水平，以及是否让患者们感觉到受重视。政府已宣布重新关注这些病患收治机构，对此我们十分欢迎，并呼吁政府着重加强这方面的工作，以便打消许多患者对此类机构的顾虑和公众对精神病患者的恐惧。我们由衷地感激来自政府方面的支持，尤其要对他们打破针对黑人和少数族裔患者的"恐惧怪圈"表示感谢，因为此举意义重大。

一些问题严重的收治机构无法提供受患者欢迎的优质监护服务，而这可能导致政府设法通过扩大强制性的法律手段来解决的守法问题。有证据表明，收治机构的医护人员和资源正在不断流失，主要流向社区服务机构，但住院床位的压力依然很大。在所有的病房中，一半以上均住满患者，或者患者比床位还多，而医护人员的短缺和恶劣的病房环境影响了病人住院的治疗效果。

我们着重指出，为确保提供足够数量的医师而将医护服务委托给其他收治机构的做法暗含一定的风险；同时，由于基金会面临财务危机，精神病患者收治机构具有很大的不确定性。患者"挑选"医护服务机构的范围不应进一步扩大，以免损害或排斥因心智能力缺失，或在法律上对其治疗有强制规定而无法运用选择权的患者们。

我们描述了处于压力下的现行心理健康法案的界限，连带讨论了约四十个庭审案例，并从更普遍意义上考察了当前以可能不同于议会初衷的方式运用法律手段的情况 – 议会往往是出于实用的目的，而某些专业人士又很喜欢对议会认为的、对个人最有利的情况或有助于维护社会秩序的措施加以干预。基于以上原因，我们敦促议会在进行新的心理健康立法时能够仔细界定和限定相关内容。

本报告从各方面讨论了与民事拘留和警察权力相关的现有心理健康法律手段的运用情况，并且将讨论范围扩大到拘留精神病罪犯的问题。我们提供了这段时间内的被拘留患者的死亡情况分析、向委员会通报的隔离事件，以及"第二意见" (Second Opinion) 活动的情况。

2004 年的斯特拉斯堡判决 HL v United Kingdom 已引发对政府的政策承诺偏向于为精神病患者提供非正式治疗的质疑，这种治疗从 NHS 成立之日起就一直存在。我们敦促政府采取适当的预防措施来避免"事实上的"拘留，同时避免无意中再次引入有关监护的家长式"糟糕法律原则"。这需要着重关注那些可以鼓励和支持为*所有*患者（包括心智能力缺失而无法作出监护决定的患者）赋予权利的措施。此类措施可以建立在近年来就人权意识在精神病患者收治机构中所做的大量工作的基础上：医疗保健机构和政府应将恰当得体的、为患者赋予权利的医疗保健视为精神病患者的一项正当权利。

最后，我们回顾了建议在将来采取的、监控精神病患者拘留情况的措施，并提出了对即将出台的《心理健康法》(Mental Health Bill) 进行完善的几点建议，以确保该法为精神病患者所接受并有效保护他们的权利。

報告概要

心理健康法案委員會 (The Mental Health Act Commission) 是依據 1983 年的《心理健康法案》管理監督執行權與解放拘留的病患的執行權。此報告是以我們在 2003/04 至 2004/05 財政年度期間的工作為依據。在此期間，我們持續造訪所有留置病患的精神病所，並私下會見病患。

此報告的標題反映 Aneurin Bevan 所著的書名。Aneurin Bevan 為第二次世界大戰後負責建立並管理全民健康醫療服務 (NHS) 的部長。在 2003 年，當時的衛生國務大臣 (Dr John Reid，議員) 引用 Bevan 的書名《In Place of Fear》說明其在政府任職的職責。他表示此角色不僅包含健康和疾病的問題，更延伸至安全、照顧及歸屬感的問題。

我們探討是否所有心理健康服務機構有為其病患提供可接受程度的安全及照顧，或讓其在治療時有受到重視的感覺。我們樂見政府宣佈將重心重新放在住院病患服務，並要求致力增進這些層面，以解除許多病患對於服務的擔憂，以及許多人對於精神病者的恐懼。我們對於政府的支援，尤其在破除社會上對於黑人及少數種族病患的恐懼之重要性方面，表示贊同。

某些急性的服務無法提供病患欣然接受的照顧品質，而這有可能導致法規遵守的問題。為此，政府透過強制的法規權限擴充，尋求因應之道。證據顯示，住院病患服務機構的員工人數在減少中，社區資源也在下降，然而病床的需求壓力仍然很高。有超過一半以上的所有病房皆住滿或病患多過病床，加上人員的短缺及令人不悅的病房環境，逐漸損及住院病患許可的治療目的。

我們強調確保適當程度的專家提供所移交的服務委任固有的危險，並留意由於機構面臨財務危機而造成心理健康醫療服務的難處。健康醫療服務提供病患「選擇」之擴展，不得進一步損害或排斥由於精神上無行為能力或治療上強制執行的法定權限而無法進行選擇的病患。

我們說明目前在壓力下的心理健康法界限、就法院中約四十個案例進行探討，並對法律被專業人士使用超出國會當初制定其法的目的，而只為了個人的利益或所認為的社會公平而介入。基於這些理由，我們強烈要求國會確保審慎定義並界定新的心理健康法。

此報告探討使用目前關於民事羈押及警察權限的心理健康權限層面，並對犯法的精神病的拘留進行廣泛的探討。我們提供拘留病患的死因分析、告知委員會的隔離事件，以及「其他意見」(Second Opinion) 活動。

2004 年在法國史特拉斯堡 (Strasbourg) 的「HL v United Kingdom」判決，使得有關偏好以非正規方式治療精神病者的政策承諾難以確定，而此不確定性自 NHS 的創立起便持續著。我們強烈要求政府採用適當的預防措施防止實際的拘留，同時防範非故意地重新引用專制的「濟貧原則」(Poor Law 原則) 式照顧。這需要強烈著重於措施，以鼓勵並支援所有病患的權力授與，其中包括沒有心智能力的病患亦能對自己所要接受的看護做某些決定。此等措施的建立，是根據近年來在人權意識的心理健康服務方面所完成的大量工作：健康服務及政府應將授權的正派保健視作精神病者的權利

最後，我們對於計劃在未來監控精神病者的拘留安排進行審核，並對即將到來的心理健康法案可改善的方法提出建議，以確保其可讓精神病者接受，以及其權利的有效保護。

25

Trosolwg o'r Adroddiad hwn

Comisiwn y Ddeddf Iechyd Meddwl sydd yn gyfrifol am fonitro gweithrediad pwerau a chyflawniad dyletswyddau mewn cysylltiad â chadw a thrin cleifion o dan Ddeddf Iechyd Meddwl 1983. Mae'r adroddiad hwn yn seiliedig ar ein gwaith yn ystod blynyddoedd ariannol 2003/04 hyd 2004/05, pryd y bu inni barhau i ymweld â phob cyfleuster seiciatrig sy'n cadw cleifion yn orfodol, a chyfarfod a chleifion yn breifat.

Mae pennawd yr adroddiad yn adleisio teitl y llyfr gan Aneurin Bevan, a oedd ar y pryd yn Weinidog gyda chyfrifoldeb am sefydlu a gweithredu'r Gwasanaeth Iechyd Gwladol ar ôl yr Ail Ryfel Byd. Yn 2003, fe wnaeth yr Ysgrifennydd Gwladol ar gyfer Iechyd ar y pryd (Dr John Reid AS) alw i gof deitl Bevan – "In Place of Fear"- er mwyn esbonio cyfrifoldebau ei swydd Lywodraethol. Dywedodd fod y rôl nid yn unig yn cwmpasu materion iechyd ac afiechyd, ond hefyd yn ymestyn i gwestiynau o ddiogelwch, gofal, a theimlad o berthyn.

Fe gwestiynwn a yw pob gwasanaeth iechyd meddwl ar gyfer cleifion preswyl yn darparu lefelau derbyniol o ddiogelwch, gofal, neu deimlad o gael eu trin fel rhywun o bwys. Croesawn ailffocws datganedig y Llywodraeth ar wasanaethau cleifion preswyl ac rydym yn galw arni i ganolbwyntio ar adeiladu ar yr agweddau hyn, yn lle'r ofn sydd gan lawer o gleifion ynglŷn â'r gwasanaethau ynghyd â'r ofn sydd gan lawer o bobl tuag at y rheini sydd ag anhwylderau meddyliol. Cydnabyddwn gefnogaeth y Weinyddiaeth, yn enwedig o ran pwysigrwydd chwalu'r fath "ofnau" ar gyfer cleifion croenddu a rhai sy'n perthyn i leiafrifoedd ethnig.

Mae rhai gwasanaethau dwys yn methu darparu ansawdd gofal y bydd cleifion yn ei groesawu, ac mi all hyn arwain at broblemau cydymffurfio y mae'r Llywodraeth yn ceisio mynd i'r afael â nhw drwy ymestyn pwerau gorfodi statudol. Mae yna dystiolaeth bod gwasanaethau cleifion preswyl yn colli staff a chyfleusterau i wasanaethau cymunedol, ond bod pwysau ar welyau ar gyfer cleifion preswyl yn parhau yn uchel. Mae dros hanner yr holl wardiau yn llawn, neu â mwy o gleifion na gwelyau, gyda phrinder staff a wardiau sy'n annymunol o ran amgylchedd yn tanseilio pwrpas therapiwtig derbyn cleifion preswyl.

Amlygwn beryglon cynhenid comisiynu gan wasanaethau wedi'u datganoli er mwyn sicrhau lefelau digonol o ddarpariaeth arbenigol, a nodwn sefyllfa fregus gwasanaethau iechyd meddwl wrth i Ymddiriedolaethau wynebu argyfwng ariannol. Ni ddylai ymestyniad "dewis" y claf ar draws darpariaeth y gwasanaethau iechyd gael diarddel ymhellach na pheri mwy o anfantais i gleifion sy'n methu gwneud dewis oherwydd eu hanalluogrwydd meddyliol neu oherwydd pwerau gorfodi cyfreithiol yng nghyswllt eu triniaeth.

Disgrifiwn derfynau'r gyfraith bresennol ar iechyd y meddwl lle mae straen yn y cwestiwn, gyda thrafodaeth o tua deugain achos yn y llys, ac archwiliad mwy cyffredinol o ddefnyddio pwerau cyfreithiol mewn ffyrdd, efallai, na fwriadwyd gan y Llywodraeth, yn aml am resymau pragmatig lle mae'r proffesiynolion yn awyddus i ymyrryd yn yr hyn y maent yn deall i fod o fudd i'r unigolyn neu fel mesur o drefn gymdeithasol. Am y rhesymau hyn, erfyniwn ar y Senedd i sicrhau bod deddfwriaeth iechyd meddwl newydd yn cael ei diffinio a'i chyfyngu'n ofalus.

Mae'r adroddiad yn trafod agweddau ar ddefnyddio pwerau iechyd meddwl presennol mewn perthynas â'r drefn sifil ar gyfer cadw'n gaeth a phwerau'r heddlu, ac rydym yn cynnwys trafodaeth estynedig ar gadw'n orfodol droseddwyr sydd ag anhwylder meddwl. Darparwn ddadansoddiad o farwolaethau cleifion a gedwid yn gaeth; digwyddiadau dal o'r neilltu y rhoddwyd gwybod amdanynt i'r Comisiwn; a gweithgarwch Ail Farn yn ystod y cyfnod hwn.

Mae dyfarniad Strasbwrg 2004 *HL yn erbyn y Deyrnas Unedig* wedi bwrw amheuaeth ar yr ymrwymiad polisi o ran ffafrio triniaeth anffurfiol i bobl ag anhwylder meddwl, sydd wedi parhau ers sefydlu'r GIG. Anogwn y Llywodraeth i fabwysiadu mesurau diogelu addas yn erbyn cadw de facto tra'n gwylio rhag ailgyflwyniad anfwriadol egwyddorion gofal nawddoglyd tebyg i drefn Deddf y Tlodion. Mae hyn yn gofyn canolbwyntio cryf ar fesurau i annog a chefnogi rhoi grym i bawb o'n cleifion, gan gynnwys y rheini sydd heb y gallu meddyliol i wneud rhai penderfyniadau ynglŷn â'u gofal. Mi all mesurau o'r fath adeiladu ar y gwaith helaeth sydd wedi'i wneud o fewn gwasanaethau iechyd meddwl yng nghyswllt ymwybyddiaeth ag iawnderau dynol dros y blynyddoedd diwethaf: dylai gwasanaethau iechyd a'r Llywodraeth weld gofal iechyd boddhaol sy'n rhoi grym yn hawl a ddylai fod yn nwylo pobl ag anhwylderau meddwl.

I gloi, adolygwn drefniadau arfaethedig y dyfodol ar gyfer monitro cadw pobl ag anhwylderau meddwl yn gaeth ac awgrymwn ffyrdd y gallai'r Mesur Iechyd Meddwl sydd ar y gweill gael ei wella er mwyn sicrhau derbynioldeb i bobl sydd ag anhwylderau meddwl yr un pryd â diogelu'u hiawnderau'n effeithiol.

I always recall that when Nye Bevan wrote his book he did not call it *In Place of Pain* or *In Place of Illness*; he called it *In Place of Fear*, and therefore the welfare of people for whom I am responsible is much wider than just disease or illness. It is about a feeling of security and a feeling of care, a feeling of belonging and a feeling of serenity.

Secretary of State for Health (Dr John Reid MP), *October 2003*

Evidence before the House of Commons Select Committee on Health[1]

Society or the Legislature, who shut up patients not only for their own benefit, but for the benefit of society as well ... should most jealously respect all [their] other rights

John Perceval, *July 1859*

Evidence before the Select Committee of the House of Commons on Lunatics[2]

---

[1] House of Commons Health Committee Minutes of evidence for Thursday 30 October 2003. HC 1109-ii. (published 4 December 2003), Q256.

[2] Quoted in Hunter, R. & McAlpine, I. (1963) *300 years of Psychiatry*, p.994

Introduction –
In Place of Fear?

(i) Fear of illness – indeed of death itself – is a constituent part of human experience. For many people mental disorder holds a particular horror, linked perhaps to the idea that some of its forms, such as psychosis or dementia, have the potential to disable our sense of selfhood or identity. Neither governments nor their health and social care services can be expected to address such existential fears, although there is a health education role to show that many people with serious mental disorder are not so affected, and have fulfilling, useful and successful lives whether or not they continue to live with a chronic condition. But if Government is not able directly to soothe the fear of the disease itself, it does have a role (which the quotation opposite from the Rt Hon Dr Reid highlights) in addressing fears over the social consequences of the disease. These fears are, again, deeply ingrained in the case of mental disorder, based perhaps upon the experience of generations for whom it could herald impoverishment, marginalisation, criminalisation or infantilisation, and ultimately incarceration in places that were held to be frightening and hopeless:

> poor thing, they say that she was but the other morning saying, she knew she must go to Bethlem for life…; that she had often as she passed Bedlam thought it likely "here it may be my fate to end my days" – conscious of a certain flightiness in her poor head oftentimes, & mindful of more than one severe illness of that Nature before.

Charles Lamb, letter to S T Coleridge, 3 October 1796[3]

(ii) Yet, despite Ministerial acknowledgement of Government's direct role in providing 'security, belonging and care' to people with mental disorder, the concept and terminology of 'fear' continues to stalk mental health services over fifty years after Bevan published his book. In the view of many mental health groups this is in part because the presentation of Government policy has overstressed the dangerousness of the seriously mentally disordered as a justification for controversial elements of the draft Mental Health Bill. Whether or not this charge has merit, it should be remembered that populist or opportunist policy approaches respond to prejudice just as much as they may cause it. The popular prejudice

---

3   From Marrs EW jr (1975) *The letters of Charles and Mary Anne Lamb Volume I: Letters of Charles Lamb 1796-1801*; Cornell University Press, p.49. The subject of this letter is Charles' sister and literary collaborator Mary, who had a fortnight before ran amok whilst setting the dinner table and killed their mother with a knife through the heart, also wounding their father with a fork. Mary's confinement was for relatively short periods (and initially not in a public hospital) in large part through her brother's intercessions, and Charles remained her principal carer for nearly forty years until his own death.

against the mentally ill is often at its most naked in community reactions against the proposed siting of mental health units in residential areas. The hostility of communities may yet undermine the successful implementation of meaningful 'care in the community' policies, leaving patients in frightened isolation in their own homes, or contained within smaller, geographically scattered versions of the institutions that community care was meant to replace.

(iii) Stigma and fear are self-perpetuating, and perpetuate poor engagement or compliance with mental health services, as the Sainsbury Centre for Mental Health 'Circles of Fear' report recognised specifically in the context of patients from Black and minority ethnic communities:

> service users become reluctant to ask for help or to comply with treatment, increasing the likelihood of a personal crisis, leading in some cases to self-harm of harm to others. In turn, prejudices are reinforced and provoke even more coercive responses, resulting in a downward spiral, which we call 'circles of fear', in which staff see service users as potentially dangerous and service users perceive services as harmful.[4]

We continue to see an acute service stretched to its limit, understaffed and undervalued, caring for patients with increasing severity of illness. Patients report being frightened in such wards, and will therefore be frightened of readmission, perhaps avoiding future contact with services as a result. As this increases the risks of readmission in an emergency, the circles of fear could be enveloping a number of acute care services.

(iv) The widespread championing of community-based interventions as the 'progressive' aspect of mental health services in contrast to inpatient admission, has damaged the status of inpatient services and been a causative factor in the relative neglect of hospital ward-based psychiatry. Staffing shortages; the widespread difficulties in recruitment and retention of experienced teams in inpatient services; and unacceptable inpatient environments are in part a result of experienced mental health professionals and resources being drawn towards more prestigious community-based services. We support the idea of community care (although we are wary of some of the practices that it may euphemistically describe[5]), and we endorse the overall cautious optimism and celebration of 'tremendous transformation' shown by the Sainsbury Centre for Mental Health in *Beyond the Water Towers*, their recent overview of twenty years of mental health services[6]. But our immediate focus is narrower than the whole of mental health services, and the sector to which our remit confines us (the care and treatment of patients who are detained under the Act) is in danger of being the poor relation of what has for many years (whether justifiably or not) been thought of as a 'Cinderella' service[7].

---

[4]   Sainsbury Centre for Mental Health (2002) *Breaking the Circles of Fear: A review of the relationship between mental health services and African and Caribbean communities.* London: Sainsbury Centre for Mental Health.

[5]   In particular, many 'community' services are residential in nature, and in some circumstances may amount to no lesser deprivation of liberty than residence in hospital (see Chapter 2.54 below).

[6]   Bell A & Lindsay P (2005) *Beyond the Water Towers: The unfinished revolution in mental health services 1985 – 2005.* London; Sainsbury Centre for Mental Health.

[7]   'For too long mental health has been seen as the 'Cinderella service' of the health service. But this has changed. Mental health is a key priority for the Government. We've invested record amounts of money in

(v)   We welcome the refocus on inpatient services promised in the National Director for Mental Health's five-year progress report on the implementation of the National Service Framework and evidenced in the announced funding for inpatient environments[8]. This should try to address the imbalances discussed above, by refocusing on the therapeutic environment in inpatient units and seeking to ensure that the rewards of nursing in inpatient care are equivalent to those for community practice. However community services may develop, admissions to hospital (or at least some form of 'asylum' in the non-pejorative sense) will still be required for acute crises where patients may pose a danger to themselves or to others, or simply cannot be properly cared for outside of a residential context. Hospital admission should not be seen as a failure of care, and the positive aspects of inpatient care need to be emphasised, along with the special skills that inpatient nursing requires[9].

(vi) We are increasingly being informed of mental health services at crisis level due to funding or other resource deficits, notwithstanding the increased funding arranged by Government. As we go to press, Commissioners are reporting some NHS Trusts reducing their spending on mental health services – often focusing on inpatient provision as the highest-cost service where most savings can be made – to meet spending deficits, not all of which relate to mental health services. Some services have frozen staff recruitment or other forms of investment, with some ward closures and mergers already having taken place and more likely. Equally worrying, we have been told by some clinicians that they have not been involved in managerial decisions and are reluctant to speak out against closures of their services, even within the Trust management structures, for fear of the consequences of being labeled as whistle-blowers. The substantial changes relating to PCT restructuring and budget overspends are having an impact both on Trusts and on the services they are able to provide. Service developments that involve significant expenditure and/or strategic decision making by purchasers are becoming increasingly problematic during this period of uncertainty. During the next twelve months of visiting it is likely that Commissioners will see the impact on local services.

(vii) There is some evidence that, under current service provision, people suffering with mental disorders do not always find it easy to get the help that they require. In a *Rethink* survey of over 3,000 service-users in 2003, one in four reported being turned away when seeking help over the previous three years[10]. This should give us pause when considering Government's plans to extend the scope of compulsion in psychiatric treatment under the next Mental Health Act. Responses from service users to those plans have already demonstrated the potential for a focus on compulsion to further alienate the people who, in the end, are the targets of the health interventions that mental health law seeks to support. There may be a case for the framework of legal compulsion to extend to patients that are not detained in

---

the service and I'm pleased to see that the money is getting through to the frontline, in the shape of a much needed boost to the mental health workforce. There will now be more people on the ground, *in the community*, providing help and support to patients where they need it'. Health Minister Rosie Winterton MP, speech to the National Mental Health Nursing Conference, July 2005. Emphasis ours. Department of Health 'Key targets met in mental health reform programme' press release 2005/0242 (11 July).

[8]   Department of Health (2004) *The National Service Framework for Mental Health – Five Years On*, (2005) Press release 2005/0354

[9]   See John Carvel 'Siege Mentality' *The Guardian*, 25 May 2005.

[10] Rethink (2003) *Just One Per Cent ; the experiences of people using mental health services.*

hospital, but in our view such an argument can be less convincingly based upon expectations of increased compliance or public safety than on an acknowledgement that many patients with admission or recall to hospital now are subject to similar coercion outside of any legal safeguards (see Chapter 3.57–8 below).

(viii)   It is important, therefore, that the Government focuses on positive measures that could improve inpatient services, which will in turn encourage patients' positive engagement, and break the circles of fear.

(ix)   Alongside the promise of increased resources for inpatient care, we are pleased to note the Ministerial-level support received for work aimed at tackling ethnic inequalities following the publication of the David Bennett Inquiry report[11]. In this reporting period the Minister has launched the *Delivering Race Equality* five-year action plan[12] and given personal support to the delivery of the National Mental Health and Ethnicity Census 2005. The report on the National results from the 2005 Census, whilst showing severe overrepresentation of Black and minority ethnic patients in inpatient care subject to compulsion, provides for the first time a base-line national picture from which to measure the effectiveness of ongoing interventions.

The need for clarity in mental health law

(x)   The title of our last Biennial Report[13] was taken from the writings of John Perceval, a service user voice of the nineteenth century, who described himself to a Parliamentary Select Committee as the 'attorney-general of all Her Majesty's madmen'[14]. The complaints that Perceval raised over his detention in hospitals during the 1830s ('I was placed amongst strangers, without introduction, explanation or exhortation … the assumed premise immediately acted upon was that I was to yield, my desires set aside, my few remaining privileges to be infringed upon for the convenience of others'), and his use of the language of rights to express his concerns, struck us as having a marked relevance today. In the quotation from Perceval at the head of this introduction we see that, standing before a Parliamentary Committee nearly 150 years ago, he acknowledged that mental health law was about personal health and public safety, but required of that law that it should jealously respect such rights that are not necessarily curtailed by psychiatric compulsion. In the last reporting period we have echoed his sentiments in the same context[15].

(xi)   Mental health law relating to compulsory detention and treatment must establish clear boundaries over its application. Only in this way can it serve its dual purpose of empowering professionals to act whilst protecting patients from unwarranted interference

---

[11]   Norfolk, Suffolk and Cambridgeshire Strategic Health Authority *Independent Inquiry into the death of David Bennett*. December 2003. See Chapters 2.33, 2.99, 4.158, 4.211 *et seq* below.

[12]   Department of Health (2005) *Delivering Race Equality in Mental Health Care*. January 2005

[13]   Mental Health Act Commission (2003) *Placed Amongst Strangers: Tenth Biennial Report 2001-2003*. London, Stationery Office. An electronic version can also be accessed at www.mhac.org.uk

[14]   See *Placed Amongst Strangers*, pages 22-3 for the quotation and details on John Perceval (1803-1876)

[15]   See Joint Committee on the Draft Mental Health Bill (2005) *Draft Mental Health Bill*. Vol 2, Ev 13-49 (evidence of MHAC).

in their human rights. Many service users and mental health organisations are concerned that the motivation behind the draft Mental Health Bills published to date have been, in the words of *Community Care*, 'an incongruous throwback to nineteenth-century ideas of social control'[16]. We do not take this view, although we do believe that Government has been slow to recognise the dangers of proposing broadly defined powers that can be used to override personal autonomy in the name of mental health interventions. We have written in detail before of our concerns over the broadly defined and therefore ambiguous powers that the Bills would have given to practitioners and authorities over patients, particularly in relation to the over-inclusive definitions of mental disorder and conditions for compulsion, and unrestricted powers to attach conditions to community-based orders that could govern any aspect of a patient's life[17]. We hope that the Mental Health Bill introduced to Parliament this session will address these concerns, or that Parliament will do so in debating the Bill.

(xii)   We frequently see the boundaries of the present law under stress. In this reporting period, for example, we have had involvement or been told of cases where authority to give a diabetic patient insulin was sought under Mental Health Act powers; where allegations were made of the use of s.136 to remove drunk persons from public places; where a 33-stone man with Prader-Willi Syndrome was detained under the Act for a week before being released on the grounds that he was not mentally disordered[18]; where prisoners under anti-terror legislation were admitted to Broadmoor Hospital against the clinical advice of the doctors who would treat them there; and where a prisoner was transferred to hospital at the end of his prison sentence despite scant evidence of a treatable mental disorder. Notwithstanding the Government's clear retraction of its proposal to extend psychiatric compulsion to within the prison curtilage, we were approached by one health authority seeking our views on whether prison facilities could be designated as hospitals to receive prisoners whose mental disorder warranted use of Mental Health Act transfer powers[19].

(xiii)   We also note the tendency for legal powers to be applied in circumstances far removed from those originally contemplated. In the last two years we have seen:

- an outcry over the use of Anti-Social Behaviour Orders in an attempt to contain the behaviour of mentally disordered people[20], including an order banning a suicidal woman from going near rivers, railways, bridges and multi-storey car parks after police complained of her repeated attempts to kill herself[21]; the application by North Wales Police for an ASBO banning a mentally-disordered woman with twenty years user-experience from local mental health clinic[22]; separate incidents where ASBOs have been

---

[16]   'Pandering to prejudice' (editorial comment) *Community Care* 4-10 July 2002, p.5

[17]   Joint Committee on the Draft Mental Health Bill (2005) *Draft Mental Health Bill*. Vol 2, Ev 13, para 3(b) (evidence of MHAC).

[18]   See 'Chris works off nine stone in gym' hastingstoday.co.uk 28 July 2005.

[19]   We responded to this request by stating that we thought the suggestion to be misconceived, in that it was and remains a policy aim that mentally disordered prisoners who require inpatient treatment should be transferred out of the prison environment to receive it.

[20]   NAPO (2005) *Anti Social Behaviour Orders – analysis of the first six years*. www.napo.org.uk; Jon Robbins 'Asbo aggro' *The Guardian* 7 July 2005.

[21]   *Solicitors Journal* Vol 149 No 9. The order was made in respect of a 23 year-old woman by magistrates in Bath in March 2005.

imposed upon a twelve year old girl and a fifteen year old boy, both with Tourette's syndrome, banning them from swearing in public; and an order banning another 15 year old boy with Aspergers' syndrome from staring over a garden fence[23]; (for discussion of MHAC concerns over the potential for proposed Mental Health Act powers to be used as a 'psychiatric ASBO' see Chapters 2.61 and 3.70 below); and

- the creep into wider use of procedures established in one exceptional context ('special advocate' arrangements developed in anti-terrorism cases, where disclosure of sources and information to the accused had been deemed inimical to national security). In July 2005 the Lords of Appeal by majority allowed that the Parole Board could adopt closed hearings, with disclosure to an appointed special advocate, when hearing the case of a man convicted in 1966 of killing three police officers on the way to commit armed robbery[24]. Arrangements that had been adopted on grounds of national security (and after Parliamentary scrutiny) were therefore applied in a quite different context not considered by Parliament[25].

(xiv) In this report we give considerable space to reporting cases in court over the last two years, and we hope that readers will find our account useful and instructive. We have written before of the increasing intensity of legal challenge to mental health legislation[26], and whilst the Council of Europe Commissioner for Human Rights has cited as exemplary the frequency and thoroughness with which Convention rights have been analysed in UK Court rulings since the adoption of the Human Rights Act[27], it is increasingly difficult for practitioners to keep up with the current state of the law.

(xv) For these reasons we cannot accept that the powers provided under mental health legislation should be curtailed only through the checks and balances of professional judgment, advocacy and the Tribunal. We do not find it difficult to envisage the inappropriate use, however well-intentioned, of mental health legislation for disproportionate medical interventions in the lives of the mentally disordered of for non-medical interventions for the purposes of social control[28]. For the law to be of value – to patients, mental health professionals, police, the courts or the Tribunal – its meaning cannot rest upon the discretion of those working within its framework.

---

[22] 'Woman's reign of terror at health centre', *North Wales Weekly News*, 6 July 2004

[23] Martin Bright 'Children with autism the target of ASBOs' *The Observer*, 22 May 2005; Robert Verkaik 'The Asbo Generation: More children than adults given antisocial orders' *The Independent* 20 June 2005. The British Institute for Brain Injured Children has unearthed a number of examples of ASBO applications and impositions against children with mental illness or learning disability. In many cases, ASBOs are now accompanied by 'naming and shaming' order, risking the public pillory of mentally disordered people.

[24] *Roberts v Parole Board* [2005] UKHL 45. In the light of this decision, it could be open to other statutory Tribunals (including the MHRT) to adopt this practice where the safety of a source of information or evidence would be endangered by disclosure to either the appellant or the appellant's legal representative. In one dissenting opinion Lord Steyn referred to the decision as potentially auguring 'an open ended process of piling exception upon exception' (paragraph 92).

[25] *per* Lord Steyn, *Roberts v Parole Board, supra.*

[26] MHAC (2003) *Placed Amongst Strangers: Tenth Biennial Report*, Chapter 6.5.

[27] Office of the Commissioner for Human Rights, Council of Europe (2005) *Report by Mr Alvaro Gil-Robles, Commissioner for Human Rights, on his visit to the United Kingdom 4th – 12th November 2004.* CommDH(2005)6. Strasbourg, 8 June 2005, para 79.

[28] Kinton M 'Mental Health Law for the 21st Century?' *Journal of Mental Health Law* (May 2005) 12: 57-69

The House of Lords' *Munjaz* ruling – 'a set-back for a modern and just mental health law'?

(xvi) Alongside many uncertainties in mental health law over this reporting period (including the content of the next Mental Health Bill, the Government's awaited response to *HL v United Kingdom*, and the future of the MHAC itself) there was also the appeal to the House of Lords of the Court of Appeal's 2003 judgment in *Munjaz*. We welcomed and discussed the 2003 *Munjaz* judgment in our last report[29].

(xvii) On the 13 October 2005 the House of Lords overturned the 2003 Court of Appeal ruling. The overturned ruling[30] had used powers under s.3 of the Human Rights Act 1998 to elevate the legal status of the Code of Practice, on the basis that only a strong Code could ensure transparency and predictability required for the lawful application of otherwise unregulated powers over psychiatric patients. The highest domestic court rejected this approach by a majority of three to two, allowing that detaining authorities may develop policies and practices of their own provided that these do not themselves breach fundamental rights established under the European Convention. The Lords of Appeal therefore declared that the Code of Practice has the status of guidance and should not be read as having legal force.

(xviii) At the heart of the House of Lords' ruling is the question of the role and responsibility of Government in ensuring that agencies to whom it delegates powers exercise these in accordance with ECHR principles. We were disappointed that the Secretary of State intervened in the case to play down her role and responsibility in ensuring that psychiatric patients are treated lawfully and without breach of their human rights. The MHAC, in a written intervention to the House of Lords, argued (alongside the patient concerned and MIND) for the Court of Appeal's ruling to be upheld on the grounds that, for practical purposes, a strong approach to the role of the Code of Practice was the most effective means of striking an appropriate and workable balance between requirements of certainty and the flexibility that may be required by local conditions. We suggested that the issue as to the status of the Code of Practice insofar as it concerned seclusion raised the same concerns as those identified by the Strasbourg Court in *HL v United Kingdom*. There, the existence of procedural safeguards was regarded as essential to ensure protection of vulnerable persons.

(xix) We highlighted to their Lordships that the position contended for by Mersey Care NHS Trust in appealing the 2003 *Munjaz* decision did and will continue to promote disparity of practice and uncertainty in relation to the practice of seclusion. This is contrary to the interests of patients (and for that matter also of healthcare professionals) and contrary to a mental health system that recognises and promotes respect for the system of rights provided for by the Human Rights Act. Our intervention was echoed in the two dissenting speeches of the judgment. In a strongly-worded speech, Lord Steyn derided the majority view as 'a lowering of the protection offered by the law to mentally disordered patients' and 'a set-back for a modern and just mental health law'[31]. Neither dissenting judge was convinced by the

---

[29] MHAC (2003) *Placed Amongst Strangers: Tenth Biennial Report*, Chapter 3.2 *et seq*; 6.17 *et seq*; and Chapter 2 generally.

[30] *R (on the application of Colonel Munjaz) v Mersey Care NHS Trust and (1) Secretary of State for Health and (2) Mind; S v Airedale NHS Trust and (1) Secretary of State for Health and (2) Mind* [2003] EWCA Civ 1036.

[31] *R v Ashworth Hospital Authority (now Mersey Care National Health Service Trust) ex parte Munjaz* [2005] UKHL 58, para 48 (Lord Steyn)

majority's emphatic rejection that the judgment created discretion for hospitals to depart from the Code as they saw fit[32]. Lord Steyn warned of a 'free-for-all in which hospitals are at liberty to depart from the published Code as they consider right'[33], and Lord Brown similarly remarked that patients and their carers must be reconciled to substantial departures from the Code on the part of individual hospitals[34]. Lord Brown further suggested that 'hospital policies themselves provide too insubstantial a foundation for practice so potentially harmful and open to abuse as… seclusion' and that such policies may 'not have the necessary legal quality to render them compatible with the rule of law'[35].

R v Ashworth Hospital Authority (now Mersey Care National Health Service Trust) ex parte Munjaz [2005] UKHL 58.

MHAC guidance on the effect of the change

The practical effect of this judgment is that detaining authorities may now lawfully adopt and apply their own policies on seclusion or any other matter dealt with in the Code of Practice, and such policies or practices may depart from the Code's guidance provided that they do not in themselves breach the ECHR. Prior to their Lordships' ruling, adoption or application of policy-level departures from the Code of Practice guidance on issues that engage European Convention on Human Rights (ECHR) issues would have been unlawful.

It was stressed by the majority view of their Lordships that their decision should not be seen as an invitation to other hospitals to substantially depart from the Code's guidance in resorting to their own policies[36]. Whilst the majority of their Lordships concluded that the Code of Practice is to be viewed as guidance rather than instruction, they also concurred that such guidance is 'more than something to which those to whom it is addressed must have regard to'[37], and which should be given due weight and from which any departure should be supported by 'cogent' reasons[38]. The MHAC will expect and require the production of full documentation by detaining authorities of their decision-making processes and reasoning behind any departures from the Code's guidance on the basis of this judgment.

The statement in the introduction to the Code of Practice is now once again an accurate description of its legal status:

> The Act does not impose a legal duty to comply with the Code but as it is a statutory document, failure to follow it could be referred to in evidence in legal proceedings.

Fig 1: MHAC summary of the effects of the House of Lords' *Munjaz* judgment

---

[32] See for example, *ibid.*, para 69 (Lord Hope)

[33] *ibid.*, para 44 (Lord Steyn)

[34] *ibid.*, para 127 (Lord Brown)

[35] *ibid.*, para 127 (Lord Brown)

[36] *ibid.*, para 99 (Lord Hope). In a dissenting speech by Lord Steyn, however, this was suggested as the practical result of the majority judgment: see paragraph (xix) above.

[37] *ibid.*, para 68 (Lord Hope)

[38] *ibid.*, paras 21 (Lord Bingham), 107 (Lord Scott)

(xx) We set out at figure 1 above a summary of our view on the effect of the change instigated by their Lordships' judgment. We discuss the case in relation to seclusion practice at Chapter 4.238 below. We will be monitoring closely the practical effects of this judgment on mental health services. Where visiting Commissioners consider that the care and treatment of any detained patient deviates from or appears unsupported by the requirements of the Code, they will emphasise to the service provider that the House of Lords' judgment maintained that authorities are expected to follow the Code's guidance except where they may have a 'cogent' reason to depart from it. It will be for future courts to define what is or is not a 'cogent' reason for departing from the Code's guidance. Commissioners will expect and require the production of full documentation by detaining authorities of their decision-making processes and reasoning behind any departures from the Code's guidance on the basis of this judgment[39].

Reception of *Placed Amongst Strangers*: the Tenth Biennial Report of the MHAC

(xxi) The Commission's Tenth Biennial Report, *Placed Amongst Strangers*, was published in December 2003. It contained 70 recommendations, most of which were addressed to Government. As this report went to press we received an official response from Government, acknowledging the report as 'an invaluable reference', whose discussion and recommendations have been considered by policy makers and cross-governmental groups (including the mental health legislation team at the Department of Health and the cross-government group for the recognition, prevention and management of violence for people with mental health problems). We continue to press for our recommendations to be implemented.

(xxii) The report has had a wide circulation amongst mental health professionals and was positively reviewed in the *Journal of Mental Health Law* as 'an important document', 'stimulating and challenging to all those involved with the operation, management or provision of mental healthcare services at whatever level, from hospital ward staff to Government Ministers' that 'should certainly be included in the library of every psychiatric unit in England and Wales where there are detained patients'[40].

The Government's response to *HL v United Kingdom* and future mental health law

(xxiii) Aneurin Bevan's *In Place of Fear* argued for the integration of mental health services into mainstream healthcare, on the grounds that 'the separation of mental and physical healthcare is a survival of primitive conceptions and is a source of endless cruelty and neglect. The mentally ill are looked upon as people who have stepped outside normal intercourse and this fact itself often accentuates and perpetuates the trouble'[41]. Bevan's solution was the siting of at least assessment-level mental health services in general hospitals, and continued stress on informal care as the treatment of choice. He included

---

[39]   As per Lord Hope, *ibid.*, para 69

[40]   Humphreys M 'The Mental Health Act Commission Tenth Biennial Report 2001-2003' *Journal of Mental Health Law* (September 2004) 11: 170-3.

[41]   Bevan A (1952) *In Place of Fear*, Chapter 5, Note 17. (London, Quartet Books, 1978)

statistics, in a book not overburdened with statistical tables, on the increase in 'voluntary' admissions from the first year of implementation of the Mental Treatment Act 1930, where 7% (1,495) of admissions were voluntary, to the first full year of the Welfare State, where 63% (32,345) of admissions were voluntary[42]. As we discuss at Chapter of 4.2 of this report, there is no simple comparable data available today to contrast informal and formal treatment, but by our calculation in this report it would appear that informal admission accounts for around 90% of all psychiatric admissions but that formal treatment occurs at some point in approximately one-fifth of all admissions[43]. In the National Mental Health and Ethnicity Census 2005 we found that roughly 60% of resident psychiatric patients were informal[44].

(xxiv) The judgment of *HL v United Kingdom* has cast into doubt the continuing policy commitment towards informal treatment which has been held by all United Kingdom governments since the founding of the NHS. The European Court determined in October 2004 that the informal reception of a patient into conditions that amount to a deprivation of liberty is incompatible with Convention rights for detention to be effected only with sufficient legal process, including established criteria and review.

(xxv) The judgment could be interpreted (and may be so interpreted unless there is a public policy decision otherwise) to limit 'voluntary' treatment to such persons as are actively capable of consent. This would be to regress to the position that pertained prior to the 1930 Act, ironically at a time when Government is undergoing its long and painful gestation of new legislation to 'modernise' the 1959 and 1983 Acts.

(xxvi) Indeed, the irony of today's 'modernisation' of mental health law is that it may create a framework that is similar structurally to that set aside in the reforms of the 1950s:

- the proposed legal framework reestablishes judicial certification as the civil compulsory commitment procedure, and will therefore having a closer resemblance to the Lunacy Act 1890 than to the twentieth century's attempts to lessen legal formalities[45], and

- it does this at a time when the European Court's decision leaves Government considering mechanisms for ensuring due legal process, criteria and review of informal

---

[42] *ibid.*

[43] According to Bartlett and Sandland, formal admissions account for around 10% of all psychiatric admissions. Our comparable calculation of 20% includes patients who are admitted informally but then made subject to the Act during that hospital episode. See Bartlett P and Sandland R (2003) *Mental Health Law: Policy and Practice*, second ed, Oxford University Press, p.24.

[44] See Healthcare Commission, MHAC, and NIMHE (2005) *Count Me In: National Mental Health and Ethnicity Census 2005*, National Results. The National Census did not extend to Learning Disability units in 2005, which limits the comparability of its findings with national statistics over MHA usage. Although only about one percent of admissions under s.3 of the Act (and less than half of one per cent of Part III admissions) in 2003/04 appear to be of patients with a primary diagnosis of Learning Disability, one in fourteen detained patients resident in hospital in 2004 had such a primary diagnosis. (See Department of Health Statistical Bulletin *Inpatients formally detained in hospitals under the Mental Health Act 1983* 2004/22).

[45] The Lunacy Act 1890 introduced judicial authority for ordering the detention of the mentally disordered through petition (supported by medical recommendations) to a justice of the peace by a patient's relative in private cases (ss.4-8); or by the Poor Law Receiving Officer or the police in pauper cases (ss.13-22). The 1890 Act was described by Kathleen Jones as 'from the legal point of view, ...very near perfect. From the medical and social point of view, it was to hamper the progress of the mental health movement for nearly seventy years' until it was replaced with the Mental Health Act 1959. The Royal Commission of 1954-7 took evidence from several sources that the process of certification was a source of stigma, which led them to recommend the abolition of all formalities in voluntary admission and a simplification of formal admission procedures (Jones K (1960) *Mental Health and Social Policy*, 1845-1959. Routledge & Kegan Paul).

treatment for incapacitated patients. Arguably, such mechanisms must mirror the essential safeguards for current civil detention, which have their basis in the 1930 Mental Treatment Act's 'temporary treatment without certification' measures[46].

(xxvii) Perhaps, however, it is possible to introduce safeguards to patients whose hospital treatment amounts to a deprivation of liberty whilst without returning to the overt paternalism of the mid-twentieth century. The key to this must be in initiating or retaining a focus on the empowerment of all patients, including persons incapacitated by their mental disorder, to play as active a role as possible in their care-planning and daily lives. Rather than envisaging 'care' as something passively received by patients, and supplied on the basis of society's moral generosity, we must ensure that decent and empowering health care and support are viewed as a *right* (indeed as a part of human rights) for all psychiatric patients[47].

> 'All the times I've been sectioned, I've never, ever been given information on the Mental Health Act. I didn't know what was going on. I thought I was being punished, and didn't know why. Because it's an 'Act', I thought I had broken the law'.
>
> *female s.2 patient, Oxfordshire*

(xxviii) From this starting-point, a framework of 'protective care'[48] in answer to the *HL v United Kingdom* would already appear to be encumbered with language that could militate against any real benefit for the patients concerned. Terminology can bring stigma and discrimination, and the reintroduction of safeguards for certain informally treated psychiatric patient must not be the cover for the unintentional reinstatement of 'Poor-Law principles'[49]. Indeed, the introduction of safeguards against inappropriate healthcare interventions in the lives of the incapacitated need not undermine an approach based upon patient empowerment, but could support it. The MHAC has long called for its own remit to be extended to patients who are *de facto* detained, and similarly automatic referrals to a tribunal-style review body and access to advocacy should have a part to play. Some form of admission record that requires professionals to justify their actions against established criteria need not mean the end of 'informal' admission; only that professionals will be accountable for their decisions. We discuss these matters in more detail at Chapter 3.1 *et seq* below.

---

[46] The Mental Treatment Act 1930 created 'temporary treatment without certification [under the Lunacy Act]' for voluntary patients (i.e. patients who had submitted to treatment by written application) who became incapable of expressing themselves as willing or unwilling to continue to accept treatment subsequent to admission. With the exception of an absolute time-limit (one year), the legal framework of safeguards built around 'temporary treatment' would be familiar to today's practitioners: it required an application by a relative or local authority worker (the latter either acting upon the instigation of the former or explaining why this is not the case); two supporting medical recommendations; an initial detention period of no more than six months before renewal; and powers of discharge afforded to the Board of Control. Thus the procedures for informal treatment after 1931 became the civil admission procedures under the 1959 Act, and provide the basis of current law for detention under civil powers. (Exley CH (1932) *The Guide to Poor Relief*. Meek, Thomas & Co Ltd., Liverpool, appendix, p.159.)

[47] See Barham P (1992) *Closing the Asylum: The Mental Patient in Modern Society*. London: Penguin, p.112-3

[48] Department of Health (2005) *Bournewood Consultation: The approach to be taken in response to the judgment of the European Court of Human Rights in the 'Bournewood' case*. March 2005, Chapter 5: 'the Government is inclined to adopt an approach entitled 'Protective Care'. This approach would consist of a new system to govern admission/detention procedures, reviews of detention and appeals'.

[49] Barham P (1992) *supra*, p.113. On the other hand, we are concerned that 'consumer-led' structures of health care delivery will not, without intervention, meet the needs of patients without capacity or who are legally disadvantaged from exercising choice (see Chapter 2.64 *et seq* below). In the case of many patients, but especially the incapacitated or detained, the consumer exercising choice on their behalf is the authority purchasing services that they will receive.

The Mental Health Act in the Courts

The wide-spread malaise of over-burdened courts and excessively slow justice does not extend to the United Kingdom, whose courts might serve … as a model of efficiency to other countries in Europe.

Alvaro Gil-Robles, *Council of Europe Commissioner for Human Rights, June 2005*[1]

As is widely known, the Administrative Court at present is inundated … with applications for judicial review…

Silber J, *January 2005*[2]

Incapacitated but compliant patients and deprivation of liberty: the *Bournewood* case

HL v the United Kingdom
(Application no 4508/99) Decision of 5th October 2004

1.1   The background and broader context of this case was discussed in our Tenth Biennial Report[3], but an outline of the domestic court proceedings is as follows.

1.2   *HL*, a profoundly autistic adult, was informally admitted to hospital in 1997 in response to a minor incident at a day-centre that he attended. His paid carers, with whom he had lived for over three years[4], but whose access to *HL* was restricted during the hospital admission, disagreed with the hospital admission and commenced judicial review proceedings with a writ of *habeas corpus* requiring his discharge. At first instance this failed because the judge

---

[1]   Office of the Commissioner for Human Rights, Council of Europe (2005) *Report by Mr Alvaro Gil-Robles, Commissioner for Human Rights, on his visit to the United Kingdom 4th – 12th November 2004.* CommDII(2005)6. Strasbourg, 8 June 2005, para 78.

[2]   Silber J, *obiter, R (on the application of B) v (1) Dr SS, (2) Dr AC and The Secretary of State for the Department of Health* [2005] EWHC 86 (Admin), para 69.

[3]   MHAC (2003) *Tenth Biennial Report; Placed Amongst Strangers.* Chapter 8.1 *et seq.*

[4]   *HL* had been placed with his carers as part of an 'adult-fostering' scheme upon the closure of the long-stay institution in which he had resided for over 30 years.

did not accept that *HL* was detained[5], but the Court of Appeal found to the contrary, on the grounds that professionals would have prevented him from leaving had he attempted to do so. The Court further determined that informal treatment was only available to patients with capacity to consent, and that the common law doctrine of necessity (by which restrictions on *HL*'s liberty of person might otherwise be justified) could only arise in relation to situations not covered by the Mental Health Act 1983[6].

1.3   This judgment was appealed to the House of Lords at Government instigation, partly on the grounds that its implications could lead to a doubling of the numbers of patients detained under the 1983 Act. In 1999, the House of Lords overturned the Court of Appeal judgment, taking the view that the common law doctrine of necessity did authorise *HL*'s admission to hospital, and that an similarly incapacitated but compliant patient could therefore be admitted and treated in hospital without recourse to the Mental Health Act, even where such admission amounted to detention[7]. Lord Steyn's remark that their Lordships' decision left 'an indefensible gap in mental health law' regarding the protection of incapacitated compliant patients gave currency to the phrase 'the Bournewood gap', and flagged a public policy issue whose resolution is still unclear at the time that we go to press. Following the House of Lords' judgment, *HL*'s carers applied to the European Court of Human Rights (ECtHR) arguing that *HL*'s human rights, particularly in relation to Article 5 of the European Convention, had been denied.

1.4   The ECtHR ruled in October 2004, more than a year after its hearing of the case. Its judgment established that:

(i)   *HL*'s hospital admission and care under common law did amount to a deprivation of liberty (and therefore 'detention') in that 'the health care professionals treating and managing the applicant exercised complete and effective control over his care and movements;'[8]

(ii)   Such detention, which involved no procedural safeguards (i.e. established criteria, thresholds or formal procedures governing admission), and had as its rationale imprecise concepts of 'best interests' and 'necessity', failed to meet the requirements of Article 5(1) of the European Convention of Human Rights (ECHR), in that it was not 'in accordance with a procedure prescribed by law'; and

(iii)   Such detention also failed the requirements of Article 5(4), in that *HL* was not afforded a right to have his detention reviewed by a court.

---

[5]   Judgment of Owen LJ, 9th October 1997

[6]   *R v Bournewood Community and Mental Health NHS Trust ex parte L* [1998] 2WLR 764, per Lord Woolf MR. As a consequence *HL* was formally detained under the 1983 Act, and his carers were able to exercise rights of requesting a review on his behalf. He was discharged from hospital by a managers' hearing within weeks of being formally detained.

[7]   *R v Bournewood Community & Mental Health NHS Trust ex parte L* [1999] AC 458

[8]   *HL v the United Kingdom* (Application no 4508/99) Judgment 5th October 2004, para 90.

Deprivation of liberty

1.5 We discuss the definition of deprivation of liberty in detail at Chapter 3.5 *et seq.* The Court did not define deprivation of liberty itself, but did conclude the following:

(i) *HL* was deprived of his liberty through health care staff's assumption of complete and effective control over his care and movements;

(ii) the distinction between restrictions upon liberty and deprivation of liberty is a matter of degree, so that cumulative restrictions will eventually amount to deprivation of liberty;

(iii) the question of whether there has been any actual restraint in preventing a patient leaving, as opposed to an intention to restrain should the patient attempt to leave, is not central to the question of whether that patient is deprived of liberty; and

(iv) an incapacitated patient's compliance with any regime cannot prevent restrictions imposed from potentially amounting to a deprivation of liberty.

Procedural safeguards

1.6 The ECtHR held that detention under UK common law is 'arbitrary', mainly because of a 'dearth of regulation' that it contrasted with 'the extensive network of safeguards' of the 1983 Act[9]. The main focus of the judgment therefore concerned the procedural aspects of common law in treating incapacitated patients, rather than the common law principles underpinning such treatment. The ruling does not, however, undermine previous findings of the ECtHR that substantive as well as procedural standards are required for Article 5 compliance[10]. In UK law, such standards (i.e. the 'best interests' test) will be incorporated into statute law with the coming into force of the Mental Capacity Act 2005. Dame Butler-Sloss has stated in *NHS Trust A v Mrs M* [2001] that the 'best interests' test at common law provides a more stringent safeguard than the Convention in terms of principle[11].

1.7 The procedural failings attributed to the common law by the ECtHR were a lack of:

- formalised admission procedures which indicate who can propose admission, for what reasons and on the basis of what kind of medical or other assessment;

- a requirement to fix the exact purpose of admission (e.g. for assessment or for treatment);

---

[9] *ibid.*, para 120

[10] *Kawka v Poland* Application no. 25874/94, 9 January 2001, '…where deprivation of liberty is concerned, it is particularly important that the general principle of legal certainty is satisfied. It is therefore essential that the conditions for deprivation of liberty under domestic law should be clearly defined, and that the law itself be foreseeable in its application, so that it meets the standard of 'lawfulness' set by the Convention, a standard which requires that all law should be sufficiently precise to allow the person – if needed, to obtain the appropriate advice – to foresee, to a degree that is reasonable in the circumstances, the consequences which a given action may entail' (para 49).

[11] Butler-Sloss P. *obiter* in *NHS Trust A v Mrs M* [2001] Lloyds Rep. Med 27, 35; this was noted by Silber J in *R (on the application of B) v Drs SS and AC* [2004], para 134, discussed below at paragraph 1.53. It may be argued, however, that judicial interpretation of Convention principles has provided a renewed focus on the extent of common-law powers and their application in restricting or depriving liberty, and so there has been a reciprocal effect between the two sources of judicial principle.

- limits set on the sorts of treatment or care attached to admission, and on the duration of admission;

- a specific provision requiring continual clinical assessment of the persistence of a disorder warranting detention; and

- the nomination of a representative to make objections and applications on the patient's behalf[12].

Review by a court

1.8 Government initially took the view that rights under Article 5(4) were sufficiently protected by existing mechanisms such as judicial review and *habeas corpus*, and that the ECtHR judgment to the contrary was specific to the legal framework prior to enactment of the Human Rights Act 1998[13]. This approach appeared to have foundered in the light of the Court of Appeal's finding in *MH* (discussed at paragraph 1.87 *et seq.*), which stated that the lack of provision in s.2 of the 1983 Act for the automatic review of detentions of incapacitated patients under its powers was incompatible with Article 5(4)[14]. The Government's appeal to the House of Lords was successful in October 2005 (see paragraph 1.90 *et seq* below).

1.9 It is difficult nevertheless to see how the requirements of ECHR Article 5 can be met for 'Bournewood' patients without some mechanism similar to that established by the MHRT for patients detained under the Mental Health Act 1983. Notwithstanding the Government's successful appeal against the Court of Appeal's judgment in *MH*, we consider that giving an incapacitated patient a right of appeal that is effectively and practically negated by his or her mental disability is no safeguard at all. The review of patient's deprivation of liberty by a court should not be predicated on the detainee having a carer or friend who will exercise their right of appeal (see Chapter 4.114 below).

The Government's response

1.10 Government was originally to have addressed the 'Bournewood gap' through provisions in the draft Mental Health Bill of 2002, but at the time of the ECtHR judgment it had already taken the view that the Mental Capacity Bill was possibly the more appropriate vehicle for safeguards. The MHAC, alongside many other 'stakeholders' in the process of developing Mental Health and Mental Capacity Bills, had already expressed concern that the removal of safeguards from the former Bill to the latter had, in part through the loss of particular elements such as a second opinion modelled on Part IV of the 1983 Act, seriously weakened the potential protection of patients[15]. Following the ECtHR ruling, Government considered introducing into the Mental Capacity Bill a power to establish by regulation new powers of detention to be known as 'protective care'. The regulations would encompass both the reach

---

[12]   *HL v the United Kingdom*, para 120

[13]   Rosie Winteron MP, Evidence to the Standing Committee on the Mental Capacity Bill. *Hansard*, 28 October 2004, Col 250; see also the Department of Health statement on the judgment at its website.

[14]   Department of Health *Bournewood* consultation March 2005.

[15]   See, for example, MHAC memoranda (DMH 20 para 8.5-8.6, DMH 90 1.8-1.9) in Joint Committee on the Draft Mental Health Bill (2005) *Draft Mental Health Bill.* Vol 2, p.37-8, 49

of such powers and the safeguards against their improper use, and such scope in delegated powers was declared unacceptable by the Delegated Powers and Regulatory Reform Committee in March 2005.

1.11   At the time of writing, Government was still indicating that it was minded towards a system of 'protective care' based upon Mental Capacity Bill principles (i.e. enacted common law of necessity and best interests) as the legal framework for the care of 'Bournewood' patients[16]. *The Mental Health Act Commission response to the Department of Health 'Bournewood' Consultation* (16 June 2005) is available from or on request from the MHAC secretariat. Our concern at the language of 'protective care' is discussed at paragraph xxviii of the introduction to this report.

1.12   Further discussion of the issues raised by this case, in addition to the discussion in our introduction mentioned above, is at Chapter 3.1 *et seq* in this report.

Application of *HL v United Kingdom* in the domestic and Strasbourg courts

Guardianship Order, Re McDougall or Muldoon
[2005] ScotsSC 6 (18 January 2005)

1.13   The only application of the principle of *HL v United Kingdom* so far in domestic courts appears to have been in relation to Scottish cases regarding Guardianship under s.57 of the Adults with Incapacity (Scotland) Act 2000. In the case of *McDougall or Muldoon*, the patient concerned, Mrs *M*, was elderly and mentally incapacitated as a result of vascular dementia. She was compliant with her care, and indeed 'happily settled' in a Glasgow nursing home for which she was self-funding. She had entered the nursing home from an admission to acute care following a stroke, which had made a return to her home impracticable. She had apparently agreed to the nursing home placement, although had expressed her wish to return home upon arrival. Her son had applied to be appointed under the terms of the Incapacity Act as Guardian with powers relating to her welfare, property and financial affairs.

1.14   The sheriff summarised the criteria against which he had to measure the application as:

(i)   whether the benefit to Mrs *M* could reasonably be achieved by other means;

(ii)   whether the intervention was the least restrictive option available to achieve the aim; and

(iii)   what the past and present wishes of Mrs *M* were, so that account may be taken of these.

1.15   Applications for Guardianship under the Scottish Incapacity Act require an accompanying report by a Mental Health Officer (MHO), which gives an opinion as to the general appropriateness of the order sought and of the suitability of the candidate to be a Guardian. There was no dispute that Mrs *M*'s son was a suitable candidate, and it was accepted that

---

[16]   Department of Health (2005) *'Bournewood' Consultation; the approach to be taken in response to the judgment of the European Court of Human Rights in the 'Bournewood' case.* London, March 2005.

Mrs *M* was permanently incapacitated and unable to manage her affairs. Whilst the MHO accepted that the granting of financial powers was therefore necessary and appropriate, he advised against the granting of welfare powers on the grounds that Mrs *M* was, so far as could be ascertained, happily compliant with her care and, although she often became confused, had stated that she did not want her son to be Guardian over her in this respect. To this extent the MHO suggested that it would be appropriate to continue to treat Mrs *M* as an informal patient at the nursing home.

1.16 The court considered a discussion paper produced by the Mental Welfare Commission for Scotland on authorising significant interventions for adults who lack capacity, published before the *HL v United Kingdom* judgment was handed down[17]. This paper discussed *HM v Switzerland* and the House of Lords' determination in the *Bournewood* case, although it was noted in court that the discussion paper had explicitly anticipated that *HL v United Kingdom* would provide a definitive answer to the question of whether an adult held in a locked facility in Scotland in the absence of consent or an appropriate order could claim breach of Article 5. The sheriff's court, of course, now knew the outcome of *HL v United Kingdom* and based its judgment upon that outcome.

1.17 The Sheriff noted that the ECtHR had distinguished *HL*'s case from *HM v Switzerland* (we discuss the latter case at Chapter 3.12 below) on the grounds that it had not been established that *HM* was incapable of expressing her wishes, that she had often said she consented to admission and had eventually agreed to stay, whereas *HL* was noted to be incapacitated. He also recognised that *HM* had been determined not to have been detained due to the openness of her care regime, whereas *HL* was detained by the breadth of the control over him exercised by professionals. It was therefore concluded that the ECtHR judgment in *HL v United Kingdom* was determinative of this case, and that:

> where the adult is compliant with the regime, but is legally incapable of consenting to or disagreeing with it, then that person is deprived of his or her liberty in breach of Article 5 of the Convention, and that step should not be taken without express statutory warrant governing it… in the present case, the appropriate statutory intervention is a Guardianship Order.

1.18 The Sheriff went on to say that:

> I believe that the effect of my ruling in this case will be that every case where a court is dealing with an adult who is incapable but compliant, the least restrictive option will be the granting of a Guardianship Order under the Act (assuming of course that all the other statutory requirements are satisfied), for that way only will the necessary safeguards and statutory and regulatory framework to protect the adult (and the Guardian) come into play.

1.19 Sheriffs' courts are not empowered under Scottish law to declare statutory provisions to be incompatible with the ECHR, and in any event the sheriff in this case explicitly stated that such incompatibility did not arise were the statute to be interpreted following his guidance (i.e. requiring the use of formal powers for incapacitated patients). The case does not

---

[17] Mental Welfare Commission for Scotland (2004) *Authorising significant interventions for adults who lack capacity.* Edinburgh. www.mwcscot.org.uk/publications

establish a precedent in accordance with Scottish law and, so far, there has been no flood of applications for Guardianship or other orders as a result of its conclusion. It would seem likely that many services in Scotland, in common with their counterparts in England and Wales, are waiting for further guidance or amendment to the statutory framework before taking precipitative action. In its discussion paper, the Mental Welfare Commission had estimated that there were some 15,000 incapable adults in Scotland who could be made subject to orders. It stated that the burden on the court system and supervisory bodies, such as the Mental Welfare Commission itself, the public guardian and local authorities could be intolerable without significant extra resources[18].

Storck v Germany

(Application No 61603/00), decision of 16 June 2005

1.20   This case concerned the confinement, at her father's demand, of an 18 year old woman in a locked ward of a German private psychiatric clinic between 1977 and 1979. Her placement was paid for through compulsory health insurance[19]. She was neither subject to guardianship proceedings, nor subject to formal detention[20]. Indeed, the clinic was not one which was entitled to detain patients under the relevant domestic laws of the Federal Republic at that time, and there were no provisions for State supervision of the lawfulness or conditions of confinement in such clinics. Her father and the presiding doctor at the clinic believed her to be suffering from psychosis and she received medication for this, from which, having had polio as an infant, she developed post-poliomyelitis syndrome. Her diagnosis with psychotic illness was disputed by subsequent medical opinion. She is now registered as 100% disabled and receives an invalidity pension.

1.21   The Strasbourg Court compared the facts of this case with the finding of *HL v United Kingdom* and determined that, as it had found *HL* to have been deprived of his liberty, so in Ms *S*'s case, *a fortiori*, deprivation of liberty must be found:

- although she presented at the clinic with her father, she had at no point signed the clinic's admission form prepared for the day of her arrival. Her actions in trying to escape from the clinic on several occasions indicated that, unlike *HL*, she was not compliant with her care;

- like *HL*, she was cared for under continuous supervision in a locked ward and was not free to leave;

- she had been prevented from trying to escape on several occasions and, when she once succeeded in escaping, she had been returned to the clinic by the police.

1.22   The Court further determined that, notwithstanding the private nature of the arrangements

---

[18]   *ibid.* p.32.

[19]   It seems unlikely that the factor of *Gesetzliche Krankenversicherung* (compulsory health insurance, see judgment, para 79) in the relationship between the Federal Republic and *S*'s healthcare provision alters the latter from being analogous to private healthcare uncontracted by the State in the United Kingdom today. This question is not, in any event, cited by the ECtHR as relevant to their finding that the State was involved in *S*'s deprivation of liberty discussed above.

[20]   Under the relevant domestic law (Law on the detention of mentally insane persons (*Geisteskranken*), mentally deficient persons and drug addicts, 1962), formal psychiatric detention could be authorised by a district court solely on the grounds that the patient posed a serious threat to public safety or order by his conduct towards himself or others which could not otherwise be averted (ss.2,3).

for *S*'s care in the psychiatric clinic, the deprivation of liberty could be imputed to the State as 'public authorities became actively involved in [*S*]'s placement in the clinic' when 'in … March 1979 the police, by use of force, had brought [*S*] back to the clinic from which she had fled'[21].

1.23 The latter finding may be of great consequence to the United Kingdom Government, particularly with regard to how it conceives the requirements upon the State to put in place safeguards found wanting by the European Court in respect of its judgment in *HL*. At the very least, it would seem that where police (or other State authorities) become involved in the return or other conveyance of any private patient to a psychiatric establishment, such action must trigger some form of Article 5 safeguard to ensure that the patient's care at that establishment is not an unlawful deprivation of liberty. Indeed, it is arguable that this consequence should extend to arrangements outside of psychiatric hospitals, including residential homes but also perhaps domestic environments.

1.24 It seems unlikely that the courts will require State supervision of arrangements made within family structures in any circumstances other than those where legal interventions (Guardianship, etc) already take place, given the requirement on the State not to interfere in private and family life without good reason. However, it is possible that State oversight should extend to situations where the State has some contractual interest in that carers are paid to provide a domestic environment (as in *HL*'s case). We are uncertain whether and how such arrangements should be distinguished from those of other carers who receive State benefits and allowances consequent upon their role.

> **Recommendation 1:** Where a patient is returned by force to a care environment there should be some form of review that this is a situation of lawful detention. Government should consider instigating some safeguard mechanism for reviewing deprivation of liberty that would be triggered when any person is returned by the police or other agencies of the State to a care-environment from which they have absented themselves. Government must consider both the nature of such a review mechanism, which we suggest could take the form of a monitoring or 'second-opinion' type visit, and the range of care-environments to which it would extend.

Nearest Relatives and the right to respect for private and family life

R (on the application of E) v Bristol City Council

[2005] EWHC 74 (Admin), 23 February 2005

1.25 This case concerned the circumstances in which an Approved Social Worker (ASW) must, under s.11 of the Mental Health Act, consult and/or inform the Nearest Relative of a patient when making or considering an application to detain the patient, or make them subject to Guardianship under the Act.

---

21   See judgment, para 90.

1.26 Under s.11(3) of the Act, an ASW making an application to admit a patient to hospital for assessment under s.2 must 'take such steps as are practicable' to inform the patient's Nearest Relative of the application and of the Nearest Relative's power of discharge under s.23(2)(a). Under s.11(4), ASWs must consult the Nearest Relative before applying to admit a patient for treatment under s.3 or to Guardianship, unless consultation is 'not reasonably practical' or would involve unreasonable delay.

1.27 The claimant, *E*, had been subject to a number of detentions under the Act over the past two decades, and continued to suffer from chronic mental health problems. She had a 'very strained' relationship with her sister, who was her Nearest Relative according to the hierarchy established at s.26 of the Act. The relationship between the two sisters was deemed to be such that *E*'s consultant psychiatrist stated that her mental health could be damaged by knowledge that consultation with her sister would take place against her wishes.

1.28 In this case, *E* had asked her social services authority for an undertaking that, in the event that they were considering an application under the Act, its ASWs would not consult or inform her sister as the Nearest Relative. The authority, although sympathetic, felt that s.11 of the Act prevented them from giving this undertaking. The sister had indicated that she was prepared to delegate her functions to the social services authority, although the latter considered that this did not relieve the authority of its legal duty to inform her of any intention to make an application for *E*'s detention under the Act. The claimant sought a declaration from the High Court that it would be unlawful for the authority or its ASWs to consult or inform her sister under ss.11(3) or (4) without her consent.

1.29 The High Court made a declaration that it was not 'practicable' for the authority to carry out its duties under ss.11(3) or (4) to involve the Nearest Relative. In doing so, the Court specifically rejected the advice in paragraph 2.16 of the Mental Health Act Code of Practice that 'practicability refers to the availability of the Nearest Relative and not to the appropriateness of informing or consulting the person concerned.'

1.30 In the light of this judgment, the Department of Health has accepted that the Code's advice at paragraph 2.16 of is no longer correct and has stated that:

> '… in determining whether it is practicable to consult and/or inform the Nearest Relative under sections 11(3) and (4), ASWs may (and should) consider whether doing so would lead to a breach of the patient's rights under Article 8 of the European Convention of Human Rights (right to respect for private and family life).

> The Court suggested that this requires a balancing act to be performed. On the one hand, Parliament clearly intended Nearest Relatives to have the opportunity of playing a significant role in the protection of the patient or otherwise acting in the patient's best interests. ASWs should not, therefore, lightly invoke 'impracticality' as a reason for excluding them. On the other hand, there may circumstances where involving the Nearest Relative would lead to an infringement of the patient's rights which could not be justified by the benefit of that involvement.

> The key factors support the finding in this case appear to have been that the patient had very strongly expressed the view that her Nearest Relative should not be involved, the

fact that the Nearest Relative herself did not wish to be involved and the likelihood that her involvement would have been distressing to the patient. It is also arguable that the issue might arise in other circumstances, for example where the Nearest Relative is known intensely to dislike the patient and/or would not act in the patient's best interests or where the involvement of the Nearest Relative might adversely affect the patient's health (eg by causing the patient severe distress).

However, in the Department's view it is very unlikely that the fact that a Nearest Relative is expected to object to admission or to seek the patient's discharge would, of itself, make their involvement impractical and therefore relieve ASWs of the duty to inform or consult them. Section 29 of the Act already provides mechanisms for displacing Nearest Relatives who exercise their powers to object and/or discharge unreasonably'.[22]

1.31 We have been asked by some practitioners whether the Department's raising of 'other circumstances' in the penultimate paragraph of the above guidance should be read to imply that contact with a Nearest Relative who is known to be personally antipathetic to a patient, or to be likely to act otherwise than in the patient's interests, could constitute an unwarranted interference in a patient's private and family life even if the patient had shown no indication that they objected to such contact. In our view it should not be read to imply this: it is difficult to see how contact could constitute an 'interference' unless it was objected to by either the patient or the relative concerned. Where a patient or relative does not show any objection to contact that is deemed undesirable by professionals, the mechanisms of s.29 alone should be available to professionals to set aside the role of the Nearest Relative.

1.32 We welcome the Court's decision as an advance on the situation where, in the absence of such official interpretation and in the face of the Code's explicit guidance, ASWs were apparently required to breach human rights. In our Eighth Biennial Report (1999) we suggested to Government ways in which the law regarding Nearest Relatives could be changed to prevent Article 8 breaches[23]. The Administrative Court's approach mirrors that advocated from the sixth edition of Richard Jones' *Mental Health Act Manual*[24] (1999), which we raised with Government in our Ninth Biennial Report (2001)[25]. We highlighted the conflicting interpretations of the requirements of law provided by Mr Jones and the Code of Practice, and suggested that Government needed to consider this when deciding how to remedy the problem of Nearest Relative consultation and Article 8. We were cautious over advocating Jones' approach without a change in the Code's guidance, which we felt might lead to the Code's guidance being viewed as having no more validity than any conflicting legal interpretation of its subject matter. In our view there are some authorities who would welcome the opportunity to reinterpret the Code for their own purposes, not all of which would be based on the interests of patients. At that time Government had already

---

[22] www.dh.gov.uk/mentalhealth, 'legal briefings' section

[23] MHAC (1999) *Eighth Biennial Report*, para 4.46-51.

[24] Jones, R. (1999) *Mental Health Act Manual*, sixth edition. London: Sweet & Maxwell, para 1-119. (see para 1-123 in the ninth edition, 2004).

[25] MHAC (2001) *Ninth Biennial Report*, para 2.56.

promised changes to the law as part of a friendly settlement to an ECtHR challenge[26]. In 2003 a declaration of incompatibility between the provisions of ss.26 and 29 of the Act and Article 8 of the ECHR was given in another case[27]. Whilst the ruling in *E v Bristol* has prevented some aspects of incompatibility between the legal framework of Nearest Relatives under the Act and Article 8, others undoubtedly remain. After five years we still do not know what action is to be taken to rectify such incompatibility.

> **Recommendation 2:** As recommended in our Tenth Biennial Report (Rec 2), Government should take action to rectify the incompatibility with European Convention rights of ss.26 and 29 of the 1983 Act by means of a Remedial Order under s.10 of the Human Rights Act 1998.

1.33 Admittedly with the benefit of hindsight, we take the view that Government missed an opportunity in not addressing the Code's guidance when we raised this matter, instead leaving it eventually to fall to the judiciary without benefit of any Government statement on its position[28]. In the years between our Ninth Report and the *E v Bristol* judgment, the Code's guidance will have continued to influence practice with detriment to the care of those patients whose objections to contact with Nearest Relatives have been overridden. In a more general sense, in which the detriment to patient care may be less immediate but no less real, by failing to update and revise the Code as necessary Government may damage professional and service users' perceptions of the Code as document that is both authoritative and fit for purpose.

1.34 This judgment is not the first to overrule Code of Practice guidance. In 2001, for example, the High Court overturned the Code's implication that 'previous acquaintance' requires personal knowledge (para 2.29)[29]. The Code, perhaps partly because of the requirement that its content is established by negative resolution of Parliament after appropriate consultation[30], has not been revised to reflect these changes. To help practitioners mark those parts of their copies of the Code of Practice which are no longer correct in law or fact, in March 2005 we published a Guidance Note showing suggested annotations that would ensure parts of the Code which have been effectively deleted by the courts are not acted upon in error[31].

---

[26] *JT v United Kingdom* [2000] 1 FLR 909 Application no. 26494/95, ECtHR 30 March 2000

[27] *R (on the application of M) v Secretary of State for Health* [2003] EWHC 1094

[28] We note that Government did not seek to intervene in E's uncontested judicial challenge.

[29] *AR (by her litigation friend JT) v Bronglais Hospital and Pembrokeshire & Derwen NHS Trust* [2001] EWHC Admin 792. See Jones R (2004) *Mental Health Act Manual* ninth ed. para 1-134 on 'previous acquaintance' for details.

[30] MHA 1983 s.118

[31] MHAC (2005) *The Mental Health Act Code of Practice: suggested annotations to reflect caselaw and other changes since publication.* Issue 4, October 2005. Nottingham, MHAC. Available from www.mhac.org.uk

Authority to obtain patient details from relatives against the patient's wishes

R (on the Application of Leonard O'Reilly) v Blenheim Healthcare Limited

[2005] EWHC 241

1.35 The patient was detained following a court order under s.37/41, having been convicted of assault occasioning actual bodily harm on his father. The patient had a history of criminal offences. He was viewed to hold a number of delusional beliefs by his clinical team relating to matters such as his communications with God, his role in the thwarting of the Millennium Dome diamond robbery, etc. He also alleged childhood abuse at the hands of his father, and ascribed his motivation for his index offence to this. It was possible that this allegation was also a manifestation of the mental illness (there was no objective evidence of such abuse), although the court was careful not to assume this to be the case.

1.36 The patient's RMO wished to enquire of the patient's parents as to his past personal history, for purposes of diagnosis, treatment, risk assessment and risk management. The patient objected to contact being made with his parents for this purpose, and sought judicial review of the RMO's determination to make such contact in the face of his opposition.

1.37 Mr Justice Stanley Burnton resisted arguments that asking questions of a third party was 'treatment' under the Mental Health Act, and therefore that authority for this in the face of the patient's opposition was given by s.63 of the Act: 'to my mind the enquiries sought to be made by the RMO ... are made with a view to treatment and do not themselves constitute treatment'[32]. Therefore the judge took the view that there was no assistance to be obtained by the RMO from the provisions of the Mental Health Act[33], and that it was consequently unnecessary for the Court to determine whether the patient had capacity to decide rationally as to whether the enquiries should be made. Capacity was assumed, notwithstanding an acknowledgement that whether or not the patient had made a rational objection was tied to the unanswerable question of the veracity of the alleged abuse[34].

1.38 It had been claimed that the proposed contact with the parents of the patient would be an infringement of his right to respect for private and family life under ECHR Article 8. This claim was rejected as unfounded, Stanley Burnton J stating that any communication of medically confidential information without consent could indeed be a breach of Article 8 and also of domestic law, but the RMO was aware of his obligations in this respect and in

---

[32] *R (on the Application of Leonard O'Reilly) v Blenheim Healthcare Limited* [2005] EWHC 241 para 14

[33] *ibid.*, para 16

[34] *ibid.*, para 9-10. In this the court appeared to adopt an approach towards capacity that encompasses an element of 'appreciation'. See Chapter 3.30 *et seq* below for further discussion of capacity principles.

this case 'the object of the enquiry is to obtain information and not to communicate it'[35]. The judge suggested that, had a breach of Article 8(1) arisen, in this case he would have been favourably disposed to the argument that it could be justified under Article 8.2[36]. The RMO's action might prevent unnecessary detention, or prevent premature or inappropriate discharge with its attendant risks.

1.39   The claim was dismissed on the grounds that there was no evidence that the RMO's enquiries would be such that it would be irrational or perverse for him to make them.

1.40   This case may be useful for ASWs considering whether their contact with a Nearest Relative in face of opposition from a patient (or prospective patient) is a justifiable infringement of that patient's Article 8 rights in the light of *E v Bristol* (see above). Of particular note, perhaps, is Stanley Burnton J's reminder that there may be competing rights involved in decisions whether to breach Article 8 in relation to a patient's private life where the patient may pose particular risks to family members or others:

> Had the claim been clearly made …that the communication of such information [relating to family history of a patient] was either a breach of confidence or infringed Article 8 rights, interesting and possibly difficult questions would arise as to whose information it was and as to the competing rights of his parents and the claimant himself. I say competing rights because it has to be borne in mind that the assault committed by the claimant on his father might indicate that his father would be at risk if the claimant were prematurely, or wrongly, discharged. That risk, if sufficiently strong, might arguably involve a breach of the father's rights under Articles 8, 3 and even Article 2[37].

Section 17 leave as a community treatment order

R (on the application of CS) v Mental Health Review Tribunal and Managers of Homerton Hospital (East London & City Mental Health NHS Trust)

[2004] EWHC 2958 (admin). December 2004

1.41   *CS*, whose diagnosis was paranoid schizophrenia, appealed against the decision of a Tribunal not to discharge her from detention under s.3. At the time of the renewal of her section (which had triggered her application to the MHRT) she had been on 'full-time section 17 leave' for three months and her contact with the detaining hospital had been reduced to a requirement to attend a hospital ward round once every four weeks. The appeal against the MHRT decision to upheld her section was dismissed:

> the RMO was engaged in a delicate balancing exercise by which she was, with as light a touch as she could, encouraging progress to discharge. Her purpose was to break the

---

[35]   *ibid.*, para 18

[36]   i.e. interference necessary in a democratic society in the interests of inter alia public safety, for the prevention of disorder or crime, for the protection of health or morals, or for the protection of rights and freedoms of others.

[37]   Burnton J *obiter* in *R (on the Application of Leonard O'Reilly)* [2005], para 20

persistent historical cycle of admission, serious relapse and readmission. It may be that in the closing stages of the treatment in hospital her grasp on the claimant was gossamer thin, but to view that grasp as insignificant is, in my view, to misunderstand the evidence. (para 46)

1.42 The judgment therefore adopts a very wide interpretation of 'treatment in hospital'. Justice Pitchford quoted from the RMO's submission that her reasons for renewing *CS*'s detention were in line with 'modern means of engaging and treating patients with severe mental illness':

> it is not appropriate to abruptly discharge a patient who has been subject to compulsory admission and treatment as an inpatient for a number of months... to allow *CS*'s section to lapse or to bring it to an abrupt end only to resection her would greatly upset *CS* and damage the relationship between her and the clinical team. It would also mean that mental health services were only able to engage once *CS* had suffered a significant deterioration... bringing her back from leave at the earliest sign of deterioration has avoided a significant descent into her severest symptoms and has led to limited rather than prolonged periods spent on the ward before further leave could be granted. (para 46)

1.43 The court rejected the appellant's call for a fixed date of release from detention, upholding the right of the RMO to 'risk' discharge based upon her own subjective judgment of *CS*'s progress and prognosis.

1.44 The appellant had argued that the renewal of s.3 in her case was a breach of the requirements established by Article 5 of the ECHR that domestic law must not provide for, or permit, detention for reasons that are arbitrary[38]. The court held, with reference to MHRT powers of discharge at s.72 of the Mental Health Act 1983, that the Act meets the requirements established under European cases[39] against arbitrary detention. There was no need to read into s.72 any additional dimension relating to 'proportionality' that is not implicit in the statutory right to discharge and the exercise of residual discretion. In the case of *CS*, Pitchford J observed that the application of the principle of proportionality led only to the conclusion that in renewing the s.3 'the interference with ... freedom of movement and choice were minimal in the context of the object to be achieved, namely her satisfactory return to community care' (para 52).

---

[38] *Nadarajah v Secretary of State for the Home Department* [2003] EWCA Civ 1768, para 54 (this is an asylum case).

[39] '... *except in emergency cases, the individual concerned should not be deprived of his liberty unless he has been reliably shown to be of 'unsound mind' [by] ... objective medical expertise. Further, the mental disorder must be of a kind or degree warranting compulsory confinement. What is more, the validity of continued confinement depends upon the persistence of such a disorder.* (Winterwerp v Netherlands (6301/73) [1979] ECHR 4 (24 October 1979) para 39). *'Whether and, if so, to what extent the expression 'lawful detention of a person of unsound mind' can be construed as including a reference not simply to actual deprivation of liberty of mental health patients but also to matters relating to execution of the detention, such as the place, environment and conditions of detention. Certainly, the 'lawfulness' of any detention is required in respect of both the ordering and the execution of the measure depriving the individual of his liberty. ...there must be some relationship between the ground of permitted deprivation of liberty relied on and the place and conditions of detention.'* (Ashingdane v UK (8225/78) [1985] ECHR 8 (28 May 1985) para 44).

The compulsory treatment under the MHA of patients refusing consent

R (on the application of PS) v (1) Dr G and (2) Dr W

[2003] EWHC 2335 (Admin), September 2003

1.45 This judgment, which was handed down as our last Biennial Report went to press, was the first to rule upon a human rights based challenge over the imposition of treatment under s.58(3)(b) of the Act to a patient judged to have made a capacitated refusal of consent, although it is one of a series in which a detained patient has used the Human Rights Act (HRA) to challenge medical treatment authorised by a Second Opinion Appointed Doctor (SOAD) under s.58 of the Act[40]. We were able to report this conclusion in our last Report but not go into detail[41]. In January 2004 we issued a guidance note on the implications of the case for services.

1.46 The claimant, *PS*, was detained in hospital under the MHA 1983. It was accepted that he possessed sufficient capacity to give or withhold consent to medical treatment, and he was refusing consent to proposed treatment with antipsychotic medication. A SOAD had approved this proposal. *PS* claimed that compulsory treatment in the face of his refusal would breach the prohibition on torture and inhuman or degrading treatment (ECHR, Article 3) and/or his right to respect for his private life (Article 8).

1.47 Mr Justice Silber dismissed the claim. Although the court accepted that the imposition of treatment to a capable patient clearly had the potential to breach Articles 3 and 8 of the ECHR, the following principles can be derived from its detailed consideration of this aspect of the case:

(i) For Article 3 to be engaged, the acts complained of must reach a minimum level of severity. This will depend on the particular circumstances of the case, but in general it would have to involve actual bodily injury or intense physical or mental suffering. In deciding whether the minimum level of severity has been reached it is also necessary to take account of any positive effects of the treatment.

(ii) Only if the treatment complained of reaches the minimum level of severity is it relevant to consider the second issue under Article 3, which is whether the medical necessity for the treatment has been convincingly shown to exist. This can be broken down into a number of elements: how certain is it that the patient does suffer from a treatable mental disorder; how serious a disorder it is; how serious a risk is presented to others; how likely is it that, if the patient does suffer from such a disorder, the proposed treatment will alleviate the condition; how much alleviation is there likely to be; how likely is it that the treatment will have adverse consequences for the patient; and how severe are they likely to be?

(iii) Even where the patient has capacity, the view of the doctors (RMO and SOAD) as to what is in his or her best interests can override the patient's objections to the treatment.

---

[40] See *R (on the application of Wilkinson) v Broadmoor Special Hospital Authority & another* [2002] 1 WLR 419 and *R (on the application of N) v Dr M* [2003] 1 WLR 562, both discussed in MHAC (2003) *Tenth Biennial Report: Placed Amongst Strangers*, Chapter 3.32 *et seq.*

[41] *ibid.* chapters 3.44, 4.2.

(iv) In relation to Article 8, non-consensual treatment will constitute an interference with Article 8 rights unless the treatment is justified under Article 8(2) as being proportionate 'in accordance with law' and 'necessary in a democratic society ... for the protection of health' (whether the patient's own health or the health and safety of others).

(v) The phrase 'in accordance with law' refers not only to the requirements of s.58 but also imports the common law best interests test. This requires a consideration of whether there is a less invasive form of treatment that could be given instead and which would be likely to achieve the same results. It also requires consideration to be given to: the nature and strength of the patient's objections to the treatment, including what resistance to its administration is likely; the degree to which treatment is likely to alleviate or prevent a deterioration of the condition; the risk the patient presents to self and to others; the consequences of the treatment not being given; and any possible adverse effects of the treatment. A relevant consideration in deciding whether the treatment is justified is whether it is likely to lead to the patient being rehabilitated rather than remaining subject to long-term hospitalisation[42].

1.48 The effect of the judgment is that the patient's capacity is not a bar to non-consensual treatment under s.58, but merely one of the factors may have to be taken into account, as far as is relevant, in deciding the questions of medical necessity and best interests. Provided that the imposition of treatment was medically necessary, being in the patient's best interests, the imposition of treatment could be justified as a proportionate response for the protection of the patient's health.

1.49 The judgment in *PS* should reinforce rather than change existing good practice as established under the Mental Health Act Code of Practice and Care Programme Approach. Prior to the judgment, medical practitioners considering the imposition of treatment in the face of a capable patient's refusal would have already applied a form of the 'best interests' test, and would be bound by their own professional ethics to only impose such treatment if the threshold set by such a test was met. Following the *PS* judgment, however, the legal position regarding such thresholds became more codified, as did, by implication, expectations regarding practice in reaching decisions to impose treatment. It is likely that future legal challenges to such imposition will examine the process of decision-making carefully.

1.50 Although this was a decision concerning treatment authorised by a SOAD under s.58, the same principles must apply in deciding whether it is lawful to treat a patient without consent under s.63, which provides power to treat a patient without consent, regardless of the patient's capacity, and without obtaining a Second Opinion. The burden on the RMO in every such case is to satisfy the common law best interests test.

1.51 In our view, this judgment therefore reinforces the existing requirements of good practice according to the Mental Health Act Code of Practice and Care Programme Approach. We set

---

[42] This analysis adapted from MHAC (2004) Guidance for Responsible Medical Officers : *R (on the application of on the application of PS) v (1) Responsible Medical Officer Dr. G, (2) Second opinion Appointed Doctor Dr. W.* GN 2/04, issued January 2004, www.mhac.org.uk. We are grateful to Mr Robert Robinson, solicitor (Scott-Moncrieff, Harbour and Sinclair) and a past member of the MHAC, for the analysis of the judgment contained in that guidance.

out an extract from our guidance note on how the case might be read to reinforce those requirements at figure 2 below.

The Commission advises that the following basic procedures, based upon guidance in the Code of Practice, and the Care Programme Approach, should be applied from the admission of any detained patient:

(i) The mental capacity of the patient in relation to decisions regarding specific treatment proposals must be assessed and recorded in the patient's notes. Capacity assessments should be kept under constant review (Code of Practice, 15.9 - 15.12).

(ii) The consent status of the patient must be recorded clearly in the notes and kept under constant review (Code of Practice, 15.13);

(iii) Patients must be provided with appropriate opportunity to receive and understand information on the nature, purpose, likely effects of and alternatives to proposed treatment (Code of Practice 15.12, 15.15). Such opportunity is likely to be a requirement in determining patient's mental capacity where capacity is unclear. A patient with limited mental capacity may be capacitated to take part in decision-making by the provision of appropriate information (see Code of Practice 15.12);

(iv) For patients with mental capacity, or whose mental capacity is in doubt, well-documented discussions regarding proposed treatment and consent to such treatment should take place from admission (even where such treatment is given without consent under the 'three-month rule') (Code of Practice 15.14 et seq, 16.11);

(v) Patients lacking mental capacity still have a right (section 132) to information on the powers under which they are held and the effects of those powers. Such information should include as much information as is practicable and clinically appropriate about proposed treatment and the legal and practical mechanisms under which it can be administered (Code of Practice 14.5).

(vi) Patients' views must be taken account of in determining their 'best interests' when the imposition of treatment is proposed (CPA requirement).

(vii) The medical practitioners should make a clear record of treatment decisions and their justification. The Commission strongly advises RMOs to ensure that this record is available in patients' clinical notes. Patients should receive a copy of their care plan, and have decisions explained to them unless this is not appropriate on clinical grounds. (CPA requirement)

Fig 2: MHAC practice guidance following the *PS* case

R (on the application of B) v (1) Dr SS, (2) Dr AC and The Secretary of State for the Department of Health

[2005] EWHC 86 (Admin), January 2005.

1.52 The case was heard by Silber J, who had ruled in *PS* discussed above. *B* was detained at Broadmoor hospital under s.37/41 following conviction for rape in 1995. He was diagnosed with bi-polar affective disorder, and deemed to have mental capacity to consent or refuse treatment. He objected to his RMO's proposal, which had been agreed to by a SOAD, to administer antipsychotic medication without his consent.

1.53 The SOAD authorisation in this case had never been implemented due to an injunction on treatment granted upon the start of legal proceedings. The authorisation had been time-limited[43] and would have expired shortly after the hearing of this case, and the patient's RMO indicated that he had no immediate plans to administer medication without consent if the injunction were lifted. In these circumstances all but the claim relating to principles involved in the application for judicial review were dismissed by consent. The first question before the judge was whether the court should permit a full hearing of the claim relating to matters that were argued to be 'academic' by the respondents.

1.54 Although the application for a full hearing of the claim on principles was refused, Silber J heard substantive points on this claim in the applications hearing and commented upon them in his judgment. Such comments do not, therefore, have the force of law.

1.55 The challenge in this case was effectively to the judgment in *PS* discussed above. It was argued that medical necessity should not in itself be deemed adequate justification for imposing treatment under the Act on a patient who refuses consent. It was suggested that, instead, either:

(i) To prevent incompatibility with Article 3 and/or Article 8 and/or Article 14 of the ECHR, s.58(3)(b) of the Act should be construed with the benefit of s.3 of the Human Rights Act (HRA) 1998 only to authorise the imposition of treatment in face of a refusal where, in addition to such treatment being medically necessary, it is also necessary to prevent the patient causing serious harm to self or others; or

(ii) If s.58(3)(b) of the Act cannot be so construed, then a declaration of incompatibility should be made under s.4 of the HRA 1998.

1.56 *B*'s case rested in part on the claim that there was a striking contrast between the right of autonomy given in law to people who are not detained patients, even in relation to refusal of life-saving treatment or interventions to save the lives of unborn children, and the way in which the Act may override decisions of mentally capable detained patients in their 'best interests'. Silber J rejected the suggestion that there was such a contrast. He suggested that detained patients who are deemed to have capacity may not have the same relevant powers of, among other things, understanding facts and making a balanced judgment on whether

---

[43] Although there is no statutory requirement for them to do so, SOADs occasionally time-limit Forms 39 authorising treatment to ensure that the authority is reviewed after a particular period of time; see also Chapter 4.58 below *et seq*.

to agree to medical treatment as people who are not detained patients[44]. The main authority for this assertion was given to be Hale J (as she then was) in *Wilkinson*:

> I do not take the view that detained patients who have the capacity to decide for themselves can never be treated against their will. Our threshold of capacity is rightly a low one. It is better to keep it that way and allow some non-consensual treatment of those who have capacity than to set such a high threshold for capacity that many would never qualify[45];

1.57 Silber J also quoted Lord Eassie in the Scottish Court of Session:

> Mental illness differed from physical illness in the important respect that even arguably 'competent' patients may lack insight or understanding of their problem, which lack of insight may be addressed by medication[46];

1.58 Rather surprisingly, he also suggested that the wording of s.58 (which in 1988 Stuart-Smith LJ had noted as employing the words 'capable of understanding' and not 'understands': 'thus the question is capacity and not actual understanding'[47]) 'might mean that a patient might be regarded as having capacity even if he does not *actually* understand the nature, purpose and likely effects of the treatment'[48]. We reject this suggestion. The MHAC took legal advice subsequent to Stuart-Smith LJ's 1988 judgment and advised SOADs that they should continue to require both capacity and an adequate understanding of the treatment and its consequences' to deem a patient capable of consent[49]. The Code of Practice (in common with professional bodies' guidance) requires that capacity is assessed in relation to a patient at a particular time, as regards the particular intervention proposed, and that patient is presumed capable unless he or she is unable to take in and retain the material information; or unable to believe that information; or is unable to weigh that information in the balance as a part of making the decision[50]. Similar approaches to assessing mental incapacity will be underpinned by statute law when the Mental Capacity Act 2005 comes into operation[51].

---

[44] This statement should not, in our view, be read to imply that any particular detained patient will be less capacitated than a similarly-placed informal patient. Indeed, even as a generalisation, the view that detained patients are on the whole less capacitated than informal patients is questionable, given that capacitated patients may be detained on best interests grounds or for the protection of other persons, and that incapacitated but essentially compliant patients are treated informally in at least similar numbers to the entire detained patient population. See Chapter 3 for a general discussion of these issues.

[45] *R (on the application of Wilkinson) v Broadmoor Special Hospital Authority & another* [2002] 1 WLR 419, *per* Hale LJ, para 80.

[46] *Petition of WM (AP) for Judicial Review* [2002] MHLR 367, para 22

[47] In *R v Mental Health Act Commission ex parte X* (1988) 9 B.M.L.R.77 at para 85

[48] *R (on the application of B) v (1) Dr SS, (2) Dr AC and The Secretary of State for the Department of Health* [2005] EWHC 86 (Admin), para 87.

[49] MHAC (1991) *Fourth Biennial Report*, Chapter 6.12. See also Jones, R (2004) *Mental Health Act Manual* ninth edition, para 1-713, on Stuart-Smith LJ's formulation of the requirements of valid consent, which itself 'is supportive of the Commission's approach'.

[50] Mental Health Act 1983 Code of Practice, paras 15.10-12 (see *Re C (Refusal of treatment)* [1994] 1 FLR 31)

[51] see Mental Capacity Act 2005, ss.2, 3.

1.59   Mr Justice Silber's remarks must not be misconstrued as leading the way to different *legal* criteria being applied to the determination of capacity in detained patients and others. Whether or not a detained patient may be more likely than an informal patient to be confused, irrational or deluded, professionals must presume capacity until evidence rebuts that assumption. However, Silber J's highlighting of what a 'low' threshold of capacity means *in practice* for detained psychiatric patients raises important questions, perhaps particularly in relation to calls for capacity to play a greater role as a threshold for future psychiatric compulsion. (see Chapter 3.27 *et seq* below).

1.60   One such question (also raised in the *PS* case above) was whether there could be cases, if doctors must always defer to a treatment refusal from a capacitated patient who is detained, where respecting a patient's right to autonomy in the short-term would preclude interventions that might provide for much greater autonomy in the longer-term, such as release from detention. Society tolerates perverse decision-making over health issues amongst capable adult persons who are not detained psychiatric patients, generally upholding their right to autonomy irrespective of the strength and nature of their objections to any proposed treatment, or the nature and possible benefits of such treatment. At the heart of this case is the question of whether it would be tolerable for us to extend such 'freedoms' to the seriously mentally disordered.

1.61   As a result of the *PS* case, it can now be said with certainty that a detained patient may be compelled to accept medical treatment for mental disorder, even though s/he is capable and opposes it. It is, of course, not certain that this position will remain. We understand that the European Court of Human Rights, which has before it an application following on from the *Wilkinson* Case, has requested and received from the UK Government the latter's observations on the issues raised in the 'academic' claim made by *B* (as discussed above)[52]. It is not known when a judgment on the *Wilkinson* application might be expected, nor whether such a judgment will ultimately deal with this issue, but it is possible that the English Courts will not have the last word in this matter.

Treatment of unclassified mental disorder under section 63

R v Ashworth Hospital Authority and another ex parte B
[2005] UKHL 20, March 2005

1.62   In our last report we discussed the Court of Appeal's 2003 ruling that s.63 of the Act only permits compulsory treatment that is appropriate to the mental disorder under which a patient is classified as suffering[53]. In March 2005 the House of Lords overturned that judgment.

1.63   The House of Lords heard the case in February 2005, and the Commission was pleased to submit a memorandum, at the request of the judicial assistant to their Lordships, providing

---

[52]   *R (on the application of B)* [2005] supra, para 61.

[53]   MHAC (2003) *Tenth Biennial Report: Placed Amongst Strangers.* Chapters 3.40 - 44, 7.28 - 32.

extracts from our Eighth and Tenth Biennial Reports, and from our submission to the 1998 Mental Health Legislation Review Team (the Richardson Committee). In this memorandum, we pointed to the overlap between diagnostic categories, particularly regarding mental illness and psychopathic disorder, and to the consequence that the option of reclassifying patients' disorders was therefore likely to be widely applicable. We also observed that, even if a secondary disorder cannot be classified because its nature or degree do not meet the criteria established by the Act[54], the Court of Appeal in the case that their Lordships were considering had recognised the precedent of *B v Croydon*[55], which would allow its treatment under s.63 where such treatment is ancilliary to, and therefore a necessary part of, the treatment of the classified mental disorder. We concluded that the protection against unwarranted treatment provided to detained patients by the Court of Appeal's ruling was rather slight, and that the case had had rather less effect in setting a real threshold around particular treatments and their application to certain types of treatment, as it had in underlining that restrictions on a patient's liberty must be proportionate and that detention under the Act does not cancel residual rights of unwarranted interference with the person.

1.64   We noted that the case was being cited as precedent in a small number of applications for the judicial review of the treatment of patients classified with personality disorder for whom Second Opinion Appointed Doctors (SOADs) had authorised antipsychotic medication under s.58 of the Act. Some of these applications had fallen before the House of Lords considered this case, but three were ongoing at the time of the judgment. As the body charged with administrating the SOAD system, we were involved in these reviews, and in each case were satisfied that the doctors involved believed that antipsychotic medication should be given, notwithstanding the patient's formal classification. All of the outstanding cases were withdrawn following their Lordships' judgment.

1.65   The leading opinion in the case was given by Baroness Hale. A close reading of the ordinary meaning, context and statutory history of s.63 showed that no link between classification of mental disorder and the scope of compulsory treatment had been intended or made. It was noted also that s.63 applies to patients detained under ss.2 and 46 of the 1983 Act, and to persons detained in hospital under the Criminal Procedure Insanity Acts. None of these patients have a 'classified' form of mental disorder, as this is not a criterion for their detention. It would be 'surprising' if the wording of s.63 had to take on a different meaning dependent on whether the patient it was applied to had a classified disorder or not[56], although this was the result of the Court of Appeal's decision.

1.66   Considering the policy aspects of the case, Lady Hale stated that the protection against inappropriate treatment purported to be extended to patients by the Court of Appeal's restriction on compulsory powers to treatment designed for 'classified' disorders was 'so

---

[55]   *B v Croydon* [1995] 2 WLR 294

[54]   The respondent in this case had argued that a patient may only be classified as suffering from a form of mental disorder if that form on its own met the criteria for detention (i.e. was of a nature or degree warranting detention in hospital). In other words, a person whose personality disorder would not in itself be of a sufficient nature or degree to warrant detention, but who has a mental illness that does meet this criteria, could not be classified as suffering from both disorders on an application for admission or a court order. Lady Hale questioned this reading of the Act, as discussed at paragraph 1.68 below.

[55]   *B v Croydon* [1995] 2 WLR 294

[56]   *R v Ashworth Hospital Authority and another ex parte B* [2005] UKHL 20, para 24

haphazard as to be scarcely any protection at all'[57]. Quoting from our Tenth Biennial Report's argument that legal classification may obscure the extensive co-morbidity between personality disorders and mental illness, and recognising that the State should be able (or possibly obliged) to provide appropriate treatment to a patients whose liberty it has removed, Lady Hale concluded that

> it would be absurd if a patient could be detained in hospital but had to be denied the treatment which his doctor thought he needed for an indefinite period while some largely irrelevant classification was rectified[58].

1.67 This absurdity would be worse, in Lady Hale's view, if a patient may only be classified as suffering from a form of mental disorder if that form on its own met the criteria for detention (i.e. was of a nature or degree warranting detention in hospital). It had been argued for *B* (with implicit success in front of the Court of Appeal, but less successfully at the Lords' hearing) that a person whose personality disorder would not in itself be of a sufficient nature or degree to warrant detention, but who has a mental illness that does meet this criteria, could not be classified or reclassified as suffering from both disorders. Because of the construction of s.63 adopted by their Lordships, the House of Lords judgment did not have to resolve this question formally. However, remarks of Lady Hale questioned this reading of the Act, stating her view that 'the language of sections 3(2)(a) and 37(2)(a)(i) … suggest, at the very least, that it may the combination of classified forms of disorder that makes it appropriate for the patient to be in hospital'[59]. Whilst this view does not set a binding legal precedent, we think that it an important interpretation of how the Act should be applied[60].

1.68 Although the powers of an RMO (or MHRT) to re-classify a patient's mental disorder under the Act are phrased in permissive terms, Lady Hale also advised that patients' classifications should be re-classified when it is appropriate to do so[61]. Reclassification by the RMO invokes a right of appeal to the MHRT. Where a patient's classification is changed to include mental illness as well or instead of psychopathic disorder, this alters the criteria to be applied at the next MHRT hearing. Reclassification from mental illness to psychopathic disorder invokes the 'treatability test', so that the RMO must consider whether discharge is appropriate. The lessening of the practical consequences of classification subsequent to the House of Lords' judgment should not, therefore, lead practitioners to ignore a patient's classification or fail to update it when diagnoses change.

---

[57] *ibid.*, para 30

[58] *ibid.*, para 31

[59] *ibid.*, para 32

[60] Lady Hale's *dicta* in the context of the House of Lords' judgment therefore would seem to override doubts cast at the earlier stages of this case over the Court of Appeal's finding in *R v Anglia and Oxfordshire Mental Health Review Tribunal ex parte Hagan* [2000] Lloyd's Law Reports Medical 119 (judgment 20 December 1999). The Court of Appeal in *Hagan* decided that an RMO was not bound to delete a mental illness from a patient's classification even though the MHRT, in refusing to discharge that patient on the grounds of his continuing psychopathic disorder, had determined that the patient's schizo-typal disorder was no longer of such a nature or degree as would, by itself, have justified continued detention.

[61] *ibid.*, para 33. This part of the judgment is also *obiter dicta*: remarks that do not set legal precedent and were not determinant to the judgment of the case.

1.69   Lady Hale rejected any suggestion that *B*'s transfer from a mental illness ward to a personality disorder ward within Ashworth Hospital could have engaged his Article 5 right to liberty. The decision in *Ashingdane v UK*[62] had acknowledged that a patient detained because of unsound mind should be detained in a place suitable for that purpose, but had not found Article 5 to be relevant to a patient's detention in a high security hospital when a lesser security hospital would have been appropriate. That approach applied *a fortiori* in this case. Their Lordships also found that 'nothing that happened to [*B*] came anywhere close to being a breach' of other rights under the ECHR[63]. Although there is a risk that the treatment of a patient in a psychiatric hospital will breach the Convention's prohibitions against inhumane or degrading treatment (Article 3) or unjustified interference with personal integrity (Article 8), such breaches cannot occur where that treatment can be shown to be medically necessary[64]. The legal safeguards of ss.57 and 58 of the 1983 Act, the ordinary law of negligence, and the remedies provided by the Human Rights Act itself provided protections to the patient. The Convention did not require prior safeguards against the inappropriate treatment of patients, but even if it did, classification was far too blunt an instrument to provide such a safeguard adequately[65].

1.70   The House of Lords' judgment in this case would seem to have definitively constrained the use of *legal* classification of mental disorder to questions of the detention, rather than treatment, of patients. In part that judgment has relied on views promulgated in our last report that psychiatric co-morbidity (i.e. the concomitance of two or more psychiatric diagnoses) is more general than the existence such legal classifications might imply. A recent editorial article in the *British Journal of Psychiatry* has argued that 'psychiatric co-morbidity' itself may be little more than an artefact of current diagnostic systems[66]. Although there may be certain profound dissimilarities between psychopathologies such as personality disorders and the psychoses, it also may be that

> the nature of psychopathology is intrinsically composite and changeable[67], and that what is currently conceptualised as the co-occurrence of multiple disorders could be better reformulated as the complexity of many psychiatric conditions (with increasing complexity being an obvious predictor of greater severity, disability and service utilisation)[68].

According to this editorial article, the practical consequences of artificially splitting complex clinical conditions into several pieces could be that clinical efforts focus on one or other of

---

[62]   *Ashingdane v UK* [1985], 7 EHRR 528, 543

[63]   *R v Ashworth Hospital Authority and another ex parte B* [2005] para 37

[64]   *Herczegfalvy v Austria* [1992] 15 EHRR 437, 484, para 82.

[65]   *R v Ashworth Hospital Authority and another ex parte B* [2005] para 37

[66]   Maj M 'Psychiatric co-morbidity: an artefact of current diagnostic systems?' *British Journal of Psychiatry* (2005) 186, 182-184. Maj suggests that the proliferation of discrete diagnostic categories is partially a result of the editorial policy of the third edition of the American Psychiatric Association's Diagnostic and Statistical Manual (DSM-III) that the same symptom should not appear in more than one disorder, and debates the theoretical bases for psychopathological classification.

[67]   Maj suggests with reference to Jaspers' classification of 'true diseases', 'circles' and 'types' in *General Psychopathology* (1913) the 'possibility … that the nature of psychopathology is intrinsically heterogeneous, consisting party of true disease entities and partly of maladaptive response patterns' *ibid*, p.183.

[68]   *ibid.*, p183

these pieces at the expense of holistic treatment, thereby encouraging unwarranted polypharmacy and reducing diagnostic reliability. It may be that such dangers are increased where legal rather than clinical definitions are the operative diagnostic boundaries that determine what types of treatment may be given without consent, or what kind of services are available.

1.71　The practical problem that psychiatric co-morbidity poses to services is, therefore, to balance sufficient specialisation to provide a quality service to patients with sufficient flexibility to avoid excluding patients on relatively arbitrary bases. Government has recognised that personality disorder has in the past been 'a diagnosis of exclusion' and that in 2002 a third or more of all NHS Trusts provided no identified services to this group of patients[69]. The apparent prevalence of psychiatric co-morbidity lends support to Government policy that NHS Trusts should not be expected to provide dedicated in-patient wards for personality disordered patients in general adult mental health services, as any personality disordered patient likely to need inpatient services outside of the forensic sector is arguably most likely to exhibit concurrent mental illness. However, forensic services are more likely to segregate their personality disorder and mental illness sectors, and registration requirements for Independent Hospitals may specify the legal categories of patient that such hospitals are entitled to admit. Whilst these forms of specialisation may have clinical justifications that outweigh potential disadvantages, Government and service commissioners should be aware that one such danger is of patients' needs 'falling between' such categories, either to the detriment of a holistic approach to patient care, or to the complete exclusion of some patients from services.

Executing section 135 warrants

Ward v Commissioner of Police for the Metropolis and others
[2005] UKHL 32, May 2005

1.72　We discussed the Court of Appeal ruling on this matter in our last Biennial Report[70]: that ruling has now been overturned in the House of Lords.

1.73　In 1997, *W* was removed from her home pursuant to a warrant issued under section 135 of MHA 1983. The warrant named the ASW who was to execute it, as well as a consultant psychiatrist and another medical practitioner. However, the warrant did not name a particular police constable, nor did it state the premises on which it was to be executed. The named ASW was present when *W* was removed to hospital, but the named consultant and the other medical practitioner were not. When, next day, *W* was released from hospital, she sought damages for false imprisonment, claiming: (1) the warrant was defective; or (2) the execution of the warrant was unlawful.

---

[69]　National Institute for Mental Health in England (2003) *Personality disorder: no longer a diagnosis of exclusion. Policy implementation guidance for the development of services for people with personality disorder.* See p.13 for stats: in response to a 2002 NIMHE survey 57% of all Trusts indicated that they provided at least some personality disorder services: 28% reported that they did not. 15% of Trusts failed to respond.

[70]　MHAC (2003) *Tenth Biennial Report; Placed Amongst Strangers.* Chapter 8.53 *et seq.*

1.74   At first instance, the Court held that the warrant was valid, even though it had been drafted sloppily, and its execution was lawful. The Court of Appeal overturned this decision, stating that:

- although ECHR Article 5 was not directly in issue, it was salutary to bear in mind the protection against deprivation of liberty that it provided;

- when utilising s.135 of the Act, the Magistrates would have an implied power to limit the length of time for which their warrant would remain valid;

- they could also impose such other conditions as could sensibly relate to the execution of the warrant, provided they protected the interests of the person liable to be removed and furthered the object of granting the warrant;

- therefore, although the warrant was valid its execution was not[71].

1.75   This matter was appealed to the House of Lords by the Trust involved in the case, which was concerned at the practical implications for the working of the law. The patient acted in person (although an *amicus curiae* was appointed to for the court). Their Lordships overturned the judgment of the Court of Appeal, ruling that, in the particular circumstances of this case, there was neither necessity nor legitimate purpose in naming the individuals. The inclusion of named professionals on the warrant in this case appeared to have stemmed from administrative error rather than any considered need, and there was 'nothing … to suggest that, in signing and issuing the warrant, the magistrate … actually … applied his mind to whether, or why, these individuals should be specified'[72].

1.76   Their Lordships noted that:

- the Mental Health Act 1959 had abolished the previously established statutory requirement to name the doctor who was to attend the execution of a warrant under s.15(2) of the Mental Deficiency Act 1913; and

- s.119 of the Police and Criminal Evidence Act 1984 had removed any requirement to name the police constable;

and agreed that this legislative history made Parliament's intention clear: there was to be no requirement to name these professionals. From that basis of agreement, their Lordships adopted slightly different approaches to the question of whether a magistrate legitimately could attach conditions to the issue of a s.135 warrant.

1.77   Lord Rodger's partially dissenting view took as its basis *Attorney-General v Great Eastern Railway Co* (1880):

whatever may be fairly regard as incidental to, or consequential upon, those things which the legislature had authorised, ought not (unless expressly prohibited) to be held, by judicial construction, to be *ultra vires*[73]

where 'incidental to' may be read to include matters which 'may reasonably and properly be

---

[71]   *W v The Commissioner of Police for the Metropolis and Epsom & St Helier NHS Trust* [2003] EWCA Civ 1152, (2003) 1 WLR 2413, July 2003

[72]   Para 7 of the House of Lords' judgment

[73]   Lord Selbourne LC at p478, *Attorney-General v Great Eastern Railway Co* (1880) 5 App Cas 473.

done under the main purpose[74]. This suggested that there could be circumstances (e.g. where a patient has a particularly good relationship with one professional, or a particularly bad relationship with another) where the naming of an individual practitioner to execute a warrant could be properly regarded as 'incidental' to the magistrates' power to issue that warrant, and therefore not *ultra vires*. Similarly, a magistrate could, in Lord Rodger's view, make other conditions on the execution of a warrant, such as that it should not take place at night.

1.78   In contrast, Lady Hale's approach, which was endorsed by Lords Steyn, Hutton and Carswell, implicitly rejected this view, adopting instead the general principle that there can be implied into a statutory power only such incidental powers as are *necessary* for its operation[75], and not such as might be 'sensible or desirable'[76]. Lady Hale concluded that it was not permissible on this basis to imply into s.135 a power to insist that named professional execute the warrant.

1.79   The Court declined to reach a final conclusion on the extent to which other specific powers (such as whether s.135 warrants may be time-limited by magistrates' upon issue), although Lady Hale's construction outlined above would presumably be the most likely test to be applied in any future legal challenge. In what may be an important *dicta*, Lady Hale inclined to the view that the provisions of ss.15 and 16 of the Police and Criminal Evidence Act 1984 apply to warrants issued under s.135 of the Mental Health Act 1983 – an interpretation that we have always supported, but which appeared to have been not followed by the Court of Appeal. Accordingly, applications for warrants should be made *ex parte* in writing; can only be used to gain entry to premises once; and expire after one month. In our last report we discussed this issue at length and called for Government guidance giving an authoritative view on the requirements for s.135 warrants in the light of PACE and human rights requirements[77]. This judgment may perhaps now enable this recommendation to be acted upon. The MHAC has made available a precedent warrant for s.135 purposes on its website (see Chapter 4.194 below).

Definition of 'a public place'

R v Leroy Lloyd Roberts
[2003] EWCA Crim 2753, October 2003

1.80   Having received an emergency call, a police officer tried to enter *R*'s house. There was a struggle in *R*'s front garden, during which *R* and the police officer fell over. It is relevant to the case that the garden was very narrow, and the gap between the house and the public highway was only one metre wide. *R* was restrained and taken to the police station, where he was searched and found to be in possession of a knife.

1.81   *R* was charged, amongst other things, with having a blade or a sharply pointed article in a

---

[74]   Lord Blackburn at p481, *Attorney-General v Great Eastern Railway Co* (1880)

[75]   Lady Hale on Bennion, *Statutory Interpretation* fourth edition, §174 (para 23 of the judgment).

[76]   Para 24 of the judgment

[77]   MHAC (2003) *Tenth Biennial Report: Placed Amongst Strangers.* Chapter 8.52 – 8.56.

public place.[78] For these purposes, 'public place' 'includes any place to which at the material time the public have or are permitted access, whether on payment or otherwise'.[79] This definition is similar to the one used in s.136 of MHA 1983, so that the 'place of safety' provisions may be used 'If a constable finds in *a place to which the public have access* a person who appears to him to be suffering from mental disorder and to be in immediate need of care or control'.[80]

1.82   When *R* came before the Crown Court, the trial judge accepted that the front garden was not a place to which the public was permitted access. However, given that it would be possible for someone standing in the garden to use his knife against a passing pedestrian, he directed the jury that the front garden was a public place for the purpose of this case. *R* was convicted, and he appealed.

1.83   The Court of Appeal held that the trial judge was wrong: land adjacent to areas to which the public had access could not be a public place, even if the harm against which the offence was designed to provide protection could be inflicted from that land. *R*'s conviction was therefore quashed.[81] This decision is consistent with an earlier decision of the Court of Criminal Appeal, to the effect that a garden is not a public place for the purposes of the Public Order Act 1936.[82]

Director of Public Prosecutions v Pauline Zhao and John Zhao

[2003] EWHC 1724 (Admin) June 2003

1.84   The defendants were charged with having a dangerous dog in a public place contrary to s. 3(1) and (4) of the Dangerous Dogs Act 1991 ('DDA 1991'). Under s.10(2) of DDA 1991, 'public place' means:

> [A]ny street, road or other place (whether or not enclosed) to which the public have or are permitted to have access whether for payment or otherwise and includes the common parts of a building containing two or more separate dwellings.

1.85   In this case, the alleged 'public place' was a cul-de-sac on which the defendants' commercial premises were situated. It was alleged that their dog bit a third person on the pavement just outside those premises. The defendants were convicted on the evidence of a police constable, who said she had seen children playing and cars parked on the cul-de-sac in question. Despite this evidence, the District Judge ruled that the street was not a public place as defined in DDA 1991, s.10(2), and he dismissed the case. The prosecution appealed.

1.86   Although the police constable had been unable to say precisely when she had seen the parked cars and the playing children, the Administrative Court held that her evidence was

---

[78]   Criminal Justice Act 1988, s 139(1).

[79]   Criminal Justice Act 1988, s 139(7).

[80]   MHA 1983, s 136(1) (emphasis added).

[81]   However, he had also been convicted of affray, and that conviction was upheld.

[82]   *R v Edwards* (1978) 67 Cr App R 228. However, other cases have determined that 'a place to which the public has access' could include premises where there are no barriers or notices restricting access, such as communal spaces in flats which may be entered by members of the public without hindrance. See Jones, R, (2004) *Mental Health Act Manual*, ninth edition, para 1-1230.

prima facie evidence that the relevant area was a 'public place'. Therefore, it allowed the appeal and remitted the matter to the magistrates' court for further hearing.

Right of access to MHRT for section 2 patients

MH v Secretary of State for Health & Others

[2005] UKHL 60, October 2005.

1.87 The original appellant, *MH*, was a woman with Downs' Syndrome. In January 2003 a social worker executed a warrant under s.135 to remove her from the sole care of her mother and take her to a place of safety, from where she was detained under s.2 of the 1983 Act. Her mother's attempt to discharge her from this section was barred under s.25 and, on the day before the s.2 would expire, proceedings began to displace the mother as Nearest Relative on the grounds that she unreasonably objected to the proposed making of a Guardianship order. Displacement proceedings took a number of weeks to resolve, during which time *MH*'s s.2 detention was extended by virtue of s.29(4). During this time the Secretary of State acceded to a request to use his discretion under s.67 to refer the case to the MHRT, where an unsuccessful appeal against detention was heard.

1.88 The original appeal claimed that *MH*'s rights under ECHR Article 5 (right to liberty) had been violated. The two key questions in the case were:

- whether patients should have a right to apply to the MHRT themselves when their detention is extended under s.29(4) pending resolution of an application to displace a Nearest Relative

- whether the case of patients who lack the capacity to make their own applications to be discharged from detention under s.2 of the Act should automatically be referred to the Tribunal.

1.89 The Court of Appeal found that there had been a violation of *MH*'s rights under Article 5(4) and made the following declaration of incompatibility under section 4 of the Human Rights Act 1998:

(i) Section 2 of the Mental Health Act 1983 is incompatible with ECHR Article 5(4) in that it is not attended by adequate provision for the reference to a court of the case of a patient detained pursuant to s.2 in circumstances where a patient has a right to make application to a Mental Health Review Tribunal but the patient is incapable of exercising that right on his own initiative;

(ii) Section 29(4) of the Mental Health Act 1983 is incompatible with ECHR Article 5(4) in that it is not attended by provision for the reference to a court of the case of a patient detained pursuant to s.2 of that Act whose period of detention is extended by the operation of the said s.29(4).

1.90 This declaration was overturned in October 2005 following appeal by the Secretary of State to the House of Lords[83]. In the only reasoned speech of the judgment, Lady Hale found nothing in law to justify an implication in Article 5(4) that an automatic reference should be made to the Tribunal in every case where a patient lacks the ability to make his or her own

---

[83] Department of Health (2005) *'Bournewood' Consultation - The approach to be taken in response to the judgment of the European Court of Human Rights in the 'Bournewood' case.* March 2005. (para 5.11)

application. Her view was rather that 'every sensible effort should be made to enable the patient to exercise [the right to take proceedings] if there is reason to think that she would wish to do so'[84]. In their Lordships' view, a mentally incapacitated patient, both in theory and according to the facts of this case, was so enabled by the existing legal mechanisms of the rights and duties given, under the 1983 Act, to hospital managers, Nearest Relatives and the Secretary of State[85].

1.91　We are sceptical of their Lordships' conclusion on this point. Some incapacitated patients will, unlike *MH*, have no carer or relative intervening on their behalf, and such patients' rights to take proceedings will now be dependent solely upon a decision by a mental health professional that the patient would exercise that right if he or she could do so.

1.92　At the start of her speech (para 5), Lady Hale referred to the fact that the European Court's ruling in *HL v United Kingdom* has necessitated a review of their Lordships' previous assumption (in their Bournewood ruling of 1999) that the powers of the 1983 Act are reserved, in cases of patients lacking capacity, for those who a evidently non-compliant with admission to hospital. Although there has as yet been no announcement over Government's legislative response to *HL v UK*, it seems likely that the service response to the ruling has already undermined this assumption. Services mindful of their duties under the Human Rights Act 1998 have already begun to detain some incapacitated but compliant patients under the powers of the 1983 Act where their failure to do so might be construed as an unlawful deprivation of liberty. It is surely a lesson of the *Bournewood* case that the decisions of mental health professionals alone offer inadequate protection to the incapacitated patient and we take the view that a more structured system of enabling such patients detained under s.2 to exercise their rights of appeal to the Tribunal would have been better, and may yet be deemed necessary by subsequent European Court rulings.

1.93　Whilst we were disappointed at the Government's decision to challenge the Court of Appeal judgment in *MH*, we hope that the success of that challenge will not preclude further consideration of how safeguards for incapacitated patients may be improved. We discuss this and make recommendations at Chapter 4.111 *et seq* below.

Standard of proof in MHRT hearings

R (on the application of DJ) v MHRT; R (on the application of AN) v MHRT (Northern region) and (1) Mersey Care Mental Health NHS Trust, (2) the Secretary of State for the Home Department and (3) Mind (The National Association for Mental Health)

[2005] EWHC 587 (Admin), April 2005

1.94　*AN* was admitted to Ashworth Hospital in 1985 having been found unfit to plead after he had killed a mother and her two children the previous year. He had subsequently been found fit to plead and returned to court where he was convicted of manslaughter on ground of diminished responsibility and returned to the hospital under s.37/41. At an MHRT hearing lasting five days in 2004 submissions were made as to the standard of proof that

---

[84]　*ibid.,* para 23

[85]　*ibid.,* paras 25-7

should be applied to the Tribunal's deliberations. In its statement of reasons for its decision not to discharge *AN*, the Tribunal concluded

> that in relation to assessment of conflicting expert opinions and diagnoses a balance of probabilities is the realistic standard. However we consider that in accordance with our normal practice wherever it is necessary to resolve important issues of fact upon which important consequence flow a much higher standard, akin to the criminal standard, is both fair and reasonable[86].

1.95 *DJ* had been detained at for eight years under s.37. His MHRT hearing in 2004 was presented with an independent social circumstances report that stated uncertainty as to whether the conditions for compulsion were met, but no expert medical evidence had been called by the patient. In its statement of reasons not to discharge *DJ*, the Tribunal,

> bearing in mind that the burden of proof lay on the detaining authority and that it needed to demonstrate a right to detain on the balance of probabilities, ...accepted the evidence of [the RMO] that the statutory criteria were met since there was no evidence to contradict this[87].

1.96 The statements of these two Tribunals gave rise to the case. It was argued by the patients' solicitors that the Tribunals had erred in accepting a too-low civil standard of proof (i.e. the balance of probabilities) where they should be required to adopt either the criminal standard of proof (beyond reasonable doubt) or the 'clear and convincing evidence' standard of proof applied by the US Supreme Court in *Addington v Texas* (1979). The MHRT and Home Secretary argued that the civil standard of proof was the appropriate standard, with the Home Secretary arguing that the Tribunal in *AN*'s case therefore misdirected itself in the patient's favour by adopting a higher standard for parts of its deliberations.

1.97 The judge, Mr Justice Munby, essentially agreed with the position of the Home Secretary. He found that the question that Tribunals must first answer in their deliberations – whether someone is suffering from mental disorder – was a matter of fact and therefore susceptible to a standard of proof, and that this standard of proof should be a balance of probabilities[88]. The remaining questions established for a Tribunal by the Mental Health Act – whether that disorder is of a nature or degree warranting detention; whether detention is necessary for the health or safety of the patient or the safety of others; and, for restricted patients, whether they should be liable to recall after discharge – are not susceptible to any standard of proof, being matters of judgment.[89] Where the Tribunal relies on allegations of past conduct, it must decide as a matter of fact whether the allegation has been proved, but only to a civil standard (i.e. on the balance of probabilities).

---

[86] *R (on the application of DJ) v MHRT; R (on the application of AN) v MHRT (Northern region) and (1) Mersey Care Mental Health NHS Trust, (2) the Secretary of State for the Home Department and (3) Mind (The National Association for Mental Health)* [2005] EWHC 587 (Admin), para 7.

[87] *ibid.*, para 12.

[88] *ibid.*, para 101. Although it is perhaps of little consequence to the legal reasoning of the judgment, we would suggest that the question of whether a person suffers from mental disorder cannot be categorised simply as a matter of 'fact'. The first principle of *values-based practice*, which is promoted by the National Institute for Mental Health for England (NIMHE), states that 'all decisions rest on values as well as facts, including decisions about diagnosis'. See MHAC (2003) *Tenth Biennial Report: Placed Amongst Strangers.* Chapter 5.6(iii) and Fig 4.

[89] Munby J relied in part for this on Lord Steyn's consideration of the burden of proof in Anti-Social Behaviour Orders in *R (on the application of McCann) v Crown Court at Manchester* [2002] UKHL 39, [2003] 1 AC 787: 'the [question of whether an ASBO is 'necessary to protect persons ... from further anti-social acts'] ... does not involve a standard of proof: it is an exercise of judgment or evaluation' (para 37).

1.98 Notwithstanding their adoption of civil standards of proof, Tribunals must:

- have regard to the particular dangers of relying upon second, third or fourth hand hearsay;

- be appropriately cautious of relying upon assertions of past events which are not securely recorded in contemporaneous notes, particularly if the evidence is only hearsay;

- be alert to the well-known problem that constant repetition in 'official' reports or statements may, in the 'official' mind, turn into established fact something which has no secure foundation in either recorded or provable fact; and

- guard against too quickly jumping to conclusions adverse to the patient in relation to past events where there is no clear account in contemporaneous notes of what is alleged to have happened.[90]

1.99 In Tribunal hearings, Munby J suggested that opportunity for cross examination of relevant witnesses may be a requirement of fairness where such witnesses' hearsay evidence is fundamental to the decision and is to be relied upon to that extent.

1.100 Munby J's warning to Tribunals that they must be alert to the dangers of relying on hearsay evidence has general relevance across mental health services, particularly with regard to incident reporting and risk-assessment. Writing in 1993, Lucy Scott-Moncrieff argued that key decision-making in forensic psychiatry may be biased against patients by false or misleading information included in their records[91]. Giving an account of some inaccuracies encountered in respect of her clients, Scott-Moncrieff suggested that risk-assessments, and therefore reports to Tribunals, may have been influenced by such inaccuracies and that patients may therefore not have been discharged on the basis of false information. A study published by two psychiatrists in 2000 found 'significant discrepancies, particularly in the reporting of aggressive behaviour' when comparing accounts of incidents and reports to the MHRT against contemporaneous records made in their own regional secure unit over two years[92]. The authors of the latter study concluded that the unit's procedures for incident recording could allow for inaccuracies and instigated measures to counter descriptions in truncated 'psychiatric jargon' (i.e. 'behaved aggressively' or 'agitated') and to 'assiduously record eye witness accounts, taking statements in criminal justice style, to incorporate into routine record-keeping and reports'.

Conflicts of interest & MHRT panels

R (PD) v West Midlands and North West MHRT & Mersey Care NHS Trust

[2004] EWCA Civ 311, March 2004

1.101 The claimant, *PD*, had applied to the MHRT against his detention at Rathbone Hospital under s.3 of the Act. The medical member of the Tribunal that considered his case was Dr *A*, a consultant psychiatrist at the Hesketh Centre. Both Rathbone Hospital and the Hesketh

---

[90] *R (on the application of DJ) v MHRT; R (on the application of AN) v MHRT, supra*, para 129

[91] Scott-Moncrieff, L (1993) 'Injustice in Forensic Psychiatry' *Journal of Forensic Psychiatry* 4: 97-108

[92] Sugarman, P., and Roychowdhury, A. (2000) 'Injustice in Forensic Psychiatry: the Scott-Moncrieff hypothesis revisited'. *Journal of Forensic Psychiatry* 11: 165-469

Centre formed part of the Mersey Care NHS Trust's Adult Mental Health Directorate. However, Dr A had never worked at Rathbone Hospital, nor had he ever met PD or any of the other witnesses at the Tribunal hearing.

1.102   PD sought to challenge the Tribunal's decision to dismiss his application. He argued that although there had been no *actual* bias on the part of Dr A, in the view of a fair-minded and informed observer there was a real possibility of *sub-conscious* bias. Therefore, the patient continued, there was a breach of the right to a fair trial guaranteed by ECHR Articles 5(4) and 6.

1.103   The court dismissed the patient's challenge at first instance[93]. First, it held that Dr A was not an 'officer' of Mersey Care NHS Trust and so would not be prohibited from sitting on Tribunals in its hospitals.[94] Second, the court held that a fair-minded and informed observer would be satisfied that there was no real possibility that the Tribunal or Dr A were biased, because:[95]

- although Rathbone Hospital and the Hesketh Centre were in the same directorate, on a day-to-day basis they were managed independently of each other;

- Dr A had had no previous dealings with PD, Rathbone Hospital, or any witness in these proceedings;

- the basic terms and conditions of Dr A's employment contract were set nationally, 'thereby removing them from Mersey Care's sphere of influence';

- there was nothing to suggest that Dr A could be disciplined by Mersey Care NHS Trust for anything he did while sitting on a MHRT;

- 'there was no evidence that there was any promotion or demotion that Mersey Care could offer consultant psychiatrist such as [Dr A]';

- if Dr A was dismissed, he would have a right of appeal to the Secretary of State;

- 'there is nothing to suggest that it was a matter of great or any importance to Mersey Care if the claimant was or was not discharged';

- Dr A had a professional obligation to act independently, in the interests of his patients and not those of his employer.

1.104   This decision was appealed. The Court of Appeal upheld the decision of the High Court, although it applied slightly different analysis and was more cautious over the relevance of apparently analogous cases, stating that:

> It is right that we should record that the initial reaction of each member of the court to the facts of this case was that the suggestion that [Dr A] might have been biased was absurd. [...] It seemed to us that [...] the argument that there was apparent bias in this case was founded on an analysis of case precedent rather than the apprehension of the reasonable observer. It also made us wonder why these proceedings had ever been brought.[96]

1.105   Notwithstanding the Court of Appeal's disdain of the case, two issues that it ruled upon are worthy of note:

---

[93]   *R (on the application of PD) v West Midlands and North West MHRT & Mersey Care NHS Trust* [2003] EWHC Admin 2469. October 2003

[94]   Mental Health Review Tribunal Rules 1983, SI 1983 No 942, r 8(2); *Re A Company* (1980) 1 CA 138

[95]   All quotations from para 67 of the judgment

[96]   Para 46 of the judgment

Definition of an 'officer'.

1.106 The MHRT Rules prohibit anyone from sitting as a Tribunal member who is 'a member or officer of a health authority which has the right to discharge the patient under section 23(3) of the [Mental Health] Act.'[97] It was accepted that Dr *A* was not a 'member' of Mersey Care NHS Trust, but was he its 'officer'? The Court of Appeal said he was not. Referring to the dictionary definition of the word,[98] it concluded that it was people who 'manage the affairs of the authority in question'[99] that would be excluded under this ground.

1.107 This may be an important decision, for the word 'officer' appears throughout MHA 1983 and often seems to be used in a less narrow sense[100]. It also leaves open the possibility of unlawfulness where a MHRT medical member exercises some degree of 'management or direction' of the detaining Trust.

Employees of detaining authorities & MHRT panel membership

1.108 Even if he wasn't an 'officer' of the detaining trust, Dr *A* was certainly it's employee, and his participation in the MHRT hearing would have been unlawful if he could thereby be seen to be neither independent nor impartial. The Court held that there was no general rule prohibiting an employee from sitting on a Tribunal in proceedings to which his employer is a party.[101] However, it found that a NHS Trust was not 'a party' to the proceedings for this purpose because it did not have 'any particular interest in the outcome.'[102] Had Dr *A* been employed at Rathbone Hospital – where the patient was detained – 'there might have been reasonable apprehension that he would have come into contact with those actually responsible for *D*'s detention.'[103] However, that was not the case here, and the Court of Appeal concluded that there was nothing in Dr *A*'s employment with the detaining Trust to give rise to an appearance of bias in this case.[104]

1.109 The Court of Appeal suggested that the *Conflict of Interest Guidelines* drawn up by the Regional Chairs of the MHRT to avoid conflicts of interest were 'incoherent'[105]. In April 2005 the guidelines were withdrawn, the Regional Chairmen of the MHRT having concluded that 'it is dangerous and probably futile to list or determine the factors which may, or may not, give rise to a real danger of bias'. In place of the Guidelines, the Regional Chairmen set out general guidance to members of questions of possible bias. We summarise the principles established in that guidance in the following points:

---

[97] Mental Health Review Tribunal Rules 1983, r 8(2)(b)

[98] 'A person holding office and taking part in the management or direction of a society or institution' – New Shorter Oxford English Dictionary

[99] Para 24 of the Judgment

[100] For example, in the case of Approved Social Workers (ASWs). Technical questions regarding the employment status and role of ASWs discussed in MHAC (2003) *Tenth Biennial Report: Placed Amongst Strangers*, Chapter 8.87-9 and recommendation 26 have not been addressed by Government to date.

[101] Para 26 of the Judgment. See also: *R v Spear* [2002] UKHL 31

[102] Para 28 of the Judgment

[103] *ibid.*, para 37

[104] *ibid.*, para 36

[105] *ibid.*, para 44

(i) The right to a fair hearing by an impartial tribunal is guaranteed in principle by the European Convention and places an obligation on MHRT members to act without partiality or prejudice;

(ii) any direct pecuniary or proprietary interest in the subject matter of a proceeding, however small, operates as an automatic disqualification;

(iii) in cases other than where automatic disqualification applies, the test is whether a fair-minded and informed observer, having considered the given facts, would conclude that there was a real possibility that the tribunal was biased[106];

(iv) this broad test requires each case to be determined on its own facts and issues: no sound objection could be based upon religion; ethnic or national origin; gender; age; class or sexual orientation etc; nor ordinarily on matters relating to employment background or history; previous political associations; extra curricular utterances or previous decisions, etc[107]; but

(v) a real danger of bias might be thought to arise from personal friendship or animosity between the MHRT panel member and any other person involved in the case; or if the member had been closely involved with any such person in a professional relationship such as court proceedings; or when, in similar circumstances, the member has in a previous case rejected the evidence of that person in such outspoken terms as to throw doubt on his ability to approach such evidence with an open mind on a later occasion; etc.

(vi) If there is any real ground for doubt, that doubt should be resolved in favour of recusal.

1.110 We discuss further aspects of conflicts of interest in MHRT panels below at Chapter 4.119 *et seq*.

The re-detention of patients after MHRT discharge

R v East London and the City Mental Health Trust and another, ex parte von Brandenburg

[2003] UKHL 58. November 2003

1.111 Against opposition from his RMO and clinical team, the patient was granted a deferred discharge from s.2 detention by the MHRT in March 2000. On the day before the discharge was to take effect, he was detained under s.3.

1.112 The patient sought judicial review of his re-detention. He said it was unlawful because there had been no relevant change of circumstances since the MHRT granted him a deferred discharge. The respondents argued that a change of circumstances was not necessary in order for a patient to be detained again.

1.113 The patient was unsuccessful at first instance and in the Court of Appeal. In the latter[108], Lord Phillips MR held that where 'a sensible period' had elapsed following discharge,

---

[106] See *Lawal v Northern Spirit* [2004] 1 All ER 187

[107] For a full list (also in relation to point (iv)), see *MHRT Conflicts of Interest: Guidance to MHRT Panel Members on Standing Down on Grounds of Possible Bias*. April 2005, available on request from MHRT secretariat.

[108] [2001] EWCA Civ 239

...to require the professionals involved to investigate […] in order to decide whether or not there has been a relevant change of circumstances would not be helpful or even meaningful.[109]

However, he warned that a very different position would obtain where the re-detention application was made 'within days' of the Tribunal discharge. In such a situation, there was likely to have been a difference of view between the patient's doctors (and social worker) and the MHRT, and, 'where such a conflict exists, it is the opinion of the Tribunal that is to prevail'.[110] Furthermore, s.13 of the 1983 Act requires the ASW who makes a fresh detention application to be satisfied that 'an application ought to be made'. Where the patient had been recently and lawfully discharged by a MHRT, it was difficult to see how the ASW could be so satisfied, and so any application s/he made in those circumstances would be irrational.

1.114 Mr Justice Sedley reverted to the judgment of Laws J in *R v Managers of South Western Hospital, ex parte M*, [1993] QB 683, which had been decisive at first instance in this case. Laws J had stated that

> [T]here is no sense in which those concerned in a section 3 application are at any stage bound by an earlier Tribunal decision. The doctors, social worker, and managers must, under the statute, exercise their independent judgment, whether or not there is an extant Tribunal decision relating to the patient.[111]

1.115 Sedley J agreed that a change of circumstances would justify a departure from a recent MHRT discharge, and he acknowledged that if there had been no such change, the ASW and the recommending doctors were not legally bound by the discharge. However, he said:

> They must have due regard to such a decision for what it is: the ruling of a body with duties and powers analogous to those of a court […] The second decision must be approached with an open mind, but it is not necessarily going to be written on a clean slate.[112]

The House of Lords

1.116 Lord Bingham delivered the only substantive speech. He said that, though it was 'narrow', the question at issue in this case was one of 'practical importance'.[113] The need to comply with Article 5(4), and with the rule of law, meant that decisions of legally constituted courts and tribunals should be respected.[114] Therefore, 'It is not open to an ASW to apply for the admission of a patient […] simply because [s/he] disagrees with a Tribunal's decision to discharge. That would make a mockery of the decision'.[115] However, Lord Bingham set out the following 'important considerations':

---

[109] *ibid*, para 30

[110] *ibid.*, para 31

[111] [1993] QB 683, at p.696

[112] [2001] EWCA Civ 239, para 42

[113] [2003] UKHL 58, para 6

[114] See, for example: *Pickering v Liverpool Daily Post & Echo Newspapers plc* [1991] 2 AC 370

[115] [2003] UKHL 58, para 8

- A MHRT can consider a patient's condition only at the time of the hearing, and it 'cannot ignore the foreseeable future consequences of discharge'.[116] However, it 'is not called upon to make an assessment which will remain accurate indefinitely or for any given period of time'.[117]

- Although a Tribunal discharge might give pause to a psychiatrist who had opposed it, he 'cannot be obliged to suppress or alter' his opinion, because his duty to his client and to the public 'require him to form, and if called upon express, the best professional judgment he can, whether or not that coincides with the judgment of the Tribunal'.[118]

- It is significant that, under s.13 of the 1983 Act, an ASW is under a duty to apply for detention where s/he is satisfied that such an application 'ought to be made'.

1.117 Although Lord Bingham concluded that the decision of the Court of Appeal was broadly correct, his test was different. He said:

'[A]n ASW may not lawfully apply for the admission of a patient whose discharge has been ordered by the decision of a Mental Health Review Tribunal of which the ASW is aware unless the ASW has formed the reasonable and *bona fide* opinion that he has information not known to the Tribunal which puts a significantly different complexion on the case as compared with that which was before the Tribunal'.[119]

1.118 Broadly speaking, information 'not known to the Tribunal' is likely to be information which existed but which was not made available to the Tribunal at the time of its hearing, or new information reflecting a change in the patient's condition or other circumstance since the Tribunal hearing. In this case, the ASW had attended the MHRT hearing, had heard its decision and read its written reasons, and so, in the view of Lord Bingham, was well placed to decide whether this test had been fulfilled[120]. However, this would not always be so, and there might be cases in which the ASW was unaware that there had been a MHRT hearing.

1.119 The patient argued that each ASW should have a duty to make reasonable enquiry as to any prior Tribunal decision, but Lord Bingham did not accept this. He noted that under s.13(2) of the Act, an ASW must 'interview the patient in a suitable manner and satisfy himself that detention in a hospital is in all the circumstances of the case the most appropriate way of providing the care and medical treatment of which the patient stands in need'. In this way, the ASW might learn of an earlier MHRT decision and the reasons for it. However, if s/he did not, Lord Bingham could 'see no ground for implying a more far-reaching duty of enquiry not expressed in the statute'.[121]

1.120 Lord Bingham thought that only a light additional duty should be imposed upon an ASW in these circumstances: 'a patient should be informed why an earlier Tribunal decision is not thought to govern his case if an application for admission is made [that is] inconsistent in

---

[116] MHA s 72(1)(a)(i) and (b)(i); *In re Waldron* [1986] QB 824, at p.846

[117] [2003] UKHL 58, para 9

[118] *ibid.*

[119] *ibid.*, para 10

[120] *ibid.*, para 11

[121] *ibid.*

effect with the earlier decision'.[122] However, even this duty would be a limited one, and an ASW could not be required to make a disclosure that would be harmful to the patient or others.

1.121 Although this case may be the last word of the judiciary on the general principle at stake, it would seem that there are still some broad uncertainties for practitioners which will have to be grappled with by authority's legal advisors and potentially the courts. One instability in the judgment would seem to be the question of what might constitute 'new' information, particularly where an authority feels that the Tribunal failed to take into account some important aspect of a case, or failed to show that it did so. In such a case, the interests of fairness and justice would seem to require that the authority seek judicial review of the decision, rather than undermine or override it through instigating a new detention, although the option of judicial review may not be attractive where a patient has already left the hospital on the basis of the contested decision[123]. In discussions with some legal advisors to detaining authorities, it has been suggested to us that the *Brandenburg* judgment might provide an alternative means for an authority to prevent what it sees as the dangerous discharge of a patient from hospital.

Requirement on MHRT to give reasons for its decisions

R (on the application of Li) v MHRT

[2004] EWHC 51 (Admin), January 2004

1.122 In this case a successful application for the judicial review of a Tribunal decision was based upon a claim that the reasons given for its decision had been inadequate. It highlights the need for full disclosure of the Tribunal's reasons for its determination. In the light of the *Von Brandenburg* case (see above), such reasons should be provided speedily upon any decision to discharge a patient, to allow an ASW to respond appropriately if re-detention becomes a possibility soon after discharge.

---

[122] *ibid.*, para 12

[123] It was established in *R (on the application of H) v Ashworth Hospital Authority & others* [2002] EWCA Civ 923 that, where an application for judicial review of an Tribunal decision is made, that application may also request a stay of that decision, even where the practical effect of granting such a stay would be to require a patient who had been discharged as a result of the contested decision to return to hospital whilst the court heard the case. Dyer LJ suggested that the jurisdiction to grant such stays should be used sparingly, and 'that the court should usually refuse to grant a stay unless there is a strong, and not merely arguable, case that the Tribunal's decision was unlawful' and there is 'cogent evidence of risk and dangerousness' (para 47). Where any stay of a Tribunal decision is granted pending judicial review, the case should be determined 'with the degree of speed appropriate and usual in a *habeas corpus* case' (i.e. if at all possible, within days of the application) (paras 47 – 48).

Tribunal hearings in public

R (on the application of Mersey Care NHS Trust) v Mental Health Review Tribunal; Ian Stuart Brady and Secretary of State for the Home Department
[2004] EWHC 1749 (Admin), July 2004

1.123 This case has been analysed in the *Journal of Mental Health Law* by David Hewitt[124].

1.124 Ian Stuart Brady is a restricted patient detained at Ashworth Hospital after having been transferred from prison. In 2000 he was unsuccessful in challenging his force-feeding by the hospital in response to his hunger-strike[125]. In 2003 his request that his next MHRT hearing be held in public was accepted by the Tribunal after an initial refusal. The hospital had opposed this request, arguing that Mr Brady did not have the capacity to request a public hearing, and that the impact of such a hearing would be inappropriate, both in its own right on clinical and security grounds and in terms of the publicity that it generated. The MHRT held that:

- a Tribunal hearing must be held in private unless the patient requests a public hearing and a public hearing is not contrary to the patient's interests;

- the Tribunal was not satisfied that Mr Brady lacked the capacity to request a public hearing and therefore presumed that he had such capacity; and

- a public hearing would not be contrary to Mr Brady's interests.

This decision was challenged at judicial review by Mersey Care NHS Trust as the hospital manager.

1.125 This judicial review took place against the background of Article 6 of the ECHR, which establishes that everyone is entitled to 'a fair and public hearing' in determination of their civil rights. The ECHR qualifies this entitlement in allowing that the press or public may be excluded from all or part of the trial for various purposes, including in the interests of morals and public order, or in special circumstances where publicity could prejudice the interests of justice.

1.126 Beatson J, presiding, found for the Trust, setting aside the MHRT decision and remitting the matter back to the MHRT for reconsideration. The judgment found the MHRT's decision to have been flawed in a number of respects, including:

- it was, in the judges' view, based upon an incorrect assumption that the MHRT's own powers to control publicity were underpinned by contempt laws[126]; and

- in part because of this over-estimation of its powers, the MHRT had failed to take account (or show that it had done so in its reasons) of relevant considerations to its decision:

---

[124] Hewitt, D (2005) 'A Private Function' *Journal of Mental Health Law*, May 2005; p 83-95. Northumbria Law Press

[125] *R v Collins and Ashworth Hospital Authority, ex parte Brady* [2000] Lloyds Medical Reports 355

[126] see Hewitt, D. (2005) 'A Private Function', *supra*, for a critical examination of this aspect of the decision.

- although the MHRT rules only relate the decision whether to hold a hearing in public to determination of interests of the patient, because those rules establish permissive powers to hold public hearings rather than a duty to do so, the MHRT should take account of wider considerations (such as issues of security, public order and the interests of other patients) when deciding whether to exercise its discretion; and
- although the MHRT had applied a test of whether Mr Brady had capacity to *request* a public hearing, it was not apparent from its decision that it had considered Mr Brady's capacity to understand issues relating to the longer-term 'impact and likely ramifications' of a public hearing.

The court's use of a capacity test to refute the patient's claim.

1.127 In his analysis of this case, David Hewitt has pointed out, amongst other things, some aspects of the use of a capacity test that should be of concern. Firstly, there is nothing in the MHRT rules that explicitly invokes mental capacity as a determining factor in whether a patient's expressed wish for a public hearing should be respected: the test is the wider one of 'the interests of the patient'[127]. It is undoubtedly the case that a patient's mental capacity in relation to a request is relevant to whether meeting the demand would be in his or her best interests, but it is only one factor. There is a danger of narrowing the scope of patients to take decisions about their lives by the importation of a capacity test into decisions that should rest on wider principles.

1.128 Furthermore, the Court showed a curious willingness in Mr Brady's case to reverse the usual presumption of capacity. It acknowledged that the MHRT had rightly considered 'whether Mr Brady gives proper regard to the risks that he runs' in requesting his public hearing (the MHRT having concluded that Mr Brady did do so, on a presumption of capacity which they found had not been refuted). But Beatson J then went on to insist upon a distinction between Mr Brady's capacity to request a public hearing and his capacity to grasp the implications of having such a hearing and, by interpreting the MHRT's decision to relate only to the former, found Mr Brady incapacitated in relation to the latter.

1.129 Mr Hewitt concludes in his review of this case that:

> Mr Brady has not enjoyed good fortunes in challenging the organs of the State. He failed to stop Ashworth force-feeding him and now he has failed to compel the MHRT to hear his case in public. A common theme of both cases is … Mr Brady's intellectual capacity. However much he has of it, it never seems to be enough. His force-feeding was lawful under the common law doctrine of 'necessity' because, although he was perfectly capable in most every other facet of his life, Maurice Kay J felt that he was not so in relation to decisions about food refusal. Now, his acknowledged capacity to request a public hearing has been held not to imply that he is capable of understanding the implications of such a course. The Court has shown itself willing to make an inference against Mr Brady from the mere absence of information to support him.

> In *Brady* the State has indeed been fortunate in its choice of adversary, for … its judges

---

[127] Mental Health Tribunal Rules 1983, rule 21(1).

have always been able to find sufficient – and sufficiently *legal* – reasons to deny him what he wants, and to do so, moreover, for his own good[128].

1.130   In our last report we discussed the potential role of mental incapacity as a threshold in the legal framework around compulsion in mental health services. We pointed to the danger of circularity of definition in making mental incapacity or its absence a fundamental criterion for compulsion. Where the request of a psychiatric patient makes professionals uncomfortable or appears to be not in a general best interest, the decision that such a request is made by an incapacitated patient too easily closes down consideration of whether it might nevertheless be honoured[129]. We believe that the above case should sound as an echo of that caution. We discuss these issues further at Chapter 3.27 *et seq* below.

Conditional discharge and aftercare duties

R (on the application of IH) v (1) Secretary of State for the Home Department (2) Secretary of State for Health and (1) Mental Health Review Tribunal (2) Nottinghamshire Healthcare NHS Trust

[2003] UKHL 59. November 2003

1.131   We discussed the Court of Appeal's 2002 ruling on this case in our last report[130]. *IH* was detained in a high secure hospital in 1995 following a finding of not guilty by reason of insanity under the Criminal Procedure Insanity Acts (CPIA). His diagnosis was paranoid psychosis, which was reported to be in remission by 1999. Tribunal hearings over 1999 and 2000 heard conflicting clinical views as to the advisability of discharge, but in February 2000 the MHRT ordered a conditional discharge, deferred until a consultant psychiatrist would agree to supervise him in the community. No such psychiatrist could be found. In 2002 the Court of Appeal gave a constructive reading of s.73 of the Act to enable Tribunals to treat as provisional decisions to discharge patients subject to conditions; to monitor progress in implementing that decision; and to amend the conditions, or determine that the patient should remain in hospital, if the original conditions could not be met. The Court of Appeal suggested that the Secretary of State should refer *IH*'s case back to the Tribunal. In March 2002 the Tribunal concluded, notwithstanding the view of its earlier hearing, that the conditions for detention in hospital continued to be met and that *IH* should remain there.

1.132   The House of Lords' judgment dealt with a number of important issues arising from the case up to this point[131].

The MHRT as a court

1.133   *IH* had claimed that because the MHRT could not compel a psychiatrist to supervise him in the community, the MHRT had no power to enforce its rulings and was not a 'court' within

---

128   Hewitt, D. (2005) 'A Private Function', *supra*, p.95

129   MHAC (2003) *Tenth Biennial Report: Placed Amongst Strangers.* Chapter 4.3 *et seq*

130   *ibid.*, Chapter 3.16-23.

131   We are grateful to David Hewitt of Hempsons Solicitors for permission to use his training material *Case Law Update* (Spring 2004) in the preparation of this report. We remain responsible for any use of his material.

the meaning of Article 5(4)[132]. Their Lordships did not agree. They said that the MHRT *does* have sufficient 'coercive power' to make it a 'court'. If a condition of discharge cannot be met, a Tribunal can order the patient's absolute discharge. The Tribunal's failure to do so in this case reflected the MHRT's opinion of the patient's mental state, not an insufficiency in its powers. Their Lordships upheld the Court of Appeal's interpretation of s.73 of the Act and its view of the options available to a Tribunal where conditions required for a discharge had not been met.

1.134 So, even though the MHRT cannot overcome the absolute refusal of clinicians to collaborate with a conditional discharge, the steps that it *can* take are more extensive than was first thought and they *do* make it a 'court' for the purposes of the ECHR.

Unlawful detention?

1.135 The patient had claimed that the period spent in hospital awaiting the fulfilment of conditional discharge arrangements should be considered as unlawful detention. In this he relied upon the case of *Johnson v United Kingdom*[133], in which the European Court of Human Rights held that a patient's continued detention was unlawful because suitable after-care arrangements could not be made. However, it was clear that whereas Johnson had not suffered from mental illness for several years of his detention, it had never been suggested that this was the case for *IH*, who had throughout satisfied the '*Winterwerp* criteria' for detention[134]. Their Lordships held that there was 'a categorical difference, not [just] a difference of degree' between the positions of Johnson and *IH*. In the latter:

> the Tribunal considered that the appellant could be satisfactorily treated and supervised in the community if its conditions were met, as it expected, but the alternative, if these conditions proved impossible to meet, was not discharge, either absolutely or subject only to a condition of recall, but continued detention.[135]

1.136 This aspect of the judgment was further debated in the subsequent case brought by another patient against Doncaster Metropolitan Borough Council, discussed at paragraph 1.143 *et seq* below.

The duty of the PCT

1.137 Where a MHRT discharges a patient subject to conditions, the after-care arrangements necessary to fulfil those conditions will be made by a PCT (jointly with a local social services

---

[132] Article 5(4) says that anyone who is detained for this reason has the right 'to take proceedings by which the lawfulness of his detention shall be decided speedily by a court and his release ordered if the detention is not lawful.'

[133] (1997) 27 EHRR 296

[134] '… except in emergency cases, the individual concerned should not be deprived of his liberty unless he has been reliably shown to be of 'unsound mind' [by] …objective medical expertise. Further, the mental disorder must be of a kind or degree warranting compulsory confinement. What is more, the validity of continued confinement depends upon the persistence of such a disorder.' (*Winterwerp v Netherlands* [1979], para 39)].

[135] Para 28 of this judgment

authority).[136] Their Lordships' judgment on this was little more than a restatement of existing law[137]:

> The duty of the health authority [...] was to use its best endeavours to procure compliance with the conditions laid down by the Tribunal. [...] It was not subject to an absolute obligation to procure compliance and was not at fault in failing to do so.[138]

1.138 In any case, Their Lordships found that aftercare authorities 'had no power to require any psychiatrist to act in a way which conflicted with the conscientious professional judgment of that psychiatrist.'[139]

The psychiatrist as a 'public authority'

1.139 It was argued on behalf of the patient that one way to ensure that MHRT conditions were met would be to make every individual psychiatrist a 'public authority' for the purpose of the Human Rights Act 1998.[140] This would compel him/her to act compatibly with a patient's ECHR rights and, for example, to supervise any patient given a conditional discharge.

1.140 In our last report we discussed this proposal at length[141], noting that, although the Mental Health Act does limit doctors' powers, it does not create any general powers or duties that compromise a doctor's autonomy to make positive clinical decisions. Under civil powers at least[142], a doctor cannot be compelled to provide treatment to a patient against his or her wishes. We hoped that the court would reach a balance in their determination of the public authority role of psychiatrists that did not impose unreasonable responsibilities of psychiatrists or absolve them of public authority responsibilities where these are warranted.

1.141 Their Lordships declined to consider this general issue. They said that as no claim arose out of the fact that Tribunal conditions were unmet, the question of public authority responsibilities for psychiatrists was academic for the determination of this case, and that 'determination of that question is best left to a case in which it is necessary to the decision'[143]. It seems likely that this issue will therefore rise again in a future challenge.

1.142 The European Court of Human Rights has ruled an attempt to take these issues to Strasbourg on appeal inadmissable.

---

[136] MHA 1983, s 117(2)

[137] See, for example: *R (on the application of K) v Camden & Islington Health Authority* [2001] EWCA Civ 240; [2002] QB 198

[138] Para 29 of this judgment

[139] *ibid.*

[140] Section 6(3)(b)

[141] MHAC (2003) *Tenth Biennial Report: Placed Amongst Strangers.* Chapter 3.21-3.

[142] The position is arguably less certain in relation to patients subject to restriction orders, where a clinician loses the right to discharge a patient from his or her care.

[143] Para 29 of this judgment

W v Doncaster Metropolitan Borough Council

[2004] EWCA Civ 378, May 2004.

1.143 W was a restricted patient in a medium secure unit (MSU), whose schizophrenia seemed to be well-controlled by medication. In July 2001 the MHRT agreed to a deferred conditional discharge on conditions that included residence at appropriate accommodation identified by his RMO. Problems in identifying place agreed as suitable by all parties, and in providing adequate social services input, delayed implementation of the discharge: in January 2002 W's solicitors made a fresh application to the MHRT. The Tribunal met in March 2002 and directed W's discharge to a named residential facility in Rotherham, notwithstanding the concerns of social services. An arrangement was agreed whereby Doncaster Metropolitan Borough Council, as W's 'home' authority, agreed to put in place community psychiatric and social supervision until such time as Rotherham could take over. These arrangements only lasted a short time, due to deterioration in W's mental state for reasons not relevant to the legal challenge.

1.144 The patient challenged the lawfulness of his detention during the eight months between MHRT hearings. The Court of Appeal rejected this on grounds established by the House of Lords in the *IH* case (see above), with Mance LJ suggesting that a careful reading of the *IH* judgment provided the key to determining all such cases as these. The central question determining whether a patient may lawfully continue to be detained in hospital where MHRT-suggested conditions for discharge cannot be met is whether that patient continues to meet the *Winterwerp* criteria of being of 'unsound mind'. In the case of *Johnson v UK*[144], because it had been determined that the patient no longer suffered from any mental disorder, any unreasonable delay in discharge could constitute a breach of Article 5. But if a patient continues to suffer from mental disorder to a nature or degree that warrants hospital treatment, or would warrant it unless particular arrangements for care outside hospital can be met, the continued detention in hospital in the absence of such arrangements will not constitute a breach of Article 5. In *IH*'s case it had been established that the Tribunal had viewed the conditions it proposed as essential prerequisites for the patient's discharge: although there was no similarly unequivocal explanation of the Tribunal's thinking in W's case, the Court determined that the Tribunal must have taken a similar view. The Court suggested that 'it would be helpful in cases … where the patient continues to suffer from an underlying mental illness which can only be managed in the community provided the conditions imposed are implemented, if the Tribunal says so when it makes the discharge order'[145].

The duty of s.117 authorities

1.145 Both the House of Lords in *IH* and the Court of Appeal in this case essentially reiterated the earlier findings of Lord Philips MR[146] on the duties of authorities to discharge their s.117 responsibilities, but added some further observations. In summary, the authority with s.117 responsibility:

---

[144] *Johnson v UK* (1997) 27 EHRR 296

[145] *W v Doncaster Metropolitan Borough Council* [2004] EWCA Civ 378, para 70(3) per Scott Baker LJ

[146] *R (on the application of K) v Camden & Islington Health Authority* [2002] QB 198, para 20

(i) is empowered, but not obliged, to take preparatory steps in making aftercare arrangements prior to a MHRT hearing. The Appeal Court in this case did not overturn Stanley Burnton J's statement at first instance that such preparation would be wasteful in contested cases, but that authorities should if practicable plan after-care before uncontested Tribunal hearings in order to be able to comply with their duties, but it did stress that such pre-Tribunal discharge planning was itself a *power* rather than a *duty*. This may conflict with the general guidance given in the Code of Practice (and reinforced by the Care Programme Approach) that discharge planning should start upon a patient's admission to hospital[147]. The Code is certainly now incorrect in stating the 1993 case of *Fox*[148] as the authoritative ruling in the matter of pre-discharge planning. Scott Baker LJ said that the suggestion that there was a duty under s.117 to establish after-care arrangements prior to discharge in *Fox*, which he himself had agreed with in the 1999 case of *Hall*[149], should no longer be followed[150];

(ii) in the exercise of its discretion as to what arrangements are appropriate, should normally give way to MHRT decisions, and should make reasonable endeavours to implement the MHRT recommendations: in the absence of strong reasons, not to do so could be an unlawful exercise of that discretion;

(iii) is not itself concerned whether the *Winterwerp* criteria for the patient's continuing detention is met pending arrangements for discharge, as this is a matter for the MHRT;

(iv) will not necessarily breach its duty under s.117 by failing to implement aftercare requirements if it has used its best endeavours to do so, within the constraints of its resources[151],and is placed under no additional legal obligations in this respect by the ECHR than already exist in domestic law[152]. Where there is a breach of s.117 duties, the true remedy is likely to be judicial review and not damages[153].

Aftercare provision

Tinsey (by his receiver and litigation friend Martin Conroy) v Sarker

[2005] EWHC 192 (QB). February 2005.

1.146 This was a dispute over an insurance claim submitted on behalf of *DT*, who sustained head injuries when knocked off his bicycle by *JS* in a road traffic accident. Subsequent to that accident *DT* had been detained under s.3 of the 1983 Act, and thus a part of the issue in contention was whether *JS*'s insurers should meet a claim that included future care costs, where there was a liability on the part of *DT*'s health and social services authorities to make appropriate provision for this under s.117 of the Act.

1.147 Mr Justice Leveson accepted that the duties on authorities to provide aftercare services to patients discharged from detention under the Act were mandatory and not subject to

---

[147] MHA 1983 Code of Practice, para 27.1

[148] *R v Ealing District Health Authority ex parte Fox* [1993] 3 All ER 170

[149] *R v Mental Health Review Tribunal ex parte Hall* [1999] 3 All ER 132

[150] *W v Doncaster Metropolitan Borough Council* [2004] *supra*, para 49 per Scott Baker LJ. See MHAC Guidance Note on suggested annotations to the MHA Code of Practice for further information.

[151] See *R (on the application of K) v Camden & Islington Health Authority* [2002] *supra*, para 29.

[152] *W v Doncaster Metropolitan Borough Council* [2004] *supra*, para 67

[153] *ibid.*, para 68.

means-testing. But neither was that duty open-ended, so that the nature and extent of after-care facilities provided to fulfil this duty must fall to the local authority's discretion[154]. Following from Scott Baker LJ in the *Doncaster* case (see discussion above), he accepted that 'there is neither a bottomless pit of funds nor an adequate supply of suitable accommodation … stretched local authorities and health care providers have to make do as best they can with the facilities and resources available'[155]. The authorities involved were entitled to consider not only what the patient's needs were, but how they could be met within resources. Whilst the authority may not means-test, it is entitled to take into account a patient's actual position with regard to what support the authority must provide (such as taking into account the fact that someone who is entitled to support under s.117 has a house that they can safely return to and therefore does not need accommodating). However, unlike under the National Assistance Act 1948, s.117 of the 1983 Act had no specific provision for patients to top-up provision so as to receive services of their choice.

1.148 In this case, there was cross-examination of the Director of Social Care for Manchester Health and Social Care Trust, who explained to the Court the serious budgetary constraints faced by the Trust. Leveson J stated that it was 'beyond doubt' that the financial position of the Trust was such that there was no question of it funding a regime that was either acceptable to *DT* or even found by the Court to be reasonable for his needs[156]. The judge was not prepared to require *DT* to accept the Trust's 'best facility for the money that [it] might be able to spend'[157], and saw no statutory means whereby such money could be contributed to off-set the costs of alternative aftercare arrangements[158]. He therefore was not prepared to discount damages awarded to *DT* for future care provision 'to reflect the chance' that the Trust might subsequently fund all or part of his future placement[159].

Conditional discharge and restrictions on liberty

R (on the application of the Secretary of State for the Home Department) v MHRT and PH

[2002] EWCA Civ 1868; [2003] M.H.L.R.

1.149 In 2001 the MHRT agreed in principle to conditionally discharge a patient (*PH*) who had spent 44 years in Broadmoor Hospital after having been found unfit to plead on two accounts of wounding with intent to cause grievous bodily harm. In 1958 he had broken into the house of a child actress with intent to kill her, and had attacked her parents as they intervened. *PH* was 77 years old and in poor physical health at the time of the MHRT

---

[154] See Lord Philips MR in *R (on the application of K) v Camden & Islington Health Authority* [2001] EWCA Civ 240 (para 29)

[155] Scott-Baker LJ in *W v Doncaster Metropolitan Borough Council* [2004] EWCA Civ 378, para 59.

[156] *Tinsey v Sarker* [2005] EWHC 192 (QB), para 126

[157] *ibid.*, paras 126, 118

[158] *ibid.*, paras 125, 127

[159] *ibid.*, para 127. Leveson J also stated that he was 'one of those judges to whom Longmore LJ was referring in *Sowden v Lodge* [[2004] EWCA Civ 1370] at paragraph 92 when he said 'Some judges also have an instinctive feeling that if no award for care is made at all, on the basis that it will be provided free by local authorities, the defendant and his insurers will have received an undeserved windfall.'

decision, although he continued to suffer from paranoid schizophrenia and express fixed delusional beliefs. The conditions of his discharge were determined to be that he should reside in a hostel which provided 24-hour trained nursing staff supervision, and that he should not go out from the hostel without being escorted. The Home Secretary challenged this decision through the courts, arguing that the MHRT had gone beyond its powers by imposing conditions that amounted to continued deprivation of liberty after formal discharge. The challenge failed, both at first instance and on appeal.

1.150   In the reasoned judgment of the Court of Appeal, Keene LJ stated five principles established by Strasbourg jurisprudence as applicable to the interpretation of ECHR Article 5(1)'s provision for 'the lawful deprivation of liberty of persons of unsound mind'[160], which we paraphrase below:

(i)   There is a basic distinction between restrictions on movement and deprivation of liberty. The former cannot engage Article 5, but are governed by Article 2.

(ii) The distinction between restrictions on and deprivation of liberty is one merely of degree or intensity, not nature or substance.

(iii) Courts must start from the actual situation of the individual concerned and take into account criteria such as type, duration, effects and manner of implementation of the measure in question.

(iv) Account must be taken of the cumulative effect of the various restrictions.

(v)   The purpose of restrictions is relevant. If they are taken principally in the interests of the individual who is being restricted, they may well not be regarded as a deprivation of liberty at all[161].

1.151   An important reason for the Courts' rejection of the Home Secretary's challenge in this case was that the conditions were considered necessary as supportive measures for *PH*, who was deemed unlikely to cope in the outside world without them, and that they could be relaxed over time as he became more confident outside of a hospital environment.

1.152   This case therefore enabled the MHRT to discharge a patient on condition that he or she continued to reside in another hospital, and where there may be considerable restrictions on that patient's liberty provided that these do not amount to deprivation of liberty and therefore detention. Cases subsequent to *PH* have already started to test the boundaries of this ruling.

R (on the application of G) v MHRT
[2004] EWHC 2193 (Admin) October 2004

1.153   The patient, *G*, was 67 years old and had been admitted to Broadmoor Hospital in 1967 under the Criminal Procedure Insanity Act having been found unfit to plead to the rape of his ten year-old niece and the attempted strangulation of her mother. He had been conditionally discharged but then recalled in the 1980s, and had been recalled to high secure

---

[160] *R (on the application of the Secretary of State for the Home Department) v MHRT and PH* [2002] EWCA Civ 1868; [2003] M.H.L.R. paras 14-16.

[161] See Chapter 3.11 *et seq* below for a discussion of the principle adopted at point (v).

care from other hospital places in 1987 and 1995 following assaults on staff in other hospitals. He suffered from paranoid schizophrenia, which was controlled with medication by the time of this case, so that he was then living in a rehabilitation flat at Thornford Park Hospital. He largely cared for himself in this flat, managing his own cooking, cleaning and finances. He was allowed unescorted leave of up to six hours a day (and indeed attended the judicial review hearing on that basis), but was required to agree with staff his times of leaving and return, and where he will be going. He had to pass through the unit's security system to leave, and was usually only permitted to go out in daylight hours.

1.154   In July 2003 the MHRT decided to conditionally discharge G from detention, subject to his living in a named hostel, and accepting treatment and supervision. The hostel place was withdrawn subsequent to this decision, and attempts to find another proved unsuccessful. After two adjournments, the MHRT determined in March 2004 that it would have no option but to revoke the conditional discharge.

1.155   The patient wanted his conditional discharge more for its symbolic than practical value. G's solicitors and RMO proposed that the conditional discharge should be implemented, with G's current rehabilitation flat being named as his place of residence. It was suggested that the change of legal status, whilst giving G the theoretical right to leave, would in fact have little effect on his day-to-day regime. He was prepared to agree to abide by 'house-rules', and would continue to be required to agree 'leave' with his Primary Care Nurse and not go out at night. If he breached such rules he could be liable to recall under formal powers.

1.156   The MHRT took the view that it could not discharge G into the same hospital place and under the same degree of scrutiny as he had experienced as a detained patient. It viewed the regime proposed as a 'significant deprivation' (*sic*) rather than a restriction of liberty, and that G would therefore not cease to be detained upon his discharge.

1.157   In his judgment, Collins J accepted that it was possible for a patient to cease to be detained if discharged with a condition that he receives and is subject to supervision *at the same hospital* in which he had been detained. He did not, however, accept that this could occur where the regime and the purpose of restrictions on liberty remain the same as before[162]. As such he agreed with the MHRT that it could not conditionally discharge G to remain where he was under the same conditions.

R (on the application of the Secretary of State for the Home Department) v MHRT

[2004] EWHC 2194 (Admin), October 2004

1.158   The patient, *MP*, was 69 years old. In 1976 he had been ordered to Broadmoor Hospital under s.37/41, having been convicted of manslaughter after strangling an 11-year old boy whom he had invited into his house. He was known to have a history of sadistic paedophilic sexual fantasies. At the time of this offence he was under community supervision, having been conditionally discharged from a previous hospital order given upon conviction of indecent assault.

---

[162]   *R (on the application of G) v MHRT* [2004] EWHC 2193 (Admin), para 17.

1.159   In June 2004 the MHRT decided provisionally that *MP* should be conditionally discharged from Thornford Park Hospital, where he was then detained in secure conditions, if suitable accommodation could be found for his placement. It would be a condition of his discharge that this accommodation was staffed round-the-clock by persons experienced in working with violent sex offenders, and that he was not allowed to leave that accommodation without being escorted by such a member of staff who would stay with him at all times when he was out. The Home Secretary challenged this provisional decision on the grounds that the conditions post-discharge would inevitably lead to a deprivation of liberty and that it was unlawful and irrational for the Tribunal to determine this result of an appeal against detention.

1.160   The case was heard on the same day and by the same judge as that of *G* above. Collins J rejected the claim of irrationality (although he allowed that the MHRT's decision was 'surprising in the light of the evidence before it'[163]), but ruled that the MHRT's decision was not lawful as it was impossible to argue that what was proposed could amount to anything less than a deprivation of liberty.[164] Whereas 'in the *PH* case it was at least hoped that the need for an escort might reduce in time and in any event it would not have been a disaster to others if *PH* did get out since he was not a danger', in this case the arrangements restricting *MP*'s freedom to leave the hostel unescorted was entirely designed to curtail his liberty because:

> if he was [at liberty], he would be a danger to young boys ...the fact that *MP* could be managed in accommodation outside of a hospital is nothing to the point if there is a need, as there is in this case, for security which will prevent him from leaving that accommodation or ever being on his own in the community[165].

1.161   In both this case and that concerning *G* above, counsel for the patients argued that even if a patient remained deprived of his liberty as a result of a conditional discharge arrangement, this need not prevent that arrangement provided that the patient consents to that deprivation and therefore remains a voluntary patient. The approach relied on the requirement in s.131 of the 1983 Act that 'nothing in this Act shall be construed as preventing a patient who requires treatment for mental disorder ... from remaining in any hospital ... after he has ceased to be liable to be detained'. Collins J rejected this approach partly on the grounds that there was 'a contradiction between the concept of remaining in hospital as a voluntary patient and being required by a condition imposed by a Tribunal so to remain', and that 'Section 131(1) only applies where there is "no order or direction rendering him liable to be detained under this Act"'[166].

1.162   We discuss general aspects of this case at Chapter 2.56 below.

---

[163]   *R (on the application of the Secretary of State for the Home Department) v MHRT* [2004] EWHC 2194 (Admin) para 14.

[164]   *ibid.*, para 12

[165]   *ibid.*

[166]   *R (on the application of G) v MHRT* [2004] EWHC 2193 (Admin), paras 22-3.

Supervised discharge applications requiring residence in hospital

1.163 The Commission is aware of at least one case of a patient being required to reside at an Independent Hospital as a condition of supervised discharge under s.25A of the Act. The extension of such arrangements to other patients was questioned by a social worker involved with the team, but the Trust solicitors advised that there was 'nothing wrong' in legal terms with such supervision arrangements 'so long as it is understood by everyone that the patients are not in any sense detained, but have freedom of movement subject to the requirements imposed under s.25D'. The basis for this advice was given as the *PH* case (see above); the solicitors concerned have since reconsidered their general approach to this question.

1.164 It is not clear to us that the original advice was correct, even upon the basis of the *PH* case. The *PH* case specifically concerned the conditional discharge of restricted patients by the MHRT. Where such powers are described in the Act (primarily at ss.73 and 74), neither the phrase 'discharge from hospital' nor its cognates are used. Even in s.42(2), which specifies the Home Secretary's power by warrant to 'discharge the patient from hospital, either absolutely or subject to conditions', the result of such action is stated to be that the patient 'shall cease to be liable to be detained', rather than necessarily discharged from the hospital bed. But the drafting of s.25A appears to be more specific:

- An application made under s.25A is made for the patient 'to be supervised after he leaves hospital' and 'with a view to ensuring that he receives the aftercare services provided for him under section 117'[167].

- This 'supervision application' only comes into force when it has been duly made and accepted 'in respect of a patient and he has left hospital'[168].

- A supervision application may only be made in respect of a patient if there would be substantial risks to the health or safety of the patient or the safety of others if the patient does not receive aftercare services under s.117 'after he leaves hospital'[169].

- The statutory purpose of any requirement under s.25D(3)(a) that the patient resides at a specified place is 'to secure that the patient receives the aftercare services provided for him under section 117'[170]. Section 117 of the Act applies only to patients who 'cease to be detained and (whether or not immediately after so ceasing) leave hospital'.[171]

---

[167] MHA 1983 s.25A(1)

[168] MHA 1983 s.25A(2)

[169] MHA 1983 s.25A(4)(b)

[170] MHA 1983 s.25D(1)

[171] MHA 1983 s.117(1)

MP v Nottingham Healthcare NHS Trust
[2003] EWHC 1782 (Admin)

1.165   The claimant, *MP*, had been admitted to Rampton Hospital under s.37/41 upon conviction of manslaughter when he was 19 years of age in 1992. In 2000 the MHRT found him not to meet the test for release from detention, but it supported his care team's suggestion that he should move to a medium secure unit. Unfortunately there were problems in locating a suitable bed and by December 2002 the MHRT sought advice as to the exercise of its legal powers through stating a special case for determination by the High Court. In giving the answer, Silber J was critical of the procedure adopted by the Tribunal in this respect.

1.166   One aspect over which advice was sought was whether the MHRT could use its powers to conditionally discharge *MP* from Rampton hospital to a medium secure unit. The answer given was that:

- the Tribunal could discharge the patient conditionally if it was not satisfied that the detention criteria set out at s.72 (as applied by s.73) were met, but was satisfied that it is appropriate for the patient to remain liable to be recalled to hospital (i.e. conditional discharge must be warranted by its statutory criteria, and is not an available tool for other purposes), and

- the Tribunal *may not* impose conditions when discharging a patient conditionally which require the patient's continued detention (for *any* period) at a medium secure or other hospital.[172]

Recall from condition discharge

R (on the application of AL) v Secretary of State for the Home Department
[2005] EWCA Civ 02. January 2005.

1.167   This case was an attempt, before the House of Lords' overturning of the Court of Appeal's judgment in *B v Ashworth* (see paragraph 1.62 above), to argue the unlawfulness of detaining a patient under s.37/41 subsequent to his recall from conditional discharge on the grounds that he is suffering from personality disorder, where it was argued that the court-order had relied upon a previous classification of mental illness.

1.168   The court rejected this specific appeal because the patient in question had originally been found 'not guilty by reason of insanity' under the Criminal Procedure Insanity Acts (CPIA), and was never therefore classified according to any statutory scheme. Such classification as took place during the patient's detention subsequent to the court order under the CPIA was a purely medical question: prior to the law changing in April 2005 (see Chapter 5.26 below) a CPIA patient ordered to hospital 'as if' under s.37 of the Mental Health Act 1983 had no statutorily required classification.

---

[172] *MP v Nottingham Healthcare NHS Trust* [2003] EWHC 1782 (Admin), para 41.

1.169 On a more general level, the court upheld the Secretary of State's contention that his powers of recall regarding a restricted patient who has been conditionally discharged are not confined to a situation where the cause of concern relates to a relapse in the classified mental disorder. It is sufficient that any mental disorder is found to be present to a degree warranting further detention subsequent to recall. The requirement that the patient's case is referred to the MHRT within a month of recall is a safeguard against unwarranted detention.

'Nature or degree' of mental disorder warranting detention under the Act.

R (on the application of the Secretary of State for the Home Department) v MHRT and (1) DH, (2) South West London & St George's Mental Health NHS Trust

[2003] EWHC 2864. November 2003

1.170 *DH* was a patient with a diagnosis of mental illness, probably schizophrenia, with an underlying personality disorder exacerbated by alcohol and substance abuse. He had a history of repeat admissions, non-compliance with psychiatric treatment, and misuse of drink and drugs, with some past threatening behaviour involving knives and screwdrivers. He was detained under s.37/41 after stabbing another patient whilst he was an inpatient in 1998. He had subsequently been conditionally discharged in 2002, but recalled in January 2003 because of concerns over his drug and alcohol use, evidence of hostile behaviour and an incident of minor self-harm.

1.171 The Home Secretary challenged a Tribunal decision of May 2003 that *DH* should again be conditionally discharged from detention. The conditions of his discharge were to be that he should reside in a staffed hostel under the care of a named RMO and social supervisor, attend at a clinic, remain compliant with medication and undertake drug screening procedures.

1.172 The Tribunal had given as a justification for its decision that 'we conclude that *DH*'s illness is of a nature to justify treatment in hospital, but not at present of a degree'.

1.173 The Home Secretary's argument was that, in determining that *DH*'s illness was of a nature but not a degree as to justify detention in hospital, the Tribunal had misdirected itself in relation to the assessment of the risk that he posed. It had construed 'nature' and 'degree' as conjunctive rather than disjunctive, whereas the Act clearly allows that conditions for compulsion can be met where one or the other can be evinced. The Home Secretary further argued that *DH*'s drug and alcohol abuse (and its exacerbation of his mental state) was a part of the *nature* of his mental illness that must be addressed in determining whether the statutory criteria for continued detention in hospital are met. The Tribunal had failed in this duty, but had instead sought to address the risks posed by *DH*'s alcohol and substance misuse only in the context of whether he should be subject to recall.

1.174 Beatson J allowed the Home Secretary's appeal on above points (but rejected a further argument that the Tribunal's decision was necessarily irrational as a consequence), stating that, as the Tribunal's misdirection over the disjunctive nature of may have 'tainted' consideration of the question of whether treatment in hospital was necessary at the time of the Tribunal hearing, the Tribunal's decision should be quashed and the matter referred back to the MHRT for reconsideration.

Transferred life-sentence prisoners and appeals against detention

R (on the application of P) v Secretary of State for the Home Department

[2003] EWHC 2953 (Admin), December 2003

1.175 This judicial review was described as 'another case concerned with the inter-related and unnecessarily labyrinthine provisions of our penal and mental health legislation relating to life prisoners detained in a mental hospital' by its presiding judge[173]. It concerned a discretionary life prisoner, P, convicted of concurrent charge of rape and manslaughter in 1986, but resident in Broadmoor Hospital since 1994 when he was transferred under s.47/49 of the Mental Health Act. His ten-year tariff had expired, but his status as a restricted patient denied him the right to have his case reviewed by the Discretionary Lifer Panel (DLP) of the parole board. Under existing legislation as interpreted and applied, P had a right to apply to the DLP only upon a finding by the MHRT that he should be discharged from hospital (whether conditionally or absolutely)[174]. P had the right to apply to the Tribunal once a year.

1.176 Article 5 of the ECHR lists the justifications for detention under six sub-headings, of which imprisonment following conviction is the first, and detention of persons of unsound mind part of the fifth. Where discrete specialist courts determine the lawfulness of detention under each heading (as with the MHRT and DLP and their respective roles), a particular problem may arise that was central to this challenge. Provided that the first court finds grounds for detention under its heading (in this case the MHRT considering the fifth heading), then the lawfulness of detention is secure for the purposes of Article 5, regardless of any finding under other heading. But if the first court finds detention unwarranted under its heading, could the delays involved in applying to the second court deny the detainee an effective 'speedy' review as required under Article 5(4)?

1.177 P argued that he was indeed denied his rights under ECHR Article 5(4) to have his detention reviewed speedily by a court that was empowered to release him if that detention was found to be unlawful. It was proposed that the remedy for this was that MHRT and DLP proceedings should be convened concurrently take place as a single court hearing. This would mean that the right to apply to the DLP should extend to all discretionary lifers whose tariff had expired, including thise transferred to hospital and detained their under restrictions.

---

[173] R (on the application of P) v Secretary of State for the Home Department [2003] EWHC 2953 (Admin), para 1.

[174] See R (on the application of D) v Secretary of State for the Home Department [2002] EWHC 2805 (Admin); [2003] 1 WLR 1318.

1.178 Mr Justice Stanley Burnton rejected these submissions, confirming the present reading of the law as correct. There was no *necessary* breach of the requirement of a speedy hearing caused by successive hearings by the MHRT and DLP, although unacceptable delays (which would have to be determined on the facts of each individual case) *could* constitute such a breach.

1.179 In finding that the two courts need not sit concurrently, Stanley Burnton J relied in part on a distinction made between the purposes served by the MHRT and the DLP in these circumstances. The MHRT was only concerned with risk due to mental disorder, but must consider risk to both the detained person and to other persons. On the other hand, the DLP was concerned only with risk to persons other than the prisoner, but was not concerned with the cause of the risk. In cases where the issues under consideration overlap completely (i.e. where a transferred prisoner whose tariff has expired is *only* dangerous to others, and only then as a result of his mental disorder), where the MHRT determines that detention is no longer warranted, then the DLP considering the case subsequently would only be entitled to reach a different conclusion if it had information unknown to that Tribunal which puts a different complexion on the case (see our discussion of *Von Brandenburg* at paragraph 1.111 *et seq* above).

1.180 In practical terms, the very small number of transferred lifers that Tribunals recommend for conditional or absolute discharge (it was stated at the hearing that only 2% of such patients' applications to the MHRT result in such recommendatons) will then be referred to the parole board, and can expect a DLP hearing after a wait averaging six-months, during which time investigations and procedures to establish a release and supervision plan by a probation officer may take place.

1.181 The European Court of Human Rights has ruled this case inadmissable.

Restriction orders and the transfer of prisoners

R (on the application of T) v Secretary of State for the Home Department
[2003] EWHC Admin 538, March 2003

1.182 In 2002 Ms *T* was serving a fifteen month sentence in Holloway Prison for failing to satisfy a confiscation order following a drug-trafficking offence dating back to 1998. Between that order and her imprisonment she had been a psychiatric inpatient on a number of occasions, both informally and under sections 3 and 37 of the Mental Health Act. She had a diagnosis of schizo-affective disorder with episodes of depression and paranoid psychosis, and a history of suicide attempts and bulimia nervosa. Her mental state deteriorated in prison and she was transferred under s.47 in June 2002. The Home Office imposed a restriction order, although the doctor who became *T*'s Responsible Medical Officer had recommended an unrestricted order on the grounds that *T* did not pose any risk to the public, a fact that was not disputed by any party to the judicial review. In August 2002 *T*'s RMO wrote to the Home Office requesting that the restriction order be lifted, as she thought it unnecessary and positively harmful as far as therapy was concerned. The Home Office refused, stating in its letter that:

our normal policy is always to make a restriction order unless it is proposed to transfer the prisoner to hospital within days of his release date and the nature of the offence suggests that restrictions are unnecessary for the protection of the public from harm over that short period.

1.183 This policy was challenged on the grounds, *inter alia*, that:

(i) the Act should be read to predicate the making of a restriction order under s.49 on the need to protect the public from harm and that, insofar as Home Office policy is to impose restriction orders irrespective of risk, it is an exercise of discretion wider than Parliament intended and contrary to Mustil J's explanation in *R v Birch* that once a person is made subject to a transfer direction under s.47 he or she 'in effect … passes out of the peal system and into the hospital regime'[175]; and

(ii) in giving no reasons for its decision to reject the RMO's requests to lift the restriction order, the Home Office had rendered that decision unfair.

1.184 The first challenge rested on an analogy made between restrictions ordered under s.49 by the Home Secretary in respect of sentenced prisoners, and restrictions imposed as part of a court disposal under s.41. In the latter case, the Act does predicate the making of a restriction order on the need for public protection. Lord Justice Kay rejected this analogy on the grounds that the Home Secretary did not stand in the shoes of a sentencing court when imposing restrictions in these circumstances, as the subject of the transfer had already been sentenced to a term of imprisonment which had yet to run its course. It was significant that there is no reference to public protection in s.49 of the Act, and indeed this significance was apparent to Parliament when it enacted the law: 'this is a policy that has endured for going on half a century without challenge'. The 1978 White Paper preceding the Act had justified Home Office policy of almost invariably imposing restrictions on prison transfers on the grounds that this serves:

(i) to preserve the right to return a patient to prison if his condition improves significantly or is found not to be treatable or not to require treatment;

(ii) to ensure that, generally speaking, a transferred prisoner is not set at liberty substantially earlier than he would have been if he had remained in prison; and

(iii) to enable arrangements for compulsory supervision of a patient to be made as a condition of his discharge where this takes place before the expiration of his original sentence[176].

1.185 Lord Justice Kay stated that the Home Office policy therefore was aimed to put into effect a clear and justified public policy in ensuring that a person sentenced to serve a term of imprisonment serves that sentence, or such part of it as statute requires. In passing a restriction order the Home Secretary could ensure that the question of the liberty of a person properly sentenced to a term of imprisonment did not rest entirely with the medical profession upon transfer to hospital. The second challenge, that the Home Office did not give reasons for refusing to lift the restriction order, fell as the policy itself made the reason manifest.

---

[175] *R v Birch* [1990] 90 Crim App R 78

[176] Review of the Mental Health Act 1959 Cmnd 7320, September 1978, para 5.43

1.186   In seeking leave to appeal, it was argued for *T* that the judgment had not considered the effect of s.42, which empowered the Home Secretary to lift any restriction order if it is not necessary in the interests of the protection of the public. The Home Secretary had been asked to do so on such grounds by the RMO, and there was no argument that such grounds were not met. The judge did state, in refusing permission to appeal, that he had considered this, implying that the distinction made in his judgment between the sentencing function of a court and the functions of the Home Secretary in granting transfers from prison was of more significance.

Delays in transferring prisoners to hospital

R (on the application of D) v The Secretary of State for the Home Office (1) The National Assembly for Wales (2), Wrexham Borough Council (3) North Wales Health Authority (4) Wrexham Local Health Board (5) Powys Local Health Board (6)

[2003] EWHC 2529 (Admin). October 2003.

1.187   *D* had been deemed suitable for transfer from a Young Offender Institution (YOI) to hospital under s.47 of the Act, but effecting the transfer had been problematic. The Home Office had undertaken to use its best endeavours to arrange such a transfer as a settlement to earlier proceedings, but the day before *D* was due to be released from the YOI he had not been transferred and the High Court was required to consider *D*'s plight as a matter of extreme urgency. It was the widely accepted view that 'to release him into the community without, at the very least, proper safeguards, would be a disaster for all concerned'.

1.188   Davis J ordered that on the basis of him acquiring the necessary medical reports (doctors were 'apparently already on the road to the YOI in question for that purpose') the Secretary of State should direct a transfer of *D* to a specified institution 'immediately'. The Judge stated:

> It is a strong thing indeed to require the Secretary of State positively to direct a transfer, rather than to consider it, but given what has happened in the past and given the potential arguments by reference to the ECHR and other such matters, I think that, although that is a strong course for me to take, it is appropriate given the rather special circumstances.

R (on the application of D) v Secretary of State for the Home Office (1) National Assembly for Wales (2)

(2004) (Admin. Court), 16 December 2004[177]

1.189   *D*'s case (see above) returned to the High Court when, relying primarily on ECHR arguments, he sought declarations and damages in respect of the delay in the securing of his transfer. On the facts he failed. Stanley Burnton J urged the setting up of a national database of psychiatric hospitals to which reference could be made (by, for example, the prison service) to identify an appropriate hospital. He also made the following observations on the principles involved:

---

[177] We are grateful to John Horne of the University of Northumbria for notes on *D*'s case.

In my judgment, once the prison service have reasonable grounds to believe that a prisoner requires treatment in a mental hospital in which he may be detained, the Home Secretary is under a duty expeditiously to take reasonable steps to obtain appropriate medical advice, and if that advice confirms the need for transfer to hospital, to take reasonable steps within a reasonable time to effect a transfer... The steps that are reasonable will depend on the circumstances, including the apparent risk to the health of the prisoner if no transfer is effected. Inappropriate retention of a prisoner in a prison or a YOI may infringe his rights under Article 8. If the consequences for the prisoner are sufficiently severe, his inappropriate retention in a prison may go so far as to bring about a breach of Article 3, in which case the state is under an absolute duty to prevent or bring an end to his inhumane treatment[178].

Return of transferred patients to prison

R (on the application of Morley) v Nottinghamshire Health Care NHS Trust

(2003) 1 All ER 784

1.190 This case concerned the procedure under s.50 of the Act allowing the Secretary of State to decide upon the release or return to prison of a prisoner who has been transferred to hospital under a restriction order, but who either no longer requires such treatment or for whom no effective treatment is available. The patient had been transferred under s.47 but his RMO recommended a return to prison because he claimed that the treatability test was not satisfied. The patient challenged this on the grounds that there was dissenting professional opinion over this issue. The court ruled that, although the RMO had a duty to make full enquiries on this matter within the hospital, the responsibility for arriving at a final view was his alone and he as under no obligation to report dissent among his clinical team when making his report. There was no requirement on the Secretary of State to permit or consider representations, although the court accepted that the situation could arise whereby information available to the Home Secretary (including information from sources other than the RMO) creates a duty upon him or her to make further enquiries before determining what action to take consequent to receiving the RMO's report.

1.191 Although the wording of s.50 allows that 'any other registered medical practitioner' than the RMO may also make a report under s.50, the court was informed by the Home Office that in practice, unless the 'other doctor' was in some sense standing in for the RMO, then any recommendation from such a source 'would have to be looked at very carefully indeed by the Home Secretary to see whether it was appropriate to act on it'.

1.192 The ECHR has ruled this case inadmissible.

---

[178] *R (on the application of D) v Secretary of State for the Home Office* (2004), para 33.

Revisiting hospital order disposals in the magistrates' courts

Stephen Bartram v Southend Magistrates' Court

[2004] EWHC 2691 (Admin). October 2004.

1.193   *B* stabbed and killed his dog in January 2003 under the delusion that it harboured an evil spirit that needed to be released. He was considered by his solicitors and a psychiatrist to be unfit to instruct his defence to the charge of causing unnecessary suffering to an animal, which is a summary offence carrying a maximum sentence of six months imprisonment. There was apparently no doubt that had killed the dog, and therefore Southend Magistrates' Court was able to decide that he did do the act and, having had written evidence from two medical practitioners, make a hospital order under the Mental Health Act in July of 2003.

1.194   Unfortunately there appears to have been some confusion over what part of the Act was invoked in the making of this hospital order. Although the High Court proceeded on the basis that the initial power used to send *B* to hospital was s.37(3) of the Act, the magistrates' court 'purported to make what is described as an interim order'[179], which it 'extended' during the period of nearly two months before the case was brought back to court with further psychiatric reports.

1.195   The medical reports available to the court in August 2003 stated that there had been such an improvement in *B*'s condition (which nonetheless continued to be diagnosed as paranoid schizophrenia) that no further inpatient treatment was necessary (*B* had in fact already been granted leave from hospital for several periods of up to a week at a time[180]). Neither psychiatric report considered Guardianship powers, but both recommended that a community rehabilitation order with a condition of psychiatric treatment could be the appropriate disposal. One report opined that *B* knew, when he harmed his dog, what he was doing and that his actions were wrong.

1.196   The judicial review was triggered by the District Judge's decision, in light of these medical reports, that *B* was now fit for trial and, as the judge believed further disposal under the Mental Health Act was now removed as an option, to take a plea of not guilty from *B* and adjourn the case for the preparation of a defence. It was determined at judicial review that the District Judge, in making this decision, had overlooked the possibility of making a Guardianship Order under s.37(3) and was therefore wrong to act as he did on an erroneous belief. The District Judge's decision was therefore set aside and the magistrates' court was ordered to deal with the claimant under the terms of s.37 of the MHA by making either a hospital or guardianship order.

1.197   The judicial review went on to consider the question of when and how a magistrate could reopen a case otherwise disposed of by the making of a hospital order under s.37. It is

---

[179]   Although the magistrates' court described its disposal as 'interim' (a word used only in s.38 of the Act), it was 'perhaps fortunate' (para 5 of the High Court judgment) that it did not refer specifically to that section, which it had no power to invoke without convicting the accused. The remand power under s.35 of the Act could have been used to remand B, as an unconvicted person, to hospital for a report on his condition.

[180]   It would appear likely from this that B's medical team assumed him to have been admitted under s.37 rather than on remand under s.35 (or even s.38), as RMOs are not empowered to grant leave to patients detained under the latter powers and there is no indication that the court had been approached to vary any 'remand' arrangement to include domiciliary leave.

perhaps odd that this should have been an issue in the case in point, where the initial disposal was considered an 'interim' measure by the magistrates' court and therefore bound, by its very nature, to be revisited[181], but the High Court's view on this issue is of interest aside from the particular facts of this case. The judgment notes that:

- *In the 1999 case of Ramadan*[182], an order made under s.37(3) that could not be implemented for want of a bed (the court having omitted to ensure that a bed was available before making the disposal) was determined to be rescindable under s.142 of the Magistrates' Courts Act 1980. This power allows the court to 'vary or rescind a[n] ... order imposed or made by it... if it appears in the interests of justice to do so; and ... to replac[e] a[n] ... order which for any reason appears invalid by another which the court has power to impose or make'.

- In addition to situations where a mistake had been made in making a hospital order, s.142 of the Magistrates' Courts Act 1980 empowers courts to revisit a hospital order (even one which appears to finally dispose of the case) in circumstances where this 'is in the interests of justice'. For example, it would be acceptable to reopen a case where the accused, who was unfit to plead at the time that the hospital order was made, regains sufficient mental competence to mount a defence against the charge laid against him and seek acquittal[183].

1.198   It is reported that the powers available to magistrates' courts to make a hospital disposal under s.37(3) are used rarely (see Chapter 5.14 below). This may account for the imprecise understanding of the Act's powers apparent in the magistrates' courts dealings with this case. We have been informed by a number of legal practitioners that, 'with one or two honourable exceptions', there can be a lack of understanding of mental health law amongst magistrates and their clerks. Given the centrality of the diversionary mechanisms for the mentally disordered to the distribution of justice such a lack must be of serious concern which we draw to the attention of the Department of Constitutional Affairs.

Lowering the threshold for breaches of Article 3

McGlinchey and others v United Kingdom

[2003] application no 50390/99, 23 April 2003

1.199   It has been suggested that there is a trend in the European Court of Human Rights towards lowering the threshold for findings of a breach in ECHR Article 3 (which prohibits torture or inhuman or degrading treatment or punishment)[184]. In *Keenan v UK* [2001] the Court found a breach of Article 3 in the lack of appropriate medical treatment and punitive

---

[181] If *B* had have been formally remanded to hospital under s.35 (as would have seemed appropriate in this case) then the District Judge would have been correct insofar as he determined that the case could be tried in the usual way without invoking special powers other than those contained within s.35 to terminate the remand.

[182] *R v Thames Magistrates Court ex parte Ramadan* [1999] 1 Cr.App.R 386

[183] The court noted that a finding under s.37(3) that an accused did the act with which he is charged is not a conviction in the normal sense, but nevertheless falls within the definition of 'conviction' used in the Rehabilitation of Offenders Act 1974 and 'would potentially remain as something against the person concerned'.

[184] We are grateful to Paul Barber of Bevan Brittan for permission to use his training material *Mental Health Case Law Update* (April 2005) in the preparation of this report: the observation here is Mr Barber's, although we remain responsible for any use of his material.

segregation of a mentally disordered prisoner known to be at risk of suicide. In *McGlinchey v UK* [2003], a breach in Article 3 was found resulting from deficient medical care of a prisoner with long-standing heroin addiction and asthma, who died in custody a week after starting her sentence following a rapid decline in her physical condition involving sustained vomiting and dramatic weight-loss. The ECtHR determined that, having regard to the prison authority's responsibility to provide a proper standard of medical care to prisoners, the failure to accurately establish the extent of Mrs McGlinchey's weight loss, a gap over a weekend in monitoring her condition and a failure to admit her earlier to hospital or seek more expert medical assistance reached the threshold for an Article 3 breach. Article 13 (which requires effective remedy) was also breached, as damages had previously been denied to her family due to a lack of established causal link between the failures of care and the death. The ECtHR awarded damages on the basis of the Article 3 breach. It is likely that, because of the enhanced duty of care towards persons detained by the State, these cases set precedents applicable to the circumstances of patients detained under the Mental Health Act.

'Slopping-out' can breach human rights requirements

Napier, Re Petition for Judicial Review

[2004] ScotCS 100 (26 April 2004)

1.200 The Scottish courts awarded damages to a prisoner who it deemed to have suffered degrading treatment in breach of ECHR Article 3 over the 40 days he spent on remand in Barlinnie Prison, Glasgow. The presiding judge also recorded that, even if he was wrong in this determination, there had been an obvious and unjustified infringement of ECHR Article 8.1 (right to respect for private life) in the conditions of the prisoner's treatment[185].

1.201 A key aspect of the regime that was found unacceptable and an infringement of the ECHR was the lack of sanitary facilities in prisoners' cells, and the subsequent requirements of 'slopping-out'.

1.202 This case could establish some precedent for legal challenges to the denial of effective sanitary facilities to detained psychiatric patients (for example during periods spent in seclusion or 'isolation' etc). Whilst many psychiatric seclusion facilities now have integral toilet facilities, this is not universally the case. Secluded patients may ask to be escorted to lavatory facilities outside of the seclusion room (just as, in the *Napier* case, prisoners could request to leave their cells to use lavatory facilities during the day) but such requests are not bound to be met, whether in UK hospitals or Scottish prisons[186], sometimes for a lack of available staff to act as escorts (see Chapter 4.248 *et seq* below).

---

[185] *Napier, Re Petition for Judicial Review* [2004] ScotCS 100, para 91

[186] Slopping-out was banned in the English prison system in the 1990s. In April 2004, 18% of Scottish prisoners (1,200 men) were estimated to still have to slop out in five of Scotland's jails (Kirsty Scott 'Slopping out judged a breach of human rights'. *The Guardian* 27/04/04).

1.203 The specifics of this case may limit its direct application to detained psychiatric patients. Particular aspects that are not likely to occur in psychiatric hospitals include the following:

- The prisoner shared a cell with others, was often confined for much of the day in that cell, and although there were partial screens for limited privacy when using a chamber pot or urine bottle, these did not obscure the whole body, nor mask noise or smell. Used receptacles would remain in the cell for long periods of time before they could be emptied.

- Prisoners were required to 'slop-out' by emptying their own receptacles at a communal washroom sluice during morning ablutions and at other set times of day.

- The prisoner was denied opportunities to get out into fresh air and was confined in 'stuffy, smelly, gloomy atmosphere' where 'many features of the regime seemed designed to stamp a mark of inferiority on the prisoner'[187].

1.204 In 1991 the ECtHR concluded that conditions in a then-overcrowded Broadmoor dormitory, where sanitary conditions involved the use of a commode at night, to be 'extremely unsatisfactory', but not to amount to inhuman or degrading treatment under Article 3 of the ECHR[188]. It is possible that a court considering the Broadmoor case today would have found differently.

1.205 In hospitals dealing with patients suffering from physical disorders, where patients may be confined to bed or otherwise prevented from using toilet facilities by their physical conditions, the use of bed-pans and urine bottles is of course a normal medical procedure that is in no sense an infringement of patients' rights. However, in such circumstances patients can expect their privacy and dignity to be upheld through use of screens and thoughtful nursing practice. In our experience, psychiatric patients held in conditions of seclusion may not always have such assurance.

1.206 The Committee for the Prevention of Torture stated, in relation to practices in English Prisons before slopping-out was abolished in the 1990s, that 'the act of discharging human waste, and more particularly of defecating, in a bucket or pot in the presence of one or more persons, in a confined space used as a living area, is degrading'[189]. The petitioner in *Napier* indicated to the court that having to use a chamber-pot had lessened his feeling of self-worth:

> 'It makes you feel like you don't exist because you are forced to use that toilet … it just makes you feel low all the time … they shouldn't make you do the toilet in a pot. There should be toilets there for you, even though you are a prisoner.'[190]

---

[187] 'He and his cell-mates had to make do with only one chair. He had to eat in the cell without getting a chance to wash first. At various times during the day he was systematically released for short periods and locked up' (*Napier*, para 77).

[188] *B v United Kingdom* (1991) 32 DR 5. This case was raised by Lord Bonomy in *Napier*, but 'because the Convention is a living instrument' the judge had 'not found particular assistance in older judgments or determinations of either the Commission or the Court' (para 64).

[189] Committee for the Prevention of Torture, report on 1990 visit to inter alia Brixton Prison, quoted in *Napier*, para 55

[190] *Napier*, para 76

1.207 It seems, therefore, that while the 'slopping-out' element (i.e. that prisoners were required to empty their own used pots at certain times of day) was important to the finding in this case, the judgment provides some indication that this is not essential for the practice to infringe the human rights of detainees.

Mandatory sentencing of mentally disordered offenders

1.208 The Powers of Criminal Courts (Sentencing) Act 2000 s.109 requires that any person over the age of 21 who has been previously convicted of a serious offence shall, upon subsequent conviction of another serious offence be given a mandatory sentence of life imprisonment, unless there are 'exceptional circumstances'. In this reporting period it has been confirmed by the highest domestic court that this requirement applies to mentally disordered offenders and that mental disorder itself is not likely to constitute 'special circumstances'. The House of Lords (*R v Drew* below) has determined that the requirements of mandatory sentencing in relation to the mentally disordered are compatible with the human rights principles of the European Convention.

1.209 The Mental Health Act 1983 was amended in 1997 to include a 'hybrid order' power (s.45A) that enables, simultaneously with the passing of a prison sentence, the court to direct that a mentally disordered offender be taken to hospital and detained there for treatment as if transferred under s.47/49. We discuss this in detail at Chapter 5.90 *et seq* below. The effect of the hybrid order is that a patient may remain in hospital without limit of time, but may (whilst the prison sentence continues to run) be sent to prison if there is no longer any need for medical treatment in hospital, or it is concluded that no effective medical treatment can be given in hospital. In its 1997 circular, the Home Office stated that 'except where the law requires the imposition of a life sentence … the court is is required [191] to consider the effect of a custodial sentence on the offender's mental disorder and on the treatment which may be available for it before passing sentence. The hospital direction does not disturb this arrangement…'[192]. The power to issue a mandatory life-sentence and a hospital direction simultaneously under s.45A applies only in respect of patients whose diagnoses include psychopathic disorder, and cannot be used with offenders with mental illness or the mental impairments[193]. Such restrictions do not operate in equivalent legislation in Scotland[194].

1.210 The cases of *Newman* and *Drew* discussed below relate to offenders suffering from mental illness for whom the law required mandatory life sentences and removal to prison.

---

[191] Now under the Powers of Criminal Courts (Sentencing) Act 2000, s.82 (at the time of the Home Office circular, under s.4 of the Criminal Justice Act 1991)

[192] Home Office Circular 52/1997

[193] MHA 1983 s.45A(2)(a)

[194] HL paper 101, para 13

R v Newman

[2000] EWCA Crim 2 (18 January 2000).

1.211　Under s.109(2) of the Criminal Courts (Sentencing) Act 2000, mandatory life sentence may be avoided 'if the court is of the opinion that there are exceptional circumstances relating to either of the offences which justify it not [passing a life sentence for the second offence]'. The reasons for such a decision, including a statement of why the circumstances are exceptional, need to be given in open court.

1.212　In *R v Newman*, the Court of Appeal determined that the defendant's mental illness was not, in itself, sufficient to constitute an 'exceptional circumstance' that would lift the requirement to impose a mandatory life sentence. The defendant's second offence had been the killing of his grandmother, with bizarre violation of the body, leading to conviction of manslaughter on grounds of diminished responsibility. *N* had previously been convicted of an unprovoked knife attack on a stranger and so, although the sentencing judge for the second offence had before him the certificates necessary to authorise *N*'s admission to Rampton Hospital, and said that he thought it 'as plain as can be that [*N* was] mentally ill', he felt obliged to sentence him to life imprisonment as the mental disorder did not in itself constitute special circumstances warranting other action[195]. The Court of Appeal dismissed *N*'s appeal against this decision, but noted in doing so that

> it is a matter of concern that a defendant so obviously and acutely suffering from mental illness should be ordered to prison and not to hospital: even though, in practical terms, the difference between the two orders may lie less in the mode of treatment after sentence than in the procedure governing release and recall, we regret our inability to make what seems on the medical evidence to make the appropriate order[196].

1.213　The Government has argued that its policy aim in the mandatory sentencing requirement is that of ensuring that the protection of the public. The legislation is 'founded upon the assumption that those who have been convicted of two qualifying serious offences present such a serious and continuing danger to the safety of the public that they should be liable to indefinite incarceration and, if released, should be liable indefinitely to recall to prison'[197].

1.214　The courts have therefore recognised that 'exceptional circumstances' relieving a sentencing judge of the duty to pass a mandatory sentence relate to the offender's dangerousness, rather than the presence or absence of mental disorder. In *R v Offen* [2001], the Court of Appeal determined that the mandatory sentencing requirements of the Criminal Courts (Sentencing) Act 2000 would be incompatible with the ECHR if they were applied to a defendant who posed no significant risk to the public, and they found accordingly that such a finding could constitute 'exceptional circumstances' under that Act lifting any duty to impose an automatic life-sentence. This approach was accepted as correct in arguments for the Home Secretary in *R v Drew*. Prior to the Court of Appeal's 2001 ruling, that Court had

---

[195]　The Judge in *Newman's* case was bound by the mandatory sentencing provisions of s.2 of the Crime (Sentences) Act 1997, which was the forerunner and equivalent of s.109 of the Criminal Courts (Sentencing) Act 2000.

[196]　*per* Lord Chief Justice, *R v Newman* [2000] *supra*

[197]　*R v Buckland* [2000] EWCA Crim 1, 1 WLR 1262, 1268 (18 January 2000).

already applied a similar interpretation of the 'exceptional circumstances' clause in the case of *R v Buckland* [2000][198]. Here the defendant was deemed likely to be suffering from amphetamine-induced psychosis (which was therefore deemed no defence) at the time of the criminal action that led to his second conviction. The offence was an attempt at a bank robbery described in the Court of Appeal as having been of unusual incompetence and lack of aggression[199]. The first offence had involved firing a starting pistol whilst drunk and disorderly. The Court of Appeal found that the original sentence of two concurrent terms of life imprisonment could not be justified by any danger to the public posed by the defendant and set aside the life sentences, and reduced the determinate sentences imposed by the first judge.

R v Drew

[2003] UKHL 259 (thirty-first report of appellate committee, HL paper 101), 8 May 2003

1.215 *D* had been convicted on two accounts of grievous bodily harm and sentenced to prison in 1995. Six months after his release from prison in 1999, he was charged with having committed a further violent assault and pleaded guilty to wounding with intent to cause grievous bodily harm. He was known to be mentally ill, but neither unfit to plead nor 'insane' (see Chapter 5.8 *et seq* below for a discussion of these terms). Whilst awaiting sentence, he was transferred to hospital after showing psychotic symptoms and messianic delusions, was diagnosed with schizophrenia and was responding well to medication by the time he came up before Cardiff Crown court for sentencing. His doctors recommended a court order with restrictions under the Mental Health Act (s.37/41). However, as this charge was *D*'s second 'serious offence' within the meaning of the Powers of Criminal Courts (Sentencing) Act 2000, that statute required the court to impose a life-sentence[200]. The Recorder of Cardiff Crown Court did so with an expression of regret, fixing the minimum term to be served at two years and eight months, and let it be known that he would have accepted the recommendation for a hospital order had the law allowed him to do so.

1.216 On *D*'s admission to HMP Cardiff his mental condition deteriorated sharply for want of the drug which he had been prescribed but which prison authorities were not empowered to administer him. Following urgent and repeated representations by the prison authorities he was transferred back to hospital under s.47/49 after eights days in prison, during which time his mental health had deteriorated to such an extent that it took several months after his return to hospital to regain control of his symptoms.

1.217 On *D*'s behalf it was argued that his imprisonment was 'inhumane or degrading treatment' under Article 3 of the ECHR and that sections 109 and 37 of the 2000 and 1983 Acts respectively were incompatible with that Article in requiring automatic life-sentences upon mentally disordered defendants.

---

[198] *ibid.*

[199] *B* had waited his turn for a cashier, presenting him with a note demanding money and stating that he had a gun (which was written on the back of an envelope showing his name and address) and then sat quietly and waited for the money. The cashier activated the silent alarm summoning the police. When arrested, he gave his occupation as 'saving planet earth' and was found to be carrying a toy plastic gun in the pocket of his tracksuit bottoms.

[200] Powers of Criminal Courts (Sentencing) Act 2000, s.109.

1.218 In May 2003, the House of Lords determined that it cannot be wrong in principle to pass a sentence of imprisonment on a mentally disordered defendant who is criminally responsible and fit to be tried (para 17). Whilst causing unnecessary suffering, humiliation or distress to such a defendant, or causing an avoidable deterioration in his condition, *could* be a beach of Article 3, the effects of *D*'s incarceration were insufficient to cause such a breach in this particular case, and as a general rule any breach could be avoided by the Home Secretary applying his powers to transfer such a defendant to hospital from prison under s.47 of the 1983 Act. Failure to do so could be amenable to judicial review.

1.219 The court noted that mental health law in England and Wales (s.45A of the 1983 Act) differed from equivalent Scottish provisions in limiting the application of 'hybrid orders' to defendants with psychopathic disorder. It was noted that, had the recorder been able to use s.45A to make such an order in *D*'s case, he would probably have done so, and *D* could have been taken directly to hospital and not suffered the ill effects of imprisonment. Their Lordships recommended further thought be given by Government to the exercise of the hybrid order power. The draft Mental Health Bill of 2004 retains a hybrid order allowing a prison sentence with immediate transfer to hospital, but dispenses with the legal classifications of mental disorder that presently curtail its general use.

1.220 Whilst the ability to pass concurrent prison sentences and hospital directions on mentally disordered offenders would at least prevent the situation in *R v Drew* from occurring again, we remain uneasy at this extension of the ability to nominally sentence mentally disordered offenders. Whilst such sentencing policy may have no immediately adverse consequences on the individuals concerned, given that they would receive the hospital care that they require without a potentially damaging committal to prison, there is a risk of perverse anti-therapeutic effects in that such patients will know that any recovery on their part could lead to transfer to prison. The potential for perversity in such a system would be greatly reduced if there were more confidence in the operation of the legal thresholds regarding criminal responsibility and mentally disordered offenders (see Chapter 5.17 *et seq* below).

1.221 The dilemmas faced by policy makers and the judiciary over mentally disordered offenders are thrown into sharp relief by the removal of judicial discretion in the disposal of cases where mental disorder is a relevant consideration in defence against a charge. In this respect, the problems which now appear to need resolution through a closer overlap between mental health and prison disposals were created by the extension of mandatory sentencing to offences other than murder without any exclusion for mental disorder (see Chapter 5.33 *et seq* below).

Investigatory obligations at Inquest

1.222 The law relating to ECHR requirements and coroners' courts is developing rapidly, at a time when Government has acknowledged that

the coroner's system has long laboured under antiquated legal provisions which were never designed to meet the demands of today's society. the shortcomings within the system have become increasingly evident and it has become essential that we build an effective, supportive and transparent system that commands public respect [201].

1.223 The Home Office position paper *Reforming the Coroner and Death Certification Service*[202] outlined the proposals below relevant to the cases discussed in this report:

- continued mandatory inquests for deaths in custody unless other investigatory measures (such as a criminal prosecution) already underway;

- juries of between seven and nine persons to determine the verdict (instead of the current maximum of 11 jurors);

- narrative verdicts to be preferred over short-form verdicts, to provide an adequate explanation of the cause of death; and

- expectations that coroner's reports be copied to the Health and Safety Executive and other inspectorate bodies, as well as those authorities directly concerned in the circumstances of the death, with an annual report by the Chief Coroner to Parliament outlining reports made, responses received and action taken.

R v Her Majesty's Coroner for the Western District of Somerset and another ex parte Middleton
[2004] UKHL 10. March 2004.

1.224 In October 2000 an inquest found that *M*, a prisoner at HMP Horfield, had hanged himself whilst the balance of his mind was disturbed. There was some question of whether the prison authorities had responded adequately to previous indications that *M* was at risk of suicide. The coroner ruled that the issue of 'neglect' was not to be left to the jury, but invited the jury to pass him a note regarding any observations they had on the evidence. The jury duly passed such a note stating its opinion that the Prison Service had failed in its duty of care to *M*. The family of the deceased asked that the note be appended to the verdict, but the coroner declined to do so and the note's content was not made public. The Coroner subsequently used the note as the basis of a letter to the Chief Inspector of Prisons.

1.225 *M*'s family challenged the fact that the jury's note had not been publicly recorded, and that no public determination of any responsibility of the Prison Service for *M*'s death was thus possible. They argued, successfully, that this failed the investigative procedural requirements of ECHR Article 2 where a person dies in the custody of the State[203].

1.226 This appeal reached the House of Lords in March 2004. Their Lordships determined that:

(i) to meet the procedural requirement of Article 2 an inquest ought ordinarily to culminate in an expression of the jury's conclusion on disputed factual issues[204];

---

[201] Paul Goggins MP quoted in the Home Office press release, *Report of the Fundamental Review of Death Certification and Coroner Services*, 4 June 2003

[202] Home Office (2004) *Reforming the Coroner and Death Certification Service – a position paper*. Cm 6159, March 2004

[203] For an analysis of these requirements, see Wilson J in *Plymouth City Council v Her Majesty's Coroner for the County of Devon (Plymouth & South West District) and The Secretary of State for Education and Skills* [2005] EWHC 1014 Admin, para 88.

[204] *Ex parte Middleton* [2004] UKHL 10, para 20.

(ii) there were some cases in which the current regime for conducting inquests in England and Wales, as hitherto understood and followed, did not meet these requirements of the Convention[205];

(iii) to rectify this, the Coroners Act 1988 and the Rules that it governs must be interpreted to broaden the scope of the inquiry of coroner's inquests to consider 'in what circumstances' a death occurred, and not just 'by what means' it occurred[206];

(iv) coroners and inquest juries remain barred from determining criminal or civil liability, and so expressions suggestive of civil liability (in particular 'neglect', 'carelessness' and related expressions) should be avoided[207].

1.227   Therefore, an inquest jury considering the death of a detained patient is entitled to consider not only the cause of death, but also 'the defects in the system which contributed towards the death; and any other factors relevant to the circumstances of the death'[208]. The coroner must ensure, unless the Article 2 requirements upon the State are satisfied through another means such as a public inquiry or criminal trial, that these matters are addressed where they arise. Parties appearing or represented at inquests can make submissions on the means of eliciting such conclusions to the coroner. This is bound to result in longer and more adversarial hearings. Where defects in the system are determined by juries, the appropriate action is still for coroners to write to the appropriate authority, but the requirements of Article 2 are such that coroners must not only state publicly that this is their intention, but also outline in neutral terms the substance of the report that they will be making[209].

R (on the application of Khan) v Secretary of State for Health
[2004] 1 WLR 971 [2003] EWCA Civ 1129. October 2003

1.228   *Khan* was not a mental health case, but concerned the question of funding for the parents to be represented at the inquest into their three-year old daughter's death due to medical error during chemotherapy. It determined that, where the inquest serves the purpose of an Article 2 investigation, its procedures must allow participation by the next of kin[210], and as such the State should fund the family's legal representation. The details of whether this liability falls to the Legal Services Commission or the hospital in which a patient died was the subject of an Appeal that had not been heard at the time our report went to press.

---

[205] *ibid*, para 32. Examples in addition to the *Middleton* case itself case where an inquest jury were unable to say how a death occurred, but restricted from expressing a conclusion as to the circumstances of that death, were given as the verdict of death by misadventure with the cause of death being asphyxiation by hanging in *Keenan v United Kingdom* (2001) 33 EHRR 913; or the unlawful killing verdicts in *Edwards v United Kingdom* (2002) 35 EHRR 487 and *R (on the application of Amin) v Secretary of State for the Home Department* [2003] UKHL 51.

[206] *ibid*, para 35

[207] *ibid*, para 37. In the case of *M*, their Lordships suggested that a narrative verdict such as 'the deceased took his own life, in part because the risk of his doing so was not recognised and appropriate precautions were not taken to prevent him doing so' would embody a judgmental decision of a factual nature without infringing the Coroners' Rules barring determination of criminal or civil liability.

[208] *ibid*, para 36: their Lordships suggested (*inter alia*) this construction (from the Fatal Accidents and Sudden Deaths Inquiry (Scotland) Act 1976, s.6) as suitable for coroners in directing juries.

[209] *ibid*, para 38.

[210] *R (on the application of Amin) v Secretary of State for the Home Department* [2003] *supra*

R (on the application of Goodson) v Bedfordshire & Luton Coroner
[2004] EWHC 2931(Admin) All ER (D) 298. December 2004.

1.229 This case, which does not involve mental health services, concerned a coroner's refusal to conduct as an investigation for the purposes of ECHR Article 2 an inquest into the death of an 83 year-old patient of peritonitis subsequent to perforation of the duodenum during an elective procedure to remove gallstones. The patient's family had requested that the inquest be considered an investigation under Article 2, as a consequence of which they argued an independent medical report to review the treatment given should be obtained. The case therefore considered the extent to which the investigative obligations of Article 2 extend to *any* hospitalised patient, given the State's duty to take adequate measures to protect life. The Court found that simple negligence in the care and treatment of a patient does not itself breach Article 2, although where agents of the State potentially bear responsibility for the loss of life, there is a need for an effective investigation. This may be discharged in a number of ways, including a combination of inquest and civil (or criminal) proceedings against the authority concerned. The Court distinguished between a case such as *Khan*, where the conduct of medical authorities had been described as 'grossly negligent' by an independent expert and where there were suspicions of a 'medically-orchestrated cover-up', and the potential liability for simple negligence. The ECtHR had determined that:

> where a Contracting State had made adequate provision for securing high professional standards among health professionals and the protection of lives of patients, it cannot accept matters such as errors of judgment on the part of a health professional or negligent co-ordination among health professionals in the treatment of a particular patient are sufficient of themselves to call a Contracting State to account from the standpoint of its positive obligations under Article 2[211].

Investigatory obligations in near-death cases

R (on the application of D) v Secretary of State for the Home Department
[2005] EWHC 728 (Admin). April 2005

1.230 *D* was a prisoner who attempted suicide by hanging in 2001 but was resuscitated by staff. As a result of his attempt he sustained brain damage leading to serious and long-term mental incapacity. Judicial review proceedings were brought on his behalf for a breach of the investigative obligations under ECHR Articles 2 and 3. The Prison Service had conducted an internal investigation, although this and various other documents were lost and only released to the claimant during proceedings, and the Home Secretary had suggested an independent investigation with published findings by the Prisons and Probation Ombudsman. This proposal allowed for some involvement of *D*'s solicitors in the investigation, although not to the extent of cross-examination in public. It was argued by the Home Secretary that this proposal would meet Article 2 investigative requirements, given that the ECHR allows flexibility in the form of investigations.

---

[211] *Powell v United Kingdom*, application no 45305/99, 4 May 2000, p.17-18.

1.231 Munby J found against the arguments of the Secretary of State, determining that the circumstances of *D*'s case required 'full and effective' investigation which, to meet Article 2 requirements, should take place in public, with the claimant's representatives able to attend all hearings and put questions to witnesses in person, and with adequate funding provided to them. He gave permission to the Home Secretary to appeal, and that appeal has been initiated.

1.232 This case may have wide ramifications for many services other than the prison service. If upheld, Munby J's determination may apply to any incident resulting in life-threatening injury to a patient detained under the 1983 Act (although each case may turn on its own facts, and the parameters of the first-instance judgment may yet be determined by the Court of Appeal).

2

The context of care

2.1 The overall picture of acute services suggests that detained patients' initial experience of mental health services are likely to be quite negative, leading to patients fearing readmission after their eventual discharge and discouraging them from maintaining contact with services. Our experience of acute wards bears out the observation of the Healthcare Commission that

> many acute mental health services are 'fire-fighting' as they struggle to work with an increasingly unwell population, some of whom have a dual diagnosis. For many, faced with high bed occupancy figures and inadequate staffing, the delivery of a therapeutic service can become impossible[1].

Bed occupancy

2.2 Bed occupancy rates are calculated by comparing the proportion of patients 'on the books' of any ward with the number of beds on that ward, and includes patients who are on leave, absent without leave, or temporarily transferred to another ward or facility without formal hand-over. Royal College of Psychiatrists' guidance suggests that an ideal average bed occupancy rate should be about 85%[2], although this is not a universally accepted recommendation.

2.3 In November 1996 we conducted a simultaneous unannounced visit to 309 acute psychiatric wards over 118 separate units (amounting to 47% of all mental health units in England and Wales)[3]. We found that the average bed occupancy, including patients on leave from the ward, was 98%. The Sainsbury Centre survey of acute psychiatric inpatient wards in England over 2004 found an average occupancy of 100%[4]. These findings contrast against Department of Health statistics on bed occupancy over the period between these two

---

[1]   Healthcare Commission (2005) *National Audit of Violence (2003-2005) Final Report.* Royal College of Psychiatrists' Research Unit / Healthcare Commission. p.7. www.healthcarecommission.org.uk.

[2]   Royal College of Psychiatrists (1998) *Psychiatric beds and Resources: Factors Influencing Bed Use and Service Planning.* London.

[3]   Sainsbury Centre for Mental Health (1997) *The National Visit: A one-day Visit to 309 Acute Psychiatric Wards by the Mental Health Act Commission in collaboration with The Sainsbury Centre for Mental Health.* London, the Sainsbury Centre for Mental Health.

[4]   Sainsbury Centre (2005) Acute Care 2004; *A national survey of adult psychiatric wards in England.* London, the Sainsbury Centre for Mental Health, p 22.

surveys, in which fairly constant average occupancy rates of about 91% have been recorded for 'short-stay mental illness beds (excluding elderly and children's services)' in England[5].

2.4 It is questionable whether a national average figure for bed-occupancy is the best measure either of the problems associated with overcrowding, or of progress in addressing such problems. In the nine months from October 2004 to July 2005, we found occupancy rates of 100% or more in over half of 1,591 wards visited. We show these findings in figures 3 and 4 below.

Bed Occupancy	Number	Percentage
under 100%	758	47.6
100%	580	36.5
over 100%	253	15.9

Fig 3: bed occupancy levels of 1,591 wards visited by the MHAC between 1 October 2004 and 1 July 2005[6]

2.5 Nearly three-quarters of these wards (1,176 wards or 74% of the total) were operating at occupancy levels higher than the 85% recommended by the Royal College of Psychiatrists.

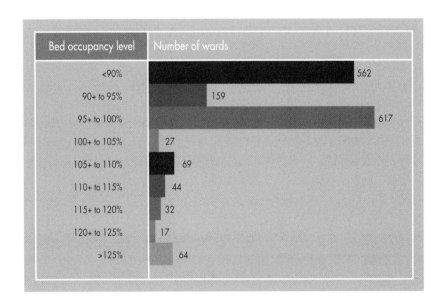

Fig 4: bed occupancy levels of 1,534 wards visited by the MHAC between 1 October 2004 and 1 July 2005[7]

---

5   Department of Health statistics for 1996/7 record an average bed occupancy of 91% for short-stay mental illness beds (excluding elderly and children's services), and an average occupancy of 90% in secure units. Average bed-occupancy for 2002/03 was reported to be 91% in both sectors. The data for 2003/4 suggested average bed occupancies of 92% in short-stay mental illness beds and 93% in secure units (Dept of Health *Hospital Activity Statistics – Beds Open Overnight, England 1996-97 and 2003/4.* www.performance.doh.gov.uk/hospitalactivity). This data is not directly comparable to MHAC and Sainsbury Centre data given the different classifications of hospital used. See also Department of Health (2004) *The National Service Framework for Mental Health – Five Years On*, p.26.

6   Data source: MHAC data collection

7   *ibid.*

2.6   The 81 wards that were operating at over 120% bed occupancy rates each had an average of 20 beds and 28 patients. Twenty-eight of the 81 wards were based in the London metropolitan area, with the rest ranging from urban areas such as Leeds, Birmingham and Nottingham to rural areas in Devon, Cornwall and North Wales.

2.7   The King's Fund 2003 report *London's State of Mind*[8] suggested that high rates of bed occupancy were the result of inadequate community services, together with high case loads and a shortage of the sorts of services (such as crisis resolution teams) that might keep patients out of hospital. This is supported by previous research findings[9], and our own observations on visits. The King's Fund argued that the relatively slow implementation of effective community mental health services in the capital lead to patients being admitted to hospital unnecessarily. Rates of compulsory admission under the Act in London can be as much as twice that in other areas of England and Wales[10].

2.8   Sainsbury Centre research has suggested that the problem of over-occupancy would be solved by the relocation of inappropriately placed patients from acute admission wards. It has identified such patients into four categories:

- Patients whose residence on the ward is relatively short but who would be more suitably accommodated elsewhere if appropriate community supports were available;

- Patients requiring longer stays who need relatively specialised and supervised care which is no longer available outside acute services ;

- A relatively small group of patients whose dangerous and violent behaviour requires higher secure care and are awaiting transfer; and

- A heterogeneous group of patients with a range of special needs, such as patients with acquired brain damage, dual diagnoses or eating disorders. Such patients may fall between different specialities (e.g. neurology or learning disabilities and general psychiatry) or may simply be insufficiently numerous for single Trusts to have specialist provision. Although each subgroup of this category is small in number, together they comprise an appreciable proportion of those misplaced on acute admission wards[11].

2.9   It is notable that a significant proportion (29%) of acute inpatient ward managers canvassed by the Sainsbury Centre in its 2004 study reported that one impact of crisis resolution teams appears to have been an *increase* in the severity of illness amongst patients who are admitted to hospital[12]. Whilst we recognise that many crisis resolution teams are in their initial stages of development and may not yet be operating entirely as envisaged by Government in its

---

[8]   King's Fund (2003) *London's State of Mind: King's Fund Mental Health Inquiry 2003.* London.

[9]   e.g. The 1997 Sainsbury Centre study found that there was a shortage of acute psychiatric beds, but that over a quarter of inpatients were considered to be inappropriately placed on admission wards for want of suitable alternative accommodation, home support or rehabilitation places. The study found that 61% of patients who had been resident on admission wards for over six months were inappropriately placed. (Shepherd, G., Beadsmore, A., Moore, C., Hardy, P., Muijen, M. 'Relation between bed use, social deprivation and overall bed availability in acute psychiatric units, and alternative residential options: a cross sectional survey, one day census data, and staff interviews'. *BMJ* 1997;314:262 (25 January)).

[10]   King's Fund (2003) *supra.*

[11]   Shepherd *et al* (1997) *supra*

[12]   Sainsbury Centre (2005) *supra*, p. 63-4.

Mental Health Policy Implementation Guidance, this does suggest that further research is needed on the impact of such teams and that we should not assume that their establishment will necessarily relieve the pressure on inpatient services. We are hopeful that the Healthcare Commission's review of acute inpatient services (which we understand to be in planning stage) will include the impact of crisis resolution teams in its scope.

2.10   We have been concerned that some services are establishing community services such as crisis resolution teams using resources from inpatient or ward-based services, in anticipation of decreasing pressure on in-patient care. Where the community services are not able rapidly to obviate the need for inpatient services the result may be an increased pressure across the service as a whole, as with the following example (see also paragraphs 2.13 *et seq* below).

Case example: over-occupancy in a London-based unit

In December 2004 we visited a unit that had long-standing capacity problems, with over-occupancy of 200% noted on some wards in past visits. We visited a ward designed for 22 patients, which was at that time used by up to 37 patients during the day (i.e. an occupancy rate of 168%). Twelve of the patients assigned to the ward were reported to have been awaiting discharge for more than a year.

Overflow wards were opened at night for sleeping accommodation for the additional patients. Patients were moved on to such wards after evening medication had been administered, and brought back in the mornings. There were examples of patients being woken in the night to change wards to make room for new admissions. Patients sleeping on overflow wards had to take their possessions with them, and although the overflow wards had lockers, these were not accessible during the daytime and patients had to carry such possessions as they required during the day[13].

The day area on the ward was too small to accommodate adequately the additional numbers of patients. The constriction of space was worse during tri-weekly ward rounds, for which one of the two day rooms on the ward was needed for half a day at a time. During wet weather the smoking rooms could not accommodate all those who wished to use them. Nursing staff reported being unable to meet all patients' nursing needs and reported being particularly stretched to provide the standard of care suited for the admission of a minor in September 2003. The MHAC identified lapses in the implementation of the Care Programme Approach, with a number of patients unaware of their care plans. Drug and alcohol misuse was evident on the wards. There were concerns over the safety of patients and staff.

Fig 5: case example of over-occupancy in a London mental health unit (for follow-up action, see paragraphs 2.11 and 2.12 below)

---

[13] Despite this the MHAC noted that the Trust had scored fully in its Commission for Healthcare Improvement performance indicator for 2003 regarding 'privacy and dignity', as the performance indictor only measured gender separation, and the wards were single-sex. Our experience of visiting the site belied any notion that patients had adequate privacy or dignity.

2.11 In the example at figure 5 above, the Commission had been expressing its concerns throughout this reporting period and visiting the hospital repeatedly. The Trust was aware of the problems of overcrowding and had identified delays in moving patients off the unit as a major contributing factor. It recognised the role of the Care Programme Approach in facilitating better discharge planning and instigated training, and had engaged a 'Supporting People Worker' to help identify and arrange supported housing for patients upon discharge. We arranged a meeting between the chief executives of our respective organisations where we urged that immediate action be taken in locating immediate resources to ease the pressures on the unacceptable patient environment in the unit.

2.12 Some progress has been made as we go to press, with average rates of 107% bed-occupancy in the first quarter of 2005, and some previously over-occupied wards now running with some spare capacity. 'Sleeping out' has now stopped: if a patient cannot be accommodated on their own ward, they are transferred fully to another ward until a bed becomes vacant. The Trust managers attributed progress in bed-occupancy reduction to the development of home treatment teams in one of the boroughs that it covers: patients from the remaining borough without such service development now account for much of the overcrowding. The changing patterns of care presented new problems: particularly in that a higher percentage of patients remaining on the wards were likely to be detained and exhibit challenging behaviour, necessitating higher staff ratios and potentially increasing the wear and tear on already unsatisfactory buildings. The Trust acknowledged that home-treatment teams may increase the pressure on carers. Limitations in hostel accommodation and 24-hour care in the boroughs served by the Trust continued to exacerbate problems of delayed discharge and prevented occupancy levels from falling further. The option has been discussed of establishing a step-down ward for patients whose discharge from hospital is delayed, although it is recognised that this is not a solution to the problem of patients remaining in hospital environments when they are fit for discharge.

Psychiatric bed provision in England

2.13 It is well known that the number of psychiatric beds has reduced dramatically from a high-point in the early 1950s. There are now *probably* less than 40% of the *total* number of hospital beds (i.e. taking into account both the NHS and independent sector) than there were when the Mental Health Act 1959 came into force. In part, of course, this reduction simply reflects the increasing use of community-based mental health care, which was made possible over the last half-century not only by improvements in medication that enabled people to be treated without lengthy hospital admissions, but also by changing social attitudes towards the treatment of the mentally disordered, coupled with the ability of the welfare state to co-ordinate what was, in its early years, called 'comprehensive care'[14].

2.14 A study of service utilisation in North-West Wales, where the population has remained similar in number, ethnic and social mix and rurality over the last century, compared

---

[14] See Bennett, D. 'The Drive Towards the Community' (p.326) in Berrios, G., & Freeman, H. [eds] (1991) *150 Years of British Psychiatry 1841 – 1991*. London, Gaskell.

morbidity and mortality associated with mental illness between 1896 and 1996[15]. The findings on length of hospitalisations for severe mental illness were startling: where, in 1896, an annual cohort of patients with schizophrenia was likely to spend 400 years in hospital per million population, every million population today will have a schizophrenic cohort who at the time of writing will have already spent that length of time in hospital and will spend several hundred more years in a service bed before they die. The first admissions were considerably shorter in 1996 than 1896, but today's patients will spend longer periods of their lives in hospital than their counterparts a century ago. This may be in part because of earlier admissions and, despite an increased rate of death by suicide[16], longer life-expectancy, but it also suggests that:

- the culture of 'assertive' interventions and risk assessment in today's mental health professions may lead to admissions that would have been less likely in the past;

- the assumption that 'early intervention' or the admission of patients with less severe problems may lead to a better rate of 'cure' may not in fact hold true; and/or

- the remissions induced by modern pharmacology may be relatively unstable, and that readmission may be a part of the pattern of treatment rather than a core attribute of the disease being treated.

2.15 The number of *NHS* mental illness beds available to services in England in the last twenty-five years is shown at figure 6. This shows a 40% reduction in such beds since the passing into law of the 1983 Act[17]. It would be misleading, however, to interpret this as indicative of a similarly proportioned reduction in bed capacity overall, as these figures do not include beds in the independent sector. At figure 7 (page 116) we have set out available data on NHS and independent bed provision since 1994-95. The data is necessarily incomplete as we have been unable to obtain numbers of independent sector beds after 2000/1[18]. Such data as we have obtained appears to show that, while the numbers of available beds in NHS facilities fell by around 20% over the seven years between 1994-95 and 2000-01, the overall decrease in bed availability during that period was approximately 5% once the growth in the independent sector is taken into account.

---

[15] Healy, D., Harris, M., Michael, P., Cattell, D., Savage, M., Chalasani, P. & Hirst, D (2005) 'Service Utilisation in 1896 and 1996: morbidity and mortality data from North Wales'. *History of Psychiatry* 16(1) 27-41

[16] The study found only three inpatient suicides and two suicides soon after discharge in the 1896 cohort: see Chapter 4.296 below for this in the context of current suicide rates.

[17] The number of available NHS learning disability beds declined even more sharply than mental illness beds (an overall reduction of 36% having occurred since 1997/8, although a small increase in bed availability occurred between 2002-03 and 2003-04, as shown in the table below). It is of relevance to note that the Commission is aware of anecdotal evidence of some learning disabled patients being admitted in emergencies to mental illness wards for want of available alternatives.

Average daily number of available learning disability beds, England						
1997-98	1998-99	1999-00	2000-01	2001-02	2002-03	2003-04
8,197	7,491	6,834	6,316	5,694	5,038	5,212

source: DH returns SH3/KH03; Hansard 1 March 2004 Col 720W (2003-04 data from www.performance.dh.gov.uk/hospital activity)

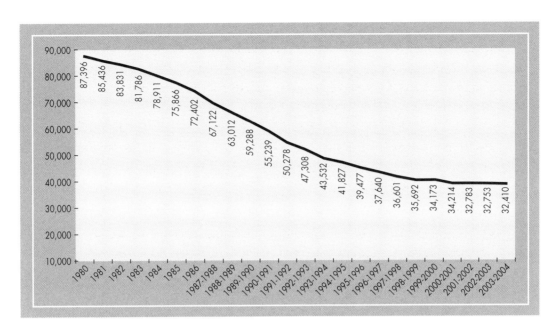

Fig 6: average daily number of mental illness beds in NHS Trusts, England, 1980 - 2003[19]

2.16 The majority of independent sector beds shown in figure 7 overleaf (88% over the period 1994-95 to 2000-01 for which data is available) were mental illness beds for the elderly, although the proportion of such beds to those provided by the independent sector for other patient groups fluctuates over the period for which we have data. In 1997-98, the proportion of mental illness beds available for patient groups other than elderly patients in the independent sector reached 32% of all independent sector provision. Even if few of these independent sector beds provided acute care services in the same way as general NHS acute wards, they will have provided a considerable number of places to patients who might otherwise be likely to be stuck within NHS acute care for want of an alternative. Such places can, however, be very costly solutions to the silting up of NHS acute care, and in our experience not every NHS Trust has or is prepared to use the resources required for buying independent sector space (or is allowed to do so by PCT commissioning bodies). In the context of learning disabilities services, the Department of Health has acknowledged that the expense of buying beds from the independent sector 'can place local commissioners in the position where they recognise the need to develop appropriate local services but are unable to do so'[20].

---

[18] Prior to 2000/1 data on all independent sector beds was published by the Department of Health. Data collections from 2002/03 fell to the Healthcare Commission and the Commission for Social Care Inspection, depending on whether the beds are classed as hospitals or residential/nursing homes. We have been unable to establish data classified into comparable categories as shown at fig 7. The Healthcare Commission has informed us that it estimates approximately 6,000 beds across 200 registered Independent Hospitals available for patients detained under the Mental Health Act on its books.

[19] Data source: Dept of Health returns SH3/KH03; *Hansard* 15 Jul 2003 Col 228W (2003-04 data from www.performance.dh.gov.uk/hospital activity)

[20] Daloni Carlisle 'DoH warns against new long-stay institutions' *Health Service Journal*, 25 Nov 2004.

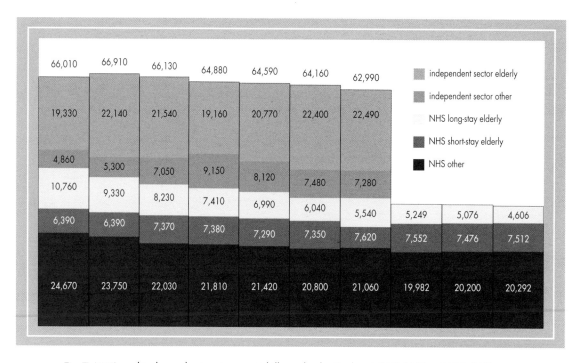

Fig 7: NHS and independent sector mental illness beds, England, 1994-95 to 2000-01[21]

(total bed numbers given at the head of columns 1994/5 to 2000/01. See note 18 for limitations on subsequent years' data.)

2.17 Mental Health Act statistics collated by the Department of Health show a significant increase in the numbers of uses of the Act in the independent sector, with increases in both civil and criminal justice admissions to independent hospitals that cannot be accounted for by a simple rise in the overall usage of the Act. The overall use of the Act has risen by approximately one-fifth since 1992-93. Over this time,

- the number of patients admitted to the independent sector through Mental Health Act court orders or prison transfers has doubled (which might be expected given the noticeable expansion of the independent sector into secure provision); and

- the number of civil admissions under the Act to Independent Hospitals appears to quadruple (see figure 8).

Since 1997, the number of detained patients *resident* in Independent Hospitals in England has more than trebled, from 705 patients in 1997 to 2,292 in 2004 (see figure 32 below).

2.18 Nevertheless, the independent sector's share of all Mental Health Act detentions is still very small, with 5% of all admissions under the Act being to Independent Hospitals in 2003-04 (4% accounted for by civil admissions under Part II, and 1% by Part III admissions), compared to 2% in 1992-93 (where Part II and Part III admissions each accounted for 1% of all admissions under the Act)[22].

---

[21] Data source: Dept of Health statistics published as *Health and Personal Care Statistics*, Table B23: '*Mental Health and Learning Disability: Hospital beds and places in residential & nursing care homes for people with mental illness*'. Data on NHS facilities are derived from available bed day figures supplied by NHS Trusts on form KH03. The figures on places in the independent sector are as at 31 March in each year (see www.performance.doh.gov.uk/hpsss/index.htm).

[22] Data source: Dept of Health Statistical Bulletins '*Inpatients formally detained in hospitals under the Mental Health Act 1983 and other legislation, England*', (1993 - 2004.)

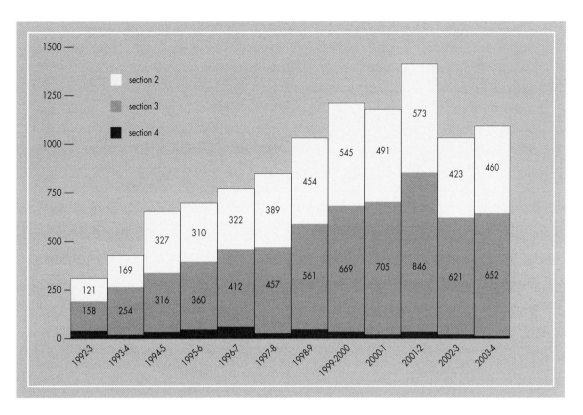

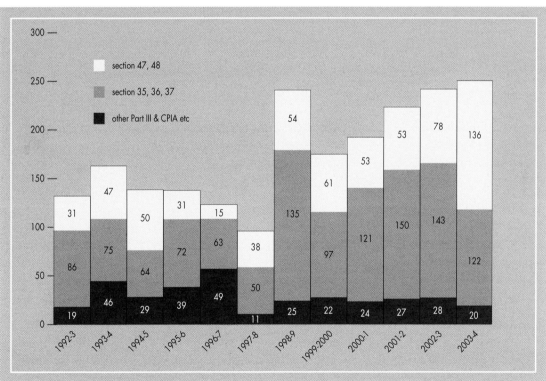

Fig 8: admissions to Independent Hospitals under Part II (civil powers – ss.2,3,4) and Part III (court orders and prison transfers – ss.35-48 etc) of the Mental Health Act 1983, 1992-93 to 2003-04[23]

23   Data source: as n.22 above, Bulletins 2003/22 and 2004/22, table 1. This figure will not include patients who are detained initially in NHS facilities and subsequently transferred to independent sector beds.

117

2.19 The debate about the role of independent sector facilities in delivering NHS care is often heated and politically charged, and has no particular place in our report. However, in our view it is appropriate to note that independent sector services, whether profit-based or not, will rise and fall according to the dictates of the market. Although 'market-discipline' may be used to good effect if referring agencies have 'a freedom of choice to select another independent unit from among twenty or more organisations who compete on the basis of quality, immediacy of response, and price'[24], there must be a question over whether too much reliance on the commercial market as the driver of service provision could have a deleterious effect on service planning overall, particularly when services are increasingly being commissioned from small, fragmented and relatively inexpert fund-holding bodies (see paragraph 2.23 below).

Out of area treatment

2.20 Where specialist or other beds are purchased from independent providers patients may be treated away from their home area. This can lead to logistical problems with:

- the commissioning authority's ability to monitor quality and cost effectiveness of the services provided;
- patients' relationships with family and friends, and possibly their ability to reintegrate into their local community upon discharge;
- social work and other care management input;
- local service development, when placements may have a high-cost to local resources.

2.21 In some cases we have heard of patients becoming 'stranded' in out of area placements whose security or clinical profile is no longer appropriate to their needs, for want of an alternative local placement. In such conditions, perhaps because of a sense of not 'moving on', or because of treatment amongst patients who remain relatively highly disturbed, such patients' clinical progress may be stalled or reversed.

> 'There are not enough medium secure beds available for local hospitalisation – I once waited three years for a bed in a MSU'
>
> *Trevor Howard, s.37/41 patient, Yorkshire*

2.22 There has been widespread concern over the out of area placement of patients from the closing NHS long-stay learning disability hospitals into Independent Hospitals, which may in effect be re-creating long-stay institutions[25]. Rob Grieg, the Head of the Government's Valuing People team and its National Director for Learning Disabilities, was reported to say

---

24 Hughes, J.C. (2002) Re: Editorial 17 August 2002 'The NHS, the Private Sector, and the Virtual Asylum' *British Medical Journal* Rapid Response, 30 August. Also: 'This market discipline has in fact ruthlessly closed more than ten independent units in the last decade via withholding referrals – and we are better off because of it'.

25 All remaining long-stay NHS hospitals for people with learning disabilities are to be closed by 2006, two years after the original deadline established by Government. Patients remaining in such institutions are likely to be detained under the Act and have complex needs, often related to challenging behaviour. See John Carvel 'Hundreds with learning disabilities kept in asylums' *The Guardian* 20 November 2003; Andalo D 'Town halls defying care in the community edict'. *The Guardian* 4 November 2004, and articles referenced below.

26 Daloni Carlisle 'DoH warns against new long-stay institutions' *Health Service Journal*, 25 November 2004.

that 'the NHS has lost quite a lot of competence around learning disability commissioning'[26] and that Independent Hospitals 'were just responding to market opportunity'[27]. In November 2004 the Department of Health issued *Commissioning service close to home*, a note of clarification on the commissioning of learning disability services[28] (see figure 9). This reinforced Government policy that people with learning disabilities should be provided with local services tailored to their individual needs, and reiterated the principles shown in the box below. We suggest that similar principles should also apply to the commissioning of general mental health services.

Recommendation 3: Principles outlined by the Department of Health for learning disability service commissioning should inform commissioning of all mental health service sectors.

Key principles for learning disability service commissioning

1. Individuals should have services provided as far as possible in community rather than institutional settings

2. People should be supported as near as possible to their homes and families

3. Development and expansion of the capacity of local services to understand and respond to challenging behaviour

4. Individuals should be in conditions of no greater security than is justified by the danger they present to themselves and others

5. Services should maximise rehabilitation and the individuals' chances of sustaining an independent living

6. The differing needs of people with challenging behaviour should be responded to by highly individualised service planning and delivery

7. Local specialist services should be provided which support good mainstream practice as well as directly serving people with the most challenging needs

Fig 9: Department of Health guidance on principles for service commissioning[29]

---

[27] Maria Ahmed 'Ladyman warns councils of a return to long-stay hospitals 'by back door'' *Community Care* 18-24 November 2004.

[28] Department of Health *Commissioning service close to home*, note of clarification for commissioners and regulation and inspection authorities. www.dh.gov.uk/assetRoot/04/09/33/23/04093323.pdf

[29] *Commissioning service close to home, supra*, p.3.

Commissioning mental health services

2.23 In our above discussion of out of area treatment and the independent sector generally we have questioned whether present arrangements for the commissioning of mental health services might not militate against the Government's concerns for service improvement and best use of resources. Mental health service chief executives have been reported to have grave concerns over the understanding of their sector by Primary Care Trust commissioning bodies[30], and the National Director for Mental Health has acknowledged that some Primary Care Trusts have 'failed to follow through the Government's commitment to mental health'[31]:

> Some of the money that has reached front-line services has been spent on the wrong things. It has been used to shore up the old services that the NSF and NHS Plan were intended to change – out of area admissions, medium secure beds for people who could be admitted locally, locum and agency costs. It has been swallowed up by historical deficits in a local health economy, whether or not these could be traced to mental health services.

> …many, though certainly not all, PCTs, faced with their own financial pressures, have not given sufficient priority to mental health care in comparison with other priorities such as access to targets and waiting lists. In a devolved system of commissioning, there is very little earmarking of money allocated, and spending has been left to local organisations to argue over[32].

2.24 These perceived failings may be exacerbated by changes planned to commissioning functions which will refocus the Primary Care Trust role to support 'practice-based commissioning' by the end of 2008, with expectations of at least 15% reductions in management and administrative costs in commissioning services and a 'progressive move towards greater use of other providers [than NHS Trusts], including those from the independent sector'[33].

Should overcrowding be addressed by increasing the numbers of beds?

2.25 In 1996 the MHAC and Sainsbury Centre wrote that:

> for nursing staff on the wards, the reduction in bed numbers has resulted in them caring for an increased number of people with more severe mental illness. This increase in their patients' difficulties, and the high throughput of patients, places a heavy burden on nursing staff. At the same time, the emphasis of policy and managerial support has been on the development of community care. The development of inpatient care has suffered from relative neglect[34].

---

30   Emma Forrest 'Chief execs fear "clueless" commissioners' *Health Service Journal* 23 February 2003.

31   Department of Health (2004) *The National Service Framework for Mental Health – Five Years On*, p.69.

32   *ibid.*

33   Department of Health (2005) *Commissioning a patient-led NHS*. 28 July 2005

34   Sainsbury Centre for Mental Health (1997) *The National Visit: A one-day Visit to 309 Acute Psychiatric Wards by the Mental Health Act Commission in collaboration with The Sainsbury Centre for Mental Health.*

2.26 Reductions in mental health beds over recent decades have been founded upon the assumption that the patient days 'lost' to inpatient services will be taken up by community services. There is some evidence that overall capital expenditure in mental health services has focussed on access and crisis services at the expense of inpatient provision[35]. Over the last two decades, community-based services have increased greatly (if not always proportionately with reductions in inpatient provision[36]), and much development focus is now on forms of community mental health provision such as assertive outreach and crisis interventions that are designed to prevent the need for hospital admission. However, some commentators have raised the possibility that the focus on community-based provision may have had unintended consequences:

> delays in admission and treatment caused by bed shortages may mean that patients' illnesses are becoming more severe and that compulsory treatment is being initiated in cases in which informal admissions would previously have been possible … the move to community care may have led to a paradoxical and unexpected increase in the use of coercion in the treatment of patients with a mental illness[37] .

2.27 The systemic relation between hospital and community elements of mental health care make it difficult to determine whether, in cases such as our example at figure 5 above, inpatient overcrowding should be addressed by increasing bed numbers or further concentration on community support. Assuming that the pressures on inpatient services *are* a result of inadequacies in community mental health services or more general community provision (and not simply a lack of adequate numbers of inpatient beds), then clearly the long-term needs of the service as a whole would be best addressed through an increased concentration on community aspects of the service. Redirecting resources to increase acute inpatient ward capacity could be counter-productive to the strategic aim of establishing a working spectrum of care with several types of residential care appropriate to different levels of need. However, in a number of instances we are aware that resources are being taken from existing inpatient budgets, including staffing budgets, to fund developments in community services. Given our estimate from figures available over the last decade that the actual reduction in beds was 5% up to 2000/1 (see paragraph 2.13 above), and the asymptotic appearance of our graphic presentations of bed reductions at figures 5 and 6 above, it could be that we have already attained the minimum number of psychiatric beds for a viable service.

> 'Services are available nearer home but the ward environment is much worse than in what we used to call 'the big bins'. There is an acute shortage of beds'.
>
> *Margaret Jessop (aged 73), ex s.3, London*

---

[35] See Department of Health (2004) *The National Service Framework for Mental Health – Five Years On*, p.40: 'between 2001/02 and 2003/4 there was a 51% investment in access and crisis services – the category most closely reflecting the NHS Plan initiatives – [but] a small fall in percentage terms [from 19.5% to 18.6% of total expenditure] in spending in clinical services (comprising predominantly inpatient spend)'.

[36] The 1997 Sainsbury centre study quoted above (see note 9 above) found that even services 'in areas with relatively low levels of social deprivation … are in difficulty for precisely the same reason as those in the inner cities – that is, they have reduced the availability of long-term, highly supervised accommodation and have not replaced it with anything else'. (Shepherd *et al* (1997), *supra*).

[37] Wall, S., Hotopft, M., Wessely, S., & Churchill, R. 'Trends in the use of the Mental Health Act 1984-96' *BMJ* 1999;318;1520-1521.

In two Trusts in the south of England, patients have been accommodated on fold-down beds in the communal lounges of acute admission wards. This compromises patients' privacy and dignity, and their safety. (Not only are such patients forced to sleep in areas open to access by any other patient, but the lounges are not designed for use as bedrooms and in at least one case have inappropriate features such as inward-opening doors, making it possible for patients to barricade themselves into the room). We understand that recent service reorganisations have reduced acute and intensive care inpatient beds, with a refocused emphasis on home treatment for crisis resolution. This refocus has been reported by staff not to have led to a reduced demand for acute inpatient beds.

Fig 10: practice example of services with bed shortages

Managing beds sparingly depends on the following factors:

• Home assessment when possible;

• Senior clinical gatekeepers for admissions;

• Clear statements of the purpose of each admission;

• Frequent inpatient review meetings with the authority to discharge patients;

• Immediate transfer to housing services where the patient is homeless; and

• Mental health teams with control over admission and discharge from their own beds.

Fig 11: guidance on bed management[38]

2.28 We are encouraged by the programme to modernise inpatient care announced by the National Director for Mental Health in 2004, which will seek to eradicate unsuitable ward environments through capital investment; develop new models of inpatient provision for flexible purpose; improve integration with community services and tackle problems of recruitment, retention, morale and therapeutic skills of staff, and improve safety on wards by addressing problems of drugs and violence[39]. Where this vulnerable patient group are forced to reside in overcrowded and possibly dangerous conditions, we do not find it acceptable for services to use developing community structures as an excuse for not addressing their immediate needs. Some direct intervention to ameliorate overcrowding and related problems must be taken, whether this involves specific actions to enable individual patient discharge, arrangements for extra-contractual or out-of-area treatment, or consideration of alternative inpatient facilities for specific groups of patients.

2.29 It is also vital that responsible authorities do not lose sight of the possibility that, notwithstanding developing community services, the local provision of inpatient beds may simply be inadequate to serve the catchment population.

---

[38] Thornicroft, G., Strathdee, G. 'How Many Psychiatric Beds?' *BMJ* 1994;309:970-971 (15 October)

[39] Department of Health (2004) *The National Service Framework for Mental Health – Five Years On*, p.73.

Staffing levels

2.30 The Sainsbury Centre for Mental Health has stated that 'the provision of adequate and appropriate staffing levels and skill mix is one of the biggest challenges facing mental health services today'[40]. Its *Acute Care 2004* report found the vacancy rate for qualified nurses (funded posts minus actual staff) to be 13% nationally, and 22% in London (see figure 12). Even considering qualified nurses and health care assistants in combination, the actual number of staff did not meet the funded establishment in any national region. On a ward with 16 beds, for example, this would suggest a difference between actual and funded staff of two whole-time equivalent posts. This gap is likely to be managed in part or in full by the use of bank and agency staff, at some additional financial cost and to the detriment of continuity of care.

> 'Sometimes there are not enough staff to take us out on leave'
>
> *male patient, Yorkshire*

- The national average sickness rate among ward staff was 6.8%

- The national average use of bank and agency staff per week per ward was 152 hours, equal to more than 4 full-time staff

- 26% of wards had lost staff to community teams in the previous year

- 12% of ward managers reported having no administrative support

- 48% of wards did not have a lead consultant and 13% had no ward manager or nurse above grade F at the time of the survey

- 35% of ward managers reported that the client group on the ward had changed due to the development of community teams

- 18% of ward managers reported that they did not have access to a Psychiatric Intensive Care Unit (PICU)

- Communication with community teams was said to be poor during patient admissions by 16% of ward managers

Fig 12: key findings of *Acute Care 2004*: staffing problems and pressures on wards[41]

2.31 Percentages of trained and agency staff on wards that we visited between October 2004 and August 2005 are given at figure 13 below. About half of wards visited had between thirty and fifty percent qualified nursing staff. More than three-quarters of wards relied on agency staffing for less than 10% of their ward complement, although one ward in ten relies on agency staff for at least 20% of its staffing complement.

---

[40] Sainsbury Centre for Mental Health (2005) *Briefing 28. Acute Care 2004: A national survey of adult psychiatric wards in England.* May 2005.

[41] *ibid.*

%age of trained staff	no. of wards	cumulative total	%age of wards	cumulative %age	%age of agency staff	no. of wards	cumulative total	%age of wards	cumulative %age
< 10%	10	10	0.57	0.57	90%+ to 100%	2	2	0.11	0.11
10%+ to 20%	102	112	5.81	6.38	80%+ to 90%	–	2	–	0.11
20%+ to 30%	179	291	10.19	16.57	70%+ to 80%	1	3	0.06	0.17
30%+ to 40%	436	727	24.83	41.40	60%+ to 70%	6	9	0.34	0.51
40%+ to 50%	451	1,178	25.68	67.08	50%+ to 60%	7	16	0.40	0.91
50%+ to 60%	219	1,397	12.47	79.56	40%+ to 50%	31	47	1.77	2.68
60%+ to 70%	149	1,546	8.49	88.04	30%+ to 40%	62	109	3.53	6.21
70%+ to 80%	148	1,694	8.43	96.47	20%+ to 30%	63	172	3.59	9.79
80%+ to 90%	16	1,710	0.91	97.38	10%+ to 20%	139	311	7.92	17.71
90%+ to 100%	46	1,756	2.62	100.00	< 10%	1,445	1,756	82.29	100.00

Fig 13: percentage of trained staff and agency staff on wards visited by the MHAC between 1 October 2004 and 31 July 2005[42]

2.32　Patients often report having inadequate attention from or opportunities to talk with staff. It is unlikely that nurses struggling to carry out their basic duties on understaffed wards can reach out towards patients in need:

> I'd really like staff to approach me to and ask how I'm feeling when I'm upset/down because that's when I really need to talk but not able to tell them… At home at least you're on your own… but to be surrounded by people who … ignore you is far worse than being alone[43].

Medical staffing

2.33　The David Bennett inquiry heard that it took the on-call psychiatrist approximately one and a half hours from being 'bleeped' to attend the clinic where Mr Bennett was under restraint[44]. The delay was in part caused by human error and failed taxi arrangements, but the inquiry took the view that it was unacceptable that a foolproof system was not in place to secure the attendance of a doctor within 30 minutes at a unit caring for seriously ill patients. The inquiry stated that, had the psychiatrists arrived within half an hour of being called, the death of Mr Bennett under restraint may have been avoided. By the time any doctor arrived on the scene on the night of the 30 October 1998, Mr Bennett was almost certainly already dead[45]. The inquiry recommended that

> there should always be a doctor in every place where a mentally ill patient is detained, or if that is not possible, foolproof arrangements should be in place twenty-four hours a day [so] that a doctor may attend within twenty minutes of any request by staff to do so[46].

---

[42]　Source: MHAC visit database

[43]　Patient quoted in Healthcare Commission (2005) *National Audit of Violence*, p.36.

[44]　Norfolk, Suffolk and Cambridgeshire Strategic Health Authority (2003) *Independent Inquiry into the death of David Bennett*. December 2003, page 29

[45]　Mr Bennett was pronounced dead at 00.20 hours but seems likely to have died prior to the arrival of an ambulance at 23.45. A second doctor called by the clinic (after the first had not appeared) arrived at this time. See *Independent Inquiry into the death of David Bennett*, pages 22 & 29.

[46]　*ibid.*, p.30.

2.34   Government has 'accepted' that appropriate medical cover is vital and 'will repeat that message to service providers' but it will leave 'precise arrangements to be decided locally in the light of local circumstances'[47]. In reality, as we discussed in our previous Biennial Report[48], the structure of service delivery in relatively small and geographically scattered units may make medical cover in an emergency a practical difficulty in a great many units in the NHS and independent sector. Dr Hadrian Ball, the Medical Director of the Norvic Clinic (where David Bennett died), has written that it is impossible to achieve the Inquiry's recommendation of medical presence within 20 minutes in Norwich, where the clinic is one of three inpatient mental health sites, two of which are at opposite ends of the city, and where the number of junior doctors on duty across Norwich reduced by a third with the implementation of the European Working Time Directive on 1 August 2004[49]. Dr Ball argues that the medical cover envisaged by the inquiry could only be met through a reversal of the policy of dispersed mental health units, culminating in the recentralisation of inpatient care into large institutions[50]. Dr Ball does not advocate such a move, and neither do we. In our last report, however, we did suggest that limitations over powers of control and restraint could be justified on safety grounds for units that do not have medical staffing to oversee their implementation[51]. There may be limitations to the extent which this recommendation can be adopted by forensic units such as the Norvic Clinic, which leads us to agree with Dr Ball that the risk posed to some elements of inpatient care should be explicitly owned by the Department of Health and Primary Care Trust commissioners, not shouldered by provider units[52].

> 'We're told the less contact with our doctor means we're getting better and don't need to talk to them as much.'
>
> Richard Holmes, s.37/41 patient, Yorkshire

2.35   We nevertheless support in principle the David Bennett Inquiry report's recommendation, although we recognise that in many units across the NHS and independent sectors it may be difficult to meet the expectation of a doctor's attendance within twenty to thirty minutes. Within such units it may be necessary to establish policies that encourage nursing staff to call for medical presence as early as possible in any situation where interventions such as restraint or seclusion may be required; consider how spaces may be set aside within the unit that may be used to contain patients without lengthy physical restraint; and train staff to consider certain forms of restraint as a very last resort. It is unacceptable that patients are being exposed to hazardous procedures in the absence of adequate medical services to ensure their safety. We discuss restraint further at Chapter 4.206-17 below.

2.36   We continue to encounter arrangements for the medical cover of units that cause us considerable concern. Some small units, particularly in the independent sector, have either

---

[47]   Department of Health (2005) *Delivering Race Equality in Mental Health Care; an action plan for reform inside and outside services and the Government's response to the independent inquiry into the death of David Bennett.* January 2005, p.36.

[48]   MHAC (2003) *Tenth Biennial Report: Placed Amongst Strangers.* Chapters 1.7, 10.32 & 11.23.

[49]   Ball, H.N. 'Death in restraint: lessons' *Psychiatric Bulletin* (2005) 29; 321-323

[50]   *ibid.*

[51]   MHAC (2003) *Tenth Biennial Report: Placed Amongst Strangers*, Chapters 10.32 & 11.23, Rec.44.

[52]   Ball, H.N. (2005) *supra*

arranged or considered medical staffing arrangements that could not possibly expect the attendance of a doctor within half an hour of an emergency call:

- A single consultant psychiatrist offered to provide 24 hour medical cover simultaneously to five independent hospitals in different locations, some of which were more than 40 miles apart; and

- A group of psychiatrists in one part of the country offered 24 hour consultant psychiatrist/RMO cover to a number of independent mental health hospitals, some of which were at great distance (i.e. 200 miles) from their location. We understand that their proposal to undertake RMO responsibilities for MHRTs and Hospital Managers' reviews by video-link has not been considered acceptable for registration purposes.

2.37   More generally, we have found the consultant psychiatrist cover in some Independent Hospitals to be inadequate. It may consist of an arrangement for a consultant psychiatrist (sometimes retired) to attend the hospital to see patients after six o'clock in the evening one day per week, or during the day at week ends. This is likely to preclude the holding of effective ward rounds involving the patient, their relatives, social worker, OT, psychologist, primary nurse/key worker, advocate, interpreter, etc.

2.38   In contrast to a number of NHS Mental Health Trusts, some Independent Hospitals (especially in the learning disability sector) can be geographically isolated from the main centres of population. Smaller Independent Hospitals do not generally have a range of other on call psychiatric/medical staff, e.g. Senior House Officers, Specialist Registrars, Associate Specialists or Staff Grade Doctors. Nor in a number of cases does the consultant psychiatrist/RMO live within a reasonable distance from the hospital, as is the expectation in the NHS. It is our perception, particularly in light of the recommendations of the David Bennett Report, that at times of a psychiatric or other medical emergency, patients in some hospitals may be at risk.

> 'Only saw doctor once a week on ward round, in a big room with other staff – felt like I was on trial.'
>
> *Deborah Hickman, ex-s.3 patient, Lancashire*

2.39   We understand that the Healthcare Commission has raised this issue with the Royal College of Psychiatrists. We would welcome a statement or guidelines in respect of a baseline requirement for consultant psychiatrist/RMO cover that all Independent Hospitals would be expected to adhere to for registration purposes. Given that approximately 95% of psychiatric patients in Independent Hospitals are NHS funded, it seems equitable that they should receive no less a service in terms of medical staffing than would be available in NHS facilities.

Ward environments

2.40   In 2003 the Secretary of State suggested that Government initiatives over patient choice (see paragraphs 2.64 *et seq* below) should benefit "all aspects of the patient experience [including] attentive staff. A clean, comfortable, friendly place to be. Safe, high-quality, co-ordinated care. And all done in a way that makes people say 'they treated me as if I mattered...' "[53]. For many detained patients the absence of these basic standards curtails choice, and can be perceived as an affront to basic rights of dignity and respect. The following problems are by no means endemic across all inpatient units, but are common enough to allow us to generalise:

- Shabby and ill-kept ward environments contribute to making patients' surroundings bleak and counter-therapeutic.

- Patient mix on wards may be inappropriate, in that patients with a wide range of age and diagnosis are placed within the same facilities. In 1999, the Department of Health recognised that up to a third of mental health inpatients would be better placed elsewhere[54].

> 'Unsafe environment – layout unsuitable for staff & patients. Men/women mixed which was not appropriate and embarrassing. Passive smoking & no quiet space'.
>
> *Yasmin Jackson, ex- s.3 patient, Wales*

- Bed pressures and overcrowding can leave patients with little personal space or 'peace and quiet', and opportunities to spend time off-ward may be limited by shortfalls in environmental or staffing arrangements, irrespective of patients' clinical needs.

- Bed pressures may lead to patients being moved around wards or transferred to out-of-area placements during periods of detention.

- Men and women are often housed together in units where this may not be appropriate or the first choice of women patients. Women in a minority on inpatient wards may feel threatened or isolated, and may still encounter poor facilities that offer little privacy or safety for sleeping, using bathrooms or simply spending time on the ward during the day.

- Drug abuse and illicit 'drug culture' in some inpatient units makes patients feel unsafe and places them at risk. In some units where illicit drugs are a problem, wards are closed to keep drugs out, limiting the movement of patients. Where this is not done, drug users and dealers from outside the ward may disrupt its functioning and environment.

- Ward arrangements may not be tailored to individual patients' needs, particularly for patients from Black and minority ethnic groups. Isolation or patient-to-patient bullying may be compounded by poor arrangements to meet cultural, religious or communication needs.

- Patients who are confined to wards are left with little to do, either in terms of leisure and recreation or activities with a more therapeutic design[55].

2.41   These observations, which we have included in previous Biennial Reports, have been confirmed in this period by other studies of inpatient environments. Whilst we recognise that many wards have made some improvements, and that some new-build wards provide an excellent environment for care, we cannot agree with the National Director for Mental Health that 'the popular image of squalid mental health wards is outdated and unrepresentative'[56].

---

53   Rt Hon John Reid MP, Secretary of State for Health, speech to the New Health Network, 15 July 2003.

54   Department of Health (1999) *A National Service Framework for Mental Health*. London, Stationery Office. See also Mental Health Act Commission (2001) *Ninth Biennial Report*, Chapter 3.5.

55   See, Mental Health Act Commission (2001) *Ninth Biennial Report*, Chapter 3.4 – 8, Mental Health Act Commission (2003) *Tenth Biennial Report* Chapter 9.29 *et seq.*

56   Department of Health (2004) *The National Service Framework for Mental Health – Five Years On*, p.73.

The Healthcare Commission National Audit of Violence, based upon returns from 265 wards or units between December 2003 and March 2005, found the following 'common factors' deleterious to patient experience in inpatient units, which it stated 'are either increasing the likelihood that violence will happen, or mean that it will not be managed effectively if it does':

- *Unsafe environments:* failure to meet basic safety standards in the design of wards. The report calls for staff and service users to be fully involved in the design process for every new build, and for great effort to upgrade and improve existing wards in ways that optimise safety.

- *Inadequate staffing:* many services are operating with vacancy factors with an on-going drain of experienced staff into higher paid, and often more highly-regarded, community posts, leaving some in-patient services reliant upon inexperienced leaders. Problems recruiting staff leads to over-reliance upon bank and agency staff. These difficulties militate against building a coherent team that works proactively to prevent and manage violence. The report calls for the status of in-patient nursing to be raised to at least that of community nursing.

- *Client mix and over-crowding:* many acute mental health services are 'fire fighting' as they struggle to work with an increasingly unwell population, some of whom will have a dual diagnosis. The conjunction of high bed occupancy figures and inadequate staffing can make the delivery of a therapeutic service impossible. The report calls for action from commissioners and managers to address the great inequities in staffing levels and skills mix across the country.

- *Substance misuse* was identified as the most common trigger for violence. The study revealed that problems associated with the use of alcohol and illegal drugs were more common in mental health services – particularly acute, PICU and forensic services (alcohol was rated as especially problematic in acute services). Staff teams need support to address the problems caused by the use of alcohol and illegal drugs in in-patient services.

- *High levels of boredom:* many services are unable to offer patients a structured and therapeutic system of care. This is linked to low staffing levels and high volumes of paperwork. As well as the obvious link between 'boredom' and 'violence', this is seen to have an impact on recovery rates for service users, and on job satisfaction for staff. The report called for 'ways to be found of supporting staff to spend more time in face-to-face contact with service users – doing the job that they were trained to do'.

- *Staff training in the prevention and management of violence:* significant numbers of staff reported dissatisfaction with the timing, content, or quality of the training they received, or with their ability to apply such training in real life situations. Training must be tailored to individual needs and more emphasis placed on the prevention rather than the management of incidents, but can only be effective if the other issues described above also addressed.

Fig 14: Healthcare Commission findings of common factors deleterious to patient experience in inpatient units, December 2003 – March 2005[57]

---

[57] Healthcare Commission (2005) *National Audit of Violence (2003-2005) Final Report.* Royal College of Psychiatrists' Research Unit / Healthcare Commission. p.63-4. www.healthcarecommission.org.uk.

2.42 At figure 15 below we set out findings from the Healthcare Commission's *Audit on Violence* regarding some basic environmental standards. There is clearly much work to be done on the inpatient environment across all sectors. It is notable that PICUs scored poorly in availability of natural fresh air and (although this is not shown on the table) also in provision of activities and service user involvement in care-planning and prescribing. Lack of space and access to fresh air can be particularly problematic in recently established smaller PICUs and Medium Secure Units. One proposal for a 70-bedded Independent Hospital in the London metropolitan area specified an Astroturf airing court of approximately 30 x 15 metres, with a minimum exercise time of one hour daily for residents. We do not know if this proposal is likely to be implemented.

'There is nowhere you can go to have space. The wards and courtyards are much too small, especially the courtyards, for the 100 service users here'.

Gul Davis, ex-s.3 patient (MSU)
Birmingham

standard	percentage met				
	acute	PICU	forensic	elderly	all units[58]
all areas look clean	67	67	74	55	71
all areas smell clean	65	58	58	64	68
all areas look friendly	53	50	53	73	58
natural daylight	63	58	68	82	68
natural fresh air	40	17	42	64	48
temperature and ventilation adequately controlled	32	33	37	36	39
noise levels are adjusted to meet the needs of residents	73	75	63	55	71
access to external space with sheltered area	42	50	32	27	37
adequate quiet spaces for staff and patients	43	50	37	18	46
adequate private spaces for interactions	53	50	26	45	53
single bedrooms provided	62	92	100	64	77
perception of space with overcrowding avoided	63	92	68	27	65
ward size and design appropriate to patient population	36	42	26	55	42

all figures are percentages

Fig 15: Healthcare Commission environmental audit national findings, by service sector, 2003-2005[59].

2.43 Mental health wards for elderly patients scored significantly low on average in cleanliness, noise levels, access to external and/or quiet spaces and single bedrooms. The incidences of violence on wards for elderly patients were, perhaps surprisingly, higher than the national average, although staff were less likely to receive adequate training or support in the prevention and management of violence. The following are extracts from letters addressed to a consultant on an elderly ward by a patient who had been detained there under section 3.

---

[58] 'All units' includes acute, PICU, forensic, rehabilitation, elderly, learning disability (short stay, lon challenging behaviour) units and small group homes.

[59] Healthcare Commission (2005) *National Audit of Violence* p.63-4.

'It would be sheer bliss to be taken for a walk round Ladywell Fields or Lewisham Park, pausing half-way round to sit and have a friendly chat. I do realise, however, that the nurses are extremely busy, struggling to cope with the individual needs of 18 elderly patients suffering from such a wide range of problems, including depression, eating disorders, various forms of dementia, brain damage, the aftermaths of a stroke, and mania like me, some of whom may be completely bedridden, so that this cannot happen as often as I would like.

The ward is often extremely noisy. On my last, oh so involuntary, stay there on top of the usual panic alarms, fire alarms, patients screaming, and the television, (an unwritten rule seems to be that this must never be turned off), which I have learned to expect and dread so much, we had a building site next door, and thus the sounds of hammering, pneumatic drills, and heavy plant machinery added to the usual din.

I profoundly believe that access to fresh air is a basic human right, and that denying me the opportunity to exercise in the garden is a very risky strategy both for my mental and physical health. ... In any case Hayworth ward is not a particularly safe place for anybody. During my various involuntary stays there has been an attempt to throttle me, I have been head-butted, and I have long lost count of the number of times I have been hit. These attacks were I feel an entirely foreseeable consequence of the policy of locking very ill people up in a fairly confined space'.

Margaret Jessop, (age 73), ex-s.3, London

The safety and security of women patients

2.44   The safety and security of women patients is a particular concern. Although Government figures claim that 98% of Trusts in England and Wales meet the national standards for single-sex accommodation, patients' own reports continue to indicate that women feel there is insufficient segregation of the sexes and/or protection from sexual harassment or violence on psychiatric wards. The difference between official and patient perceptions is due to the fact that Trusts may meet the standards for 'single-sex accommodation' through segregation of sleeping areas, designation of bathroom facilities, and the provision of some women-only space such as a day-lounge. Patients may still experience such facilities as essentially 'mixed-sex', particularly when undertaking activities or at meal-times. In the 2003 implementation guidance *Mainstreaming Gender and Women's Health*, Government recognised a wish for women-only facilities to avoid what one female patient described as 'sitting down to breakfast with a group of strange men, all in varying states of undress'[60]. For women to both feel and be secure much wider use of genuinely women-only wards should be encouraged.

2.45   Between November 2003 and July 2004 we asked services to notify us of any admission of a female detained patient to a mixed ward where women constituted less than ten per cent of the patient population. We were notified of 105 such admissions, relating to 97 patients (eight patients in the sample were admitted on two different occasions during the notification period). On average, this amounts to roughly three admissions every week. We set out some of the information gathered from the notification procedure at figure 16 below. Of this sample (we do not know the rate of under-reporting from our notification exercise),

---

[60]   Department of Health (2003) *Mainstreaming Gender and Women's Health*

one fifth of women patients were known to have a history of being abused by men, but twice this number had no access to women-only areas on the ward, nearly a quarter were required to use the same bathrooms as male patients, seventeen percent had sleeping arrangements that were not separated from male bedroom areas and a quarter had to walk through areas of the ward used mostly by males to reach women-only washing, toilet or day facilities. A significant minority of these women patients (13%) had raised concerns over their personal safety on the ward.

	Yes	%	No	%	N/S[61]
Is there a policy relating to the care a treatment of women patients?	29	28	33	31	42
Are staff provided with special training in dealing with issues relating to women?	15	14	25	24	21
Are women on duty every shift on these wards?	59	56	13	12	32
Is the patient's primary nurse female?	77	73	17	16	11
Does the patient have access to independent advocacy?	57	54	10	10	29
Has the patient raised concern/s over personal safety?	14	13	48	46	42
Has the patient a history of abuse by men?	21	20	49	47	51
Do women have access to a women-only area?	21	20	43	41	40
Do women have access to a women-only toilet?	55	52	11	10	38
Do women have access to women-only bathrooms?	40	38	24	23	40
Do women have to walk through a mostly male area to access bathrooms / toilet etc?	27	25	34	32	43
Are women patients' bedrooms separate from men patients' bedrooms?	45	43	18	17	41

Fig 16: 105 responses to MHAC questionnaires relating to the situation of women admitted to mixed wards where they constitute less than 10% of the total patient population, Nov 2003 – July 2004

2.46   Whilst some ward staff reported that they could offer a safe, supportive environment for women patients, a number expressed their concerns that this was not the case. A number of units acknowledged that they had inadequate facilities and/or space to designate women-only areas within the ward or to offer care to the standards of safety, privacy and dignity that they would prefer:

- 'the facilities on this unit are not conducive to catering for both sexes';
- 'patient isolated due to age and gender';
- 'male and female service user bedrooms in the same corridor is not ideal. Is at times restrictive…';
- 'we feel that [the patient's] recovery is compromised by at least one male patient who is intrusive and insensitive to the needs of others. Patient has been offered nursing in isolation but she does not wish to accept the offer'[62].

---

[61] 'N/S' or 'not stated' category includes all returns that gave neither 'yes' nor 'no' in answer to our questions.

[62] The quotations are taken from returned notifications on Form MHAC8.

2.47   At figure 17 we reproduce the key findings of Mind's *Ward Watch* campaign, which highlighted a number of shortfalls in patient experience of inpatient care between 2002 and 2004.

Key findings of Mind's Ward Watch survey of 335 current or recent inpatients, 2004[63]

- Two years after the Government's own target for the elimination of mixed sex wards, and less than a year after it claimed that 99 per cent of NHS Trusts met Government targets, 23% of recent and current inpatient respondents have been accommodated in mixed sex wards.

- Thirty one per cent of respondents did not have access to single sex bathroom facilities. Only 30% of respondents had access to single sex daytime facilities.

- Over a quarter of respondents (27%) said that they rarely felt safe while in hospital. Only 44% of respondents felt safe all or most of the time.

- Over half (51%) of recent or current inpatients reported being verbally or physically threatened during their stay with 20% reporting physical assault.

- Nearly one in five (18%) respondents reported sexual harassment in hospital; 5% of respondents reported sexual assault.

- Seven per cent of respondents reported being subject to harassment because of their race while 3% reported racially motivated assault.

- Ten per cent reported being subject to harassment because of their sexuality; 5% reported being assaulted because of their sexuality.

- Fifty-six per cent of harassment or assault episodes were perpetrated by a patient or service user. 31% of harassment or assault episodes were perpetrated by a ward staff member.

- Fifty-three per cent of respondents thought that the hospital surroundings had not helped their recovery. 31% thought that it had made their health worse.

- One in five (20%) of respondents felt that they were treated with respect and dignity by staff. Almost the same proportion (17%) stated that they were never treated with respect and dignity by staff.

Fig 17: key findings of Mind's *Ward Watch* campaign.

The detention of children and adolescents in adult services

2.48   In December 2004 we published our study of the detention of children and adolescents in adult services over the 18-month period between April 2002 and September 2003[64]. Over this time were notified of 270 such placements and made 122 visits to detained children and adolescents (in the remaining notifications, the patient would have either been made

---

[63] Mind (2004) *Ward Watch: Mind's campaign to improve hospital conditions for mental health patients.* Of the 335 respondents to Mind's questionnaire (March 2004), just under a quarter were current inpatients; others had been inpatients in the previous two years. Just over half identified themselves as female; four-fifths as white British. 44 (13%) identified their area of residence as Wales.

[64] MHAC (2004) *Safeguarding children and adolescents detained under the Mental Health Act 1983 on adult psychiatric wards.* London; TSO, December 2004. Also at www.mhac.org.uk

informal or transferred before we could arrange a visit). Less than 13% of such placements related to children under 16 years of age, and two-thirds of all notifications related to male patients. There was very significant over-representation (26%) of Black and minority ethnic patients in the notifications as a whole, with children and adolescents of Black African or Black Caribbean origin comprising 13.1% of notifications but only 2.7% of the child population.

2.49   Less than half (43%) of services had policies or protocols relating to the admission of a minor to an adult facility; only ten per cent had trained staff in issues to do with the care of minors and a third had not carried out of completed police checks on staff working with minors in these circumstances. Only a quarter of wards had access to a copy of the Children Act 1989. On a number of visits staff expressed their concern at their own lack of skills or knowledge to work with minors, and some reported that their role was limited to containment until a more suitable place was found. Whilst transfers to age-appropriate facilities were planned for most of the children under 16 years of age, such plans were in place at the time of our visit in less than 30% of all the cases of minors' admission to adult facilities. A number of patients reported feeling frightened by other patients on the adult ward, and many spoke of boredom and lack of appropriate activities.

2.50   We concluded that inappropriate admissions of minors to adult wards occur apparently as a result of inadequate provision of child and adolescent beds nationally, confounded by unequal geographic distribution and very little provision for emergency admissions to Child and Adolescent Mental Health Services (CAMHS). Our recommendations called upon:

- the Department of Health to issue guidance and standards for NHS-commissioned CAMHS services, including guidelines on the admission of minors to adult facilities, similar to those issued in 2002 by the Welsh Assembly Government[65];

- commissioners of CAMHS to
    - ensure that admission policies for children and minors are agreed with all service provider units; and
    - identify the number of specialist beds needed;

- CAMHS services to review access to their services by young people and their families from Black and minority ethnic groups and ensure ethnic monitoring is implemented fully;

- adult wards which are designated to admit minors to implement fifteen specific recommendations designed to ensure wards staff are trained, adequately police-checked, supported by CAMHS services; and able to provide a single room for the patient, assess and respond to educational and activity needs of patients, and make provision for suitable visiting facilities. Such wards should also have access to trained advocates and written information on legal rights accessible to minors[66].

---

[65] Welsh Assembly Government (2002) *Mental Health Policy Implementation Guidance for Child and Adolescent Mental Health Services.* Cardiff: Welsh Assembly Government

[66] MHAC (2004) *Safeguarding children and adolescents detained under the Mental Health Act* pages 6-10

Recommendation 4: Government, commissioners of CAMHS and service managers should implement the recommendations of our 2004 report *Safeguarding children and adolescents detained under the Mental Health Act 1983 on adult psychiatric wards.*

Therapies and activities

2.51   The Sainsbury Centre for Mental Health's 1998 report *Acute Problems* found that as many as 30% of service users said they were not involved in any therapeutic or recreational activity at all during their hospital stay (SCMH, 1998). The Sainsbury Centre *Acute Care 2004* report found that:

- Art therapy was routinely available on 49% of wards and psycho-social interventions were routinely available on 35%.

- Fewer than 20% of ward managers reported that cognitive behavioural therapy (CBT) was routinely available.

- Practical therapeutic activities such as learning cooking skills or financial management were reported as being available routinely on 73% of wards.

> 'I'd like to see alternative therapies on offer, such as massage with a safe, trained person…as a service user, when was the last time you were touched? Hospitals should be therapeutic settings, exploring different therapies'.
>
> *Abina Parshad-Griffin, ex s.3, Oxford*

- Leisure and social activities, such as coffee mornings, karaoke, music events and going to the gym, were routinely provided on 64% of wards.

- Nurses and occupational therapists provide the bulk of input into activities with just under a quarter of ward managers reporting that they had input from psychologists.

Residents of Ashley House (Care Principles Ltd), whose primarily diagnoses are predominantly Learning Disability, have timetabled activity programmes that specify key worker involvement and recreational/ therapeutic activities which are regularly reviewed, and form part of a goal achievement programme. We saw encouraging signs of user-involvement in formulating the plans on a recent visit, and noted the use of the programme as a therapeutic tool through the award of points for the completion of 'coping goals'.

Ashley House, Market Drayton, tel: 01630 673 800

Fig 18: practice example – patient activity

2.52   We support the Sainsbury Centre's recommendations on therapies and activities:

Recommendation 5:

- Health care assistants, volunteers and activity workers should be involved in facilitating a broader range of activities.

- Ward staff need training in therapies such as CBT, and sufficient opportunities to practise afterwards.

- Inpatient wards need greater input from psychologists (and adult psychotherapists) in delivering therapies and activities.

The debate over 'reinstitutionalisation'

'In 2003 the conditions and atmosphere on the ward were significantly worse than they had been a decade earlier. The door was now locked at 5pm, and the practical obstacles to getting both in and out often made it more effort than it was worth to enjoy a quiet stroll outside. There is now a lovely and safely enclosed garden … yet I was refused access to it until after morning handover, so I could not enjoy the beauty of the dawn. The arbitrary exercise of power like this is so destructive to the spirit of those who are subjected to it and contradicts the true function of the ward. There was no longer any occupational therapy on the ward itself, and only very limited provision elsewhere in the hospital for patients who were well enough to leave the ward. The intense boredom and resulting tensions could not be more counterproductive. The nursing staff seemed to be far more preoccupied than before with form-filling and observations, leaving reduced time and energy for real human interaction. Morale seemed lower, while the therapeutic groups had disappeared'.

Emma Laughton, ex-s.2 patient, Devon

2.53   It is perhaps unwise to generalise over the 'direction' of mental health care, which is a complex and sectorised system subject to a number of competing pressures. However, we are struck by a number of debates over the question of 'reinstitutionalisation' over this reporting period. It should perhaps be expected that the enactment of human rights legislation, coupled with a public policy focus on expanding community-based services for both the mental illness and learning disability sectors (with the latter having a delayed target for the closure of all long-stay institutions by next year), would herald the end of 'institutionalisation' in mental health care. But this may not be the case.

2.54   In the first place, it must not be assumed that smaller-scale, geographically scattered units are necessarily less 'institutional' than the larger hospitals that they are replacing. Bartlett and Sandland have warned that 'wards ostensibly in the community may in fact be more secure than those in hospitals' and that we risk making the mistake of 'spinning a tale of the shift from institutional to community-based provision, when in fact much of that provision in the community is in residential form' [67]. Patients moving 'down' from high secure care, which might be assumed necessarily to be the most 'institutional' sector in mental health services, may find themselves housed in one of the increasing number of small low and medium security units whose practices may be more restrictive than the high secure

---

[67]   Bartlett, P. & Sandland, R (2004) *Mental Health Law Policy and Practice* Second Ed, Oxford University Press p.126

135

rehabilitation wards they have come from. We are pleased that Ministers spoke out against the commissioning of out of area placements for learning disabled patients as 'reinventing the long-stay hospital by the back door'[68] and that the Department of Health issued guidance to service commissioners reminding them of Government policy over this matter (see paragraph 2.22 above). The burgeoning provision of independent sector 'low secure' facilities is clearly a response to a market need in relation not only to learning disabled but also general mental health patients. We are concerned that this market may be distorted or exaggerated through the relative lack of expertise in Primary Care Trusts regarding special sector commissioning:

> private hospitals offer an easy solution to what are often challenging commissioning problems. It's much simpler to make a one-off hospital placement than to construct a complex, multi-service support network in the community[69].

2.55 Second, the focus on community-level residential units and home-based treatment has perhaps been at the expense of inpatient services that will and must be left to accommodate patients who, for whatever reason, cannot be treated in community settings (see paragraph 2.24 *et seq* above). In our last Biennial Report we raised our concern that

> in the absence of sufficient central guidance and monitoring, laudable aims of less formality with greater immediacy of response and availability of appropriate care could lead in practice, to casual and unregulated application of powers of coercion[70].

In particular we raised the spectre of the workhouse 'casual wards', where admission was relatively open but at much cost to civil liberties and human dignity. It should not be tolerable today that patients entering acute psychiatric wards may have either of these rights compromised, although our experience in visiting some such facilities, and a number of reports on acute service published in the last two years, worryingly suggest that this happens too often.

2.56 Earlier in this report, we discussed case-law regarding conditional discharge of patients from one hospital to another (see Chapter 1.149-62). These cases give an interesting insight to the way in which the Human Rights Act, by defining rights more closely, in fact can result in the extension of powers over patients' lives. In 1986 the courts took the view that a condition of remaining in a hospital is inconsistent with the meaning of 'discharge' in the Act[71]. By approaching this question afresh according to principles of Strasbourg jurisprudence (see Chapter 1.150 above), the courts have subsequently determined otherwise, so that the key issue is no longer whether an establishment is a hospital or not (which, in any case, is an arbitrary distinction based solely upon legal registration status), but whether arrangements for patients post-discharge from hospital continue to amount to a deprivation of liberty or not. This is undoubtedly a sensible approach to constructing the

---

[68] Maria Ahmed 'Ladyman warns councils of a return to long-stay hospitals "by back door"' *Community Care* 18-24 Nov 2004

[69] David Brindle 'Private care for learning disabled people is a return to Victorian values' *The Guardian* 4 August 2004.

[70] MHAC (2003) *Tenth Biennial Report: Placed Amongst Strangers.* Chapter 1.7

[71] *Secretary of State for the Home Department v MHRT for the Mersey Regional Health Authority* [1986] 3 All E.R. 233

meaning of the law (i.e. on principles rather than on technicalities of language), but it is interesting that its immediate result has been that the MHRT may 'discharge' restricted patients on condition that they remain in hospital subject to numerous restrictions on their liberty. This further demonstrates how 'deinstitutionalisation' has a potential to put pressures on 'community services' to become more 'institutional' (or at least restrictive) as they take on patients coming from institutional culture, and how this move can even appear to be a necessary requirement in the patients' best interests.

2.57   Third, overemphasis or misrepresentation of psychiatry's role in risk-assessment for public protection may distort service priorities. The table at figure 19 overleaf is adapted from a comparison of service provision in six western countries by Priebe *et al*, published in the *British Medical Journal* in January 2005[72]. In a controversial editorial, Priebe and Turner argued that mental health services are undergoing a process of 'reinstitutionalisation' characterised by:

(i)   rising numbers of forensic beds (with dramatic increases in private sector provision the UK), 'sucking funds away from the more financially stretched areas, especially in London';

(ii)   changing attitudes towards compulsion, with rising numbers of detentions and plans to widen the criteria for compulsory treatment;

(iii) increased placements in supported housing 'taking the place ...[of] the old-style asylums' with many facilities run by private providers ('this and the aforementioned rising number of privately provided secure units might lead to the conclusion that 'private madhouses' are back, no matter the official names');

(iv)   the establishment of assertive outreach that exercise powers of coercion in practice and 'turn individuals who otherwise would not yet be treated into psychiatric patients and subjects of ongoing treatment interventions'.

2.58   Further, Priebe and Turner argued that reinstitutionalisation may be an effect that could be limited to patients with more severe mental disorders who are unable or unwilling to engage with an increasing market for patients who actively seek treatment and can directly or indirectly pay for it. This echoes our own discomfort over the potential for 'contestability' to lead to two-tier services, with underperforming services being utilised mainly by patients whose choices are restricted through the use of mental health powers (see paragraph 2.90 below).

2.59   It may be that the terminology of 'institutionalisation' is unhelpful: one correspondent to the BMJ suggested that 'deinstitutionalisation is just the transfer of a patient from what is perceived to be a less appropriate institution to one that is perceived to be more appropriate, reinstutionalisation is the reverse'[73]. Professor Priebe himself has said elsewhere that 'professional mental health care is probably impossible to conceive without institutions'[76]. Dr Rob Poole has written that 'the essential feature of a 'total institution' is

---

[72]   Priebe, S., Badesconyi, A., Fioritti, A., Hansson, L., Kilian, R., Torres-Gonzales, F., Turner, T., Wiersma, D. 'Reinstitutionalisation in mental health care: comparison of data on service provision from six European countries'. BMJ 2005;330:123-126.

[73]   Dubourg G 'reinstitutionalisation' bmj.com rapid response to Priebe & Turner, 13/02/03.

	Numbers per 100,000 population				% Change
	1990s		2000s		
Involuntary admissions	40.5	(1990)	50.3	(2001)	+24
Restricted patients admitted[74]	1.3	(1991)	1.8	(2001)	+38
Places in supported housing	15.9	(1997)	22.3	(2002)	+40
Psychiatric hospital beds	131.8	(1990)	62.8	(2001)	–52
Prison population	90	(1992)	141	(2003)	+57

Fig 19: number of involuntary hospital admissions; admissions of restricted patients; places in residential care or supported housing; psychiatric hospital beds; and prison population: percentage changes over a decade[75]

that its residents are not free to pass through its doors unimpeded. The loss of this freedom brings other processes into play which lead to the adverse consequence of institutionalisation. No matter how intrusive community services may be, they cannot inflict the damage caused by losing control over where you go and who you associate with'[77].

2.60 For the majority of the patients who fall within our remit (including those who are subject to the Act in 'community-based' residential units), impediments to 'passing through the ward door' are a basic fact of life. Our further concern is that an increasing prominence of criminal-justice concepts and measures in mental health law for civil compulsion could result in many inpatient units becoming increasingly custodial-based and 'total institutions' than at present. The reverse side of the rights-based legalism in mental health compulsion is that the processes through which a patient passes increasingly resemble those of the criminal law[78]. This need not be an inevitable consequence: other court-based systems (such as child welfare) are clearly established as civil processes, although children under the age of 16 are, of course, already the ward of someone and the basic issues of personal liberty and detention are not so clearly engaged.

'When I was on full observations, I said to the nurse, jokingly, "you know, I have the strangest feeling I'm being watched and followed!" and she wrote it down in my notes – if you're detained even your humour is pathologised!'

Abina Parshad-Griffin, ex s.32.60, Oxford

---

[74] Priebe *et al* interpret this figure in their multi-national comparison as an indicator of 'forensic beds' in England, and count it, alongside 'places in supported housing', as defining 'institutions as defined by bricks and mortar'. We have not followed them in this, as we consider this too much of a generalisation for our purposes. The number of forensic beds cannot be considered equivalent to the number of admissions of restricted patients because, *inter alia*, not all 'forensic' patients are subject to restriction orders (and neither is a restriction order a guarantee of a bed in a 'forensic' service), and a considerable proportion of forensic beds are occupied by the same patient for a number of years.

[75] Table adapted from Priebe *et al*; *supra*

[76] Priebe S 'Institutionalisation revisited – with and without walls'. *Acta Psychiatr Scand* 2004;110:81-2

[77] Poole R 'Institutions have walls' bmj.com rapid response to Priebe & Turner, 23 February 2003.

[78] Kinton M 'Mental Health Law for the 21st Century?' *Journal of Mental Health Law* (May 2005) 12;57-69

2.61 In this way it is unfortunate that the draft Mental Health Bill 2004 would import into civil psychiatric compulsion a number of mechanisms that could distort clinical priorities and that gave the Bill the flavour of a criminal justice measure. The most striking examples are:

- The particular provisions in the conditions for compulsion of civil patients who are deemed to be at 'substantial risk of serious harm' to others, above and beyond those provisions that set a threshold for the compulsion of any other civil patient for the protection of other persons[79];

- The provision allowing the Tribunal to make an order requiring a civil patient to be detained in hospital for a fixed period of time[80];

- The introduction of the equivalent of restriction orders for civil patients deemed to be at substantial risk of serious harm to others, where the Tribunal may reserve unto itself powers of leave, discharge or transfer[81]; and

- The powers given to the Tribunal or a court to attach any sort of conditions to the imposition of a non-residential treatment orders, where breach of such conditions could result in detention in hospital, thus providing a potential 'Anti-Social Behaviour Order' use of mental health powers[82] (see paragraph xii of the introduction to this report, and Chapter 3.70 below).

2.62 We have no doubt that there is a political will to modernise mental health legislation and services to the benefit of those to whom they are applied. It is important that this aim is not undermined by the unintended consequences of measures taken (or not taken) by Government in implementing its policy aims.

2.63 We are encouraged by other currents in thinking about mental health care. The Sainsbury Centre *Search for Acute Solutions* project, based upon workshops attended by staff and service users, synthesised a description of the role and function of acute inpatient care that provides a positive model of the goals for policy development. We have summarised the description below (figure 20): a fuller version is given in the Sainsbury Centre book *Beyond the Water Towers; the unfinished revolution in mental health services 1985-2005*[83].

The role and function of acute inpatient care is to provide:
- Crisis resolution for people who are too distressed to be beneficially treated at home;

- Respite, asylum or sanctuary in a secure, calm, dignified and homely environment;

- Rapid multi-disciplinary assessment (including risk-assessment) centred upon the patient as expert and focussing on strengths as well as needs;

- Planned admissions as part of crisis prevention where appropriate;

---

[79] Draft Mental Health Bill 2004, clause 9(7)

[80] *ibid.* clause 46(6).

[81] *ibid.*, clause 46(4)

[82] *ibid.*, clauses 48(4), 119(5), 121(3).

[83] Sainsbury Centre (2005) *Beyond the Water Towers; The unfinished revolution in mental health services 1985-2005.* London, SCMH, pages 46-7

- Therapeutic treatment and care focussed on recovery, initiating or continuing a range of therapies that will be continued in the community;

- Assertive discharge that supports community inclusion including making links to appropriate community resources and agencies; support to maintain existing positive networks and links (including with family, friends, care co-ordinator, employers etc); developing relapse prevention and coping strategies;

- One part of an integrated whole system of mental health services, linked into community services to facilitate timely admissions and early discharge.

Fig 20: the role and function of acute inpatient care (summarised from Sainsbury Centre for Mental Health *Beyond the Water Towers*)

User involvement, choice, and psychiatric compulsion

2.64   Over the last decade increasing official attention has been paid to user involvement and the service user perspective is now a recognised part of Government consultation processes over legal and policy provision in mental health. Service user perspectives are also much in evidence in work undertaken by, for example, the National Institute for Mental Health for England and, within these bodies and their networks of similarly grass-roots agencies effecting local arrangements and services, we do not doubt that service users' input is valued and valuable.

2.65   But service user involvement can still be marginalised in relation to the issues concerning psychiatric compulsion. In part, this may be because those who are identified and who self-identify by the administrative category of psychiatric 'service user' have disparate backgrounds which may not include detention, or in which detention is no longer likely (although there are, of course, activists in the various service user movements and in the MHAC for whom psychiatric compulsion remains a current or sporadic element of their experience of services), but it can also be because service users from the 'survivor' perspective may be marginalised as necessarily 'anti' compulsion *per se*, when the ultimate requirement for compulsion of some sort is assumed within the context of debates between Government and professional bodies. These are matters that can be overcome, firstly through care not to homogenise an imposed category of 'service user' into a single imaginary whole, any element of which can stand as the token for patients' perspectives; and secondly by not allowing different core assumptions about service provision to preclude dialogue over details.

> 'At first I felt totally crushed and disempowered and got a strong message that I had no voice. Gradually I won back little bits of autonomy, even big bits sometimes, but often still with a sense that this was illegitimate defiance'.
>
> *Emma Laughton, ex-s.2 patient, Devon*

2.66   A greater threat to service user involvement in public policy on psychiatric services involving compulsion may, in some senses, stem from the very success that the service user 'movement' has had in becoming recognised as a part of the policy machinery of Government. The main emphasis in 'user involvement' since the 1990s has been closely tied to 'the parallel shift to the market in welfare, with new emphasis on the 'welfare consumer', 'user-centred services' and 'needs-led provision" [84]. It is a glib response to mental health service user demands for involvement to address them as any if they were simply another consumer group, especially when compulsory powers are in play that may preclude choice over engagement with services; where patient decisions over the timing and type of intervention may be overridden; and where the choice agenda itself does not reflect the needs of patients subject to compulsory powers (see paragraphs 2.67 *et seq* below).

Mental Health Act Commission Service User Reference Panel

The Mental Health Act Commission is committed to involving service users who have had experience of detention under the Act in its work.

In 2005, we set up the Mental Health Act Commission Service User Reference Panel (SURP) as an important part of our service user involvement strategy. The SURP, which is led by a service user member of the MHAC Board, has been widely publicised through service user organisations; our website; and outreach work by Commissioners, generating a large and very positive response from service users. Twenty-four service users have so far been appointed to the SURP, on the basis of their experience of detention and using mental health services. The panel is diverse, including men and women from different ethnic backgrounds, covering all age groups from all over England and Wales. All members of the panel are either currently detained, or have recent experience of detention, but their experience encompasses a range of different mental health sectors and sections of the Act.

The panel's main brief is:

- To provide the Commission with a service user perspective on all aspects of its current and planned activity;

- To influence the Commission's work programme, including advising and commenting on visiting priorities, development work, and publications;

- To advise on how the Commission can involve users meaningfully and effectively in its work.

The emphasis on the experience of detention is a unique aspect of the Commission SURP. As some of the members are currently detained, most of the panel's input is facilitated 'remotely' – by post, telephone and email. Panel members' first activity has been to give their views on how they would like the panel to work and on what constitutes good service user involvement: our SURP terms of reference are being amended to reflect its members' views, which will help to shape the MHAC service user involvement strategy more generally. The SURP has also contributed to this report, with members giving a service user view on many of the issues covered in the report and providing 'vignettes' from personal experience.

For further information on the MHAC Service User Reference Panel please visit the service user involvement page on our website at www.mhac.org.uk or contact Rose Sibley on 0115 9437111.

Fig 21: the MHAC service user reference panel

---

[84] Beresford P (1997) 'The Last Social Division? Revisiting the Relationship Between Social Policy, Its Producers and Consumers' in May M, Brunsdon E & Craig G (eds) *Social Policy Review* 9, Social Policy Association, London Guildhall University.

The scope for choice within a framework of compulsion

2.67 The 'choice' agenda currently promoted by Government has yet to show any meaningful engagement with issues of compulsion. In the absence of such engagement, patients subject to compulsion risk being further marginalised through the 'choice' agenda, and there must be a danger of a two-tier health service, with patients who are clinically or legally disabled from exercising choice being compelled towards services that are rejected by patients who have the opportunity to choose. In this way "one patient's choice may deny another patient's treatment"[85]. Patients subject to compulsion may be particularly disadvantaged in any system where there is competition for access to services. It is conceivable that patients who are subject to compulsory powers, who will by definition require some sort of healthcare intervention and will often be in crisis, will have to accept whatever services are available, which may mean those that are 'left-over' from elective service uptake. Something like this may already be at work in admissions to many acute wards in areas where community teams operate to prevent hospital admission except as a last resort (see also paragraph 2.90 *et seq* below).

2.68 We are also concerned that the language of choice and patient involvement is not used to mask the realities of patients' experience of coercion. There already exists a range of psychiatric patients who, although not formally subject to the powers of the Mental Health Act 1983, are subject to *de facto* coercion and constraints, and we discuss these at Chapter 3.18. The decision of *HL v United Kingdom* (Chapter 1.1 -19 above) has now made it imperative to ensure that compulsion amounting to deprivation of liberty is acknowledged and that safeguards are provided for patients who are compelled to engage with services. Patients whose choices are limited by circumstance or by imposed legal powers are not served by a lack of formal recognition of their situation[86]. There already exists in some services a tendency to use euphemisms for specific areas of compulsion (such as the rebranding, in some services, of 'control and restraint' as 'care and responsibility', or 'seclusion' as 'nursing in isolation' etc, discussed further at Chapter 4.230 below). In the Commission's view, patients' rights are poorly served, and patients are not respected, by any system that does not acknowledge its coercive aspects.

2.69 We do, however, believe that it is possible and desirable to promote patient choice, even within a framework of compulsory hospital admission and treatment. Many services are already establishing strong user involvement components in their day-to-day practice and at other levels of their organisations, but there remain a considerable number who report little progress in this area[87].

---

[85] 'There is an irreconcilable conflict – in the context of a fixed health care budget – between allowing individual patients unconstrained choice of treatments that are free at the point of consumption, and the allocation of resources in a cost-effective manner. Individuals may choose treatments that are the most effective (and that best meet their preferences) but not the most cost-effective (or that reflect the preferences of society as a whole) – with corresponding opportunity costs in terms of health gain foregone by other patients. One patient's choice may deny another patient's treatment.' Appleby, J., Harrison, A. & Devlin N. (2003) *What is the Real Cost of More Patient Choice?* London: King's Fund. June 2003, page 3

[86] See MHAC (2003) *Tenth Biennial Report: Placed Amongst Strangers.* Chapters 1.7, 8.1–5 & 15.9.

[87] MHAC (2003) *Tenth Biennial Report: Placed Amongst Strangers* Chapter 9.6– 9.8.

Patients on a hospital ward in Sussex complained to a visiting Commissioner that, in anticipation of negative local media coverage of an incident on their ward, their television had been removed from the ward by staff. When the Commission challenged the hospital management over their action, we were told that the decision to remove the television had been taken to avoid further distress to patients on the ward after a previous critical TV report had caused 'very significant' distress to patients who knew the patient concerned. We were not satisfied by this explanation, and pointed out that the decision to remove the patients' television was difficult to reconcile with the principles of promoting patients' autonomy, recognising their preferences insofar as is possible and personalising services around their needs. The action of removing the television had distressed those patients who had complained to us. We suggested that a less disempowering intervention would have been for staff to inform patients of the possibly distressing content of the programme and offered them the option of not watching it.

Fig 22: practice example - reducing patients' autonomy

2.70   Within the framework of compulsion there is opportunity for individually tailored consensual practice. The 1983 Act recognises explicitly that patients may consent to specific treatment whilst detained in hospital under its powers, and requires medical staff to engage with detained patients on questions of consent to treatment with ECT and/or medication for mental disorder[88]. Almost all other aspects of care and treatment in hospital are subsumed under the general power of detention[89], and detained patients may therefore be denied autonomy over much of their day-to-day experience in hospital. But the principles of the Care Programme Approach (CPA) should ensure that, even in the absence of any legal requirement to defer to detained patients' wishes, there is still scope for choice and ways of enabling choice to happen.

2.71   The practical reality of bed-provision in acute mental health units, and the great difficulties experienced by doctors in identifying available beds for patients in need of compulsory admission, suggest that there may be insurmountable practical difficulties in enabling patients' choices between hospitals in acute mental health care. However, although most mental health service users who are detained under the Act are detained at a point of crisis in the management of their condition, for all but first-time admissions it may be

'Most places I have been the decisions affecting the hospital are left up to staff'

Dawn Cutler, (ex-ss.3, 37, 47), Cheshire

---

[88]   See MHA 1983, s.58, and Code of Practice Chapters 15 & 16. Detained patients may consent to their medical treatment and have that consent certified by their doctor. Non-consenting detained patients may not be treated with medication for more than three months or ECT at any time, except for in an emergency, unless a Second Opinion Appointed Doctor has certified that the treatment should be given notwithstanding the absence of consent. We were concerned that proposals under the draft Mental Health Bill of 2004 apparently excluded such issues of treatment under consent from its statutory framework on the assumption that consenting to treatment was a matter for the common law. We await the revised proposals in light of our criticisms, and those of the Joint Parliamentary Committee on the draft Bill, with interest.

[89]   In particular, under the broad powers of the Mental Health Act 1983, s.63 (as defined by s.145 and subsequent case law), which allow that the consent of any detained patients is not required for any aspect of nursing care, habilitation or rehabilitation given under medical supervision.

possible to plan for the eventuality of such crises. Patients' care-plans under the Care Programme Approach (see below) are supposed to anticipate crises, and should take account of patients' preferences in interventions. If care plans can specify actions on the part of the patient or services that will intervene in the early stages of any crisis and possibly avert it, the need to override the patient's choices for care through compulsory admission may be avoided altogether. Effective choice in the community could obviate many compulsory admissions.

2.72   The infringement of personal liberty involved in the compulsory admission of a patient to hospital under the 1983 Act must, to be compatible with human rights requirements, be justifiable as necessary in that patient's best interests. We have suggested that one of the factors influencing the use of formal detention under the 1983 Act may be the need to engage patients with services that they view with hostility or fear due to inadequacies of provision[90] (see introduction, para iii and Chapter 4.4 below). It is difficult to reconcile such use of compulsory powers with human rights requirements, and the need to address ill-suited or substandard therapeutic environments or care provision is therefore a requirement of the fundamental legality of psychiatric provision under compulsion. In addition, however, an emphasis on providing basically acceptable inpatient mental health units across the whole service sector would address many aspects encompassed within the wider focus of Government in introducing 'patient choice' as a motor for quality development, as outlined in 2003 by the Secretary of State (see paragraph 2.40 above). Exercising a choice to avoid admission to substandard facilities may not be to exercise free choice at all, but to be forced into making a choice for want of reasonable alternative. In such circumstances, use of the language of 'choice' is inappropriate and disingenuous.

> 'Often you find yourself "second guessing" what the care plan is – the reasons why some things are being done. Often feel as though you don't have much choice i.e. you are officially informal but if you want to leave you will be sectioned. This is often very intimidating and leaves you confused as to what your rights are or where you stand'.
>
> *anonymous patient quoted in Healthcare Commission (2005) The National Audit of Violence*[91].

2.73   Once detained, the Mental Health Act Code of Practice requires that patients are treated according to a set of basic guiding principles, central to which are allowing patients the greatest possible degree of self-determination and responsibility, respecting diversity and treating patients in the least controlled and segregated facilities that are practicable for therapeutic and safety purposes. These principles should be reflected in patients' care plans, which should have been drawn up with the involvement of the patient concerned.

2.74   To make inpatient environments 'homely', patients should be provided with as much opportunity as possible to exercise choice over diet and activities, and be enabled to fulfil their religious and spiritual needs, by an appropriate range of options being available.

---

[90]   see MHAC (2001) *Ninth Biennial Report 1999-01*, Chapter 3.1-2, and MHAC (2003) *Tenth Biennial Report: Placed Amongst Strangers*, Chapter 8.27.

[91]   Healthcare Commission (2005) *National Audit of Violence (2003-2005) Final Report*. Royal College of Psychiatrists' Research Unit / Healthcare Commission. p.37. www.healthcarecommission.org.uk.

> **Recommendation 6:** Government should own and promote policy guidance on promoting patient autonomy and choice in the context of psychiatric compulsion.

Choice of care and treatment options: the potential role of the CPA

2.75   The Care Programme Approach (CPA) provides an existing mechanism for patient engagement and choice in mental health services extending to patients who are subject to the Mental Health Act. The CPA has now been operative for over a decade and was last updated in 2000. The principles of CPA, which are based around the provision of an individualised, patient-centred care package, should already provide patients with a real say in their treatment and care by mental health services. It is likely that those service providers who operate CPA successfully will feel that they already engage with patient's choices about care within restrictions set by the law and best practice. However, effective implementation of the CPA is far from universal[92]. Central to effective use of CPA is the individual tailoring of care plans to patients' needs and wishes. Commissioners report that patients often feel that their care plan could apply to anyone and is not personal to them. In part, achieving truly personalised services may depend on challenging stigma and stereotypes about mental illness amongst medical and nursing staff, so that patients are recognised as individuals, and not simply categorised by legal status or diagnosis[93]. The widespread and effective implementation of the CPA across all psychiatric services would go some way towards implementing the suggestions that we make below.

> 'Care plans are pre-written and you are expected to 'read and sign' – no consultation with what's in the care plans.'
>
> *Trevor Howard, s.37/41 patient, Nottinghamshire*

> 'I was given no opportunity to contribute to the planning of my care. In fact, I was threatened with a renewal of my section if I didn't accept my care plan. Ward planning weekly meetings were held but they were ineffective.'
>
> *male s.3 patient, Middlesex*

> 'I was not consulted on decisions about my care plan'
>
> *male s.3 patient, London*

2.76   The effective use of the CPA process is crucial to enabling patients to operate choice in relation to care and treatment options. Without the involvement of the patient in drawing up his or her care plan, and without that patient having a physical copy of the care plan to refer to, CPA cannot work effectively in enabling patients to partner services in the management of their conditions. As discussed in relation to the report *Back on Track?* below, many patients encountered by Commissioners do not know the details of their plan, appear not to be involved in its ongoing development and do not have a copy of it[94].

---

[92]   See MHAC (2001) *Ninth Biennial Report 1999-01*, Chapters 2.68-2.73 & 4.62-3; and MHAC (2003) *Tenth Biennial Report: Placed Amongst Strangers*, Chapter 9.1-3.

[93]   See North East London Strategic Health Authority (2003) *Report of an Independent Inquiry into the Care and Treatment of Daksha Emson M.B.B.S., MRCPsych, MSc. and her Daughter Freya.* October 2003, Recommendation 1: Stigma, pages v, 23-4. www.nelondon.nhs.uk.

[94]   See also Rose D (2001) *Users Voices: The Perspectives of Mental Health Service Users on Community & Hospital Care.* London: Sainsbury Centre for Mental Health.

2.77 The following areas are those where collaborative CPA planning could engage with patients and set out preferences and choices for an individually-tailored care plan:

(i) It is already a legal requirement on professionals to provide detained patients with sufficient information about proposed medical treatment so that they can make an informed choice over giving or withholding their consent[95]. In practice, many patients do not receive adequate information, or do not receive it in useable form, to engage fully in this process. Information should encompass side-effects, alternatives and the likely consequences of not giving the treatment.

(ii) Patients often express concern that professionals do not take their abilities and strengths into account when planning treatment[96]. An effective CPA process would recognise that all patients are 'experts' and would seek to encourage and develop self-management.

(iii) Services should seek to engage with and make available to patients user-led and peer support services (e.g. Hearing Voices groups, self-help groups). This should include approaches from within Black and minority ethnic cultures and communities where possible.

(iv) Patients frequently complain to Mental Health Act Commissioners that insufficient 'talking treatments' and occupational therapies are available, and that consequently their choices of treatment are constrained.

(v) Actions to be taken to manage behaviour on the ward at times of crisis (i.e. relating to restraint, seclusion and sedative medication) can be negotiated with patients. Some units have successfully negotiated planned responses to risk behaviour with patients on an individual basis, so that professionals are aware of patients' preferences in their management, and patients are less disturbed by action taken by staff if their acting out is presenting a risk to themselves or others.

(vi) Physical health needs, such as women's/men's health; dentists; physiotherapy; 'weight-watchers'; diabetes management, smoking cessation etc, are frequently not met for patients detained in mental health units (see Chapter 4.86 *et seq* below).

(vii) Effective discharge planning must be timely, involve patients (and carers/family), encompass crisis planning, and address vocational/educational needs.

2.78 In this reporting period, we collaborated with the Sainsbury Centre for Mental Health over a project aimed to:

- examine and describe the quality of CPA care planning for patients who were detained at the time of the survey, and had been admitted under detention on another occasion in the previous three years;

- assess the factors that contribute to the best quality of care and the most effective care planning for these service users, and

- develop a tool for use in monitoring, assessing and evaluating care planning.

The project was carried out through an examination of CPA care plans and case notes, and interviews with service users.

---

95 Section 58(3)(a) of the 1983 Act implies such a duty in respect of medication for mental disorder or ECT, in that consent for such treatment must be certified to be based upon an understanding of the nature, purpose and likely effect of treatment. More specific requirements covering the wider definition of medical treatment are provided by Chapters 15 and 16 of the Code of Practice.

96 Rose D (2001) *Users Voices: The Perspectives of Mental Health Service Users on Community & Hospital Care.* London: Sainsbury Centre for Mental Health.

2.79 The project report *Back on Track? CPA care planning for service users who are repeatedly detained under the Mental Health Act*[97] was published in June 2005. The key findings and recommendations are shown below and on pages 148 and 149.

Back on Track? – summary findings and recommendations

This joint project between the MHAC and SCMH aimed to examine and describe the quality of CPA care planning for people who had been detained under the Act more than once in a three year period. Mental Health Act Commissioners, as part of their normal visiting programme, visited 119 wards in 57 units within 15 NHS Trusts, drawn from all eight National Institute for Mental Health in England (NIMHE) regions. Information was collected from the case notes of 277 service users, 151 of whom were also interviewed.

Ensuring equitable service delivery

Ethnicity was not recorded for all the service users whose case notes we examined. We also found some statistically significant differences between the way different groups of service users had their needs assessed, their care planned, and help provided after discharge from hospital. Service users in Black and Asian groups had fewer needs assessed and planned for than those in White groups. Similarly, people over 40 did less well than younger people, and those whose previous admission had been on an assessment section of the Act had fewer needs assessed or met than those who had been on a treatment section. Women service users reported having fewer needs met after discharge from hospital than did the men. Having identified 17 areas of an individual's functioning which should be assessed as part of CPA care planning, based on the key documents and examples of good practice nationally, we found that not all types of needs were equally well assessed and planned for.

Recommendations:

1. NHS Trusts should record the ethnicity of all service users, in order to ensure that the services planned and delivered meet service users' cultural needs and to avoid inequalities in the delivery of care.

2. Regular monitoring should enable NHS Trusts to assess whether some groups of service users – e.g. those of different gender, age, and ethnicity – are being treated less equitably than others. Where such inequities are detected, they should be addressed.

3. Service providers should ensure that aftercare services are provided equitably to men and women, and to people who were admitted on all assessment and treatment Sections of the Mental Health Act.

Information sharing

In some instances, case notes were difficult or impossible for Commissioners to find. Two thirds of the service users had a copy of the CPA care plan relating to their previous discharge from hospital in their inpatient notes. Few wards had access to an electronic CPA system.

---

[97] Sainsbury Centre for Mental Health (2005) *Back on Track? CPA care planning for service users who are repeatedly detained under the Mental Health Act.* Published in association with the Mental Health Act Commission. Available @ £10 plus 10% p&p from SCMH publications on 020 7827 8352 or www.scmh.org.uk.

Recommendations:

4.   Local systems should ensure that case notes are securely stored and easy to access, so that information on previous care planning and interventions delivered is available to contribute to current care planning.

5. Local systems should ensure that CPA care plans are shared between hospital and community services, and with other service providers who are involved in an individual's care. Effective liaison when planning service users' aftercare may reduce the number of readmissions within 90 days.

6. Electronic CPA systems should be fully implemented in each NHS Trust to enable crucial information to be easily shared between staff across hospital and community sites, and between disciplines, and so facilitate coordinated planning and delivery of care.

Inpatient care

At the time of their current admission, most service users were described in their case notes as being either a danger to themselves or to other people. More than half were said to be non-compliant with treatment in the community. In a small number of cases, non-compliance was the only recorded reason for their compulsory admission. Over 40% of the service user interviewees were generally positive about being in hospital, while a similar number had negative feelings about their admission, reiterating concerns identified in other national studies.

Recommendations:

7.   NHS Trusts should ensure that the criteria for compulsory admission are correctly applied.

8. Managers of acute inpatient care should ensure that an adequate range of therapeutic activities is provided, along with social and recreational occupation, especially for detained patients who are unable to leave the ward.

9. All inpatients should be on the enhanced level of CPA, and this should be recorded in their notes.

10.   Copies of CPA care plans relating to service users' previous discharges from hospital should be kept in their inpatient notes to facilitate continuity of care.

Discharge planning and provision of aftercare

Gaps were identified in the CPA information recorded in some service users' case notes. The CPA level was recorded for less than two thirds of the service users, and the date of the next CPA review was recorded in just over half the care plans. The CPA Care Co-ordinator was recorded as attending the post-discharge CPA review in a third of cases, and a fifth of service user interviewees said their Care Coordinator was involved in drawing up their care plan. A fifth of the service users were readmitted to hospital within 90 days, with seven people being readmitted within two weeks of their previous discharge. Readmissions within 90 days were found in 14 of the 15 Trusts visited. In terms of the care provided after their previous discharge from hospital, not all groups of needs were equally well met. Some groups of service users had their needs less well met than others. The Care Co-ordinator should have face to face contact with the service user within a week of discharge from hospital, as evidence shows this is a crucial time period in order to minimise suicide, self harm and readmission. 60% of interviewees said they had been seen by a mental health worker in that time.

Recommendations:

11.   The date of the next CPA review should be recorded in service users' case notes before they are discharged from hospital.

12.   The CPA Care Co-ordinator should take the lead in drawing up service users' care plans, and should attend the CPA review meetings.

13.   CPA assessment and care planning should be comprehensive, with all needs included. Individuals' cultural and spiritual needs, at present rarely assessed and planned for, should be included in CPA care planning.

14.   Timely discharge planning should enable appropriate community-based services – including housing, financial and occupational – to be arranged so that service users can be discharged as soon as their clinical need for inpatient care has ended.

15.   Local systems should ensure that community services have face to face contact with all formerly detained patients within a week of their discharge from hospital.

16.   Having a comprehensive CPA care plan is not an end in itself. Services should ensure that the interventions specified in the care plan are actually delivered to the service user.

Involving service users in the CPA

A quarter of the service users interviewed said they knew a lot about the CPA while almost half said they had heard of it. A quarter of the interviewees said they had been involved in drawing up their CPA care plan at the time of their last discharge from hospital, and a third remembered being given a written copy of it. It was recorded that a third of the service users had signed their CPA care plan, and a fifth had been given a copy of it.

Recommendations:

17. Service users should be informed about the CPA, and fully involved in drawing up their care plans and participating in CPA reviews, with access to an independent advocate if they request this. Their own assessment of their strengths and needs, as 'experts by experience', should inform the care planning process. They should be asked to sign their care plan, and be given a written copy of it.

Conclusions

The study found some examples of good practice, and identified areas in which Trusts need to do much more to ensure the CPA is effectively implemented – particularly, though not exclusively – for service users who are repeatedly admitted compulsorily and have a range of complex needs. Effective use of the CPA, the single care coordination approach for adults of working age with mental health needs, has the potential to make a big difference to improving the lives of service users.

Choice of professional workers

2.80 Patients who are made subject to compulsory powers may have had difficult relationships with medical professionals in the past, and may, for example, have experience of changing their GP. We receive numerous requests for advice from patients about how, once detained in hospital, they can go about changing their doctor, or be assigned to a different key-worker. We advise that all patients have a right to ask for such a change, but that patients who are subject to compulsory treatment under the care of particular staff cannot expect of right to remove themselves from the care of such staff.

2.81 Many requests to change doctors or key-workers may be motivated by resentment at the role of those professionals in compulsion, rather than in their respective personal abilities or approaches. As such, the change of consultant or other professional may not resolve a patient's concerns. However, some patients will have other reasons for preferring a particular professional over another (such as previous treatment history), and the fact of detention need not prevent such preferences being respected where it is practically possible to do so. The Commission has stated that hospital managers should treat with respect all patients' requests to change professionals and give clear reasons why the request cannot or will not be met where this is the case[98]. It is important that mechanisms ensure that there are no deleterious repercussions for patients who request a change of doctor or other professional involved in their care.

2.82 Patients' relationships with professionals will not be nurtured where there are staffing shortages, or where the staffing composition and skill-mix does not meet the profile of patients detained on the ward in terms of culture, gender etc. Managers should seek to ensure that staffing of wards reflect, as far as possible, the profile of patients. Similarly, specialist medical staff (old-age psychiatry, CAMHS etc) should be engaged with patients falling within specialist categories. By addressing these issues, services may avoid placing patients in the position of needing to exercise 'choice' in an attempt to obtain adequate services to meet their needs.

2.83 If detained patients were extended a true choice in their doctor, this could require a number of structural changes to the service. For instance, present Government policy advises that each acute adult inpatient ward should have a dedicated lead consultant psychiatrist, who would be responsible for each patient on that ward[99]. This requirement is not met by some current arrangements, where a number of psychiatrists, each with responsibilities in community provision, may share authority in a ward. Such existing structures (which are not universal) appear more flexible and able to respond to patient choice than arrangements suggested under the Government's good practice requirement. Existing flexible structures can allow for continuity of care unaffected by alternate periods of inpatient and community treatment, and could help to maintain clinical relationships that work (similarly, outreach teams should be encouraged to visit patients who are detained in hospital to take part in

---

[98] This position has been taken in response to individual queries and is outlined in MHAC (2003) *Tenth Biennial Report: Placed Amongst Strangers,* Chapter 9.28.

[99] Department of Health (2002) *Mental Health Policy Implementation Guide: Acute Adult Inpatient Care Provison.* p.32-4.

their discharge planning). The fixed allocation of consultants to wards could, therefore, provide a bureaucratic obstacle to patient choice. It is possible that similar tensions will occur throughout mental health services between the economic and workforce need to rationalise service provision and the maintenance of sufficient flexibility to meet the demands of patients empowered to choose modes of treatment.

Choices in social care

2.84   Under s.117 of the 1983 Act, health and social services authorities share responsibilities for providing and funding such aftercare needs as a detained patient is jointly assessed to require upon discharge from hospital. Many patients who receive such aftercare services may be ineligible for direct payments under present arrangements, although we know of no blanket restriction. There is a potential broad scope for patient choice to be exercised in aftercare provision, and we do not doubt that much current aftercare planning seeks to involve patients in decision-making as far as possible. The most likely limitations on patient choice are not professionals' attitudes, but the availability of alternative options to the aftercare services in use. Voluntary organisations have an important role both in hospital and community, but provision overall can be patchy and often under-resourced.

2.85   We discuss Government plans to introduce means-testing for services provided after six weeks of a patients from discharge under proposed legislation at Chapter 4.131 *et seq* below.

Areas of support required by patients to exercise choice
- Provider policies that support user and carer involvement[100].
- Effective use of the Care Programme Approach, by staff who are committed to patient involvement.
- Advocacy.
- User-led groups and service user councils.
- Opportunities for patients to comment on ward environment, administration etc, through ward community meetings, questionnaires or suggestion boxes.
- Links with self-help groups and cultural organisations.
- Ensuring that mental health is not marginalised within Public and Patient Involvement Forums.
- Information and support to make complaints or raise concerns - advocacy, PALS, legal representation, the Mental Health Act Commission and its successor body.
- A copy of an individualised care plan produced through effective CPA practice.
- Access to other health care records, including copies of letters between professionals

---

[100]   NIMHE have published a summary of available research on user involvement: Department of Health (2003) *Cases for Change: User Involvement*. Leeds: National Institute for Mental Health in England. www.nimhe.org.uk.

- Information on the range of available treatments, their effectiveness, adverse effects etc.

- Information (through discussion and support etc) on 'how to make a choice' – how to weigh options (e.g. quality of life v. impact of treatment), etc.

- When to make a choice – understanding the system of compulsion and its limitations on choices for detained patients.

- Information required to be given under s.132, Mental Health Act 1983: covering a detained patient's legal situation, rights of appeal, existence of the MHAC and Code of Practice. This information should be repeated and reinforced if required.

- Access to a copy of the Code of Practice.

- Access to the internet.

- Information on standards - what service users can expect from a service, treatment or therapy.

Fig 23: areas of support required by patients to exercise choice

2.86 There does need to be a change in culture for mental health services operating compulsion to become truly patient-centred. We are encouraged by the National Institute for Mental Health in England's promotion of Values-Based Practice, and by the issue of training material under the tutelage of NIMHE National Fellow for Values-Based Practice, Professor K W M Fulford[101]. Values-Based Practice can be a complementary counter-balance to Evidence-Based Practice through refocusing decision-making on patient-centered approaches, fostering collaboration between patients and professionals and overcoming some of the difficulties and tensions inherent in focussing on patient choice within a framework of compulsion. Specifically in relation to compulsion, Values-Based Practice shifts the emphasis in decision-making from (a negative) denial of patients' values to (a positive) balancing of patients' current values against their own future values and the values of others.

2.87 With such a refocus, existing mechanisms (e.g. clinical governance, accountable care, quality standards, service development) can be used to develop a culture of patient involvement. These do need to be reinforced by the recognition and resourcing of user-led groups and user involvement in commissioning and monitoring services, and in staff-training.

> **Recommendation 7:** Service users and ex-service users (and their carers) should be encouraged to apply for both dedicated and generic posts within hospital staffing.

---

[101] see NIMHE Values Framework at www.connects.org.uk/conferences; MHAC (2003) *Tenth Biennial Report: Placed Amongst Strangers*, Chapter 5; Woodbridge K & Fulford, KWM 'Right, Wrong & Respect' *Mental Health Today* Sept 2004 28-30; Woodbridge K & Fulford KWM (2004) *Whose values? A workbook for values-based practice in mental health care.* Sainsbury Centre for Mental Health (SCMH); NIMHE /SCMH joint workforce support unit *Ten shared capabilities: a framework and list of the ten essential shared capabilities for the whole of the mental health workforce.* SCMH, 2004.

Payment by results

2.88 Payment by Results (PbR) is planned to be operational across all health services by 2008. Government has accepted that it has proved difficult to adapt the systems of PbR to mental health services[102]. The Sainsbury Centre for Mental Health stated in December 2004 that 'a workable system of payment by results [in mental health] is still some way off. Reasons include the long-term and often episodic nature of mental health problems, the diversity of services and the wide range of factors in addition to diagnosis that influence the costs of care'[103].

2.89 The National PbR Expert Reference Group is reported to be considering 'a case-managed model where funding is provided on a capitation basis', with 'tariffs based upon projected resource consumption for a given population' and 'unit costs… defined in terms of social outcomes not volume of intervention'. However this might signal that the final PbR model for mental health services may differ from that applied to other aspects of NHS provision, the political aims are identical:

> The emerging models for the application of payment by results in mental health services… demonstrate that in future financial flows for the provision of services will increasingly be defined by the choices people make in accessing services.[104]

Whilst we take no position on the overall advantages or disadvantages of PbR systems, we recognise the concerns expressed by the Sainsbury Centre that the potential benefits of PbR over block-budgeting arrangements come with considerable risks to services, including potential for perverse incentives that may distort service priorities or undermine the proper implementation of the Care Programme Approach[105]. We have noted increasing concern amongst some mental health professionals that PbR will provide a financial disincentive to inpatient treatment that may override the clinical needs of patients, by reinforcing existing financial pressures for the discharge of patients shortly after their admission whether or not they are ready to leave hospital.

Contestability

2.90 Government has suggested that 'combined with payment systems which allow money to follow the patient, contestability can provide incentives for greater organisational efficiency and greater responsiveness'[106]. In our discussion at paragraph 2.67 above we have pointed to the danger that patients who are compelled through mental health legislation to engage

---

[102] In particular, Government has had 'limited success' in modelling PbR based upon models involving health resource groups (HRGs), or groupings of individual cases that are clinically similar and require similar amounts of resources for their treatment. See *Care Services Improvement Partnership Choices Checklist, step 4*, p.2-3, 2005 (www.doh.gov.uk). See also Department of Health (2002) *Reforming NHS Financial Flows: Introducing Payment by Results*; (2003) *Payment by Results: Preparing for 2005*.

[103] Sainsbury Centre for Mental Health (2004) *Policy Paper 4 Payment by Results: what does it mean for mental health?* p.1

[104] Care Services Improvement Partnership *Choices Checklist*, step 4, p.2. 2005

[105] see Sainsbury Centre for Mental Health (2004) *supra*, p.14

[106] Department of Health (2003) *Fair for all personal to you. Choice, responsiveness and equity in the NHS and social care. A National Consultation*. London: DoH. page 15

with services may be disadvantaged in a market environment because of the limitations placed upon their ability to pick and choose services.

2.91 It is conceivable that whole areas of mental health services could be disadvantaged by a process similar to that described by the health economists writing for the King's Fund in June 2003:

> ... hospitals that lose patients to other establishments because of patient choice could face a spiral of financial decline. Such hospitals might then have difficulty in responding to the 'market signals' of patient choice, resulting in poorer services for those patients remaining with their 'home' hospital – and a consequent widening of inequality[107].

As mental health services develop into a wider range of structures, with increasing emphasis placed on community-based assertive outreach interventions, the remaining acute inpatient wards could be caught in a cycle of decline.

2.92 We have noted some examples of decline in acute inpatient units as service managers focus on alternative services. For example, one pioneering service in the field of community care in the 1990s did experience a marked decline in its remaining inpatient units' environment and practice in administering inpatient care and treatment. In this particular example, service managers were responsive to our concerns and sought to address the situation by reallocating resources. There is a danger that in a system where direct payments follow patients, such reallocation may not be possible, or will serve as an incentive to allocate patients whose choices can be limited under mental health legislation into such services to continue their funding.

2.93 Any funding system, or system involving patient choice in uptake of mental health services, must therefore have some mechanism to guard against perverse incentives to allocate patients subject to compulsion to failing units and wards. This may involve additional investment for extra capacity in the system, so that choice of services for some is not given at the expense of services for others. This suggests that whatever organisational efficiency is encouraged in the field of, for example, community-based services, cost savings across mental health services overall which are driven by patient choice and resulting 'contestability' could only be achieved by reducing services to patients.

2.94 However, the 'choices' that may be enabled through building on existing opportunities and emerging structures for patient involvement and partnership (such as the CPA, patient-centred approaches and Value-Based Practice) have little potential for increasing inequity of provision other than through uneven development of services and consequent geographic variation in patient experience of mental health services. Such inequalities can best be addressed through strong policy initiatives, sharing good practice and mentoring less successful services, as exemplified by the Government's programme relating to *Delivering Race Equality*.

---

[107] Appleby, J., Harrison, A. & Devlin N. (2003) *What is the Real Cost of More Patient Choice?* London: King's Fund. June 2003, page 33.

Stigma

'The paradoxical thing is that stigma, while often totally overt, can also be both very hidden and yet still very obvious. Stigma feeds paranoia because people often try to hide it. When applying for jobs now you know that they know that they can't express discriminatory attitudes – so it will be almost impossible to be sure that you have a straight view of why you've been rejected. On the other hand, people can be laughably naïve in thinking that they can simply assure you that they are not at all prejudiced. They forget that you started out in life with all the cultural assumptions and typical discriminatory attitudes, so you know them very well; in order to survive you have had to wake up and question everything'.

Emma Laughton, ex-s.2 patient, Devon

2.95 The reduction of stigma and discrimination against people with mental health problems is part of the first standard to be implemented under the National Service Framework for Mental Health. In this reporting period we have seen continued work in health promotion and anti-stigma interventions, such as the Department of Health's *Mindout for Mental Health* campaign, which ended in March 2004, followed by the launch in June 2004 of the National Institute for Mental Health (England) (NIMHE) five-year plan to tackle stigma and discrimination on grounds of mental health, entitled *From Here to Equality*. This programme will include training for people with mental health problems to engage with the media and a 'media alert system' for people to give positive and negative feedback to journalists and their regulatory bodies. We hope that every effort will be made to involve issues concerning psychiatric detention in this work, and so to help dispel some of the myths concerning why compulsion may be used. The Commission is regularly approached by journalists covering news stories or by television producers involved in the dramatisation of fictional events involving the use of Mental Health Act powers, and we have been pleased to give contextual or technical advice.

''Friends' now walk on the other side of road. 'Friends' don't know how to talk to me. People are scared of me.'

Yasmin Jackson, ex-s.3 patient, Wales

2.96 Our own experiences as mental health professionals and/or service users confirm the observation of Richard Brook, Chief Executive of Mind, that 'widespread prejudices – from being denied insurance to being shunned by neighbours – have a massive negative effect on people's quality of life'[108]. This has been the position for many years[109]. The Government's Social Exclusion Unit report *Mental Health and Social Exclusion* suggested that 'stigma and discrimination can have a greater impact on people's lives than the mental health problems themselves'[110]. We believe that this may be true even of the more severe mental illnesses that can lead to the use of Mental Health Act powers.

---

[108] John Carvel 'Stigma of mental illness 'ruins lives'' *The Guardian* 14 June 2004

[109] See Campbell T.D. & Heginbotham C.J. (1991) *Mental Illness: Prejudice, Discrimination and the Law.* Aldershot: Gower.

[110] Social Exclusion Unit (2004) *Mental Health and Social Exclusion.* Office of the Deputy Prime Minister, London, June 2004, p.33. See also Rethink (2003) *Just One Per Cent ; the experiences of people using mental health services:* When asked to name a single change that would improve the quality of their life 62% of service users named a non-medical change, such as more money, improved social relationships or an end to stigma and discrimination.

2.97   We commend the work leading to publication of *Mental Health and Social Exclusion*, and the action plan that it has established. However, it is of some concern that there is no guaranteed funding after the first year for implementation of its wide-ranging recommendations[111], and we note the criticisms of Citizens Advice that the report side-stepped issues regarding problems faced by people with mental health problems in dealing with the benefits system and handling consumer affairs[112]. Citizens Advice have pointed to an example during this reporting period where a Benefits Agency decision to stop incapacity benefit after many years, and against medical evidence of unfitness to work, precipitated a relapse and admission under s.2 of the Act to a service user in Berkshire. Given the way in which mentally disordered benefits claimants may be disadvantaged by the benefits system generally, or in appealing against highly contestable decisions to stop benefits[113], we share the concerns of Citizens Advice over Government's intention to use a reduction in the number of claimants of incapacity benefit as a measurement of progress in the implementation of the Social Exclusion Unit's recommendations.

> 'My family was deeply ashamed of my section, and interrupted all contact for more than two years to the detriment of my well-being. In my housing estate an individual attempted to get me evicted ... by way of a petition'.
>
> *male s.3 patient, Middlesex*

Patients' benefits and the abolition of 'hospital downrating'.

2.98   In 2003 the Government abolished the practice of downrating state pension payments to persons who had been hospital inpatients for more than a year. In the 2005 budget, the practice of downrating other state benefits after their recipients have been in hospital for over a year was similarly abolished. The latter decision comes into effect on the 1 April 2006, after which time any patient who has been in hospital for more than a year and has had their Incapacity Benefit, Severe Disablement Allowance or Income Support downrated in consequence will have their benefits restored to the full amount. The Treasury has stated that this change is 'in recognition of the fact that individuals have many on-going fixed commitments such as housing costs and utility bills while they are in hospital'[114].

2.99   For patients under longer-term mental health care the effects of 'hospital downrating' may have perpetuated social exclusion and stigma. Unlike many other longer-term patients with an in-patient status, psychiatric patients can spend large amounts of time off hospital

---

[111]   Implementation has been tasked to the National Institute for Mental Health in England: see NIMHE (2004) *From Here to Equality: A Strategic Plan to Tackle Stigma and Discrimination on Mental Health Grounds 2004-2009.*

[112]   Lesley Cullen 'Of little benefit' *Community Care* 11-17 November 2004. See also Citizens Advice (2004) *Out of the Picture.* April 2004. www.citizensadvice.org.uk

[113]   About a third of all paper and oral appeal hearings against Incapacity Benefit decisions are decided in favour of the appellant (Dept of Work & Pensions, Quarterly Appeal Tribunal Statistics www.dwp.gov.uk/asd/qat.asp). The article by Cullen referenced above appears to overstate the appellant success rate by quoting only data from oral hearings (where nearly half of appellants are successful). In any case, it is clear that benefit decisions are highly contestable, which raises additional concerns when they are used as measures of Government policy implementation.

[114]   HM Treasury (2005) *Budget 2005 'Investing for our future: Fairness and opportunity for Britain's hard-working families' Economic and Fiscal Strategy Report and Financial Statement and Budget Report – March 2005.* HC 372. London, The Stationery Office, para 5.67.

premises (under leave arrangements if they are detained), and may therefore be particularly exposed to the effects of poverty. Current downrating of benefits can leave patients with an income of less than £16 per week. Mind's campaign against downrating highlighted the inadequacy of such provision, which denies patients opportunity to adjust to independent living and maintain dignity and self-respect[115]. The David Bennett inquiry heard how patients whose benefits were downrated did not have enough money to dress properly or lead a normal life, and how fear of losing benefits through downrating could lead informal patients to discharge themselves against medical advice, perpetuating problems of poor treatment compliance[116]. The Bennett inquiry recommended that the Government consider modifications to state benefits arrangements to ensure that psychiatric patients receive adequate financial assistance[118]. We are pleased that the Government has done so and that detained and informal patients will receive more adequate benefits from next year.

> 'My care-plan involves home visits but I can't afford to pay for a taxi'.
> 'The boredom of hospital as a long-term patient was massive. I didn't have money for activities to occupy and distract me and I think this made me more preoccupied with the treatment and my illness'
> 'Me and my fellow patients rely on nurses to cut our hair as we can't afford a proper hairdresser'
>
> *Quotes from service users about surviving on £15.90 per week* [117]

2.100   In this reporting period we have noted questions over who is responsible for providing basic needs to patients who are impoverished by reduced benefit entitlements. According to Mind, there has been a widespread failure by NHS Trusts to honour their obligations under the National Service Framework to ensure that arrangements are in place to provide good standards of privacy and dignity, such as essential clothing[119]. The Minister appears to have confirmed to Parliament that the obligations of the Care Programme Approach are such that provision of these items falls to NHS Trusts in the last instance, and that Government 'would expect the Trust to take account of the basic needs of the patient and assess these in the context of his or her wishes, the length of the hospital stay, and any other available resources'[120]. For detained patients, we would suggest that the detaining authority responsible for any patient care for under Mental Health Act powers has an unequivocal duty to ensure that the requirements of privacy and dignity are met.

---

[115]   See Mind (2004) *Why the Downrating of benefits for long-term hospital inpatients with mental health problems is wrong.* December 2004

[116]   Norfolk, Suffolk and Cambridgeshire Strategic Health Authority *Independent Inquiry into the death of David Bennett.* December 2003, p.68.

[117]   Quotes taken from Mind campaign material 'Quotes from service users about surviving on £15.90 per week', www.mind.org.uk.

[118]   *ibid.,* recommendation 18.

[119]   'patients rely on charities for new clothes as Trusts 'shirk obligations'. *Community Care,* 8 April 2004.

[120]   Hansard 29 March 2004, Col 1220W. Written answers from Ms Rosie Winterton MP in response to questions 163261/2 (Mr David Taylor MP).

Compulsory psychiatric treatment as a bar to engagement in civic responsibilities

Membership of public bodies

2.101 In our last report we discussed irrational and potentially unlawful discrimination against people who have been detained under the 1983 Act by public authorities accountable to Government[121]. We focussed upon the Department of Education and Skill's *Guides to the Law for School Governors*, which explained regulations appearing to bar any person 'liable to be detained' from serving on school governors' bodies. We highlighted the unclear meaning of the guidance, and suggested that in any case there should be no automatic bar on people who have been or are detained under the Act from taking or continuing to hold public office. Our comments have had a limited effect, in that the school governors' regulations and guidance have now been revised, although only to clarify that 'a person is disqualified from holding or continuing to hold office as a governor of a school at any time when he is detained under the Mental Health Act 1983'. We regret that there was no consultation with us on these revisions, which were made in 2004 and publicised in the Deputy Prime Minister's Social Exclusion report, as they do not go nearly far enough to remove the discriminatory aspect of these rules.

2.102 There is no reason why an episode of detention under the 1983 Act should trigger the end of an appointment to public office. Indeed, in the case of the public office of membership of Parliament itself, the law is carefully constructed so as to avoid this effect. The provisions of the 1983 Act specify that any Member of Parliament detained under its powers on the grounds of mental illness will only forfeit his or her seat after a period of six months in hospital[122]. In its proposals for the 2004 Mental Health Bill, Government suggested that there should be no automatic point at which a sitting MPs must vacate their seat upon being made subject to powers of compulsory psychiatric treatment, but that a review would be in the hands of the speaker after one year and the matter determined simply upon the basis of whether such status is likely to affect to a significant extent the member's ability to attend the legislature[123].

2.103 We fully support the proposed amendment in the 2004 Bill of the rules relating to membership of Parliament and compulsion under Mental Health Act powers. It is fitting that the test of whether a holder of public office may continue to have such status upon being made subject to compulsory mental health powers should relate solely to the question of whether such powers (which in practice should mean detention) prevent him or her from exercising the duties of that office. The law should neither make generalised assumptions about the nature of mental disorders themselves, nor apply these assumptions (which, given the broad range and effects of mental disorders that might lead to compulsion, can only be prejudices) to deterministic rules over questions of fitness for public office. It is hypocritical of Government ministers, who are themselves subject to relatively enlightened rules in this respect that will be further improved by the proposals in the Mental Health Bill, to allow

---

[121] MHAC (2003) *Tenth Biennial Report: Placed Amongst Strangers*. Chapter 6.34 *et seq.*

[122] See MHA 1983 s.141. There are no general provisions in this matter for members of the House of Lords, who do not therefore automatically forfeit their status at any point. MPs detained as suffering from psychopathic disorder would seem to be immune from removal from office altogether.

[123] See Draft Mental Health Bill 2004, clauses 294-7 and its Explanatory Notes, paragraph 490.

discriminatory rules relating to other public offices to continue, or to present minor changes to such rules that do not end their discriminatory basis as anti-discriminatory measures.

> **Recommendation 8:** School governor regulations, and any other regulations relating to fitness for public office consequent to mental health compulsion, should apply the same criteria regarding fitness for office as are applicable to Members of Parliament.

2.104 We are pleased to note intentions to consult upon the modernisation of eligibility criteria for jury service[124].

Detained patients and the right to vote

2.105 In our Ninth report we welcomed the Representation of the People Act 2000, which extended the effective franchise to some detained and informal patients resident in psychiatric hospitals through a removal of the bar on the use of a psychiatric hospital address for electoral registration purposes. Patients resident in hospital may now be entered in the electoral register giving the hospital address or any other address with which they have a 'local connection'. In this reporting period, the first to hold a General Election since the enactment of the new law, we produced a guidance note on detained patients and voting and answered many queries on the matter from patients and mental health professionals.

2.106 Alongside other legal commentators, we had not noticed prior to the election period that the 2000 Act provides that those patients detained under the Mental Health Act who may vote may *only* do so by post or proxy[125]. It would appear that it is not lawful for a detained patient to vote in person at a polling station even if given leave from hospital for this purpose. We do not know the justification for this effect of the drafting of the law, as we were neither party to its development nor consulted on its policy aim. However, in our view this legal bar is indefensible, not only on the grounds that it is unnecessarily discriminatory, but also because it is impossible to put into practice. Electoral officers, who have the final decision over eligibility to appear on an electoral register but also a responsibility to uphold the law, have no way of knowing whether voters on their register are subject to powers under the Mental Health Act, and cannot therefore prevent the technical unlawfulness of detained patients who are on the electoral register and who have practical access to polling stations casting their vote in person.

2.107 The Representation of the People Act 2000 continued the disenfranchisement of all sentenced prisoners; patients detained under Part III powers of the Mental Health Act (other than transferred remand prisoners); and patients detained under the Criminal Insanity Acts. It was noted before the passing of the 2000 Act that the law creates anomalies in voting rights for convicted offenders, in that the removal of voting rights is not

---

[124] Social Exclusion Unit (2004) *supra*, p.107.

[125] 'A person to whom section 7 of the [Representation of the People Act 1983] (mental patients who are not detained offenders) applies and who is liable, by virtue of any enactment, to be detained in the mental hospital in question; or a person to whom section 7A of that Act (persons remanded in custody) applies … may only vote by post or by proxy (where he is entitled as an elector to vote by post or, as the case may be, by proxy at the election)'. (Representation of the People Act 2000, Schedule 4, para 2(6))

determined by conviction of any criminal offence but upon the sentencing disposal subsequent to such conviction[126]. Therefore community disposals do not disenfranchise offenders, whereas custodial disposals do, even in some cases where the period of custody ends before an election takes place but after registration closes. Whilst these anomalies already extend to mentally disordered offenders who are diverted from the criminal justice system (for instance in relation to persons given hospital orders rather than psychiatric probation orders), they would have become all the more acute under proposals for the new Mental Health Act that introduce more non-residential treatment options upon conviction.

2.108 In October 2005 the European Court's judgment in *Hirst v United Kingdom No.2*[127] declared the UK's blanket disenfranchisement of convicted prisoners to be a violation of Article 3 to protocol No.1 of the Convention. It seems likely (given that the UK Government appears to be disinclined to extend the franchise to all prisoners in response to the judgment) that the Representation of the People Acts will have to be amended further to define more carefully who will be disenfranchised as the result of criminal conviction and imprisonment. For example, it may be that disenfranchisement extends only to persons serving sentences for 'the most serious offences'.[128]

2.109 We have written to Government on this issue. We consider it to be indefensible that patients detained under Criminal Procedure Insanity Act powers (see Chapter 5 below), who have by definition not been convicted of any crime, should continue to be disenfranchised. Further, given that the Government defended its disenfranchisement of prisoners to the European Court as a punitive and deterrent measure of criminal justice[129], we have questioned why such measures should be applied to patients who receive a hospital order rather than a prison disposal from the courts.

> **Recommendation 9:** The Representation of the People Act 2000 should be amended at the earliest opportunity to:
>
> - redress the violation of ECHR rights to vote in respect of detained patients, ensuring in particular that unconvicted patients and convicted patients who are not given prison sentences are not caught in any framework deigned for punitive disenfranchisement; and
>
> - ensure that all enfranchised patients who are also subject to compulsory mental health powers are legally enabled to vote in person at polling stations where their leave or care arrangements would provide practical opportunity to do so.

---

[126] Smith H & Humphreys M 'Mental disorder and voting' *Journal of Forensic Psychiatry* Vol 9 No 2 Sept 1998

[127] *Hirst v United Kingdom (No.2)* Application No. 74025/01, 6 October 2005.

[128] *ibid.*, para 49

[129] *ibid.*, paras 24, 50. See also concurring opinion of Judge Caflish, para 8(c).

3

Future Directions

Addressing the 'Bournewood gap': *de facto* detention and legal safeguards

'I was given virtually no information regarding my section, both when I was put onto my section 3 and, almost more importantly, when I came off my section 3 but remained a voluntary rather than detained inpatient. When I came off section I found myself without rights and with no-one I could appeal to, as I was no longer entitled to a Tribunal or managers' hearings or a second opinion. I was not made aware that as an informal service user the legal position was that I had to consent to any treatment or restriction they were imposing else it could not be done to me on an informal basis. They carried on imposing the blanket restriction regardless of how I felt about it, regardless that I did not consent and wanted to leave and did not realise this was not allowed. Everybody agreed that I was inappropriately placed, but as I am not yet well enough to look after myself independently without somewhere to go, I could not just up and leave.

I was told I was not entitled to a managers' hearing or Tribunal, and that MHAC could not help me because I was not on section. It was a very desperate time for me. Fortunately a solicitor got involved, made me and my clinical team aware of the legal requirement for a CPA document and the legal and human rights implication of imposing restrictions upon me without consent while voluntary in the hospital. I have now been referred to supportive housing and have a wonderful psychologist and CPA care plan that makes sense.'

Gul Davis, ex-s.3 patient, Birmingham

Addressing the Bournewood gap

3.1   The lack of safeguards against unregulated, 'informal' deprivation of liberty has been a recognised gap in public policy for over five years (see Chapter 1.3 above). In the absence of a domestic solution to extend protections such as automatic review mechanisms to the *de facto* detained, the European Court decision in *HL v United Kingdom* (see Chapter 1.1 *et seq* above) has dealt a heavy blow to the concept of common law treatment of non-voluntary patients[1]. The dilemma for Government in the light of that judgment is how to avoid restricting the status of 'informal' patient to those who can competently consent to

---

[1]   Hewitt, D (2004) 'Effective, unqualified control' *New Law Journal* 22 October 2004, p1553-5

treatment. It is felt by many that redrawing the threshold of formal admission systems for psychiatric care to encompass all but 'voluntary' patients would be a seriously regressive step, reminiscent of mental health law at the start of the last century (see introduction, paragraph xxvi *et seq*).

3.2 The disadvantages of extending formal admission requirements to all incapacitated patients relate to resource implications, and the notion that formal admission is stigmatising. We accept that resources concerning *de facto* detention should be targeted to where they will be effective. The blanket-coverage of a system of formal admissions for all incapacitated patients could stretch resources too thinly to be effective, or lose focus through encompassing patients who are unlikely to be deprived of liberty in any meaningful sense. We also accept that it would be regressive to reintroduce, in the name of human rights, systems of psychiatric admission that undo the assumptions that informal care is to be preferred wherever possible. We do, however, believe that Government can reduce the stigmatising impact of formal procedures for admission or review of treatment through its handling of the issues involved, both for the incapacitated patients who are the focus of the *HL v UK* judgment and for those whose treatment already falls under domestic mental health legislation.

3.3 We have serious doubts that domestic mental health legislation, in the form either of the Mental Health Act 1983 or any planned successor, can encompass without distinction incapacitated compliant patients without seriously lowering the operative thresholds of compulsion. It would, however, be possible to introduce mental incapacity as a factor differentiating separate thresholds in the criteria for compulsion, so that the broad reach of the Act in relation to incapacitated patients was narrowed when it was applied in the context of a competent refusal of consent. The solution provided in the 2002 draft Mental Health Bill, of having a separate part of the Bill to extend some of that Bill's safeguards to informal patients who are compliant with treatment but not capable of consenting, appears to us to be a model that can be adapted for use in the circumstances that the legislature is now in. It would make most sense for safeguards relating to deprivation of liberty for compliant patients to be provided through the vehicle of the Mental Health Act, given that this deals with precisely this issue for the non-compliant patient. Because, however, there is a more urgent need for legislation to deal with the common-law *de facto* detention of patients than there is for a new Mental Health Act, it may be appropriate to establish separate legislation that will provide safeguards to the *de facto* detained modelled upon those available for patients subject to formal detention, if not necessarily identical to them.

3.4 It is extremely important that any framework for safeguarding the rights of *de facto* detained patients does not create confusion over the application of existing legislation such as the Mental Health Act 1983 or its successor. In our view the 1983 Act, or whatever forms of formal psychiatric admission succeed it, must not be used exclusively to compel patients with mental capacity whose objections to treatment are overruled following assessments of dangerousness. Our concerns that this could result from the interaction of the Mental Capacity Act and (in particular) the proposals for the next Mental Health Act are discussed at paragraph 3.32 below. We do not believe that a Mental Health Act that operates in practice solely upon such criteria would promote humane treatment of the patients falling within its powers, or extend to all patients who are in need of intervention. For this reason very close attention must be given to ensuring that incapacitated patients who resist admission are afforded the full protection of the 1983 Act, and not dealt with under less rigorous safeguards. We have urged Government to ensure that, for example, distinctions made between resistance to admission and resistance to treatment are not allowed to become loop-holes allowing 'protective care'[2] arrangements to provide authority to treat incapacitated patients by force for any extended period.

Defining deprivation of liberty

3.5 The *HL v United Kingdom* judgment did not provide any new definition or objective threshold of what is meant by 'deprivation of liberty'. It confirmed previous ECtHR findings that it is the cumulative effect of restrictions[3] placed upon a patient by a public authority, the threshold of which can only be determined in relation to the specific situation of the individual.

3.6 In the case of *HL*, health care professionals treating and managing him 'exercised complete and effective control over his care and movements'[4]. *HL* was under constant supervision and control and not free to leave, but furthermore:

> the hospital's health care professionals assumed full control of the liberty and treatment of a vulnerable incapacitated patient solely on the basis of their own clinical assessments completed as and when they considered fit … this left effective and unqualified control in their hands[5].

3.7 Importantly, the ECtHR rejected submissions that deprivation of liberty was dependent upon actual restraint in preventing a patient leaving, as opposed to an intention to restrain should the patient attempt to leave[6]. As such, paragraph 2.8 of the Code of Practice, which states a preference for the informal hospital admission of incapacitated compliant patients must now be interpreted as no longer applicable to a patient who was in a situation identical to that of *HL*, or whose admission to hospital would equally amount to a deprivation of liberty. Where hospital admission deprives a patient of his or her liberty, and the criteria for

---

[2] See introduction to this report, para xxviii, for our reservations over the use of this term.

[3] In this, the judgment confirmed the previous ECtHR finding of *Ashingdane v United Kingdom* [1985] 7 EHRR 528, ECHR, judgment of 28 May 1985, application no.8225/78, §.41: 'The difference between a deprivation of, and restriction upon, liberty is merely one of degree or intensity and not one of nature or substance' (*HL v the United Kingdom*, para 89).

[4] See *HL v the United Kingdom*, paras 89-91.

[5] *ibid.*, para 121.

[6] See *HL v United Kingdom*, para 90: '…considerable emphasis was placed by the domestic courts, and by the Government, on the fact that the applicant was compliant and never attempted, or expressed the wish, to leave. The majority of the House of Lords specifically distinguished actual restraint of a person (which would amount to false imprisonment) and restraint which was conditional upon his seeking to leave (which would not constitute false imprisonment). The Court does not consider such a distinction to be of central importance under the Convention. Nor, for the same reason, can the Court accept as determinative the fact relied on by the Government that the regime applied to the applicant (as a compliant incapacitated patient) did not materially differ from that applied to a person who had the capacity to consent to hospital treatment, neither objecting to their admission to hospital. The Court recalls that the right to liberty is too important in a democratic society for a person to lose the benefit of Convention protection for the single reason that he may have given himself up to be taken into detention (*De Wilde, Ooms and Versyp v. Belgium* judgment of 18 June 1971, Series A no. 12, §§ 64-65), especially when it is not disputed that that person is legally incapable of consenting to, or disagreeing with, the proposed action'.

detention under the Act are otherwise met, then the powers of the 1983 Act should be used rather than informal arrangements: there is no room for the doubt implied by the Code (see also paragraph 3.20 below).

3.8   It has been argued in an article for the *Journal of Mental Health Law* by Robert Robinson (who was *HL*'s solicitor[7]) and Lucy Scott-Moncrieff[8] that the finding of a deprivation of liberty in *HL*'s case can be read to be at least partly consequent upon the hospital's *assumption* of control, in the sense that *HL* was not *uncontrolled* at the time of his admission, but lived with and was looked after by his carers, who were opposed to his admission. This raises the possibility that, had *HL* been without carers or family, or had his admission been at the behest of his carers, the court (if the matter could have been brought to court in such circumstances) may not have found that a deprivation of liberty occurred. Robinson and Scott-Moncrieff argue that *HL*'s carers also had 'complete and effective control over his care and movements' prior to his admission to hospital, and yet the deprivation of liberty was deemed to have occurred with *HL*'s removal from their care into that of the hospital. In one sense, this is simply because the law only recognises 'deprivation of liberty' engaging Article 5 in relation to public authorities, and does not extend this concept to private individuals and what we might loosely term 'family structures'. But Robinson and Scott-Moncrieff also propose that *HL*'s domestic situation prior to admission was of specific relevance to the court's determination that a deprivation of liberty had occurred in his case, particularly when this determination is compared to previous rulings of the ECtHR which were considered during the hearing[9]. They argue that three factors 'stand out' in *HL*'s case:

- *HL*'s admission to hospital was effected against the wishes of those with whom he shared his home and family life;
- There was at all times an alternative to institutional care (and indeed his carers were opposed to admission and wanted him to return home, and in addition were initially prevented from seeing him); and
- The quality of his life in hospital 'was not only worse that that with his carers, but was more restrictive than it needed to be in an institutional setting'[10].

3.9   Robinson and Scott-Moncrieff suggest that taking into account these factors could help Government in establishing workable and proportionate measures to address the incompatibility of UK law with Article 5 that concentrate on the most vulnerable patients and prevent the wholesale formal 'detention' of incapacitated patients by authorities to anxious to avoid risk of litigation. We support the general *aims* of this approach (if not the specific analyses discussed below), and agree that guidance is needed to help services recognise and also avoid deprivation of liberty. The authors also propose two specific consequences of their reading of the judgment, which we attempt to summarise below:

---

[7]   Robert Robinson is also a past-member of the Mental Health Act Commission.

[8]   Robinson, R., & Scott-Moncrieff, L. (2005) 'Making Sense of Bournewood' *Journal of Mental Health Law*, May 2005, p.17-25.

[9]   In particular, the case of *HM v Switzerland* [2002] ECHR 157, outlined at para 3.12 below.

[10]   Robinson, R., & Scott-Moncrieff, L. *supra.* p.22-3

(i) Should admission on the agreement of family or carers be deemed not to engage Article 8?

3.10   Robinson and Scott-Moncrieff suggest that guidance for services on what is meant by 'deprivation of liberty', as well as the eventual legal structure of admission and review procedures, could allow that there is no deprivation of liberty where an incapacitated patient's admission to an institution is undertaken with the agreement of that patient's family or main carers. In such circumstances, professionals (and through them the State) would not be exercising 'complete and effective control' over the patient, but would be acting in co-operation with those who would otherwise be caring for the patient. There are attractions to this formulation, which would have the advantage, amongst other things, of solving the problem of how respite care might fit into a system of formal admission procedures required by Article 5. However, there are practical risks in assuming that a patient's carer or perhaps especially 'Nearest Relative' would in fact make decisions in the best interests of the incapacitated person[11], or be able in practice to resist professional pressure for an intervention that they do not wholly endorse. This would suggest that some form of review mechanism could be a necessary protection even for those patients who, under a 'protective care' framework, enter hospitals or other establishments with the sanction of their relatives. Such a protection (in the form of the MHRT) is, after all, extended to such patients who are admitted to hospital or Guardianship under the 1983 Act with the support of relatives.

(ii) Should care for patients unable to exercise liberty be presumed not to engage Article 8?

3.11   Robinson and Scott-Moncrieff further suggest that there should be a presumption of no deprivation of liberty where the admission of a patient to an institution is a response to a situation the patient is 'not capable of enjoying their liberty' and it is, for example, not safe for him or her to be living at home[12].

3.12   The authors suggest the case *HM v Switzerland* as a precedent for this view. *HM* was an elderly woman removed by police into residential care from the unheated and, according to the welfare assistance removal order, 'intolerable conditions' of the flat that she shared with her son. She was deemed to be suffering from dementia, but had not been medically examined, as this was not strictly relevant to the Swiss legislative powers under which the order was made. Despite the fact that *HM* was taken against her will (and also against the wishes of her son), and was not free to leave the institution to go home, the ECtHR found by majority that *HM*'s placement in the nursing home (which they noted was an open institution with no or few restrictions placed on her contacts or daily movements, factors

---

[11]   In the context of discussions over how persons might be protected from over-coercive use of State power, it is perhaps salutary to remember Farge and Foucault's presentation of the use of *lettres de cachet* in *Ancien Régime* France. Although nominally a system allowing the most arbitrary detention at the king's pleasure, the authors show that its practical implementation was often at the representation or insistence of family members in response to problems on a domestic level. See Farge A & Foucault M (1982) *Le Désordre des Familles; Lettres de cachet des Archives de la Bastille.* Editions Gallimard, Paris.

[12]   Robinson, R., & Scott-Moncrieff, L. (2005) *supra* p.24. A similar argument (albeit in the context of a patient's release from detention in hospital rather than the instigation of detention) was adopted by the Court of Appeal in the *PH* case, discussed at Chapter 1.149 above.

that did not prevent deprivation of liberty in the leading case of *Ashingdane v UK*[13]) did not amount to a deprivation of liberty within the meaning of Article 5 'but was a responsible measure taken by the competent authorities in the applicant's interests'[14].

3.13 The authors suggest that 'the liberty which the Convention exists to protect does not include the liberty to neglect oneself to the detriment of one's health or safety'[15]. When applied to persons who are mentally incapacitated by their mental disorder, this statement appears to us to be uncontroversial. But the very real difficulties in determining whether a patient is genuinely incapacitated in relation to specific decisions, or is simply disagreeing with professional judgment (see paragraph 3.27 *et seq* below), should warn us that that this approach is not without danger. Eccentric or unwise[16] decisions over lifestyle may be falsely interpreted as resultant from, and indeed evidence for, incapacitating mental disorder. Some groups of the population (such as elderly patients[17], but also the learning disabled) could be at particular risk of such speculative diagnoses, and particularly disadvantaged in trying to refute them. The *HM v Switzerland* judgment demonstrates this danger.

3.14 Under the 1983 Act, the risk that a patient poses to his or her own health or safety must be connected to the existence of their mental disorder, and must be shown to be of a certain magnitude to warrant admission[18]. The *HL* judgment pointed precisely to the danger of arbitrariness when such risks, and the consequent action of authorities to meet such risks, are determined without formal procedures. The dissenting judge in *HM v Switzerland* warned against the approach adopted by the majority of the court:

> if it were true that those responsible for the application or interpretation of the Convention were free to establish other categories of 'deprivation of liberty' in respect of which the prohibition of Article 5 would be inapplicable, either because the compulsory restriction of a person's physical freedom is a 'responsible measure' for his own good (as in the present case) or for any other 'useful' purpose, this would render the prohibition meaningless and make a mockery of its objectives[19].

3.15 In *HM v Switzerland*, the finding that Article 5 was not engaged by the majority of the court precluded resolution as to whether *HM* was in fact mentally disordered and, if so, whether this was sufficient justification in itself for her admission. There was evidence either way[20].

---

[13] *Ashingdane v UK* [1985] *supra*.

[14] *HM v Switzerland* [2002] ECHR 157, para 48.

[15] The authors cite Sedley LJ in Re F (*Adult: Court's Jurisdiction*) [2000] 2 FLR, 512: 'The purpose of [Article 8], in my view, is to assure within proper limits the entitlement of individuals to the benefit of what is benign and positive in family life. It is not to allow other individuals, however closely related and well-intentioned, to create or perpetuate situations which jeopardise their welfare.'

[16] See Mental Capacity Act 2005, s.1(4): 'a person is not to be treated as unable to make a decision merely because he makes an unwise decision'. This general principle should apply to all decisions over mental capacity, but may be difficult to enforce.

[17] This is especially true of diagnoses of 'incipient' or 'apparent' dementia.

[18] See, for example, MHA 1983 s.3(2).

[19] Dissenting opinion of Judge Loucaides, *HM v Switzerland* [2002] ECHR 157.

[20] In a view concurring with the majority that there had been no Article 5 violation, Judge Gaukur Jörundsson nevertheless found that Article 5 had been engaged, but that detention was justifiable on grounds of mental disorder. The dissenting view of Judge Loucaides disagreed with this on the grounds that no medical examination had ever taken place to determine the presence or seriousness of any mental disorder.

It is possible that, without some formal procedure in UK law to test this sort of question when an incapacitated patient is admitted to an institution, a presumption against deprivation of liberty on the grounds of what amounts to 'last resort' could perpetuate the lack of safeguards that the ECtHR in *HL v UK* criticised in the present informally-applied 'best interests' test.

3.16 We note that the UK Government argued in the Strasbourg hearing of *HL v United Kingdom* itself that Article 5 would not be engaged where a patient is admitted to hospital in his own interests to provide him with necessary medical care, using the *HM v Switzerland* case as a precedent. The ECtHR rejected this argument and the equivalence being made between *HL* and *HM* in the Swiss case[21].

3.17 In some cases we continue to observe practices which are clearly in breach of human rights requirements as determined by the European Court in *HL v United Kingdom*. The MHAC remit does not extend to informal patients. Where in the course of a visit a Commissioner has serious concerns about an informal patient the issues will be referred to the Healthcare Commission. The following example of *de facto* detention is taken from a Commission visit in June 2005.

On a visit to an Independent Hospital that predominantly cared for learning disability patients, we found that many staff did not know which patients under their care were detained under the Act and which were informal. We met with and interviewed two patients at the unit who were not detained before we realised their legal status. Thirty-seven patients (21 detained) resided at the hospital in locked 'apartments', either as sole occupants or in groups of up to six patients. Patients only left these apartments – in some cases even to go to the smoking room – under the escort of staff.

Whilst we found that staff at the unit showed a caring attitude towards patients, it was apparent that the majority of them were inexperienced and had received very little training in the legal aspects of their role. The unit manager informed us that Mental Health Act training was included in the first-day induction training for staff, although one staff member had already informed us that on her induction day this aspect had been 'skipped' for pressure of time.

It was clear that the clinician in charge of the patient's treatment viewed detention under the Act as unnecessary and stigmatising for his patients.

The above meetings with informal patients caused us some concern. One patient, who was unusual in having a primary diagnosis of mental illness with only mild learning disability, had resided at the unit for three years after spending much of his life in and out of prison. He told us that the hospital was 'better than prison' and appeared to be compliant with his care, but showed little understanding of his rights. The second patient's compliance with medication and general care appeared questionable, and his understanding of his rights very poor. One patient whose s.3 detention had recently been rescinded after over a decade of uninterrupted detention under the Act, told us that she was 'excited' that the section had been removed,

---

[21] See *HL v UK*, para 93.

although we gained no sense that she appreciated how her rights might now be different or that she was now treated any differently by staff. The first patient was deemed by staff to pose a danger to other people, and the other two a danger to themselves if allowed to leave the hospital.

We raised our concerns about the unit with the psychiatrist responsible for the patients, the management of the Hospital and the Healthcare Commission.

Fig 24: practice example 1 – unlawful deprivation of liberty?

Locked wards and unlawful deprivation of liberty

3.18 Despite the Code of Practice's presumption against locked wards (Code of Practice, 19.24 *et seq*) Commissioners report that they increasingly find adult acute wards locked as a matter of course. In our visiting activities in the nine months from October 2004 to July 2005, we found 931 locked wards compared to 590 unlocked wards[22]. Any psychiatric ward that has detained patients on its books is therefore more likely than not to be a locked ward. It has been observed that the widespread locking of acute psychiatric wards is a relatively new phenomenon in the United Kingdom whose implications have yet to be worked out[23].

3.19 In some cases wards or units are locked not to keep the patients in, but to keep others out, whether this is because of security concerns regarding thefts of hospital or patient property, or to prevent predatory access by members of the public who may pose a basic risk to vulnerable patients, or who may try to sell illicit drugs or entice patients into shop-lifting, etc. In many cases, however, locked doors restrict patients' movements on and off the ward in ways that are disproportionate to the level of risk. In part this may simply be an unintended consequence of the reducing culture of open wards, although the prevalence of locked wards can quickly lead to changes in the management of patients. Some units, who have either low staffing levels and/or a heavy reliance on agency or unqualified staff, may simply be locking doors in the interests of the management, security or safety of patients (and therefore in contradistinction to the reasons suggested by the Code of Practice) where this could otherwise be achieved by means of adequate staffing.

3.20 The Code's guidance on locking ward doors (Code of Practice, 19.24 *et seq*) is written on the assumption that this is a time-limited intervention on an otherwise open ward, and requires in part that:

---

[22] Data from MHAC reports between 1 October 2004 and 1 July 2005. The data also showed 91 'unknown' returns. Locked wards therefore accounted for between 58 and 63% of all wards visited that figure in this data capture.

[23] Bowers, L 'Runaway patients' *Mental Health Practice* September 2003 vol 7 No 1;10-12. It is, of course, the case that most mental health wards were locked in the early decades of the last century and that some wards have never been open. But it has been argued that 'in 1983 the open nature of acute psychiatric wards was accepted. Now the positive side of taking the risk of opening psychiatric wards tends not to be appreciated and in many ways we have returned to the worst institutionalised behaviour of the asylum' (Dr D C Double, letter to Critical Psychiatry Website, September 2003, www.critpsynet.freeuk.com/Editor.htm).

- patients whose behaviour has caused the ward to be locked should be informed of the reasons for this action, and

- all other patients should be informed that they may leave on request at any time with someone being available at all times to unlock the door.

The Code requires that all patients have a written care-plan which states explicitly why and when he or she will be prevented from leaving the ward. There should be clear instructions and advice visible for all to see about why the ward door is locked and what rights and freedoms people have to pass through these doors. It is notable that the Healthcare Commission's audit of 111 acute wards in this reporting period found more than a fifth to have no policy on locking the ward[24]. The Code also requires that, where an informal patient persistently or purposefully tries to leave the ward or unit, and is prevented from doing so, consideration should be given to whether that patient is being deprived of his or her liberty and whether detention under the Act is appropriate. This latter requirement rather understates the legal position following *HL v United Kingdom*, where the European Court concluded that, for the purpose of determining whether restrictions on liberty amount to a deprivation of liberty, the question of whether a patient had been restrained from leaving or *would be* restrained from leaving was not of central importance[25]. Nevertheless, we find that consideration of whether it is appropriate to assess for possible detention under the Act is not always given, sometimes for surprising reasons, as in the following example.

> In one case noted in March 2005, the need to contain an informal patient who was unwell at the time of our visit was given as the reason for the locking of a unit both informal and detained patients. Some patients were given a key but others, including informal patients, had to ask staff to be allowed out. The patient for whose benefit the unit had been locked was clearly deprived of his liberty in this situation. The unit staff explained the man's continued informal status as a consequence of the fact that the nursing home to which it was hoped he would be transferred was not registered to take detained patients.

Fig 25: practice example 2 – unlawful deprivation of liberty?

3.21 Commissioners report that it is rare to see notices or other information provided to indicate to informal patients how they may exercise their rights to leave the ward environment at will. It appears that informal patients often must request from staff that the door be opened, and it is apparent that such patients do not fully understand their true legal rights in this respect and that their requests to leave the ward or unit are not always granted. It is not uncommon to encounter the use of the concept of 'authorised leave' in relation to informal patient's absences, and to find that systems not unlike those used to grant s.17 leave to detained patients are in use for informal patients. In some cases, as with the example below, informal patients may be 'marked' as 'not to go of the ward'.

---

[24] Healthcare Commission (2005) *National Audit of Violence (2003-2005) Final Report.* Royal College of Psychiatrists' Research Unit / Healthcare Commission. p.47. Twenty-four of the 111 acute wards indicated to the Healthcare Commission that they had no such policy. A further two wards stated that the question was not applicable (presumably on the grounds that the wards were always locked).

[25] See *HL v United Kingdom*, para 90 (reproduced at footnote 6 above).

While interviewing detained patients in a London hospital in March 2005, a Commissioner overheard an informal patient repeatedly asking nursing staff in the ward office to allow him to go for a short 15-minute walk. The patient, who had put on his outdoor clothes, subsequently approached the Commissioner for assistance. She asked a member of staff to address his request and was told that staff were waiting for a doctor to see him. Over the next half hour she overheard him repeat his request, and be told to wait for a doctor or to wait for another nurse (whom it seemed might escort him on leave) to arrive. Upon the arrival of the nurse, he was told that the nurse who had arrived would not go out as it had started to rain, and he was waiting for the rain to stop when the Commissioner left the ward area.

This patient and two other informal patients on the ward had an orange square placed against their names on the ward office admissions board. The Commissioner learned that this symbol meant 'not to go off the ward' without a nursing escort.

Fig 26: practice example 3 – unlawful deprivation of liberty?

3.22   In the above example, we find it doubly unacceptable that the patient was being stopped from leaving upon no proper legal grounds, and that the staff preventing the patient from going for a walk did so through prevarication and less than honest means. Such practices are likely to exasperate and frustrate patients and are likely to be counter-therapeutic as well as being legally questionable. We deplore the use of concepts of formal 'leave' in the care of informal patients. Such terminology creates confusion amongst staff and patients concerned as to the legal position of patients, and runs a high risk of staff acting in ways that amount to unlawful deprivation of liberty.

3.23   This is not to say that it is never appropriate to ask informal patients to inform a member of staff when leaving the ward, indicating where they are going and how long they expect to be. It can be legitimate, and indeed may be sensible health and safety practice, to ask patients to 'sign out' when leaving the ward. Some wards are so arranged that nursing stations are near the exits and this can facilitate such 'common-sense' means of ensuring that the general whereabouts of patients is known to staff. At a recent visit we made to Merley Ward, St Anne's Hospital, Poole, patients on this open ward were very positive about this arrangement which ensured that the door was always open but that staff knew of patients' whereabouts.

3.24   Some wards view restrictions over patient's movements as a part of the 'contract of care' in the patient's care plan. This may indicate that the patient has agreed to abide by certain rules whilst admitted to the ward. In practice, such 'contracts' and care-plans may often be just a note in the patient's records, and not necessarily a document that is copied to, signed by or even shared with the patient concerned. House rules, being expectations on a patient's behaviour, should be clearly spelt out to patients in advance and the rules, and the likely consequence of a patient not abiding by them, should be fully documented as a part of the patient's care plan, a physical copy of which is provided to the patient (see paragraphs 2.75 *et seq* above). Whilst it may be legally justifiable to ask a patient to 'contract' to abide by house rules that place *restrictions* on his or her liberties (provided that this is done openly and that any restriction upon a patient's liberty as a result is one that the patient understands and freely consents to when signing up to the contract), the European Court has rejected the notion that a patient can contract to *deprivation of liberty*:

> the right to liberty is too important in a democratic society for a person to lose the benefit of Convention protection for the single reason that he may have given himself up to it … especially [but not exclusively] when… that person is legally incapable of consenting to, or disagreeing with, the proposed action[26].

Where informal patients properly understand that any treatment 'contract' does not prevent them from discharging themselves from hospital, and that such a contract has no legally binding character in any other sense, it seems likely that any restrictions implied by that contract cannot amount to a deprivation of liberty.

3.25 All wards have certain stated and unstated house rules or practices which contain patient behaviour or protect patients on the ward. We do not question the legal basis or practical need for the front door of hospitals or units being locked at night, for example, or for rules banning alcohol or drugs, or for requirements upon patients to behave in ways that do not impair or restrict the rights of others, such as rules about smoking or noise. In our view the validity of any 'contract' basis for restricting patient liberties over and above any generally applied house rules must be based upon:

- individual risk assessments as to the need for such restrictions;
- written confirmation in the form of a plan that informs all staff of the unit who have responsibilities in providing care to the patient and who have the power to restrict liberty of the level and conditions of that restriction;
- copying of that plan to the patient;
- the patient's willingness to comply with such restrictions; and
- a contingency plan in the event that the patient is not prepared to comply, or that changes occur in the patient's needs or the environment in which those needs are being met.

3.26 The statutory requirements over the provision of information to patients detained under the Mental Health Act are provided by s.132 of that Act. By contrast, there are no statutory requirements to provide informal patients with information about their legal position and rights. However, it is our view that it is imperative for ethical and legal good practice that informal patients are fully informed of their legal position and rights and their movement is not restricted by covert rules or vague assumptions regarding contracts. A patient who is allowed to believe that he or she is under a legal obligation to that hospital authority may well be deprived of liberty as a consequence. Some services are developing patient information leaflets for informal patients.

---

[26]   *HL v United Kingdom*, para 90

Key points about locked wards and identifying unlawful deprivation of liberty

Information for patients

(i) All patients must have a written care-plan which states explicitly when and when he or she will be prevented from leaving the ward (Code of Practice, 19.27).

(ii) All patients should be provided with a copy of their care-plan and efforts should have been made by ward staff to ensure that patients understand its content; the expectations placed upon them; and the expectations that they may have of ward staff.

(iii) Informal patients should realise that they are not bound by their care-plan, but may terminate their involvement in it by discharging themselves from hospital.

(iv) It should be clear to such patients that assessment for detention under the Act may be undertaken in circumstances where they seek their own discharge, but neither care-plans nor staff should prejudge that such detention would necessarily result from an informal patient's decision to discharge.

House rules and patient contracts

(v) Where there are house rules on a ward regarding locked doors, there should be clear instructions and advice visible for all to see about why the ward door is locked and what rights and freedoms people have to pass through these doors (Code of Practice 19.25).

(vi) Patients may be asked to 'contract' to individualised rules of conduct, including in relation to their leaving the ward. Such 'contracts' must be transparent and should be treated as care-plans described above, so that, whether the 'contract' itself is a written or verbal agreement, it should be documented in the care plan. A patient's signature to a contract does not make it legally binding. The MHAC neither encourages nor discourages the use of patient contracts in inpatient wards.

(vii) A capacitated patient may agree to restrictions upon his or her liberty but not to a deprivation of his or her liberty. Contracts and house-rules, however much they may regulate ward-life, may not necessarily amount to a deprivation of liberty where the patient concerned (i) has capacity to agree to restrictions and does so; and (ii) understands that such agreement may be terminated by discharging him or herself from hospital. The distinction between a restriction and deprivation of liberty is therefore in part described by a patient's ability to discharge him or herself from hospital care. It is important that the quasi-legal 'feel' of a contract is not allowed to mislead the patient into thinking that he or she has made a binding legal agreement.

(viii) Informal patients must therefore realise that they are not bound by house-rules or any 'contract' entered into with the hospital, and are free to discharge themselves from hospital and any requirements consequent to hospital care.

Incapacitated patients

(ix) Patients' capacity should be judged in the context of particular decisions rather than as an overall measure of mental state (Code of Practice 15.10).

(x) Incapacitated patients may have their liberty restricted but not removed under common-law powers. The point at which restriction of liberty becomes a deprivation of liberty is one of degree, but mental incapacity may preclude the ability or volition to exercise rights of self-discharge, implying that the threshold may be lower for incapacitated than capacitated patients.

(xi) Where restrictions over incapacitated but compliant patients amount to a deprivation of liberty and cannot in any way be relaxed, then detention under the Act should be considered.

Fig 27: Key points about locked wards and identifying unlawful deprivation of liberty

Capacity-tests and future legislation

3.27   In our last report we discussed the potential role of mental capacity in future mental health legislation and practice[27]. We noted the considerable support amongst stakeholders for a legal framework where the threshold for the imposition of treatment without consent is established by a patient's loss of mental capacity to give or withhold such consent. We do, however, continue to have concerns over whether the nature and application of the concept of mental capacity (even as this is applied in the Mental Capacity Act, as discussed below) is sufficiently developed to operate as a threshold determining whether mental health treatment should or should not be given[28]. The indeterminacy of the use and conception of mental capacity is twofold:

---

[27]   MHAC (2003) *Tenth Biennial Report: Placed Amongst Strangers*, Chapter 4.2 – 4.10.

[28]   Even amongst those who have argued most vociferously to the Joint Committee on the Draft Mental Health Bill for a capacity threshold for compulsory powers, very few adopt a purist approach to whether or not treatment could be refused where, for example, a patient poses a significant risk to others if left untreated. The Richardson and Millan Committees, and the Scottish Parliament, allowed that such patients should be treated against their will even in a capacity-based framework. As such any capacity-based legislative framework would not be entirely analogous with the law regarding physical health (with the possible but not necessarily helpful exception of certain approaches to communicable diseases), but could at best be what Campbell & Heginbotham described in 1991 as 'justifiable non-discriminatory paternalism' (see Campbell T & Heginbotham C (1991), *Mental Illness: Prejudice, Discrimination and the Law*, Aldershot: Dartmouth, p.124).

- there is a potential for circularity in the determination of mental incapacity as a point on a sliding scale which must take account of both the patient's mental state and the circumstances in which a decision is made, whereby any decision to refuse treatment that is considered necessary by medical opinion might be deemed to result from impaired judgment by mental disorder[29];

- there continues to be a wide variety of definitions and tests adopted by different authorities and jurisdictions in which the concept of mental capacity is used, and there is no consensus over how capacity should operate as a threshold in mental health interventions. Particular dilemmas are posed by deteriorating patients, for whom many professionals would propose intervention prior to a loss of capacity, or persons whose behaviour places other persons at risk of harm. Most systems establishing capacity-based thresholds for intervention do not operate these consistently for all such patients, but instead allow that, for example, interventions may be imposed against a capacitated refusal of consent where the patient presents a danger to self or others.

3.28 In our last report we stated that the potential for mental incapacity to be defined circularly by clinicians, as any resistance to interventions that they feel to be necessary, could be ameliorated through having some other authority determine whether the patient is capable of refusing consent[30]. It is not at all clear, however, that entrusting the determination of capacity to judicial authorities protects against the danger that a patient's decisions which are inconvenient or unacceptable in the view of the assessor will not be deemed to be invalid on grounds of mental incapacity. In our discussions of legal cases above (see Chapter 1.27 *et seq* above) we highlight the courts' determination of mental capacity in cases involving Ian Stewart Brady, where we concur that the courts appear all too willing to refute Mr Brady's wishes by declaring him incompetent to make decisions. If the determination in 2000 that Mr Brady was not competent to hunger-strike had the implication that 'it may be very difficult for anyone detained in hospital with a psychopathic disorder to protest against medical treatment without that protest being characterised as a symptom of that mental disorder'[31], the subsequent decision in 2004, with its apparent reversal of the usual presumption of capacity in relation to Mr Brady's decision to request a public MHRT hearing, has even wider implications, not limited or excused by pragmatic questions of the imposition of medical treatment on best interests criteria.

3.29 In June 2005 the courts refused an application from the Official Solicitor for an injunction against the television broadcast of a documentary about *E*, a woman suffering from mental disorder[32]. The judge rejected the Official Solicitor's claim that *E* would be likely at trial to be

---

[29] In part this circularity stems from the determination of mental capacity in relation to the nature of the decision at hand, but other approaches such as a 'status' test approach, whereby the general attributes of a patient may be considered to render that patient incapacitated, have limited application and may be unacceptable in terms of human rights expectations of non-discrimination.

[30] MHAC (2003) *Tenth Biennial Report: Placed Amongst Strangers.*, Chapter 4.3

[31] Jane Scott (2003) 'Tests for Decision-making Capacity in Medical Treatment – Practical or merely theoretical?' LLM Dissertation, University of Northumbria, December 2003.

[32] *E v Channel Four & Another* [2005] EWHC 1144 (Fam)

shown to lack capacity to make her own decision on the broadcast. Although that determination was enough to reject the application, the judge also criticised the Official Solicitor for making a determination of *E*'s best interests without consulting *E* to ascertain her own wishes and feelings. It is striking that such assumptions as were criticised by the judge in this case were made by the Official Solicitor, whom we might expect to show exemplary legal practice regarding the questions of capacity and consent.

3.30 The common-law definition of mental incapacity been codified in statute through enactment of the Mental Capacity Act 2005. Although, in strict legal terms, the definition applies only in the context of decisions taken under the Mental Capacity Act, in practice it is expected that the definition and two-stage test[33] for mental incapacity is used, where appropriate, in relation to other proceedings[34]. The test does, in any case, mirror that which was applied in previous case-law determinations regarding consent to medical treatment[35]. As a codification it perhaps inherits some of the uncertainties of case-law in England and Wales, such as the extent to which the requirement to 'weigh' information as part of the process of making a decision reflects or encompasses a test of 'appreciation', the latter describing an aspect of mental capacity that includes but goes beyond cognitive ability; which incorporates emotional or evaluative criteria and which may be compromised by delusions or other distorting effects of belief[36]. 'Appreciation' is not an established concept in English law, although some approaches in UK cases that are reflected in the Codes of Practice for the Mental Health and Mental Capacity Acts have encompassed some of its elements[37]. We would welcome the adoption of 'appreciation' criteria in determining

---

[33] The 'two-stage test' requires assessors to determine firstly that there is an impairment of or disturbance of a person's brain and, secondly, if so, whether that makes that person unable to make a decision. See Department of Constitutional Affairs (2004) *Mental Capacity Bill: Draft Code of Practice*, para 3.5 www.dca.gov.uk/menincap/mcbdraftcode.pdf. The first stage will always be met by any patient subject to mental health compulsion. The second stage (which has three components relating to ability to (i) understand (ii) retain and (iii) weigh information) may or may not be met by patients subject to Mental Health Act powers. The ability to weigh information may be compromised by pathological evaluative perspectives, but any formal system of measuring capacity on these terms must recognise the pitfalls of imposed professional or normative value-systems (see note 36 below).

[34] Department of Constitutional Affairs (2004) *Mental Capacity Bill: Draft Code of Practice*, para 3.26.

[35] In our Tenth Biennial Report (Chapter 4.4) we pointed to the differences between the *Re C (Adult refusal of treatment)* [1994] application of a capacity test (including the consideration of whether a person can 'weigh' the information) and the specific wording in the Draft Mental Incapacity Bill of 2003 (Cm 5859-I), which described only the 'use' of the information as criteria. The Bill was amended in its passage to enactment so that the Mental Capacity Act 2005 now refers to an ability 'to use or weigh' information.

[36] 'Appreciation' is a term appearing in case law and statutes in the United States, including tests of criminal responsibility (see Chapter 5.23 below). It has been both formulated and championed as a component of decisional capacity by Paul S Appelbaum and Thomas Grisso, who have recently suggested approaches that recognise a more complex view of appreciation than was first envisaged (Grisso & Appelbaum 'Appreciation as a dimension of decision-making capacity' NIMHE conference presentation, 2-3 September 2004). They have sought to classify the various 'evaluative processes' in decision making into four types, not all of which will be relevant to conceptualising medicolegal incapacity: (i) applied beliefs with patently false premises (i.e. rigidly held beliefs that offer a distorted perspective on meaning regarding consequences, often associated with psychotic or affective thought disorder); (ii) applied impoverished perspectives related to cognitive immaturity or deficiency; (iii) applied adaptive distortions (associated with defence mechanisms under stress, or scripted decision-making heuristics typical of severe depressive or anxiety disorders, such as minimisation; rationalisation; avoidance; selective attention, etc); (iv) applied non-logical evaluative premises (i.e. belief-systems, including religious or moral beliefs, subjective likes etc). In such classification, evaluative processes of the fourth type would be generally inviolate, and decisions that a patient is incapable of a particular decision on the basis of the third type would perhaps require more justification than those on the basis of either of the first two types.

[37] See *Mental Capacity Bill: Draft Code of Practice*, para 3.12: the Code gives an example of an anorectic patient who is able to understand rationally the consequences of not eating but who lacks capacity to weigh these against the desire not to eat. **175**

decision-making[38] capacity, to ensure that the legal test for mental incapacity is flexible enough to recognise incapacity that is not linked to cognitive impairment (we are critical of the overly cognitive bias of tests of legal *culpability* in Chapter 5.17 & 5.22 below). But we also recognise that an 'appreciation' element in capacity tests might reduce the impression of objectivity in their use and *could* increase the likelihood of circular definitions of capacity as discussed above. To prevent this, careful attention must be given to the design and definition of capacity tests, mental health professionals must be conscious of and sensitive to the play of values in decision-making[38], and the safeguards of reviewing mechanisms should be sufficiently robust.

3.31   We discuss the introduction of a capacity-test specific to the imposition of ECT under Mental Health Act powers at Chapter 4. 71 *et seq* below.

The interface between the Mental Capacity and Mental Health Acts

3.32   The Mental Capacity Act received Royal Assent on 7 April 2005 and is scheduled to come in to force on 1 April 2007. It codifies (and possibly extends) common-law powers relating to the treatment of patients who lose capacity to provide consent, including powers of restraint and coercive treatment[39]. We have argued alongside other commentators that the Mental Capacity Act may come into contention with the Mental Health Act, and especially the draft Mental Health Bill, in relation to which authority may appropriately be used, or may be available, for compulsory treatment for mental disorder[40].

3.33   The Government initially rejected that such contention had any real basis, primarily on the grounds that the Mental Capacity Bill is worded carefully to authorise '*restrictions*' on liberty, whereas Mental Health Act powers are concerned with '*deprivation*' of liberty[41]. Insofar as the case-law of the European Court of Human Rights (ECtHR) makes a clear distinction between restriction of liberty (which does not engage Article 5 rights)[42] and deprivation of liberty (which does engage such rights), this distinction would form the operative threshold between the two Bills. At paragraphs 3.5 *et seq* of this report we have questioned how easily

---

[38]   See MHAC (2003) *Tenth Biennial Report: Placed Amongst Strangers*, Chapter 5 (and Chapter 2.87 of this report, above) on values-based practice.

[39]   See Mental Capacity Act 2005 ss.5 and 6, which provide powers to 'restrain' incapacitated patients, provided that such restraining actions are: (i) believed to be in the patient's best interests; (ii) not in conflict with any decision taken by a donee of lasting power of attorney or a deputy appointed by the court; (iii) believed necessary to prevent harm coming to that patient; and (iv) a proportionate response to the likelihood of that harm and its seriousness. Restraint is defined (s.6(4)) as the use, or threatened use, of force to secure the doing of an act which the patient resists, or an act which restricts the patient's liberty of movement whether or not s\he resists.

[40]   See, for example, Joint Committee on the Draft Mental Health Bill (2005) *Draft Mental Health Bill*, Vol 2, Ev 9 (Memorandum from Genevra Richardson) and Ev 37, 48 (Memorandum & Supplementary memorandum from the Mental Health Act Commission). See also Kinton M 'Mental Health Law for the 21st Century?' *Journal of Mental Health Law* 12;57-69 May 2005

[41]   Joint Committee on Human Rights (2005) *Scrutiny: First Progress Report. Fourth Report of Session* 2004-05. HL paper 26, HC 224, January 2005. See Appendix 4: *Mental Capacity Bill. Letter from Baroness Ashton of Upholland to the Chair*, response to Q2.

[42]   See discussion of *HL v United Kingdom* & *Storck v Germany* at Chapter 1.1-1.24 above.

this distinction between restricting and depriving liberty can be applied to practical examples of health and social care interventions in the lives of the mentally disordered. As Government 'is minded' to allow an aspect of clinical discretion over whether any particular patient falls within the frameworks of either mental health or mental incapacity law (similar to the scope for discretion in using child protection powers or the 1983 Act in certain circumstances)[43], it could be for the practitioners themselves to decide whether their actions amount to deprivation of liberty and should be subject to the formal admission and review mechanisms that are required following the ECtHR ruling last year.

3.34   Furthermore, the interactions of mental capacity and mental health legislation may undermine the intended reforms of the latter. One of the premises of the draft Mental Health Bill is that a modernised framework of mental health powers would not be concerned simply with the detention of patients in hospital (which, of necessity, amounts to a deprivation of liberty)[44] but would also extend to compulsion on a non-residential basis (which would normally amount only to restrictions upon liberty). But, as the Mental Capacity Bill also provides powers to impose restrictions upon liberty to the same end (including the imposition of psychiatric medication and possibly ECT[45]), it would appear to be doubtful that practitioners would feel able to invoke Mental Health Act powers for compulsion that does not amount to detention, given the requirement in the Mental Health Act to use the least restriction necessary[46] and use Mental Health Act powers only where no other legal authority exists[47]. There is consequently a considerable overlap in the each of the two legislative frameworks.

3.35   The Mental Health Act's full range of powers could thereby become reserved for the imposition of treatment to mentally capable patients and, perhaps, to mentally incapacitated patients who pose 'a substantial risk of serious harm to others'. This would have the practical consequence of establishing a capacity-test as the effective threshold for use of the Mental Health Act for many patients, but not as a basis for psychiatric compulsion *per se* (given that incapacitated patients would still be liable to compulsion, but under the Mental Capacity Act's presently lesser safeguards). In our view, there would be no advantage in having a two-tier system based upon such distinctions, which could reduce safeguards for the incapacitated and reinforce prejudice against capacitated patients made subject to Mental Health Act powers by labelling these as in some sense 'dangerous'[48].

---

[43]   Joint Committee on the Draft Mental Health Bill (2005) *Draft Mental Health Bill*, Volume 2, Ev 518, Q847 (Ms Rosie Winterton MP, Professor Appleby).

[44]   Department of Health (2004) *Improving Mental Health Law: Towards a New Mental Health Act* (Summary) p.4

[45]   It may be that the procedural requirements of ECT treatment (i.e. anaesthesia) would always amount to a deprivation of liberty – see paragraph 3.37 below.

[46]   *Draft Mental Health Bill* clause 1(3)(c)

[47]   *Draft Mental Health Bill* clause 9(5)

[48]   It is disappointing in this respect that the phrasing of the Mental Capacity Act 2005 *draft Code of Practice* reinforces the common assumption that a patient may only be admitted to hospital under the Mental Health Act 1983 because of danger to self or others, when another criteria for admission is 'necessary for health' (s.3(2)(c)). See *draft Code of Practice* para 2.14: 'The Mental Health Act provides a much narrower legal authority [than the Mental Capacity Act] for the admission to hospital and treatment (where appropriate without consent) of people with a mental disorder when this is necessary in certain circumstances, because of the risk posed to themselves or others'.

	Restriction of liberty	deprivation of liberty
Incapacitated but compliant (not resisting) patient	Mental Capacity Act	'protective care' framework[49] (or Mental Health Act if conditions are met).
Incapacitated but non-compliant (resisting) patient	Mental Capacity Act / Mental Health Act?	Mental Health Act if conditions are met, otherwise no statutory basis.

Fig 28: the interrelation of the Mental Capacity and Mental Health Acts for patients lacking mental capacity

3.36   Figure 28 above attempts to show the interrelationship between the Mental Capacity and Mental Health Acts in relation to the variables of compliance with treatment and whether the intervention is a restriction upon or deprivation of liberty. As a schematic presentation it necessarily compartmentalises these variations rather more neatly than may be apparent in real-life situations.

3.37   Leaving aside the question of how Government is to address the 'Bournewood gap' described in the quadrant of the above matrix concerning the deprivation of the liberty of incapacitated compliant patients, we can see that the primary uncertainty rests in the quadrants describing non-compliant incapacitated patients. There is no apparent limitation on the use of Mental Capacity Act powers to impose treatments actively resisted by incapacitated patients, provided that such imposition does not extend to a deprivation of liberty, although under the current legal framework (prior to the coming into force of the Mental Capacity Act) such interventions would be likely to fall only within the scope of Mental Health Act powers. Thus, for example, it may be that the forcible imposition of ECT (requiring the anaesthesia of a patient, which might be presumed to amount to deprivation of liberty) might be outwith the scope of Mental Capacity Act powers, but forcible medication is not. Perhaps, however, the realities of imposing psychiatric medication (i.e. administering a depot injection in a clinical setting) will also mean that this should be considered implicitly as a deprivation of liberty (albeit of a limited duration). These questions are not answered by the Mental Capacity Act *draft Code of Practice*, but we imagine that they will quickly come to the fore with its implementation.

3.38   Further difficulties will arise where a patient's capacity fluctuates throughout the medical intervention. The *draft Code of Practice* for the Mental Capacity Act understandably expects capacity to be assessed at the point that the decision is made, as the capacity-test is a functional test, relating to particular circumstances, rather than a status test that identifies particular attributes of patients that serve to invalidate their decision-making abilities in any circumstance. The latter approach has been specifically rejected in UK law[50] and would be likely to contravene the ECHR[51]. Fluctuating capacity may be practically accommodated

---

[49]   At the time of writing (November 2005) it is not known whether the Government will propose specific 'protective care' arrangements in answer to the ECtHR's finding that informal care amounting to a deprivation of liberty is incompatible with the requirements of Article 5 of the ECHR, nor what the details of any such proposal might entail.

[50]   See *Re C (Adult refusal of treatment)* [1994] and its reflection in the Mental Health Act Code of Practice, para 15.10.

[51]   See note 29 above.

under the Mental Capacity Act in relation to a patient whose incapacitation interrupts periods of voluntary consent to medical interventions, but the legal framework may be less clear where incapacitation interrupts capacitated refusal of consent. Where psychiatric treatment is imposed under the Mental Health Act to a capacitated but refusing patient, it would seem ethically appropriate to continue under such a legal framework when the patient loses capacity, rather than lessen the safeguards and continue treatment under the powers of the Mental Capacity Act. This may, however, be problematic both because of the expectation that the Mental Health Act can only be used as a last legal resort (see paragraph 3.34 above), and because allowing a patient's legal status under the Mental Health Act to continue unchanged in the face of a change in mental capacity may be deemed an unacceptable adoption of a 'status' determination of mental capacity.

3.39 Left to find its own level, the practical threshold of using Mental Health Act over Mental Capacity Act powers could act as a curious disincentive towards the making of advance directives (which we discuss more generally below). It would seem to be the case that non-compliance in itself will not necessitate the use of Mental Health Act powers where the intervention does not amount to a deprivation of liberty. However, an advance directive (for example, against psychiatric medication) could not be set aside within the framework of the Mental Capacity Act, but could be set aside under the Mental Health Act, and may even provide the rationale for the use of the latter[52]. Patients with serious mental disorder who make their wishes known about future treatment may therefore ultimately be no better protected from having such wishes overridden, but may rather call down upon themselves the powers of the Mental Health Act, in that their advance refusal of treatment could ensure that they meet any 'last legal resort' criterion for the invocation of Mental Health Act powers, where they would otherwise be treated under Mental Capacity Act powers. In some ways this is not unreasonable, as the increased safeguards of the Mental Health Act may be appropriate where advance directives are to be overridden, but patients may not see it this way and may be concerned at the potential stigma of being 'sectioned'.

3.40 The problems inherent in the complexities of the two systems can be shown by the following example:

(i) Mr K expressly refuses consent to ECT, even as a life-saving intervention, in an advance directive under the terms of the Mental Capacity Act. He is subsequently incapacitated by treatment-resistant depressive illness.

(ii) Mr K's clinical team decides that ECT is his only hope of recovery or respite from this illness, excepting neurosurgery, which they have no inclination to propose to a court, especially without having attempted ECT.

(iii) Whilst treating Mr K under the authority of the Mental Capacity Act, the clinicians must respect the advance directive: but advance directives generally can be overridden by invoking the powers of the Mental Health Act. Indeed, the conditions for use of the new Mental Health Act mean that the need to give treatment for which consent has been refused in an advance directive is generally sufficient cause.

---

[52]   See Joint Committee on the Draft Mental Health Bill (2005) *Draft Mental Health Bill*, Vol 2, Ev 37 (MHAC) para 8.3.

(iv) The Mental Health Act requires clinicians to respect capacitated refusal of consent to ECT, except where 'emergency conditions' (which extend to the immediate necessity to relieve serious suffering) are met. 'Capacitated refusal' appears to include advance directives in the context of the Act. There is a split within the clinical team as to whether emergency powers can be invoked in Mr K's case, but those arguing that he does not meet the criteria of being in need of 'immediate' treatment concede that ECT remains the 'last hope' for recovery or improvement and that, untreated, Mr K will undergo serious suffering. On the basis that emergency powers under the Mental Health Act 'trump' powers and duties under the Mental Capacity Act, the clinicians therefore disregard Mr K's advance statement of refusal, even though this was made whilst he was capacitated and was designed specifically to apply and remain valid in the face of incapacitating illness.

We envisage that such cases may provide early opportunities for judicial review of the proposed legal frameworks. It does seem likely that there will be considerable pressure for standardisation of the effects of different parts of the statute with respect to psychiatric treatment without consent: the piecemeal introduction of capacity-test based legislation may have opened a door that Government will not easily be able to shut.

Advance directives

3.41   Notwithstanding the uncertainties over the future place of advance directives in mental health services that have resort to compulsory powers (see above), there appears to be a small but significant use of advance directives in the current legal framework. Respondents to the Healthcare Commission audit between 2003 and 2005 reported whether staff had access to advance directives drawn up by service users[53]. In the acute sector, about 30% of respondents reported some use of advance directives (figure 29). On average, about 30% of all wards across all sectors reported some access to advance directives, with considerable variation between sectors, but the numbers of returns in sectors other than acute are low and make generalisation difficult. It should be noted that this data reflects the numbers of units who have encountered advance directives, rather than the numbers of patients making them. We can neither tell from the audit how many advance directives were recognised; nor what proportion of patients subject to compulsion had made advance directives; nor what the nature of such advance directives might have been; nor whether they had been overridden by the use of compulsory powers[54].

---

[53]   Healthcare Commission (2005) *National Audit of Violence (2003-2005) Final Report* p.48.

[54]   It may also be that less-formal agreements and understandings between patients and staff were not recognised in this survey, or that staff interpreted the survey's interest only to relate to advance directives concerning the management of behaviour, rather than concerning treatment generally.

	acute		PICU		forensic		elderly		learning disability (short-stay)		learning disability (long-stay)		all units[55]	
staff have access to advance directives drawn up by service users	number	% in category	number	% in category	number	% in category	number	% in category	number	% in category	number	% in category	number	% in category
	31	30	8	44	2	13	5	15	1	8	18	86	68	30

Fig 29: Healthcare Commission findings on staff access to advance directives, by service sector, 2003-2005[56].

3.42 We expect the use and recognition of advance directives to increase in coming years, provided that continued emphasis is placed upon patient choice and involvement in the care-planning process. Patients can currently make advance directives, although they will have no statutory basis in England and Wales until the Mental Capacity Act 2005 comes into force, and even then may be overridden by Mental Health Act powers (see paragraph 3.39 above). Scottish mental health legislation now on the statute book explicitly recognises advance directives and, although they may be overridden by compulsory powers, requires that they are taken into account[57]. The Joint Committees on Human Rights[58] and on the draft Mental Health Bill[59] have called for legislation applicable to England and Wales to be similarly explicit. The Government has indicated that it is considering how to achieve this[60].

3.43 Advance directives in the form of 'crisis cards' were pioneered two decades ago by user groups such as Survivors Speak Out[61], and endorsed (as an alternative to community treatment powers) by the House of Commons Health Committee over a decade ago[62]. The Committee recognised that there were some questions over how such crisis cards might be given a statutory role in treatment. One such problem is whether the statutory role for advance directives can encompass directives that 'opt-in' to treatment by stating preferences, as opposed to 'opting-out' of treatment through stating advance refusal of consent[63]. In

[55] 'All units' includes acute, PICU, forensic, rehabilitation, elderly, learning disability (short stay, long stay and challenging behaviour) units and small group homes.

[56] Source: Healthcare Commission (2005) *National Audit of Violence*

[57] Mental Health (Care and Treatment) (Scotland) Act 2003, ss.275-6

[58] Joint Committee on Human Rights (2005) *Draft Mental Health Bill*. HL 181, HC 1294, November 2002. Para 91.

[59] Joint Committee on the Draft Mental Health Bill (2005) *Draft Mental Health Bill*. Vol 1, para 170-2.

[60] *Government Response to the Report of the Joint Committee on the Draft Mental Health Bill*. Cm 6624, July 05, p.17

[61] Thomas P & Cahill A 'Compulsion and psychiatry—the role of advance statements' *BMJ* 2004; 329: 122-123

[62] House of Commons Health Committee (1993) *Community Supervision Orders* Fifth Report of Session 1992-93, Vol 1, HC 667-1, para 86.

[63] On the distinctions between 'opting-in' and 'opting-out' see Atkinson J 'Advance planning in mental health' bmj.com rapid responses for Henderson *et al.*, (see note 66 below) 329 (7458) 136, 30 July 2004.

particular, it is difficult to see any role for advance directives opting into any intervention that would take place prior to a patient's incapacitation through illness, given that it is neither practical nor desirable for an advance directive to override a patient's capable decision over treatment at the time of the intervention. It is important, as we note below (paragraph 3.45) that advance directives do not become another form of compulsion or duress. In practice, however, a 'crisis card' system must take into account the positive wishes of the patient regarding treatment, and not only state what he or she would refuse if allowed to do so. At present, Scottish legislation adopts this approach, describing an advance directive as a statement specifying ways that a person wishes to be treated for mental disorder and ways in which that person wishes not to be treated[64]. The Mental Capacity Act 2005 covering England and Wales adopts a more restricted description, referring to 'advance decisions' as statements that, in certain circumstances, specified treatments are not to be carried out or continued[65]. If advance directives *as they are used in practice* are to be given a statutory basis in England and Wales something closer to the Scottish definition will have to be adopted.

3.44 In a detailed study of advance directives published in our reporting period, Henderson *et al* looked at the use of joint crisis plans agreed between 160 patients and their community mental health teams to manage psychotic relapses[66]. The crisis plans contained contact information; details of mental and physical illnesses; treatments; indicators for relapse; and advance statements of preferences for care in the event of future relapse. The study found that the crisis plans significantly reduced use of the Mental Health Act, even if it did not necessarily reduce the frequency or length of hospital admissions. However, only 36% of eligible patients agreed to participate in the study, with those who declined reporting variously that the crisis plan could not help them; that they were unlikely to relapse in any case; that they already had a plan or that no-one would take any notice of a plan. he group who benefited from drawing up plans may therefore have been fairly self-selecting.

3.45 Patients who 'opt-in' to intervention through use of agreed crisis-plans, etc, may avoid admission to hospital under the formal compulsion of the Mental Health Act, but also are denied the safeguards of formal admission such as criteria for interventions and formal review mechanisms. If the particular circumstances of admission or care in hospital initiated as a result of a crisis plan amounts to a deprivation of liberty (see paragraph 3.1 *et seq* above), the lack of safeguards could prevent the State from fulfilling its duties under Article 5 of the ECHR. Government must consider how mechanisms might be introduced that fulfil its duties in this respect and safeguard against crisis-plans heightening patients' sense of coercion or duress to accept interventions on an informal basis. The so-called 'Ulysses-contract' form of opt-in to services recently discussed in the literature[67] (by which

---

64 Mental Health (Care and Treatment) (Scotland) Act 2003, s.275(1)

65 Mental Capacity Act 2005 s.24(1)

66 Henderson C, Flood C, Leese M, Thornicroft G, Sutherby K, and Szmukler G. 'Effect of joint crisis plans on use of compulsory treatment in psychiatry: single blind randomised controlled trial' *BMJ* 2004; 329: 136-0. Training materials by the authors on developing a joint crisis plan involving 'crisis cards' is available from www.bmj.bmjjournals.com/cgi/content/full/bmj.38155.585046.63/DC1.

67 See Atkinson J 'Ulysses' crew or Circe? – the implications of advance directives in mental health for psychiatrists'. *Psychiatric Bulletin* (2004) 28, 3-4. This article references American sources of debate about 'Ulysses contracts' from the 1980s.

patients might contract to services as Ulysses did to his crew, commanding them to bind him to the mast of his ship and 'if I beg and command you to release me, you must tighten and add to my bonds'[68]), does not seem legally tenable in this light. But if such an 'opt-in' must be considered invalidated by a patient's subsequent opposition, even if such opposition is expressed in the circumstances that the advance directive was designed to address and/or when that patient's decision-making abilities are incapacitated by illness, then it is difficult to see how the 'opt-in' can ever be effected.

3.46   Nevertheless, the potential for advance directives to alter the landscape of mental health services should not be underestimated. Perhaps most importantly

>   advance directives require changes on the part of both staff and patients. Staff would have to accept not only patients' choices, but the experience that leads to those choices. Patients would need to accept the responsibility that comes with having their choices honoured, even if these choices do not always have the expected outcomes[69].

3.47   For staff, advance directives can be one way in which values-based practice could extend further into mental health services. For patients, a system that encompasses advance directives has the potential to be empowering, but also retains a vestige of the nineteenth-century's 'moral treatment' approaches, with the potential for twisting *empowerment* in dealing with one's illness into *responsibility* for dealing with it. Legal developments in the United States[70], where advance directives have been generally operative for at least a decade and have been increasingly applied in a psychiatric context in recent years[71], have 'raised the prospect of a class of patients who would become permanently untreatable, even if… psychotic and… hospitalised involuntarily'[72] because they had precluded effective interventions through advance directives. Whilst this may not be the eventual outcome of the U.S. legal system's dealings with psychiatric advance directives, the prospect of advance

---

[68]   Homer *The Odyssey* London; Penguin, p.161.

[69]   Atkinson J 'Ulysses' crew or Circe? – the implications of advance directives in mental health for psychiatrists'. *Psychiatric Bulletin* (2004) 28, 3-4.

[70]   *Hargrave v Vermont*, 340 F.3d 27 (2nd Cir 2003). This second circuit appeals court decision, which established precedent only in Vermont and New York but may yet be echoed in other U.S. circuit decisions, allows mentally disordered persons who are able to complete advance directives (i.e. when capacitated to make a decision) to preclude any future involuntary treatment with medications, even if they are involuntarily committed. The judgment was in effect an application of principles of non-discrimination enshrined in the Americans with Disabilities Act for which European equivalents might be found in the ECHR. For debate on the potential effects and efficacy of this ruling, see Appelbaum P S 'Psychiatric Advance Directives and the Treatment of Committed Patients' *Psychiatric Services* July 2004 vol 55, no.7; 751-763; and subsequent correspondence between Allen M and Appelbaum P S in *Psychiatric Services* September 2004 Vol 55 No.9 p.1067-1068.

[71]   The Patient Self-Determination Act (PSDA) of 1991 introduced new federal requirements across the United States intended to implement advance directive policies at all healthcare facilities funded through Medicaid and Medicare programmes. Impetus behind the interpretation of these requirements in the context of mental health care came from the reaction by 'mental health legal scholars and consumer activists' to community treatment powers ('outpatient commitment') introduced during the same period (see paragraph 3.61 et seq below). As of 2003, 16 state legislatures had introduced specific Psychiatric Advance Directive statutes. Swanson J W, Swartz M S, Hannon M J, Elbogen E B, Ryan Wagner H, McCauley B J, Butterfield M I 'Psychiatric Advance Directives: A Study of Persons with Schizophrenia, Family Members, and Treatment Providers'. *International Journal of Forensic Mental Health* 2003 Vol 2 No 1 p73-86.

[72]   Appelbaum P S 'Psychiatric Advance Directives and the Treatment of Committed Patients' *Psychiatric Services* July 2004 vol 55, no.7; 751-763.

directives that cannot be overridden by compulsory interventions may diminish clinicians' promotion of them to patients and therefore restrict their overall use[73].

3.48 As we note at paragraph 3.60 below, there is considerable unease amongst mental health professionals and patients in England and Wales at the potential for the draft Mental Health Bill proposals to extend compulsion further across psychiatric services, particularly with regard to the advent of community treatment powers. This may make the American experience especially relevant, and points to the Scylla and Charybdis that mental health policy must steer between. On the one hand, advance directives which can be overridden through use of legal powers of compulsion may not be effective in providing a counter-weight to sustain or develop patient empowerment and autonomy in the face of widening criteria for psychiatric compulsion. In a risk-averse society the ability to 'play safe' and override a patient's wishes could prove more powerful than respecting advance directives against certain psychiatric treatments. On the other hand, there are patients whose disorders preclude the building of sufficient trust with clinicians to initiate or continue psychiatric treatment, or even the recognition of the profoundly disabling aspects of their illness. If compulsory psychiatric interventions are ever justifiable it must be for this group of patients, and abandoning them to initiate treatment as consumers of mental health services could be a perverse moral position to take in defence of negative freedoms. But we see no reason why these extreme positions cannot be avoided.

3.49 We hope that the legislature for England and Wales will give close attention and consideration to the Scottish example of establishing advance directives (and not just advance refusals of consent) within a statutory framework. It would appear to us that one way in which the Scottish law could have been immediately improved upon would be to require (as the American Patient Self-Determination Act does) that patients must be notified when they come into contact with services of their right to prepare advance directives[74].

> **Recommendation 10:** We recommend Government gives close attention and consideration to the Scottish example of establishing advance directives (and not just advance refusals of consent) within a statutory framework, with a right to information about advance directives included within the draft Mental Health Bill's provisions.

---

[73] *ibid.*

[74] The Mental Health (Care and Treatment) (Scotland) Act 2003, s.260 (the equivalent of s.132 of the Mental Health Act 1983) has no explicit requirement that patients are informed of their right to make advance directives under s.275. We suggest that the duty to provide information should encompass telling patients about advance directives. It could also be a statutory duty of advocacy services to promote or help patients complete advance directives with existing inpatients. Swanson *et al* (see note 69 above) found that significant reasons for the low uptake of advance directives in North Carolina were lack of understanding about what they were; beliefs that drafting a directive would take much time and trouble and that it would be difficult to find help; not knowing what to put in such a directive; and not believing that it would make any difference to treatment.

Community treatment orders

3.50 In 1993 the then Secretary of State for Health stated that the question to be addressed by her officials in considering changes to mental health legislation was:

> whether or not there is some better way between either total loss of freedom in an institution or being in the community with precious few ways of ensuring sufficient compliance with a treatment programme.[75]

3.51 The Minister of State's evidence to the Joint Committee on the draft Mental Health Bill 2004 suggested that the Government believes that there is now a better way, and that this has been facilitated by the increasing use of community-based mental health teams trained for crisis resolution and early intervention. Community treatment orders (or 'non-residential compulsion') were therefore an important aspect of the Government's 2004 Bill to enable patients subject to compulsion to be treated in the least restrictive manner possible, including in community settings[76].

3.52 A requirement that a patient should be detained in hospital as a precondition of compulsory treatment carries the danger that patients may be deprived of their liberty to satisfy the needs of law rather than medicine. However, neither the problem nor its solution can be viewed in such simple terms. On the one hand, existing legal structures already allow limited coercion of patients without hospitalisation through Guardianship, leave or conditional discharge; and on the other, the Government has conceded to its critics that community treatment orders will not be applicable without recent inpatient assessment.

3.53 The 1993 Health Committee considering proposals for community treatment orders warned against the view that 'treatment and care' in mental health services should be considered to be synonymous with the administration of psychiatric medication, clearly recognising that this does nothing to promote holistic and enabling treatment or care for people with mental disorder, and does much to perpetuate the problems of non-compliance that it seeks to address[77]. Whilst we recognise and agree with the Health Committee's warning, in practice it is clear that it is the power to compel patients to take prescribed medication that is at the heart of the current community treatment order debate. Existing community powers such as Guardianship enable professionals to specify patients' place of residence; attendance at specified places for health, education or rehabilitation purposes; and that patients must provide them with supervisory access. These powers are both uncontroversial and underused.

3.54 Community treatment measures entailing compulsory powers (including the power to enforce compliance with psychiatric medication) can be classified into three types:

(a) a variant of conditional release from hospital, where the condition of such release is continuance with treatment in the community;

---

[75] House of Commons Health Committee (1993) *Community Supervision Orders* Fifth Report of Session 1992-93, Vol 1, HC 667-1, p.vi.

[76] Joint Committee on the Draft Mental Health Bill (2005) *Draft Mental Health Bill* . Vil 2, p.521 Q.858 (Ms Winterton MP).

[77] House of Commons Health Committee (1993) *supra*, page xiv.

(b) an alternative to hospital for people who meet the criteria for involuntary hospitalisation; and

(c) preventive hospitalisation of people who do not currently meet the criteria for compulsory inpatient admission but are believed to be at risk of deterioration or relapse to the point that, without such intervention, they will meet such criteria at a future point[78].

It is already the case that the law of England and Wales permits the first type of compulsion. It has done so in the case of conditionally discharged restricted patients throughout the lifetime of the 1959 and 1983 Acts (see Chapter 5.136 *et seq*), and the courts' interpretation of the conditions under which patients' detention may be renewed whilst they are on long-term leave from hospital (see Chapters 1.42 *et seq* and 4.41) has extended compulsion into the community for civil patients under the current Act[79]. In our last report we pointed out the irony that the judiciary, largely unheeded[80], had broken the link between inpatient hospital treatment and compulsion at the time of a wide and polarised debate on Government proposals over non-residential treatment orders[81]. There is a further irony that, although the debate over community treatment orders has been engaged for over a decade in England and Wales, and the introduction of community powers has been stated Government policy for at least six years, as we prepare this report for publication it is not yet certain which type of community treatment outlined above will be put into effect by the draft Bill.

3.55 In part this uncertainty is the result of the detail of the application of non-residential orders being left to unwritten regulations and the Code of Practice at the time of the publication and debate upon the draft Bill of 2004. Government stated that the 'prime group' intended for the new powers would be those 'whose conditions and treatment are already familiar to the clinical team and who have recently been assessed as a hospital inpatient. The regulations are likely to describe the minimum length of earlier hospital admission; confirm whether that period must have been under compulsory powers; and will also need to set the period within which the earlier hospital stay must have occurred'. Government was quite correctly concerned not to create 'an obstacle to sensible clinical decision-making' with such regulations'[82].

3.56 Clearly, the exact nature of the regulations established on these matters will determine the extent to which non-residential treatment orders are alternatives to hospitalisation (i.e. type

---

[78] Adapted from Monahan J, Bonnie R J, Appelbaum P S, Hyde P S, Steadman H J, Swartz M S 'Mandated Community Treatment: Beyond Outpatient Commitment' *Psychiatric Services* Vol 52 No 9 p.1198-1205; September 2001.

[79] Thus returning the law to a position held prior to the *Hallstrom/Gardner* decisions of the mid-1980s. See MHAC (2003) *Tenth Biennial Report: Placed Amongst Strangers*, Chapter 9.48.

[80] Certainly Government did not seek intervention as an interested party in cases relating to the reach of compulsory powers for community-based patients.

[81] MHAC (2003) *Tenth Biennial Report: Placed Amongst Strangers*, Chapter 9.52. See also MHAC (2003) Chapter 9.47-54 for a general discussion of leave as a form of community treatment order; for our previous comments on the risks inherent in extending compulsion's reach see MHAC (2003) Chapter 1.5 *et seq*.

[82] Joint Committee on the Draft Mental Health Bill (2005) *Draft Mental Health Bill*. Vol 1, p.210.

(b) community powers described at paragraph 3.54 above), or a second-tier of compulsion with lower thresholds of application than residential orders (i.e a type (c) community power as described above). The Joint Committee on the draft Mental Health Bill was clearly opposed to the latter, and recommended that 'the primary legislation and its regulations should provide a robust safeguard against the emergence of any two-tier threshold for the imposition of compulsory powers'[83].

> 'Certain professionals use section 117 to give the impression you're still on a section and can be recalled to hospital without any fuss'.
>
> *female s.2 patient, Oxfordshire*

3.57 In its response to the Joint Committee, the Government stressed that the criteria applicable for the imposition of residential and non-residential treatment orders 'set a single threshold' but failed to take account of the fact that those criteria are in part established by the sort of intervention proposed. It is therefore still the case that the justification for imposing a community treatment order may be less burdensome than the justification for detention in hospital. The Government's indication that these matters might be dealt with through guidance such as the Code of Practice is not reassuring[84].

3.58 In her evidence to the Joint Committee, the Minister did recognise the possibility that existing arrangements for community treatment may be coercive in effect if not in law[85] (see paragraph 3.67 below), and that a benefit of formalising such arrangements through the use of community treatment orders would be that the latter are subject to safeguards, including a means of appeal through the Tribunal. We agree that formalising coercion would have this advantage, but note that this implies something of an expansion of formal coercive power over existing patients, whereas planning assumptions appear to be that the overall numbers of patients under compulsion will remain as they are when the new Act is introduced[86].

3.59 That existing powers of Guardianship are so little used suggests that professionals rarely see its powers as appropriate vehicles for coercive measures to support patients in the community. We suggest that there are likely to be two principal reasons for this attitude:

(i) in a majority of cases the practical threshold for *any* formally coercive intervention (whether this is established by questions of ethics or the limitations of resources) may be at a level where detention in hospital is the most immediate need to ensure the health or safety of the patient or the safety of others, so that the professionals concerned would not consider it safe to leave the patient in their community setting whilst providing crisis intervention; and / or

---

[83] *ibid.*, recommendation 32, para 198.

[84] See *The Government's response to the report of the Joint Committee on the Draft Mental Health Bill 2004.* Cm 6624, p.18-19.

[85] Joint Committee on the Draft Mental Health Bill (2005) *Draft Mental Health Bill.* Vol 2, p.523 Q.863 (Ms Winterton).

[86] Adrian Sieff, Head of Mental Health Legislation, Department of Health: interview reported in King's Fund Working Paper '*A Question of Numbers*', (see note 87).

(ii) 'treatment' considered in the context of compulsion may be essentially synonymous with the administration without consent of psychiatric medication or ECT, for which the powers of Guardianship provide no statutory basis.

If the current lack of professional enthusiasm for Guardianship is a result mainly or exclusively of (i) above, then the passing into law of 'non-residential' treatment orders will have little effect. If professional practice is explained by both (i) and (ii) above, then the introduction of 'non-residential' coercion could either have the effect of lowering the legal threshold for coercion so that, for example, patients currently subject to forms of assertive outreach are to be drawn into a framework of formal compulsion, or else it is likely to be used only in place of existing long-term leave arrangements. If professionals are dissuaded from using Guardianship solely because their attitudes are described by (ii) above, then the introduction of a community treatment order could lead to a substantial increase in the numbers of people subject to compulsion under mental health legislation. We discuss the community supervision of mentally disordered offenders at Chapter 5.132 below.

3.60 Research undertaken by Simon Lawton-Smith of the King's Fund has attempted to quantify the number of patients who may fall within the ambit of non-residential orders under a new Mental Health Act[87]. In the first instance, the analysis notes that up to 1,000 existing Guardianship and approximately 600 Supervised Discharge patients could become subject to the powers soon after their implementation, given that the new Act replaces the powers to which they are now subject. Home Office estimates have suggested a further two to three hundred mentally disordered offenders would otherwise be placed in prisons or hospitals could be eligible for non-residential treatment orders. Government planning estimates assume that about 10% of the current detained patient population (i.e. less than 1,500 people) would be made subject to non-residential orders. Although there is a strong descriptive similarity between the 'revolving door' patient that the Government wishes to target and the nearly 15,000 patients subject to Assertive Outreach Treatment (AOT)[88], Lawton-Smith has suggested that, from existing studies of the characteristics of patients receiving AOT, it may be reasonable to surmise that up to one third (i.e. 5,000) of these patients are likely to fit criteria relating to limited or non-compliance with medication[89]; history of violence[90]; or likelihood of hospital readmission[91]. In summary, and taking into account international comparisons, Lawton-Smith suggests that the likely use of non-residential orders in England and Wales could build over some years to between 15 and 30 people per 100,000 population, leading to a population of between 7,800 and 15,600 people.

---

[87] King's Fund Working Paper 'A Question of Numbers: the potential impact of community-based treatment orders in England and Wales'. September 2005 (www.kingsfund.org.uk). See also Lawton-Smith S 'Increasing returns' Mental Health Today, Sept 2005 p.16-8.

[88] The Department of Health reported 14,882 people looked after by Assertive Outreach Teams as of 31 December 2004 in a personal communication to the King's Fund.

[89] McPherson R (2004) 'The role of psychiatrist in assertive outreach' (talk given in Leeds, 24 September 2004) www.scmh.org.uk/website/SCMH_Conferences

[90] Priebe S, Fakhoury W, Watts, J, Bebbington P, Burns T, Johnson S, Muijen M, Ryrie I, White I & Wright C 'Assertive outreach teams in London: patient characteristics and outcomes: Pan-London Assertive Outreach Study, Part 3'. British Journal of Psychiatry, Aug 2003; 183: 148 - 154.

[91] ibid.

The New York State experience

3.61   In 1999 New York State passed a law providing for compulsory mental health treatment on a non-residential basis in response to the death of Kendra Webdale, a commuter who was pushed under the path of an oncoming subway train by a man diagnosed with schizophrenia[92]. 'Kendra's Law'[93] provided that courts could mandate 'assisted outpatient treatment' for renewable periods of six months, requiring patients to reside at a certain place, attend places for treatment, submit to blood or urine testing to measure psychiatric or other drug levels and self-administer or accept administration of psychotropic drugs. Failure to comply with such an order could lead to removal to hospital for up to 72 hours.

3.62   Although New York State's 'Kendra's Law' was established and named in response to an apparently random act of violence by a mentally disordered person, and promoted as a public protection measure, its criteria for application were not limited to mentally disordered people who pose a risk to others, but encompassed 'revolving door' patients more generally. Analysis of the use of Kendra's Law in its first five years showed that only 15% of those made subject to its community powers of compulsion had a record of physical harm to others, although 33% had a record of verbally assaulting others and 28% had a record of threatening physical harm to others. Thirteen per cent had a record of damaging property. Almost all had a history of admission to hospital, with an average of three admissions each during the three years before being made subject to community compulsion[94]. Overall, therefore, the law was used less for public protection than it was used to coerce vulnerable patients into accepting treatment 'for their own good'. The State Governor's Office found significant reduction in hospitalisation, homelessness, substance abuse, threat of harm to others, arrest and imprisonment. Adherence to medication rose from 41% to 62%[95].

---

[92] There is a notable irony that the killer of Kendra Webdale, 'far from rejecting treatment like the prototypical target of outpatient commitment laws, had actually sought assistance on several occasion, only to be turned away because of lack of available slot in the treatment programs' (Appelbaum, P S 'Thinking Carefully About Outpatient Commitment' *Psychiatric Services* Vol 52 No 3 p347-350; March 2001). UK cases of 'failed' community treatment related to violent or dangerous incidents have similarly involved patients who have been turned away from services rather than who have avoided contact with services. As such, it may be argued that an element of 'compulsion' involved in community treatment orders is implicitly or explicitly targeted at service providers, rather than service users (see paragraph 3.71 below).

[93] The official naming of outpatient commitment laws after the victims of random violence also occurred in Ontario, Canada (Brian's Law) and California (Laura's Law). The latter was passed in the wake of New York legislation but is more restrictive in its application, with criteria based upon the principle of using the least restrictive alternative and requiring that any county implementing the powers must first have established elaborate panning and service provision to all patients, and not just those subject to compulsion, that may be beyond the practical reach of the Californian mental health infrastructure (see Appelbaum P S 'Ambivalence Codified: California's New Outpatient Commitment Statute' *Psychiatric Services* Vol 54 No 1 p26-28; January 2003).

[94] New York State Office of Mental Health (2005) *Kendra's Law: Final Report on the Status of Assisted Outpatient Treatment.* New York, March 2005, p. 9, 16. www.omh.state.ny.us/omhweb/Kendra_web/finalreport/

[95] *ibid.*

3.63 Department of Health research on the use of supervision registers[96], which were similarly promoted as a public protection measure but were applicable to patients at risk to others or to themselves (including through 'self-neglect'), found that although two thirds of the 113 patients on supervision registers in 1997 were identified as a risk to others, for almost half of these no actual incidents of violence to others had ever been recorded. The researchers noted that objective histories of risk were variable across all categories on the register. They concluded that although decisions about compulsory treatment are dependent upon an assessment of the degree of risk which patients pose to themselves or others, the study highlighted the problem of achieving valid and consistent risk assessment in community samples.

3.64 New York's Kendra's Law had a sunset clause operative after five years of implementation. Despite the State Governor's wish to make the law permanent, in July 2005 the Legislature voted only for its extension for a further five years. The law and its implementation have been controversial[97]. It is claimed unconstitutional by the New York Civil Liberties Union[98]. The group New York Lawyers for the Public Interest published a report in April 2005[99] disputing the benign analysis of the State Governor's report on the use of the power[100]. Of particular concern to the group was the fact that 42% of the nearly 4,000 uses of Kendra's Law related to Black patients. Based on population, this made Black patients five times more likely than White patients to be made subject to the powers. If state-wide statistics relating to the incidence of severe and persistent mental illness are used as the comparator, Black patients are still almost three times as likely to be subjected to the law as their White counterparts[101]. The State Governor's Office counter that the proportions of Black patients being made subject to the law are similar to those observed for all adults receiving intensive case-management and assertive community treatment in urban areas. This response slightly begs the question of why Black patients are over-represented in other 'assertive' and therefore often coercive intervention programmes[102].

3.65 Most other U.S. states have passed some form of involuntary outpatient commitment law, but most of these laws apply only to such persons who meet the criteria for involuntary hospitalisation[103]. Under Kendra's Law, the key criteria are that the patient:

---

[96] Supervision registers were introduced in 1994, requiring Trusts to identify patients at risk in various ways, and ensure that they received care under the Care Programme Approach (CPA). The implementation of *Modernising the Care Programme Approach* (1999), which created the current system of standard and enhanced CPA, foreshadows their eventual discontinuance. The effectiveness of supervision registers probably was curtailed as no new resources were provided to establish them or meet the inevitable increase in sessional commitment from health and social service professionals. See Coid J 'Failure in Community Care: Psychiatry's Dilemma' *BMJ* 1994; 308; 805-6 (26 March).

[97] Michael Cooper *Racial Disproportion Seen in Applying 'Kendra's Law'*. New York Times, April 7 2005

[98] www.nyclu.org/aot_program_pr_062305.html

[99] New York Lawyers for the Public Interest (2005) *Implementation of 'Kendra's Law' is Severely Biased*. New York, April 7, 2005. www.nylpi.org

[100] New York State Office of Mental Health (2005) *Kendra's Law: Final Report on the Status of Assisted Outpatient Treatment*. New York, March 2005. www.omh.state.ny.us/omhweb/Kendra_web/finalreport/

[101] New York Lawyers for the Public Interest (2005) *supra*, p.9

[102] Davis S 'Autonomy Versus Coercion: Reconciling Competing Perspectives in Community Mental Health' *Community Mental Health Journal* Vol 38 No 3, p.239-250 at pp.245, June 2002.

[103] *ibid.*, p.14. see also Torrey E F and Kaplan, R J (1995) 'A National Survey of the Use of Outpatient Commitment' *Psychiatric Services* 46:78.

- is aged over 18 and suffering from mental illness;

- has a history of a lack of compliance with treatment evidenced either by

  - at least two admissions to psychiatric or correctional facilities over the last three years; or

  - by one or more threats, attempts, or acts of serious harm to self or others within the last four years; and

- is unlikely to participate voluntarily in a treatment plan designed to prevent relapse or deterioration of the condition.

> 'One of my CPNs said to me, if I came off my medication I'd be sectioned. I felt really threatened, and it silenced me from talking to my GP, psychiatrist and CPN. It left me feeling paralysed and unable to discuss my medication'
>
> *Abina Parshad-Griffin, ex s.2 patient*

3.66 In our responses to the UK Government and the Joint Committee on the draft Mental Health Bill, we have stated our concern that the draft Mental Health Bill 2004 implied that non-residential treatment orders could be imposed in England and Wales using a lower threshold than would be operative for involuntary hospitalisation[104]. The 2005 census appears to confirm previous findings that Black patients are already roughly six-times as likely as White patients to be subjected to the powers of the 1983 Act[105]. We recognise and support the Government's clearly genuine intention to try to address this disproportionate use of legal powers, but we are not reassured by the Government's response to the Joint Committee's concern over the two-tier model of compulsion implied by the draft Bill's provisions (see paragraph 3.57 above). The lowering of the threshold for imposing compulsory powers must carry a risk of exacerbating the apparent overrepresentation of Black people subject to their use.

3.67 The expansion of compulsory powers into community-based treatment using a lower practical threshold of imposition would increase the proportion of mental health service users whose voluntary agreement to accept services is overshadowed by a potential use of compulsion and force. The New York State experience has been argued to show the distorting effect of such an expansion of compulsion on 'voluntary agreements' to undergo treatment. One county in the State, Erie County, showed a proportionately low use of court orders under Kendra's Law, but a proportionately high use of written 'voluntary agreements'. The New York Lawyers for the Public Interest studied these agreements and concluded that:

> 'voluntary agreements' are voluntary only in name. They are entered under the threat of court proceedings… and … often extracted without the individual having the advice of a lawyer. It is clear that at least some who sign them are thoroughly intimidated and unsure of their options. Patients picked out for voluntary agreements are asked to adhere to a prescribed treatment plan … similar in coercion to court orders. The monitoring arrangements that make up a large part of the coercive effect of court orders are present. So alas is the threat of being taken to hospital for evaluation. [With voluntary agreements] the intimidating court hearing hangs over the individual's head, whereas under an order it has already occurred[106].

---

[104] see, for example, Joint Committee on the Draft Mental Health Bill (2005) *Draft Mental Health Bill*. Vol 2, Ev24. (MHAC Memorandum DMH 20, para 2.32 et seq)

[105] See MHAC (2003) *Tenth Biennial Report: Placed Amongst Strangers*, Chapter 16.10.

[106] New York Lawyers for the Public Interest (2005) *supra*, p.10

3.68   It is already our experience that many 'informal' hospital inpatients are voluntary only to the extent that the threat of detention under the 1983 Act hangs over them. Indeed this fact has been recognised by the Department of Health's own research programme:

> From the viewpoint of patients admitted to hospital, the distinction between legal compulsion and voluntary treatment is not always clear. Many informal patients feel coerced, and only a minority are confident of their freedom to leave the ward. If compulsory treatment is extended to the community, it may be that even patients who are not in fact subject to compulsion will feel increased coercion in their relationship with services[107].

3.69   This presents something of a dilemma for a legislature seeking to provide both powers of intervention and safeguards against the over-use of such powers. One real danger, in our view, is that any two-tier system of compulsion (i.e. where community treatment powers have a lower operative threshold than powers enabling compulsory admission to hospital) may actually extend the number of patients over whose heads the threat of compulsion hangs, in effect restricting choices for groups of patients who have not previously been within reach of the State's coercive health powers.

3.70   Our concerns over the broad scope for the application of community treatment orders is compounded by the even broader scope over what the effect of such powers could be on patients who are subjected to them. The draft Bill proposals up to 2004 have not specified any parameters to the requirements that may be placed upon a person subject to a community treatment order, such as are given in relation to the powers that may be exercised under supervised discharge or Guardianship. We raised our concern to the Joint Committee on the draft Mental Health Bill that this opened the way for misuse of community treatment orders as a form of psychiatric Anti-Social Behaviour Order (ASBO)[108], where all sorts of restrictions on a patient's lifestyle, associations or activities would be enforceable under the threat of compulsory hospitalisation. The Committee subsequently recommended that the provisions for non-residential orders should be simple and used only to specify requirements on treatment and requirements or limitations on place of residence[109]. The Government has responded that this would limit the scope of non-residential orders in managing risk and therefore make them unworkable[110]. This response, and the suggestion that the scope of community powers will be subject only to guidance in a Code of Practice, causes us great concern. In the introduction to this report (paragraph xiii) we noted reports of the way in which ASBOs as civil-law measures have been applied questionably to vulnerable patients and for purposes other than that which they appear to have been intended for. We see no cause for complacency over the way in

---

[107] Professor Graham Thornicroft (2000) *Supervision and Coercion Studies*. Shaping the New Mental Health Act: Key Messages from the Department of Health Research Programme. www.doh.gov.uk/mhar/mha_use3.htm. See also Bindman J, Reid Y, Szmukler G, Tiller J, Thornicroft G, Leese M. 'Perceived Coercion at admission to psychiatric hospital and engagement with follow-up; a cohort study *Soc Psychiary Psychiatr Epidemiol* (2005) 40 160-166.

[108] See Joint Committee on the Draft Mental Health Bill (2005) *Draft Mental Health Bill*. Vol 1, p.69

[109] *ibid.*, recommendation 33, page 71.

[110] *The Government's response to the report of the Joint Committee on the Draft Mental Health Bill 2004*. Cm 6624, p.18

which community mental health powers could be applied similarly. Non-residential powers must not become a blank slate upon which *any* requirement may be made of psychiatric patients in the name of safety.

3.71   Kendra's Law also required mental health systems to give priority access to case management and other services necessary to successful community living (including, for example, housing services) to patients subject to its powers. As the sole legal means of arguing a 'right' to outpatient treatment, this does create something of a perverse incentive for the use of its powers of compulsion. Although the draft Mental Health Bill of 2004 for England and Wales is carefully framed not to imply any right to treatment, there is a danger of similar perverse incentives under the proposed framework of its powers in that patients remaining subject to non-residential compulsion will not be eligible to be charged for such services, but will become so eligible six weeks after discharge. Government has not explicitly addressed concerns that this might lead to inappropriate extension of such compulsion, although it has emphasised that means-testing will ensure that no-one is deprived of treatment because they cannot afford it, and that the relatively easy transition from non-resident compulsion to 'voluntary' patient status should ensure that there is no inappropriate extension of detention whilst aftercare is being arranged[111]. This may be the case, but the fact that exactly the same services may be provided to a patient as 'aftercare' as were provided under non-residential compulsion (i.e. there is no significant event in service provision, equivalent to the discharge from hospital of a patient subject to detention under a residential order, that marks the beginning of aftercare for non-residential patients) may make the potential for perverse incentives to continue compulsion all the harder to resist. A patient who wished to avoid means-tested charging for services that he or she is already in receipt of under compulsory powers could ensure that exemption from charging persists simply by refusing to sign their consent to such services[112]. It is not inconceivable that patients' families will challenge the patient's reclassification as a 'voluntary' patient when the most notable effect of this classification is to initiate means-testing and self-funding.

3.72   It is axiomatic that quality community and hospital-based mental health care services aiming to enhance rather than remove patients' autonomy are the most likely to achieve good patient compliance and best results. We do not doubt that compulsory powers have a role in such services, and we do not object in principle to the idea that, in certain carefully defined circumstances, compulsion might follow a patient out of hospital into a community setting. That there may or should be very strict limitations on the way in which this can take place, either because of legal or practical constraints on how compulsion can operate, may not be a bad thing. Legislative solutions such as community treatment orders may not always offer a solution to the need to provide appropriate services for psychiatric patients within limited resources.

---

[111] Joint Committee on the Draft Mental Health Bill (2005) *Draft Mental Health Bill* Vol 1, p.208

[112] *ibid.*, p.207: 'the Bill provides (clause 53) that where acceptance of a service is a relevant requirement imposed upon a patient, then no charge can be made for that service'.

The future of the Mental Health Act Commission

3.73   In our last report we described Government proposals for the future of the Mental Health Act Commission[114]. The draft Mental Health Bill 2002 contained clauses that transferred the majority of the Commission's monitoring functions to the Healthcare Commission (at that time known under its statutory name as the Commission for Healthcare Audit and Inspection (CHAI)). The Second Opinion Appointed Doctor functions would cease on repeal of the 1983 Act and implementation of the Bill once enacted, and the general functions of clinical review of cases and general advice to the Mental Health Tribunal would be the responsibility of the proposed Expert Panel. The 2004 Bill repeated these broad proposals, although the Government's response to the Joint Committee on that draft Bill suggests that the Department of Health is reviewing the way in which monitoring and inspection arrangements will be fulfilled under the Bill once enacted[115].

3.74   The Joint Committee on the draft Mental Health Bill noted that many witnesses were concerned about the proposed changes to the visiting function. They recognised that the Commission has a 'pro-active visiting regime involving announced and unannounced visits… [with] a duty to visit routinely mental health facilities and individual patients'[116]. They also noted that the Institute of Mental Health Practitioners had said:

> … getting rid of a small stand alone semi-independent specialist Mental Health Commission will do enormous harm [….] the danger is that the constitutional imperative will be consumed by a larger political imperatives if the MHAC becomes one small division within a super-Commission dedicated to monitoring compliance with the NHS programme[117].

3.75   We were pleased to note the recommendation in the report that the Mental Health Bill should set out powers and duties that will ensure the preservation of a specialised system to monitor all patients subject to powers of compulsion in the Bill, including restricted patients[118]. Similarly, we were pleased to note their recommendation that the body charged with monitoring patients subject to compulsion should have a duty similar to the visiting duty already undertaken by the Mental Health Act Commission, including a duty to visit routinely mental health facilities to interview patients[119]. We have argued strenuously that it is only by visiting services regularly, frequently and flexibly that the lawfulness of detention of patients can be checked and abuses of patients abrogated[120].

3.76   We are less certain about the Joint Committee's recommendation that the powers and duties that they described should be given to a reformed Mental Health Act Commission. The Commission has always had a 'self denying ordinance' and has not wanted to argue for its

---

[114]   MHAC (2003) *Tenth Biennial Report: Placed Amongst Strangers*, Chapter 20

[115]   *The Government's response to the report of the Joint Committee on the Draft Mental Health Bill 2004.* Cm 6624, p.41

[116]   Joint Committee on the Draft Mental Health Bill (2005) *Draft Mental Health Bill*, Vol I, p.105

[117]   *ibid.*, p.107

[118]   *ibid.*

[119]   *ibid.*

[120]   See, for example, MHAC (2003) *Tenth Biennial Report: Placed Amongst Strangers*, Chapter 20.12 *et seq.*

own preservation. Any argument in favour of our own retention would be to a large degree self-serving, however strongly we believe that there is a need for a separate standalone inspectorate. We *do* believe there are strong arguments for retaining an independent and monitoring inspectorate body as we set out below, but we *also* recognise also that there are arguments in favour of incorporating the Mental Health Act Commission's functions into a larger inspectorate body that has the resources and sanctions to ensure compliance with recommendations for improvement.

3.77   The future of the Mental Health Act Commission may not be determined solely by changes to mental health legislation, although we believe that any merger of the Mental Health Act Commission into another body should not take place prior to the enactment of the draft Mental Health Bill. The Commission was established by the 1983 Act and has important duties to undertake until such time as that Act is repealed and different legislation with appropriate safeguards is introduced. We note that the Department of Health's Arms Length Body Review (2004) proposed that the Mental Health Act Commission should be merged with the Healthcare Commission only subject to the passage of the Mental Health Bill through Parliament.

3.78   During informal discussions with the Healthcare Commission in 2004, shortly after it had come into being in its current form, we agreed that an appropriate time for the Mental Health Act Commission to merge with the Healthcare Commission, subject to the passage of legislation, would be 1 April 2007. Subsequently a number of changes have taken place that alter the context in which these discussions have been held. Two changes in particular are worth noting:

- The publication of the Joint Committee report with the recommendations as described above; and

- The decision by the Government, announced by the Chancellor of the Exchequer in his budget speech just before Easter 2005, that the Healthcare Commission and the Commission for Social Care Inspection would merge as soon as practicable, probably in 2007/8.

3.79   The proposed merger of the Healthcare Commission and CSCI is being considered by the Department of Health within the context of a major review of the regulatory environment for health and social care. This review is scheduled to take place over the winter of 2005. The Arms Length Body Review 2004 made proposals for a 20% cut in the funding of the Department of Health Arms Length Bodies (from £2.5 billion to £2.0 billion) and a reduction in overall staffing by some 25%. The total number of Arms Length Bodies was to be reduced from 39 to 19. These objectives remain Government policy and the Mental Health Act Commission is not immune from the broader context in which healthcare inspection, regulation, monitoring and review is undertaken.

3.80   We have argued to Departmental officials that if the Healthcare Commission and CSCI are to merge, then the Mental Health Act Commission is not truly merging with the Healthcare Commission but with a new body. This new organisation may have a different culture to the Healthcare Commission, which could be reflected in differing duties, responsibilities, or assessment processes to those presently adopted by the Healthcare Commission. If the

Mental Health Act Commission is to merge with another body or bodies it will be essential to have been part of the wider review which establishes functions that need to be undertaken before the form of the organisation is agreed.

3.81 There are nevertheless strong arguments for retaining a separate standalone Mental Health Act Commission. Although the Government has, we understand, turned its back on this proposal for the reasons set out above, we think it is worth rehearsing the arguments here for completeness and to ensure that, whatever form of inspectorate and monitoring body emerges, the necessary safeguards for patients are put in place in way that will be effective and can be seen by patients, service users, carers and professional staff to be effective.

3.82 In making proposals for alternative arrangements we are mindful of the very different circumstances that prevail in mental health services in comparison to other areas of health care and the need to review the assumptions on which the monitoring of mental health care is based. Much mental healthcare in the public and independent sectors is very different from general acute medicine and surgery, and has more in common with the agenda of social care and social inclusion. Unlike patients in general health services, people with mental disorder are, with one or two rare exceptions, the only group of patients whose liberty is deprived ostensibly in their own best interests, and whose circumstances frequently engage civil, legal and human rights notably the European Convention on Human Rights (ECHR) and Human Rights Act 1998. Consequently the Government's proposal to abolish the Mental Health Act Commission and merge the visiting and inspection functions into the Healthcare Commission is only one of a number of possible options to improve regulation and reduce the burden of inspection on providers. A future arrangement that focuses on civil and human rights rather than on health and social care may be worth exploring.

Changes to the policy environment since Government's decision to merge many of the Commission's functions with the Healthcare Commission:

(i) The Joint Committee on the draft Mental Health Bill's recommendations about the monitoring process for the Mental Health Act and proposed retention of a Mental Health Act Commission.

(ii) Government's increasing emphasis on reducing the burden of inspection and regulation. For mental health services the burden of inspection is already light (the MHAC costs c.£3m for monitoring and £2m for SOADs) and could be argued to be in need of strengthening.

(iii) Following the Chancellor of the Exchequer's announcement in his budget speech in March 2005, the MHAC will now not be merging with the Healthcare Commission in its present form, but with a new body whose functions are at present uncertain.

(iv) One of the new agencies to be created from the ALB review, an organisation established specifically for the purpose, or another emergent body, may be a more appropriate partner for mental health monitoring.

> (v) Over the five years since implementation of the Human Rights Act 1998 there has been a steadily increasing emphasis on equality and human rights in health care. Detained patients fundamentally engage the Human Rights Act 1998 and European Convention on Human Rights.
>
> (vi) Race, gender and disability equality is now firmly established in the Government's programme. The MHAC has been at the forefront in developing work to take forward Government's emphasis on respecting diversity particularly race and gender equality.

Fig 30: policy environment changes since Government's decision to merge many MHAC functions with the Healthcare Commission

3.83 The MHAC acts as one of the assurances for Government that its policies and statutes are being applied fairly, without discrimination, and without abuse of patients or the abrogation of their rights. Abolition of a specialist monitoring body (unless the functions are replicated elsewhere) could have a significant impact on the ability of the State to protect the rights of mentally disordered patients, where the MHAC assists in reducing risks to patients from abuse and the sometimes fatal consequences of that abuse; and on the State's ability to protect its own interests where abuses of patients' rights may occur, including financial risks to its delegated bodies from litigation by aggrieved patients or families.

3.84 It is difficult to see how an inspectorate body can contain readily within it both systems for assessment against standards and prioriities, and appraisal of individual patients' rights. Experience suggests that the one will be in constant tension with the other; but more importantly the opportunity to take an external independent perspective on rights where they conflict with systems will at best be compromised and at worst lost entirely. We are concerned that systems-based assessment processes, although valuable in themselves, are insufficient and inappropriate for monitoring the needs of detained patients. Systems are flexible, malleable and adaptable: rights are personal, indivisible and inalienable. A system of assessment methodology that is based on provider self-assessment and sample checks will not get to the heart of mental healthcare. A strengthened MHAC (whether wholly independent or part of another independent inspectorate) could benefit greatly from the ability to issue improvement or enforcement notices with recourse to the courts in a way similar to that available to the Health and Safety Executive.

3.85 Not only are there arguments for retention of the present functions of the MHAC as a standalone body, there are other functions that a revised MHAC might take on. A further extension of the powers of monitoring could include the implications of the Mental Capacity Act 2005, in particular to ensure that patients' (in)capacity has been correctly assessed; that they are not being deprived of their liberty without appropriate safeguards; and to fulfil whatever arrangements and safeguards emerge from the 'Bournewood' consultation. Similarly, a revised MHAC might be the ideal vehicle for monitoring services to older people with mental disorder, and ensuring the NSF standards (for Mental Health and Older People) are being achieved.

3.86 In developing proposals for any future Commission arrangements we believe that firm achievable objectives should be established.

(i) *The State must have the ability to protect itself and patients.* Effective protections require the achievement of minimum legal compliance and structures designed purposively to protect and promote human rights;

(ii) *Monitoring must be based on a robust human rights framework.* It is essential to retain a 'benchmark' or reference point against which to measure the role of the State in applying compulsion to patients and the role of inspectorate agencies in regulating care services. A regime based on moveable system standards that are not rooted in the needs of mentally disordered people themselves will be inadequate for the protection of those individuals.

(iii) *The significant changes to be brought about by the draft Mental Health Bill, once enacted,* must be monitored adequately. Given the huge changes that will occur on implementation of new legislation it is essential to have an expert body with the knowledge and experience to ensure the smooth introduction of new statutory arrangements.

(iv) *The Government's policy on enhancing choice for patients must extend to detained patients.* The choices of detained patients are limited in the extreme, although ways in which their choices can be increased should be explored in the context of the legal basis of compulsion.

(v) *The human rights of detained patients should be ensured through an objectively impartial monitoring system.* Article 6 distinguishes between subjective and objective impartiality, or in lay terms between actual and perceived fairness. Retaining an organisation that provides an objectively impartial scrutiny of the treatment of detained patients (in other words having a regulatory process that is not only fair but is seen to be fair) is a protection for both the State and the patient.

(vi) *Attention to race and gender equality and anti-discrimination work must be ensured.* Significant developments have taken place recently in tackling inequality and discrimination, and these alone could constitute reason for reviewing the protections required.

(vii) *Provision must be made for monitoring of the Mental Capacity Act 2005 and the care of incapacitated compliant patients.* The effective monitoring of the implementation of the Mental Capacity Act 2005 in psychiatric contexts could be subsumed into a revamped Commission.

> **Recommendation 11:** We commend to Government the objectives set out at paragraph 3.86 above for its consideration when establishing future Mental Health Act monitoring arrangements.

Partnership working

3.87 Whatever the outcome of the Government's current deliberations about the future of health and social care regulation, including the future of the MHAC, there are benefits in the meantime to collaborating with other bodies whose remits impact directly or indirectly on the care of detained patients. Since our last Biennial Report, we have strengthened the MHAC's links with a number of inspectorates, most notably the Healthcare Commission, to try to ensure that a coherent approach is taken to planning projects within an overall mental health work programme. In June 2004 the MHAC joined nine other organisations in signing a concordat[121] between bodies inspecting, regulating and auditing healthcare. The concordat sets out a number of objectives and practices, agreed by the signatories, which aim to deliver more consistent and coherent programmes of inspection, improve services for patients, clients and their carers, and reduce unnecessary burdens of inspection on staff providing healthcare. Whether the activity of the various working groups set up to help implementation of the concordat will result in tangible benefits to patients or to providers of services is yet to be tested; but over a year on, some good progress has been made in understanding others' business, sharing information and on managing the scheduling of visits and inspections. An important practice within the concordat is reliance on other inspecting bodies' reviews and findings where this is both legal and appropriate. From 2005-06 the Healthcare Commission is using published MHAC annual reports on providers as corroborative evidence to support (or refute) self-assessment by NHS mental health Trusts. A key tenet of our response to the Healthcare Commission's consultation on its assessment methodology in early 2005[122] was concern about over-reliance on self-assessment, particularly in areas of healthcare where patients are not able to exercise freedom of choice, and we were pleased that the Healthcare Commission listened to our concerns (and those of others) and have introduced a greater emphasis on spot check visits than was originally envisaged. The Healthcare Commission is partway through full implementation of its assessment methodology and regional structures. We advocate the need for specialist mental health input to inspections of mental health services, and will continue to work closely with the Healthcare Commission operations teams to ensure effective monitoring and inspection of services within the available public resources and to the benefit of patients.

---

[121] www.healthcarecommission.org.uk/concordat

[122] The MHAC's response to the Healthcare Commission's consultation 'Assessment for Improvement' is available on the MHAC website (www.mhac.org.uk). The Healthcare Commission's final proposals ('Assessment for Improvement: the annual healthcheck') were published on 31 March 2005 and are available at www.healthcarecommission.org.uk

4

The Mental Health Act in Practice

Admission trends under the Mental Health Act 1983

4.1 The annual number of patients admitted under the 'civil' powers of Part II of the Act has been roughly stable for the last six years (see figure 31 below). Over the lifetime of the Act that number has doubled. It may be that the apparent levelling off is a sign of services running at their maximum capacity (see Chapter 2 above).

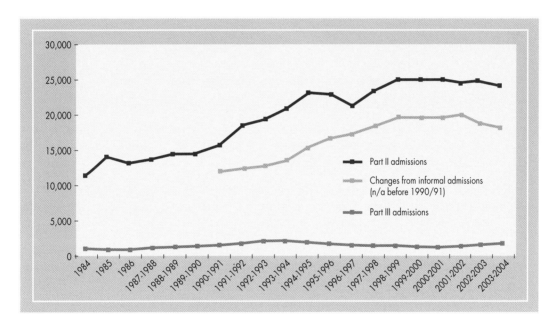

Fig. 31: Mental Health Act admission trends, England, 1984 – 2003/4[1]

4.2 In our previous Biennial Reports we have pointed to the rising proportion of inpatients who are detained compared to the informal patient population[2]. The proportion of inpatients who are detained appears still to be relatively large, and is probably higher than in the early

---

[1] Data source: DHSS (1987) *Mental Health Statistics for England 1986* Booklet 11, Legal Status Table D1; Department of Health (1995) *Statistical Bulletin 1995/4*; DH (1996) *Statistical Bulletin 1996/10*; DH (1999) *Statistical Bulletin 1999/25*; DH (2002) *Statistical Bulletin 2002/26*. DH (2004) *Statistical Bulletin 2004/22* (tables 1 and 7). Data accuracy is compromised by its several sources, mixture of calendar years and financial years and possible discrepancies in categorisation over time.

[2] See for example MHAC (2001) *Ninth Biennial Report 1999-01*. Chapter 3.1 - 3.2

years of the Act. In some medium and high secure units, of course, all or almost all patients are detained, but the rise is also notable in acute and admission wards. We note the following national data:

- Although it is difficult to determine an exact figure of 'informal' admissions for comparison, published hospital episode statistics suggest that approximately one fifth of all admissions to psychiatric inpatient beds involve detention under the Mental Health Act 1983, either at the point of admission or during the patients' stay in hospital[3].

- The most recent Department of Health statistics on the number of detained patients resident at any one time (31 March 2004) showed 14,000 patients subject to the Act[4] (figure 33 below). This is an increase of about 4% on the 2002 total given in our last report, and is marginally the highest figure recorded to date[5], at a time of the lowest inpatient bed provision in the last half-century (see Chapter 2.13 et seq above).

- The *Count Me In* National Mental Health and Ethnicity Census 2005 found that three-fifths of resident mental health patients[6] had informal status, with the remaining two-fifths detained.

4.3 At Figures 32 and 33 below we show the numbers of detained patients resident in hospital since 1997. The overall increase is by about one-fifth, although there is some fluctuation in numbers. The most striking pattern, as we have noted in Chapter 2.17 is that the number of detained patients resident in the independent sector has more than trebled over the last eight years.

4.4 In our last report[7] we suggested that the general increase in the use of the Act proportionate to inpatient admissions on some wards may be due to a number of factors:

- In part, it simply may be a reflection of decreasing numbers of inpatient beds, and increasing community-based treatment of patients who may in the past have been admitted to hospital on an informal basis.

- Bed pressures may also lead to only the most severely ill being detained for shorter but more frequent periods than previously. Such patients may be likely to be detained due to the severity of their illness at the point of admission.

- The promotion of risk-management by mental health policy makers, the criticisms of post-incident inquiries or even generally less permissive societal attitudes may account

---

3   See Department of Health Hospital Episode Statistics 2003-04, tables 2, 7; for all mental health / learning disability categories these report between 213,000 and 233,000 finished episodes for 2003/04: in that year 47,300 detentions (both admissions and of patients already informally admitted) were recorded by the Department of Health (DH (2004) *Statistical Bulletin 2004/22*).

4   *Inpatients formally detained under the Mental Health Act 1983 and other legislation, 2003-04*, table 14.

5   Official statistics for 2005 from the Department of Health (Statistical Bulletin *In-patients formally detained in hospitals under the Mental Health Act 1983 and other legislation, England: 1994-95 to 2004-05)* should be published in December 2005 or January 2006. In the 2005 National Census, we counted 13,172 patients detained under the Act. An estimated 1% of all eligible patients (detained or informal) would have been missed from the total Census collection due to failures to return data in approximately a quarter of independent sector providers. As the Census did not extend to learning disability services, and as learning disability patients counted for at least 1,100 of the 14,000 total in 2004, it seems doubtful that the total number of resident detained patients will be fewer than approximately 14,000 in 2005. See Healthcare Commission, MHAC, and NIMHE (2005) *Count Me In: National Mental Health and Ethnicity Census 2005*, in press.

6   See note 5 above on the coverage of the 2005 census.

7   MHAC (2003) *Tenth Biennial Report: Placed Amongst Strangers*, Chapter 8.27

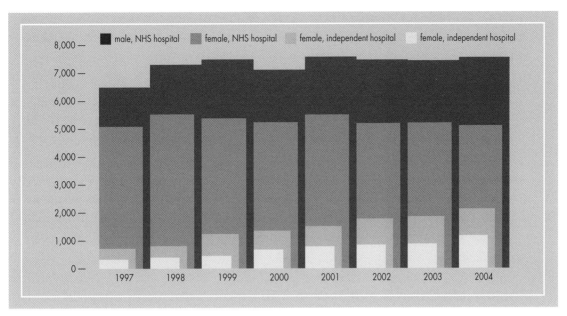

Fig 32: detained patients resident in hospital by gender and NHS or independent sector, England, 1997-2004[8]

		1997	% change	1998	% change	1999	% change	2000	% change	2001	% change	2002	% change	2003	% change	2004
Male	NHS	6,878	8	7,515	2	7,647	-3	7,421	5	7,790	-4	7,515	-0.1	7,506	3	7,727
	Ind. hosp	505	12	574	30	832	13	957	16	1,136	14	1,314	5	1,383	9	1,516
Female	NHS	3,886	10	4,315	-3	4,176	-3	4,052	7	4,360	-7	4,051	0.8	4,083	2	3,981
	Ind. hosp	200	29	280	17	338	20	425	22	543	6	579	6	616	20	776
total		11,469	10	12,684	2	12,993	-1	12,855	7	13,829	-3	13,459	1	13,588	3	14,000

Fig 33: detained patients resident in hospital by gender and NHS or independent sector, England, 1997-2004, showing percentage change[9]

for some of the rise. These factors may encourage medical and social care professionals to use the Act more readily, either through lowering the perceived thresholds for such use or through fostering defensive professional practice.

- Increases in drug and alcohol abuse co-morbidity might explain apparent rises in severity of mental disordered persons, given that drug/alcohol abuse may make mentally ill persons more disinhibited or may aggravate their symptoms, thus making their detention more likely.

- The environmental conditions on inpatient wards may be responsible for an increase in the detention of patients who would otherwise discharge themselves against medical advice.

---

8   Data source: as for fig 31 (footnote 1) above.

9   Data source: as above.

With the possible exception of the first entry on this list, none of these factors are the inevitable consequences of societal shifts beyond governmental control, but could be addressed through targeted actions. It is widely agreed that the basic structure of the legal framework for mental health care has remained essentially similar for nearly fifty years, and is predicated upon the assumption that informal treatment is to be preferred over any formal compulsion. Although in the introduction to this report (paragraph xxiii *et seq*) we recognised the potential of the judgment in *HL v United Kingdom* to undermine that structure by removing the legal basis for certain incapacitated patients' informal care, it would be a great irony were, in the decades to come, the informal hospital treatment of psychiatric patients overall to become a rarity due to failures of service provision and service capacity. In our view, as we discussed in Chapter 2.26 *et seq* above, the focus on establishing community interventions to keep patients from hospital admission must not blind us to the continuing need for inpatient care that patients will enter and reside in voluntarily.

The use of section 2 and section 3 to detain patients in hospital

4.5   Most patients who are made subject to the Act are detained under sections 2 or 3. These detention powers have slightly different criteria and safeguards: s.2 allows detention for assessment and/or treatment for a maximum of 28 days, whilst the renewable powers of s.3, although lasting for up to six months in the first instance, effectively allow for indefinite detention for treatment. It is a matter of professional judgment as to which section is initially appropriate in any particular case.

4.6   Figures 34 and 35 below show the uses of ss.2 and 3 to admit patients to hospital under each power over the lifetime of the Act.

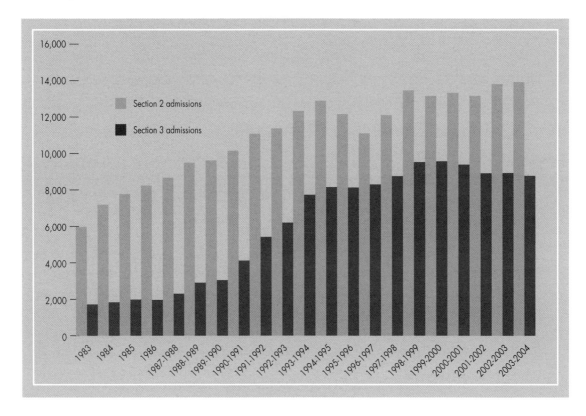

Fig 34: admissions under sections 2 and 3, England, 1983 - 2004[10]

---

[10]   Data source: as for fig 31 above.

4.7   The overall rise in the number and proportion of s.3 admissions during the lifetime of the Act is probably due to the influence of the Code of Practice guidance on the use of the Act, which was first published in 1990 and suggested that the key determinant in choosing between s.2 as an assessment power and s.3 as power of admission for treatment was the diagnostic and prognostic confidence of the clinical team in respect of a particular patient[11]. The current edition of the Code continues to suggest that s.3 may be used as an admission section where, for example, a patient is known to services and has had a recent assessment, but that s.2 should be used if the diagnosis or prognosis is unclear, or there is a need for inpatient assessment to formulate a treatment plan.

4.8   It is therefore to be expected that proportionally more patients should be detained under s.2 than s.3 upon admission to hospital, and that the reverse would be true for informal inpatients made subject to the Act (figure 35).

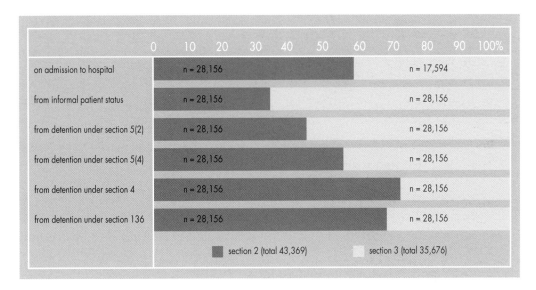

Fig 35: uses of sections 2 and 3, NHS and Independent Hospitals, England, 2002-03 to 2003-04[12]

4.9   Figure 36 below shows trends in the use of ss.2 and 3 since the publication of the Code of Practice in 1990. This appears to suggest that the proportionate use of s.3 for both hospital admission and detentions of informal patients already in hospital grew in the decade following the Code's publication, but that the growth may now have been checked. There is a notable decline since 1999 in the proportionate use of s.3 rather than s.2 as the power under which patients are admitted to hospital.

4.10   It may be that these changes in patterns of practice are a reflection of commentary in Richard Jones' *Mental Health Act Manual* on the way in which the Code's guidance should be interpreted. From 1999, the *Manual* has argued that the Code's guidance had been

---

[11]   See Mental Health Act Code of Practice, Chapter 5.

[12]   Data source: Department of Health Bulletin 2004/22 *Inpatients formally detained in hospitals under the Mental Health Act 1983 and other legislation, England 1993-94 to 2003-04,* tables 8 and 9; *Inpatients formally detained in hospitals under the the Mental Health Act 1983 and other legislation, NHS Trusts, Care Trusts, Primary Care Trusts and Independent Hospitals 2002-03 (table 9a) and 2003-04* (table 9a). The above data table does not show 9,003 recorded changes from s.2 to s.3 during this period.

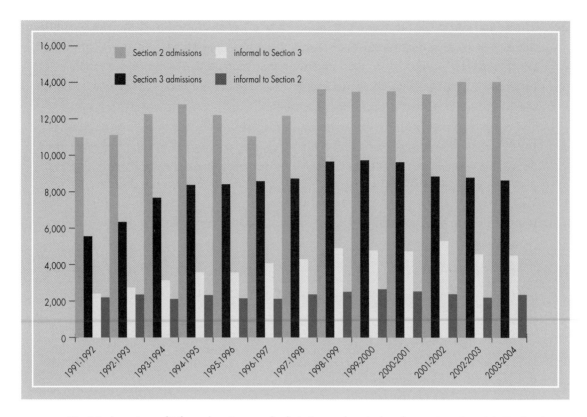

Fig 36: detentions of informal patients and admissions to hospital under sections 2 and 3, England, 1991-02 to 2003-04[13]

vulgarised, in part as a result of the MHAC's past advice, including statements in our past Biennial Reports[14]. Jones challenges the simplification of the Code's guidance to mean that a patient who is simply 'well-known' to services should therefore be admitted under s.3, pointing out that

> the extent of any prior knowledge that might exist about the patient does not deflect from the need to assess a patient's *current* situation… something has happened in that patient's life to justify intervention under this Act and it is the factors that precipitated the detention and their impact on the patient that need to be assessed[15].

4.11   Services should note the Code's suggestion that s.3 may be an appropriate admission section where the patient is known to the clinical team *and has been assessed in the recent past by that team*[16]. In our view, such a condition should be met where a patient has been in good contact with community services. We accept that the MHAC's own past statements may not have given sufficient emphasis to this aspect of the Code's guidance.

---

[13]   Data source: as for fig 31 above.

[14]   See, for example, MHAC (1995) *Sixth Biennial Report*, para 3.1; MHAC (1997) *Seventh Biennial Report*, page 41, where the criteria for s.3 admission is given as the patient being 'well-known' to services, without reference to the Code's further criteria that the patient has been recently assessed.

[15]   Jones, R (2004) *Mental Health Act Manual*, ninth edition, para 1-033 (order of sentences reversed). Similar advice has been given by the *Mental Health Act Manual* since its sixth edition (1999).

[16]   Mental Health Act Code of Practice, para 5.3a

4.12 We continue to advise services to monitor their ratios of s.2 to s.3 admissions and look carefully at the possible reasons for any unusual practices, particularly against the possibility that the additional safeguards of s.3 detention may be creating a perverse incentive against its use, or that frequent s.2 use (particularly for re-admissions) might indicate that services are losing contact with patients in the community[17].

4.13 In our last report we called for Government to confirm or update its Code of Practice guidance to services on the use of ss.2 and 3 of the Act in the light of the *Mental Health Act Manual*'s criticism of current practice[18]. This recommendation has not yet been taken up. We remain of the view that such guidance would be helpful to services, and that practitioners should not be left with uncertainty over how the law should be applied.

> **Recommendation 12:** Government should confirm or update its Code of Practice guidance to services on the use of ss.2 and 3 of the Act in the light of the *Mental Health Act Manual*'s criticism of current practice.

Reasons for use of the Mental Health Act

4.14 As a part of the work leading to publication of *Back on Track?*, the Sainsbury Centre and MHAC report on implementation of care planning under the Care Programme Approach (see Chapter 2.78 *et seq*)[19], Commissioners on their visits collected information on the reasons for admission in relation to 277 adult detained patients who had at least one previous formal admission in the past three years[20]. For 256 (92%) of these patients, we found a reference in the patients' notes as to whether admission was arranged in response to risks posed to the patients themselves; to other people; or to both patients and others (see figure 37 below).

4.15 Twelve patients (5%) of the sample shown at figure 37 were deemed to be at risk of harming both themselves and other people. Of the 111 patients believed to be a risk only to themselves, about a quarter were considered vulnerable but only at risk of self-neglect; the remaining three quarters were judged to be at risk of self-harm or suicide[21]. Of the 133 patients deemed to pose a risk only to others, 43 (16% of all patients admitted in the sample,

---

[17] See MHAC (2003) *Tenth Biennial Report: Placed Amongst Strangers*, Chapter 8.32 for a fuller list of issues to consider where s.2 use appears to be higher than average.

[18] *ibid.*, Chapter 8.29 – 8.34 and recommendation 19. See Chapter 5 of the MHA Code of Practice for extant guidance on the use of ss.2 and 3.

[19] Sainsbury Centre for Mental Health (2005) *Back on Track? CPA Care planning for service users who are repeatedly detained under the Mental Health Act.* Sainsbury Centre for Mental Health in association with the Mental Health Act Commission, 2005

[20] Data was collected from 119 wards in 57 units spread across 15 Trusts registering high use of the MHA according to Department of Health Statistics. Patients were detained mostly under ss.2 (15%) and 3 (76%) with a small number of detentions under ss.4, 37,47, 48, 135 and 136. For details see *Back on Track?* pp.16.

[21] A precise figure cannot be given because of the overlapping category of patients at risk to both self and others, which could distort the total by no more than 5%. This is true of comparisons within this paragraph on the proportions within each category.

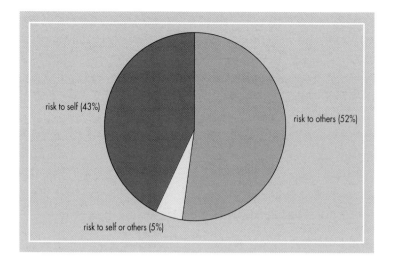

Fig 37: reason for repeated admission in 256 detained patients[22]

and roughly a third of all patients believed to be a risk to others) were reported to have behaved violently to people or property. A further 16 patients (6% of all patients) were reported to have been carrying a weapon, and a further 86 patients (31% of the total, nearly two-thirds of those reported as a risk to others) were reported as having shown threatening behaviour with no actual incidence of violence recorded.

4.16   Underlying these determinations of general risk, a further precipitative factor in 57% of these returning patients' admissions (159 patients) was failure to comply with some aspect of treatment offered in the community. For 39% of these patients (108 patients) this was failure to comply with medication. It is notable that, in seven cases (or 2.5% of all 277 patients studied), the sole reason given in the patient's notes for their readmission was non-compliance with treatment, even though this in itself is clearly no justification for detention under the Act.

4.17   The above findings cannot be assumed to represent the reasons behind all admissions under civil powers of the Act, given the potential distortion caused by our focus on patients who had already had at least one formal admission in the previous three years and were therefore already likely to be in contact with community services. Nevertheless they offer some evidence of how the Act is applied.

Ethnicity of Mental Health Act admissions

4.18   Figure 38 below shows the admission rates under the Act by gender and ethnicity for the last three financial years, according to returns from MHAC data questionnaires. The percentages roughly correlate to those found for resident patients in the National Mental Health and Ethnicity Census 2005 (figure 39), although the percentages of Black patients overall in the latter data collection are slightly higher[23].

---

22   Data source: MHAC data published in *Back on Track?* pp.44.

23   Healthcare Commission, MHAC, and NIMHE (2005) *Count Me In: National Mental Health and Ethnicity Census 2005*, National Results. In press.

Ethnic category	2002/03			2003/04			2004/05		
	M n=14,146	F n=11,266	Total n=25,412	M n=14,963	F n=12,205	Total n=27,168	M n=20,974	F n=17,630	Total n=38,604
British (White)	69.11	74.49	71.50	66.46	72.61	69.22	67.20	74.07	70.34
Irish (White)	0.86	0.83	0.84	1.06	0.93	1.00	1.08	0.97	1.03
Any Other White Background (White)	4.40	4.71	4.54	4.48	4.92	4.68	0.19	4.68	4.75
White & Black Caribbean (Mixed)	0.80	0.49	0.66	0.80	0.29	0.57	0.82	0.41	0.63
White & Black African (Mixed)	0.28	0.23	0.26	0.45	0.28	0.38	0.41	0.37	0.86
White & Asian (Mixed)	0.17	0.20	0.18	0.24	0.23	0.24	0.29	0.28	0.29
Any Other Mixed Background (Mixed)	0.47	0.36	0.42	0.57	0.31	0.45	0.83	0.62	0.73
Indian (Asian or Asian British)	1.85	1.62	1.75	1.77	1.72	1.75	1.66	1.27	1.48
Pakistani (Asian or Asian British)	1.51	1.17	1.36	1.74	1.13	1.46	1.80	0.89	1.38
Bangladeshi (Asian or Asian British)	0.38	0.20	0.30	0.81	0.46	0.65	0.06	0.34	0.48
Other Asian Background (Asian or Asian British)	0.82	0.56	0.70	0.91	0.70	0.81	1.30	1.07	1.20
Caribbean (Black or Black British)	5.40	3.29	4.47	5.72	3.15	4.57	5.10	3.13	4.20
African (Black or Black British)	2.80	1.78	2.35	3.33	2.55	2.98	3.48	2.54	3.05
Any other Black Background	2.45	1.43	2.00	2.28	1.40	1.88	3.02	1.48	2.32
Chinese (Other Ethnic Groups)	0.32	0.39	0.35	0.19	0.42	0.29	0.30	0.29	0.35
Any Other Ethnic Group	1.98	1.22	1.64	1.97	1.45	1.74	3.02	1.48	2.32
Not Stated	6.50	6.92	6.69	7.23	7.46	7.33	6.17	5.63	5.93
Total	**100**	**100**	**100**	**100**	**100**	**100**	**100**	**100**	**100**

Figure 38: admissions of patients detained under the Mental Health Act 1983 by ethnicity and gender, 2002/3 to 2004/5[24]

(figures in table show percentage of ethic category group for male, female and total admissions)

4.19 The 2005 census appears to confirm the assertion in published literature to date that Black patients overall suffer a higher than average likelihood of detention under the Act. Black groups overall appear to be three to five times more likely to be detained under the Act than the national average for all ethnic groups. These findings are discussed in more detail in the National Mental Health and Ethnicity Census 2005 National Results report[25].

---

[24] Data source: returns from MHAC questionnaires. A total of 288 questionnaires were issued for the 2002/03 to 2003/04 data, with 167 (58%) responses received. A total of 235 questionnaires were issued for the 2004/05 data, with 171 (73%) responses received.

[25] See note 23 above.

Ethnic category	Detained patients as of 31 March 20005	
	number	%
British (White)	9,090	69.01
Irish (White)	251	1.91
Any Other White Background (White)	413	3.14
White & Black Caribbean (Mixed)	169	1.28
White & Black African (Mixed)	40	0.30
White & Asian (Mixed)	60	0.46
Any Other Mixed Background (Mixed)	109	0.83
Indian (Asian or Asian British)	206	1.56
Pakistani (Asian or Asian British)	191	1.45
Bangladeshi (Asian or Asian British)	93	0.71
Other Asian Background (Asian or Asian British)	130	0.99
Caribbean (Black or Black British)	895	6.79
African (Black or Black British)	425	3.23
Any other Black Background	405	3.07
Chinese (Other Ethnic Groups)	45	0.34
Any Other Ethnic Group	196	1.49
Not Stated / Not counted in this table	454	3.45
Total	**13,172**	**100**

Figure 39: ethnic category of patients detained as of 31 March 2005[26]

The use of part II emergency and holding powers

Emergency admissions under section 4

4.20   In emergency situations, s.4 of the 1983 Act allows that an application for admission may be based upon a single medical recommendation. The criteria for such admissions are that it is urgently necessary that a patient be detained under s.2, and that the urgency precludes compliance with the safeguard of obtaining the second medical recommendation that s.2 detention requires. Patients admitted under s.4 powers may be held for up to 72 hours, during which time a further medical recommendation may be sought and the detention 'converted' to s.2.

4.21   The recorded incidence of uses under s.4 during the lifetime of the Act is shown at figure 40 below. In our last report, published in 2003, we indicated our concern that the use of emergency powers appeared to be on the rise, and that we would regret a return to the frequencies of use shown with equivalent powers before the 1983 Act came into force[27]. We are aware that many services use our report's discussions to prompt reviews of their use of the Act, and we are pleased to note that recorded incidences of the emergency power's use

---

26   Data source: National Mental Health and Ethnicity Census 2005.

27   MHAC (2003) *Tenth Biennial Report: Placed Amongst Strangers*, chapter 8.41 *et seq.*

have sharply declined in the last two years. There is always a danger that emergency powers, which are necessarily less burdensome to administer than other admission powers, become the route of detention of choice for reasons of administrative convenience. We continue to hear of problems in accessing second medical recommendations and indeed some authorities, faced with severe problems in locating medical recommendations which have been exacerbated by the implementation of new consultant contracts, appear to tolerate the use of 'emergency' powers for administrative reasons and may even advise their social workers to use s.4 as a matter of course.

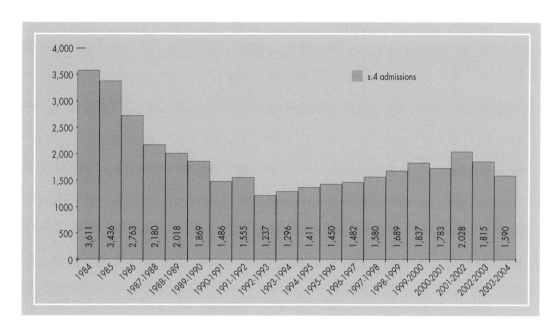

Fig 40: admissions to hospital under s.4 MHA 1883, England, NHS and Independent Hospitals, 1984 – 2003/4[28]

4.22 The outcomes of s.4 admissions, from data reported in Department of Health statistical bulletins, are set out at figure 41 below. Although Department of Health statistics record a category of conversions from s.4 to s.3, this is a technical impossibility under the 1983 Act, as an admission under s.4 is technically an incomplete s.2 application which cannot be converted directly to an application for s.3 admission. It would seem likely that services are recognising the ultimate detention of a patient under s.3 when returning these statistics to the Department. Although we have shown the category 'section 4 to 3' on our diagram, we have counted the significant numbers of admissions involved (19% of all uses of s.4 in the last five years recorded) into our category 'section 4 to 2' so as not to allow these returns to distort the overall figures.

4.23 We note that a significant number of patients brought into hospital under emergency powers revert to informal status once there. Over the last five years recorded above

28 Data sources: DHSS (1987) *Mental Health Statistics for England 1986* Booklet 11, Legal Status Table D1; Department of Health (1995) *Statistical Bulletin 1995/4*; DH (1996) *Statistical Bulletin 1996/10*; DH (1999) *Statistical Bulletin 1999/25*; DH (2002) *Statistical Bulletin 2002/26*; DH (2004) 2004/22. Data accuracy is compromised by its several sources, mixture of calendar years and financial years and possible discrepancies in categorisation over time.

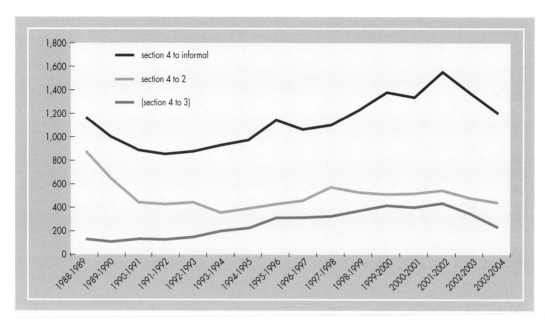

Fig 41: outcomes of s.4 emergency admissions, England, 1988/9 to 2003/4[29]

(1999/0 – 2003/4), just over a quarter (26%) of all s.4 admissions led to informal status. In past years this proportion has been considerably higher: 30% between 1994/5 and 1998/9, and 34% between 1989/0 and 1993/4. At the end of the 1980s, when the Commission was perhaps most concerned that emergency powers were being used for administrative rather than clinical reasons, more than 40% of patients admitted under s.4 were not detained under any further powers. It is not possible to say from these statistical returns whether such patients remained in hospital as informal inpatients; were released back home to continue contact with services on an outpatient basis; or whether 'informal status' is a euphemism for an absolute discharge from service. We consider it likely that the term encompasses all three outcomes.

4.24   The changing legal landscape in the wake of the European Court decisions in *HL v United Kingdom* and *Storck v Germany* (see Chapters 1.1 & 3.3 *et seq* above) could call into question whether a patient who has been brought into hospital under emergency powers can subsequently agree to remain there informally. If the resulting hospital care amounted to a deprivation of liberty it could be argued that the State's duty to provide safeguards under ECHR Article 5 cannot be signed away by a patient's apparent consent to remain under such conditions[30]. At the very least, should such an analysis be accepted by our domestic legislature or upheld by our courts, then some form of review mechanism for such patient's care will be required.

---

29   Data source: as for fig 40 above (see paragraph 4.22 above on the spurious category 'section 4 to 3').

30   See *HL v United Kingdom* para 90: 'the right to liberty is too important in a democratic society for a person to lose the benefit of Convention protection for the single reason that he has given himself up to it'; and the decision in *Storck v Germany* that the State's involvement in a patient's placement in a clinic meant that any deprivation of liberty once there could be imputed to the State (see Chapter 1.1 and 3.3 *et seq* above).

Section 5 holding powers

4.25 Section 5 holding powers may be used to prevent an informal inpatient from leaving hospital whilst consideration is given to detention under an assessment or treatment section of the Act. Section 5(2) provides a doctor with a 72-hour holding power for this purpose, and s.5(4) provides nurses with a six-hour holding power.

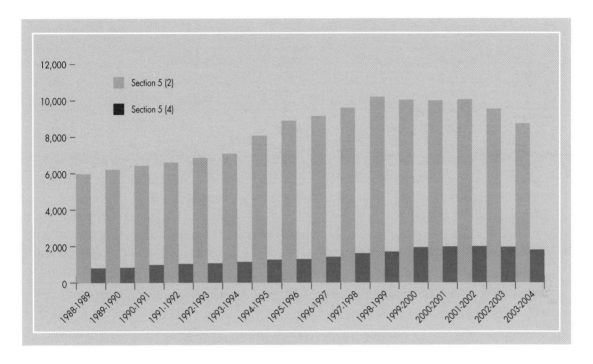

Fig 42: use of section 5, England, 1988/9 to 2003/4[31]

4.26 The recorded use of these powers since 1988/9 is shown at figure 42 above. The decline in the use of s.5 shown over this reporting period should *probably* be welcomed, although it is perhaps unwise to generalise from a national figure. From 1997 we have stated our concern at the high use of holding powers, given that this indicates large numbers of patients who initially engage voluntarily with services but have to be coerced to remain in hospital. This could be a sign that acute wards running under pressure are unattractive places for patients, who try to discharge themselves before it is clinically appropriate to do so. High-use of holding powers could also indicate that the thresholds for using holding powers are operating at too low a level in a particularly risk-averse environment, although alternatively it could indicate that patients are generally admitted informally on the principle of the least restrictive option, even where a patient might otherwise meet the criteria for detention. It is also possible, of course, that a drop in the use of formal holding powers of detention is not reflected in any lessening of coercion in mental health services: more patients may simply be being thwarted from discharging themselves by means that amount to '*de facto*' detention. It seems possible, despite the high profile of questions of deprivation of liberty raised after the European Court ruling in *HL v UK* (see Chapters 1.1 and 3.3), that there continue to be significant levels of *de facto* detention on mental health wards. However, we also recognise that there could be a number of alternative causes behind the use of holding

---

[31] Data source: as for fig 40 above

powers, some of which (for instance, a patient's condition may worsen due to non-iatrogenic causes) can be held as neither indicative of service quality nor of professionals' attitude to compulsion.

Recommendation 13: We advise services to audit their own use of holding powers carefully and in context to:

(a) determine whether lessons for local practice can be learned; and

(b) establish clear policies based upon the Code of Practice guidance with comprehensive training of nursing staff.

4.27 We would expect that on most occasions nurses' holding powers are used, as the statutory context implies, to prevent a patient from leaving hospital whilst a doctor is called. Most nurses' holding powers are therefore terminated when the doctor arrives and places the patient under a 72-hour holding power to allow assessment for detention under ss.2 or 3 to take place. In a relatively small number of cases (less than 4% over the last five years for which data is available, although an average of about 6% in the previous decade) an assessment for admission under ss.2 or 3 was completed whilst the patient remained under the nurses' holding power.

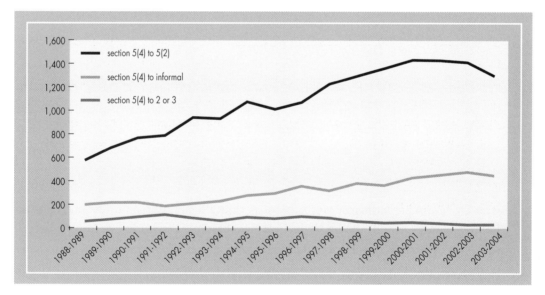

Fig 43: outcomes of s.5(4) holding powers, England, 1988/9 to 2003/4[32]

4.28 Over the last five years for which data is available (1999/0 – 2003/4), the holding power was cancelled or lapsed and the patient returned to informal status in 23% of uses of s.5(4), and 37% of uses of 5(2). In this reporting period there has been a numerical decline consistent with the falling rate of use of these powers, although proportionally the rate at which patients are returned to informal status from s.5(2) has remained stable and the rate

---

[32] Data source: as for fig 40 above

returned to informal status from s.5(4) has increased[33]. As discussed at paragraph 4.26 above, the approach adopted in the European Court in *HL v United Kingdom* and *Storck v Germany* during 2004 may have changed the legal landscape and made it less likely that patients who have been deprived of their liberty using holding powers can now be returned to informal status if they are to remain in hospital in conditions that could amount to '*de facto*' detention.

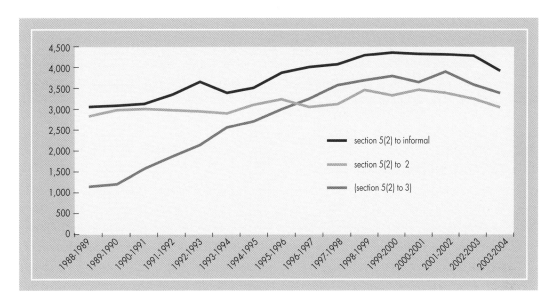

Fig 44: outcomes of s.5(2) holding powers, England, 1988/9 to 2003/4[34]

4.29 The statutory form that nurses are required to complete when using section 5(4) holding powers is now outdated (as is the Code of Practice guidance on this issue). Form 13 of the Mental Health Regulations 1983 requires nurses to indicate by deletion their 'class' (i.e. that part of the nursing register under which their qualification is listed). The categories of nursing qualification described in the register maintained under s.7 of the Nurses, Midwives and Health Visitors Act 1997 have now changed from those described on the form and in the note to chapter 9.1 of the Code of Practice. The Nursing and Midwifery Council has confirmed to the MHAC that the qualifications falling into 'the prescribed class' are now described as follows:

(i) Registered Nurse Level 1 Mental Health

(ii) Registered Nurse Level 2 Mental Health

(iii) Registered Nurse Level 1 Learning Disability

(iv) Registered Nurse Level 2 Learning Disability

---

[33] The percentage of patients returned to informal status after being held under ss.5(2) & 5(4) is as follows, according to Department of Health data:

	1988/9	1989/0	1990/1	1991/2	1992/3	1993/4	1994/5	1995/6	1996/7	1997/8	1998/9	1999/0	2000/1	2001/2	2002/3	2003/4
s.5(2)	44	43	41	43	42	38	38	38	38	40	37	37	37	37	37	37
s.5(4)	24	22	20	18	16	18	18	19	22	19	21	20	22	23	24	24

[34] Source: as for fig 40 above

215

The first four categories described on the statutory form are essentially similar and therefore equivalent to these descriptions. The fifth category on the statutory form (Part 13 of the old register) now falls within the new category (i) above, and the sixth category on the statutory form (Part 14 of the old register) falls within the new category (iii). In our view, it is acceptable to indicate the category on the statutory form that is equivalent to the current definition, and (given that the form invites deletion of that which does not apply) to cross through the now redundant parts of the description and write in the correct terms[35].

> **Recommendation 14:** The Department of Health should update Form 13 of the Mental Health Regulations 1983 to ensure that nurses using the form can accurately record their status.

Admission trends in Wales

The context of care in Wales

4.30   At Chapter 2 above we discussed generally the context within which our observations on the use of the Act should be set. Considered specific to Wales, it should be noted that, over the last decade:

- beds in the mental health sector in Wales fell by 1,950 (43%) to 2,630[36];

- average bed occupancy (i.e. average daily occupied beds as a percentage of average daily available beds) for mental illness beds increased from 80.8% to 88.9%[37];

- throughput (the number of formal and informal inpatient cases treated in the year per average daily available bed) increased from 4.9 to 6.5[38];

- The average duration of a formal or informal inpatient admission fell from 59.8 to 50 days[39] (although at Chapter 2.14 we highlight research published in this reporting period based upon North Wales service provision, which found, rather surprisingly, that today's patients spend longer in hospital over their lifetimes than patients did a century ago[40]).

4.31   We note that our observations regarding service pressures across mental health services generally apply *a fortiori* in Wales. Some Welsh services have great problems in attracting

---

[35]   Corrected descriptions of nursing qualifications on the statutory form would be as follows:
  (a) in Pt 3 (first level nurse trained in the nursing of persons suffering from mental ~~illness~~ *health*)
  (b) in Pt 4 (second level nurse trained in the nursing of persons suffering from mental ~~illness~~ *health*)
  (c) in Pt 5 (first level nurse trained in the nursing of persons suffering from learning disabilities)
  (d) in Pt 6 (second level nurse trained in the nursing of persons suffering from learning disabilities)
  ~~(e) in Pt 13 (nurses qualified following a course of preparation in mental health nursing)~~
  ~~(f) in Pt 13 (nurses qualified following a course of preparation in learning disabilities nursing)~~

[36]   Data source: National Assembly for Wales Statistical Directorate (2004) *First release: NHS Beds 2003-04* SB 61/2004, Sept 2004. Data refers from 1993-94 to 2003/04.

[37]   *ibid.*

[38]   *ibid.*

[39]   *ibid.*

[40]   Healy, D., Harris, M., Michael, P., Cattell, D., Savage, M., Chalasani, P. & Hirst, D (2005) 'Service Utilisation in 1896 and 1996: morbidity and mortality data from North Wales'. *History of Psychiatry* 16(1) 27-41

sufficient qualified staff and at least one unit in Wales has closed for want of sufficient staffing[41]. Out of area treatment appears to be widespread. Several Welsh mental health groups have expressed doubts whether the infrastructure exists or can be put in place to implement the legal framework proposed in the 2004 Bill[42].

The use of the Act in Wales

4.32 The overall use of the Act in Wales over the last eight years for which data is available is shown at figure 45 below.

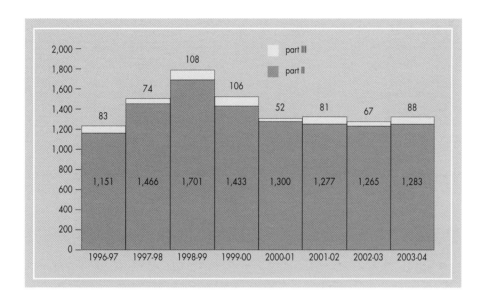

Fig 45: admissions under Part II (civil) and Part III (criminal justice) powers of the MHA 1983, Wales, NHS and Independent Hospitals, 1996-7 to 2003/4[43]

4.33 Statistics collated and published by the National Assembly allow for a much greater detailed picture of the operation of the Act in Wales than can be given for England. We hope that the ongoing commitment to a census of mental health patients in England will produce similar data for comparison in future. The numbers of resident patients by gender, legal status and length of stay in hospital is shown at figure 46 overleaf. It is apparent from this data that a quarter of male admissions under s.3, and one fifth of female admissions under that section, result in hospitalisation of over a year. An average of a further one-fifth of all uses of s.3 result in discharge within one month. Two-thirds of all s.3 detentions are rescinded within six months.

---

[41]   The Llangwyn unit at Llandrindod Wells Hospital, Powys, closed in September 2005 with patients transferred to the Bronllys Hospital, Brecon. See 'Staff crisis forces unit closure' BBC News, 4 Sept 2005.

[42]   Joint Committee on the Draft Mental Health Bill (2005) *Draft Mental Health Bill*, Vol 1, Chapter 11

[43]   Data source: National Assembly for Wales, Health Statistics and Analysis Unit (2002) *Admission of patients to mental health facilities in Wales 2001-02 (including patients detained under the MHA 1983)* SDB 32/2002; SB 69/2004

	Informal		s.2		s.3		s.37		s.37/41		s.47, 48	
	M	F	M	F	M	F	M	F	M	F	M	F
0-1 month	239	310	27	24	36	32	-	-	1	-	3	-
1-3 months	153	189	-	2	65	36	2	-	2	-	-	-
3-6 months	84	94	-	-	41	27	3	-	5	-	4	1
6-12 months	77	70	-	-	26	15	6	1	14	2	2	-
1-2 years	54	80	-	-	20	13	5	1	6	1	2	-
2-5 years	65	94	-	-	18	10	-	-	12	2	1	-
5-10 years	33	50	-	-	6	1	-	-	3	-	-	-
10-15 years	15	12	-	-	3	3	-	-	-	-	-	-
15-20 years	3	4	-	-	3	1	-	-	-	-	-	-
20 years and over	15	13	-	-	-	-	-	-	-	-	-	-
totals	738	916	27	26	218	138	16	2	43	5	12	1
	1,654		53		356		18		48		13	

Fig 46: patients resident in hospitals by gender, duration of stay and legal status, Wales, 31 March 2004[44]

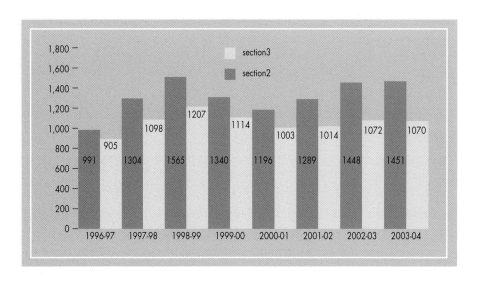

Fig 47: total uses of sections 2 and 3, Wales, independent and NHS facilities, 1996/7 – 2003/4[45]

4.34 Figure 47 above shows the total use of s.2 and s.3 over this period. The most recent year's data on usage of s.2 and s.3, showing total usage broken down to show the patients' legal status at the time of that use, is shown at figure 48. The most notable difference in pattern

---

44 Data source: National Assembly for Wales Statistical Directorate (2004) *Hospitals and Units for People with a Mental Illness in Wales; Census of Patients at 31 March 2004. SB 70/2004, Sept 2004*, Table 15. The data given above excludes 10 patients (8 male) listed as detained under 'other powers' in the original data set.

45 Data from National Assembly for Wales Statistical Bulletins *Admission of Patients to Mental Health Facilities in Wales*. Note that, in contrast to statistics published in our Tenth Biennial Report (Fig 56, p.258), this data includes uses of ss.2 or 3 following holding powers and place of safety detentions. Data from National Assembly for Wales Statistical Bulletins *Admission of Patients to Mental Health Facilities in Wales*.

from English use of the Act is the prevalence of use of s.2 to detain patients who are already in hospital with informal status. In Wales 50% of all detentions of informal patients are under s.2; in England only 30% of such detentions use s.2 rather than s.3.

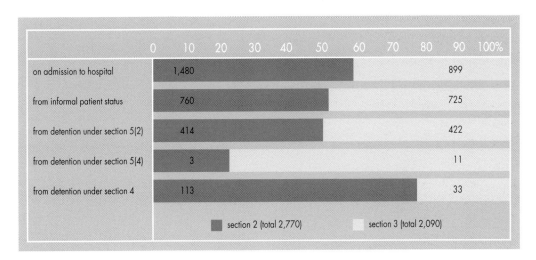

Fig 48: uses of sections 2 and 3, NHS and independent facilities, Wales, 2002/03 to 2003/04[46]

4.35 Figure 49 below shows an apparent rise in use of s.136 in Wales, but this is likely to be a misleading effect of the increasing use of places of safety in hospitals (where they are noted in statistical returns) rather than police stations (where they are not).

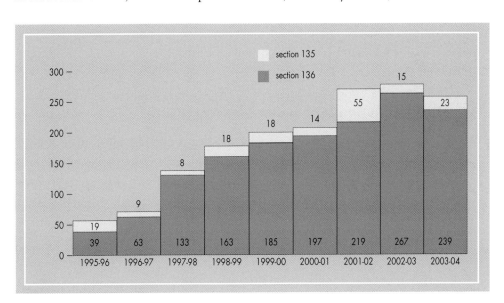

Fig 49: use of sections 135 and 136 (where place of safety is a hospital), Wales, 1995-6 to 2003-4[47]

4.36 Although only around 30% of hospital-based detentions under s.136 result in further detention under the Act (figure 50), this is neither untypical of what we know of practice in

---

[46] Data source: SB69/2004, table 4.6

[47] Data source: National Assembly for Wales, Health Statistics and Analysis Unit (2002) *Admission of patients to mental health facilities in Wales 2001-02* (including patients detained under the MHA 1983) Report No: SDB 32/2002; SB69/2004, table 4.5

England (see figure 77 below) nor necessarily a sign of poor practice. We discuss the use of s.136 more generally at paragraph 4.164 *et seq* below.

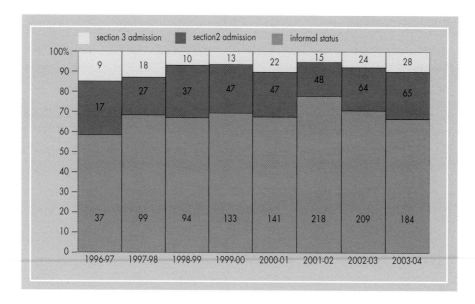

Fig 50: outcomes of section 136 use, Wales, 1996-97 to 2003-4[48]

Leave and absence without leave

4.37   Commission guidance on good practice in relation to the administration of s.17 leave is available in our Guidance Note, which includes model forms for use or adaptation by services[49].

Leave from independent sector placements

4.38   We are concerned to hear that the use of s.17 leave may be constrained within some Independent Hospitals because of an understandable reluctance by the relevant commissioning authorities to fund a bed that is not being occupied. Such constraints are most likely to affect longer-term leave arrangements, including forms of trial leave that may be particularly applicable to secure units. We understand that some authorities do not object to patients being granted limited leave from the independent sector beds that they are funding, but if constraints upon leave arrangements are being imposed by funding issues this is clearly a matter for concern and could raise a potential for legal challenge.

4.39   At the time of writing this report we have been unable to confirm or investigate further reports of differing approaches towards leave across the NHS and independent sector. The issues raised by such reports are potentially wide-ranging, however, especially given the expanding independent secure sector and Government proposals for future 'non-residential' arrangements for psychiatric care under legal control. Our particular concern is that, when the service that is commissioned for a patient under compulsion is presaged on

---

[48]   Data source: SB 96/2002 table 4.6; SB69/2004 table 4.5

[49]   *MHAC Guidance Note: Issues surrounding sections 17, 18 and 19 of the Mental Health Act 1983*, available from www.mhac.org.uk.

the purchase of a 'bed' from the independent sector, funding issues over the commissioning of independent sector healthcare could operate as a restriction on the likelihood of that residential order progressing to a non-residential order, or could raise the likelihood of patients who become eligible for non-residential orders being quickly passed out of independent sector structures with concomitant strains on NHS resources and continuity of care. Alternatively, perhaps, the independent sector will quickly move to fill gaps in provision of non-residential care (which is, after all, the major focus of the commercial sector in the United States). We invite Government to indicate how it envisages the increasing role of the independent sector will mesh with future legal frameworks. Health authorities responsible for commissioning mental health services may need to consider these issues carefully in the coming period.

Shadowing

4.40 During this reporting period we were informed of an apparent agreement by the Home Office to the 'shadowing' of a restricted patient during agreed leave periods. 'Shadowing' in this context referred to a patient being nominally granted unescorted leave, on condition that he was kept under surreptitious surveillance whilst outside the hospital. In the case in question, a Home Office review accepted that the suggestion in the particular case was an error based upon a series of misunderstandings (and the shadowing was not implemented to our knowledge), although the Home Office did reserve the position that the Act does not preclude such arrangements, which could be lawful and justifiable in exceptional circumstances. As a general rule we would consider such arrangements to be unacceptable on principle. We would have grave concerns at a patient being misinformed over the true status of his or her leave in this way and believe that the circumstances would have to be exceptional indeed to justify either such deception or the risk taken by authorities in allowing a patient leave in these circumstances.

Section 17 as community treatment order

4.41 In our last report we reported on developing case-law which we contended to have created a form of long-term community treatment order by allowing s.3 detention to be renewed even though a patient remained on s.17 leave of absence from hospital[50]. The 2002 judgment in the *DR v Mersey Care NHS Trust*[51] held that it was an impermissible and illogical gloss on the criteria for renewal of detention powers to read the phrase 'treatment in hospital' at s.20(4)(c) to necessarily mean *inpatient* treatment (i.e. where a patient is admitted to a hospital bed). Thus a renewal was deemed lawful although the patient's only hospital treatment amounted to weekly attendance at a hospital for occupational therapy and a ward round. At Chapter 1.37-40 above we discuss the 2004 judgment in the *CS* case[52], which confirmed the approach of previous rulings and allowed the renewal of detention when the patient's only hospital-based treatment consisted of attendance at a monthly

---

[50]   MHAC (2003) *Tenth Biennial Report: Placed Amongst Strangers.* Chapter 9.47 *et seq*

[51]   *R (on the application of D.R.) v Mersey Care NHS Trust* [2002] EWHC 1810 Admin

[52]   *R (on the application of CS) v Mental Health Review Tribunal and Managers of Homerton Hospital (East London & City Mental Health NHS Trust)* [2004] EWHC 2958 (Admin)

ward-round. Thus the present law provides a form of community treatment order that is, in effect, a form of conditional release from hospital. Whilst this is nominally concerned with eventual discharge from compulsion, it is determinedly open-ended[53] and may continue indefinitely (see also Chapter 3.54 above).

4.42   The extent of use of these community powers is uncertain, although we are aware anecdotally of patients whose detentions have been renewed several times without recall to hospital. The focus of Commissioners on their visits to hospital is inevitably those patients who are detained on the wards visited, although we do examine documents of patients who are on leave. In the spring of 2004 we requested information from all hospitals that we visit on patients whose detentions had been renewed whilst they were on leave during the first three months of that year, but we received very small number of returns with the details of only eight patients. We suspect that there were many more patients not brought to our attention through this exercise, and aim to conduct a more rigorous exercise in the coming period. It was interesting to note that four of the patients about whom we were notified had been determined to be consenting to treatment by their Responsible Medical Officer, either at the time of their renewal or subsequent to it, and were therefore being prescribed medication under the authority of Form 38. In these cases detention under the Act was at least theoretically being used to enforce requirements that could be made under Guardianship or supervised discharge arrangements. However, Justice Pitchford rejected arguments in the *CS* case that a patient's consent to receiving medication meant that supervised discharge or Guardianship should have been preferred over what the MHRT called 'full-time section 17 leave'[54]. First, the judge stated that the disruption of moving from one statutory framework to another may have not been in the patient's interests, but second (and perhaps more questionably as a precedent for future judgments, given the Code of Practice definition of consent as voluntary permission not given under unfair or undue pressure[55]) because 'CS's knowledge of the RMO's powers was a significant element in her willingness to accept the treatment plan'[56]. We are disappointed at this judicial attitude and understanding of the nature of consent to treatment.

Patients absent without leave

4.43   Services have a duty to look after people whose liberty they have taken away. This should include not allowing patients to go absent without leave (AWOL). The majority of AWOL incidents pass off without any recorded harm to anyone: it has been suggested that most patients who abscond simply go home, and return to hospital of their own accord the same day[57]. However, patients who abscond are at increased risk of harm, whether this is because they may go without medication; consume alcohol or drugs; intend self-harm or suicide; or simply be exposed and vulnerable when outside the hospital which has a duty of care towards them. Some patients may pose a risk to other people whilst AWOL. Absconsions

---

[53]   *ibid.*, para 49

[54]   *ibid.*, para 27

[55]   Mental Health Act Code of Practice, Chapter 15.13

[56]   *R (on the application of CS), supra*, para 48

[57]   Bowers, L 'Runaway patients' *Mental Health Practice* September 2003 vol 7 No 1;10-12

may need to be reported to the police, who must then spend resources trying to return patients to hospital.

4.44 Unnatural deaths of detained patients who are absent without leave from hospital appear to be reducing in number. In the three years up to the end of January 2000, eighty-three patients (33% of all unnatural deaths) died whilst AWOL[58]. In our prior study, covering 1992-1994, 35% of unnatural deaths involved AWOL patients. In the five years up to 2004, 70 deaths (18% of all unnatural deaths) were of AWOL patients. The decline in numbers is shown at figure 51 below. We discuss deaths of detained patients more generally following paragraph 4.279 below.

'I often absconded and was picked up in various public paces or went to police station. Police were good to me! Even tried to return me to hospital when genuinely allowed out!'

Yasmin Jackson, ex-s.3 patient, Wales

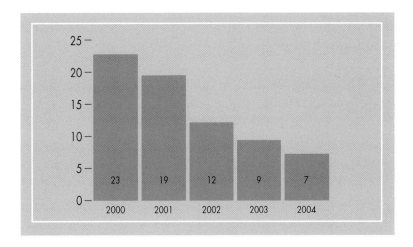

Fig 51: unnatural deaths of detained patients AWOL from hospital 2000-04[59]

Recommendation 15: Units should look at their AWOL incidents carefully, and should audit incidents (comparing the results across services) to try to identify:

• Any *patterns* to the absconsions: it may be that patients go AWOL on particular shifts, at particular times of day, or during shift-changeovers; or

• *Root causes* of absconsions: services should be particularly alert to problems of boredom or lack of therapeutic contact; ward environment or patient mix; the possibility of bullying or harassment; drug and alcohol use on the ward; lack of access to fresh air or peaceful surroundings, etc.

---

[58] MHAC (2001) *Deaths of Detained Patients in England and Wales. A Report by the Mental Health Act Commission on Information Collected from 1 February 1997 to 31 January 2000.* Nottingham, MHAC. p.15

[59] Source: MHAC data (see paragraph 4.279 below).

4.45   Research into the problems of absconding by City University in partnership with East London and the City Mental Health Trust has been continuing since 1997, and has led to a training package for acute ward nurses describing nursing intervention to reduce absconsion. The package contains a handbook for the ward manager on how to organise implementation, a poster for the ward, workbooks for all staff, pocket reminder cards, and copies of research reports and publications on absconding. This package been shown to reduce officially reported rates of absconding from partly locked or open wards by twenty-five percent[61]. The six key elements of this package are listed at figure 52.

City University London anti-absconding intervention.

The intervention consists of six elements:

1. Rule clarity through the use of a signing in and out book

2. Identification of those at high risk of absconding

3. Targeted nursing time for those at high risk

4. Careful breaking of bad news

5. Post-incident debriefing

6. Multi-disciplinary-team review after two absconds.

Fig 52: anti-absconding measures[60]

4.46   Professor Len Bowers has written that addressing the causes of absconding requires a change of perception on the part of mental health professionals, who need to recapture the sense of what admission means to individual patients on wards and not, through their own immersion in the culture of the ward, lose sight of how unsettling admission to that environment can be:

> We professionals all too easily lose sight of what an admission actually means to the patient. From the nursing point of view, admissions are short and we know that most patients are discharged within a few weeks. The constraints on patients seem, from our point of view, to be few, temporary, and trivial. This is not necessarily the way it seems to patients. To our patients, admission can be a serious derailment of their lives. They may have had to leave home in a hurry, without making sure that everything was prepared or safe. They might find themselves on a ward with a bunch of strangers, some of whom behave in ways that are frightening, and that can feel very lonely. They may feel separated from their normal conduct with friends and family, forced to take treatment

---

[60]   see www.citypsych.com/absconding/index.htm for further details

[61]   Bowers, L., Alexander, J. & Gaskell, C. 'A Controlled Trial Of An Intervention To Reduce Absconding From Acute Psychiatric Wards'. *Journal of Psychiatric and Mental Health Nursing* 10:410–416; Simpson, A. & Bowers, L. 'Runaway Success'. *Nursing Standard* 18(19)18-19; Bowers, L., Alexander, J. & Simpson, A. (under review) 'Absconding by psychiatric patients in East London: relationship to ethnicity and culture'. *International Journal of Mental Health Nursing*; Bowers, L., Simpson, A. & Alexander, J. (under review) 'Real world application of an intervention to reduce absconding'. *Journal of Psychiatric and Mental Health Nursing*.

unwillingly, and required to stay in a limited, monitored environment, unable to go out whenever they want[62].

Nursing staff in particular need to be attentive to individual patients' concerns about their home life; and responses to disappointments (for example in progress towards discharge) or to unsettling or frightening events on the ward, even if these seem unexceptional to staff.

4.47 Where a patient is at risk of absconding because of his or her concerns about, or need for the reassurance of, their relatives, friends, homes or property, it may be appropriate to consider whether leave arrangements could be provided to address such concerns or needs within a structured context. However, it is important that services remember that their first duty is towards the safety of the patient whom they have detained. In the following practice example this duty appeared to have been overlooked.

On a visit to a London hospital a Commissioner noted from medical files that a patient detained under s.3, who had absconded over the ward garden fence on the day of his detention, appeared to have been given one month's unrestricted leave on the explicit grounds that it was impossible to keep him on the ward given the ease with which absconsion through the garden could take place. We asked the Trust to revisit these arrangements to ensure, firstly, that the patient continued to meet the criteria for detention under the Act and then, if he was detainable, to ensure that conditions were specified regarding his leave from hospital, including where he was expected to reside if on long-leave and when he was expected to return to the ward.

The Trust responded within a week of our visit to inform us that the issue had been discussed with the RMO for the patient, and that it had been agreed that leave conditions should be more structured; seen as a part of the treatment plan; and that the patient should be aware of this and agreeable to the conditions of leave before the leave is granted. Patients will be made aware that breaking the conditions of leave may lead to them being brought back to hospital and s.17 leave forms will state clearly the time to implement the AWOL policy if a patient fails to return to the ward when required as a condition of leave.

Fig 53: practice example of inappropriate rationale for leave

---

[62]   Bowers, L 'Runaway patients' *Mental Health Practice* September 2003 vol 7 No 1;10-12

The administration of Part IV of the Act: consent to treatment

4.48   Commissioners spend considerable amounts of their time on visits examining consent to treatment documentation and discussing questions of the administration of Part IV of the Act with patients and staff. At figure 54 we set out ten common problems that we encounter on such visits.

4.49   In past reports we have written a great deal about our concerns over the reality of consent. Commissioners continue to encounter patients who are certified as having given informed consent to the treatments given to them, but who tell us that they do not do so or whose presentation is such that we doubt that they *can* do so. There is, of course, an element of subjectivity in assessing whether a patient appears capable of giving informed consent, and Commissioners are careful not to substitute their own judgment for that of Responsible Medical Officer and the clinical team. However, it is still common to find a lack of documented discussions about treatment with patients or assessments of mental capacity that would reassure us of the integrity of decision-making about mental capacity and consent at ward level.

> 'The physical effects of medications are ignored. Many service users cannot read due to blurred vision from the medication, are constantly restless or tremble terribly, yet these symptoms are left unaddressed despite the impact they are having on service user quality of life and how it increases the possibility of non-compliance with medication on discharge'.
>
> *Gul Davis, ex-s.3 patient (MSU)*
> *Birmingham*

4.50   The documentation of discussions and assessments is not simply a bureaucratic requirement, but (in the best services) is also a part of the structure of procedures and assessments that ensure the patient is provided with the maximum autonomy practicable and is suitably involved in decision-making. Although the responsibility for explaining treatments and assessing capacity rests with the patient's RMO, recording of processes is a vital way to ensure that these processes are being initiated and kept under constant review within the multi-disciplinary team. Too many patients feel that they are excluded from decision-making and the exercise of choice in their hospital treatment, and unable to discuss their subjective experiences of therapeutic effect or adverse side-effects. This is likely to exacerbate the likelihood of non-compliance after discharge and may contribute to the problems of 'revolving door' readmissions. Over a decade ago the Parliamentary Health Committee recognised that the 'solutions' of community treatment orders ignored the causes of patients' non-compliance:

> If professionals were to spend more time explaining the advantages and disadvantages of particular drugs and the various dosage options available to the patient, he or she is more likely to make an informed choice about whether or not to take that medication[64].

The Healthcare Commission's patient survey 2004 elicited responses from 11,350 patients who had been prescribed medication in the previous year (at least four-fifths of whom had no experience of detention under the Act): 35% reported not having been told about

---

[64]   House of Commons Health Committee Fifth Report of Session 1992-93, *Community Supervision Orders* Vol 1, HC 667-1, p.xiv

[65]   Healthcare Commission (2004) *Patient Survey report 2004 – Mental Health.* Section C1.

possible side-effects of medication; and 11% said that had not had the purpose of the medication explained to them[65].

(i)   No record of discussion with patient regarding proposed treatment

(ii) No record of assessment of patient's capacity to consent to treatment

(iii) Patients telling visiting Commissioners that they are not happy taking their medication when this is covered under a Form 38 certifying their informed consent

(iv) Patients for whom there is a Form 38 appearing to Commissioners have doubtful capacity to give informed consent

(v)   Consent to treatment Forms 38 completed, or SOAD visit requested, after the expiry of the three-month rule

(vi) No review of treatment or consent status after change of RMO

(vii) Old but uncancelled Forms 38 or 39 mistaken for current authority

(viii) Current Form 38 or 39 not kept with the patient's medicine card to ensure dispensation of authorised medication

(ix) Medication prescribed or administered outside of limits authorised on Form 38 or 39

(x)   Forms 38 completed by RMOs with no reference to the upper limits of dosage or numbers of drugs authorised under the patient's agreement

Fig 54: ten common problems with the administration of Part IV of the Act encountered by the MHAC on visits

4.51   Many hospitals have introduced standardised record forms for:

- RMOs to record discussions with patients over proposed treatment, and assessments of patients' mental capacity;
- Discussions between the Second Opinion Appointed Doctors (SOADs) and statutory consultees;
- Discussions between RMOs and patients on the outcome of the Second Opinion process.

Such forms should not be limited to 'tick-boxes' but should include space for free text to encourage narrative accounts of consultations and consideration of issues such as mental capacity. South West London & St George's Mental Health Trust's *Record of RMO's competence and consent interview* form is in our view a reasonable compromise between a structured record form and a space for more detailed narrative accounts. The Royal Glamorgan Hospital (Pontypridd & Rhondda NHS Trust) introduced all three types of documentation listed above in 2005; and statutory consultees for SOADs visiting Cedars House, Canterbury (an Independent Hospital managed by Care Principles UK) are issued with a standard form to make a record of their consultation, which also outlines the role of the statutory consultee in the Second Opinion process[66].

---

[66]   For a copy of the standard record form contact Neil Sinclair, Head of Psychology and Unit General Manager, at Neil.Sinclair@careprinciples.com

> Commissioners visiting an NHS Trust in the North of England in 2004 found a Form 39 dated to the previous month which had subsequently and unlawfully been altered by the Responsible Medical Officer. It appeared to be the case that, in the month following the SOAD's authorisation of a treatment plan of medication on Form 39, further drugs had been prescribed by the RMO which significantly changed the emphasis of the treatment. Instead of contacting the MHAC for a further Second Opinion to consider the new prescription, the RMO unlawfully altered the extant Form 39 to provide erroneous authority for the new treatment plan. We requested that the Trust investigate this serious breach of the protections of the Act, conduct a systematic audit of their s.58 practices and arrange training for staff.

Fig 55: practice example of unlawful alteration of Form 39 by an RMO

High-dose medication

4.52 Evidence put to the Joint Committee on the Draft Mental Health Bill by the National Voices Forum called for new legislation to require Tribunal approval for any medication doses that are above *British National Formulary* (BNF) levels, outside of product licence or that constitute polypharmacy[67]. The Committee agreed and recommended that doses above BNF levels should be authorised by Tribunals, and that the use of such doses should be reserved for 'exceptional circumstances'[68]. Government has indicated that this is a matter for clinical practice and appropriate for clinical governance rather than legislation[69]. We have some sympathy with the Government's position, although we fear that the debate may have become clouded by concerns over the fitness of the BNF recommendations, especially when applied to specialist psychiatric inpatient treatment, as legal thresholds.

4.53 We believe that the current Act provides insufficient protection to patients in the first three months of their treatment under detention, when they may be forcibly given medication in doses or combinations that are outside of product guidelines and recommendations without the oversight of a Second Opinion Appointed Doctor. Some RMOs appear to share our unease: we receive (but have to decline) occasional requests for statutory Second Opinions in relation to such patients. Under the present legal framework, for a relatively small increase in resources, it could be possible to formulate a requirement that the normal 'three-month period' would not apply where medication is prescribed outside of BNF or other relevant guidelines. Under the proposed legislative framework, the equivalent of the 'three-month period' is reduced to 28 days. Depending on the arrangements made for

---

[67] Joint Committee on the Draft Mental Health Bill (2005) *Draft Mental Health Bill.* Vol 1, para 372; Vol 3 Ev 963.

[68] *ibid.*, Vol 1, para 372, recommendation 80.

[69] *The Government's response to the report of the Joint Committee on the Draft Mental Health Bill* 2004. Cm 6624, p.39. We welcome the 'additional safeguard' proposed in this response of ensuring that care-plans indicate the maximum dose of medications or classes of medication for which Tribunal approval is sought, which should prevent the safeguards of current practice with statutory forms 38 and 39 from being diluted under new legislation, but we await details of this proposal (see also para 4.67 below).

considering and authorising the detail of care plans under that framework[70], there could be some scope for a similar arrangement whereby a form of 'second opinion' authorisation is required for high-dose medication or polypharmacy in the first 28 days of detention.

4.54   Over the last financial year, prescriptions involving dosages in excess of BNF limits have accounted for about 11% of all Second Opinion visits to consider the authorisation of medication. The results of such visits are shown at figure 56 below.

	2003/04		2004-05	
	Number	% of Total	Number	% of Total
RMO's plan unchanged	614	82.9	738	82.1
Plan slightly changed	110	14.8	139	15.4
Plan significantly changed	16	2.3	22	2.5
Totals	**740**	**100.0**	**899**	**100.0**

Fig 56: result of SOAD visits to patients prescribed medication in excess of BNF recommended doses[71]

4.55   There is certainly scope for critical approaches to the general patterns of psychotropic medication prescribing, and bodies such as the Royal College of Psychiatrists have questioned whether widespread prescribing of high-dosage antipsychotic drugs is fully justified on a clinical basis[72]. However, it would be a mistake to conclude from this that it is necessarily an error or 'bad' practice to use drugs above the recommended levels or outside of the categorised indications of the *British National Formulary* or product licenses.

4.56   We were concerned at the conflation of 'errors' reported through medication incident reports and 'off-label prescribing' in the National Patient Safety Agency Report *Building a memory: preventing harm, reducing risks and improving patient safety*[73]. Examples of such 'errors' according to this report include 'the use of psychotropics above recommended levels and the use of anti-epileptic drugs as mood-stabilisers'. The BNF continues to include guidelines from the Royal College of Psychiatrists over the management of such doses, and in the case of paediatric prescribing, includes advice on the use of unlicensed medicines or of licensed medicines for unlicensed purposes[74]. We advise SOADs that we see nothing

---

[70]   At the time of writing Government has indicated that it is reviewing the workability of the new Tribunal process and is taking into account the Committee's endorsement of our criticisms of it in relation to authorising care plans. See *The Government's response to the report of the Joint Committee on the Draft Mental Health Bill*, pages 30, 38.

[71]   source: MHAC data. These figures do not include 47 authorisations above BNF limits (17 in 2004/05) where the outcome classification was not recorded.

[72]   Royal College of Psychiatrists (1993) *Consensus statement on the use of high dose antipsychotic medication.* CR26, p.17. This document is currently has been reviewed and a revised statement adopted for publication over the winter of 2005.

[73]   National Patient Safety Agency (2005) *Building a memory: preventing harm , reducing risks and improving patient safety. The first report of the National reporting and Learning System and the Patient Safety Observatory.* July 2005. Page 44.

[74]   See *British National Formulary for Children 2005*, p.3.

wrong in principle in authorising treatment outside of product licences or BNF recommendations where the potential benefits appear to outweigh risks and disbenefits. This includes the prescription of medicines, such as anti-epileptic drugs, which are not listed for the treatment of mental disorder but are widely used for that purpose[75]; unlicensed drugs or drugs that are not yet listed in the BNF; and dosages of psychotropic medication above the BNF recommended limits:

- In July 2005 an MHAC Second Opinion Appointed Doctor reviewed and approved medication given to the minor *X* (whose case we refer to at paragraph 4.219 & figure 77 below, in the context of mechanical restraint), including an SSRI antidepressant. Although guidance from the Committee on the Safety of Medicines advises against prescription of SSRIs to under-18 year olds, in the view of the RMO and SOAD prescription of the drug in *X*'s case was justified on grounds of the severity of his illness and because this was on a closely-monitored inpatient basis.

- In many other cases, patients who are detained under the Act may be severely unwell and, given that such patients will be treated under conditions of close supervision on hospital wards and have the safeguard of a statutory Second Opinion[76], we do not think that artificial or inflexible constraints should be placed on the prescription of psychotropic medication.

4.57   Many service providers have policies on the use of high-dose medication. West London Mental Health NHS Trust's policy defines high dose antipsychotics as 'a total daily dose of a single antipsychotic which exceeds the upper limit stated in the Summary of Product Characteristics (SPC) or BNF' or 'a total daily dose of two or more antipsychotics which exceeds the SPC or BNF maximum using the percentage method'[77]. The policy requires that:

- any medication prescribed in excess of BNF recommended doses must be recorded in the patient's notes, with an explanation and a clear care plan which will be reviewed by the multidisciplinary team at regular intervals. The patient should be informed that they are receiving 'high dose' medication and this too should be recorded.

- Monitoring requirements for pulse, temperature and blood pressure must be outlined clearly in the care plan for the individual patient. An ECG, taken before treatment is started, must be available for comparison at regular intervals to observe any changes during treatment.

- All patients who are on high dose antipsychotics are encouraged to have a good fluid intake of at least two litres daily, which is recorded in their care plan and monitored on a fluid chart; and

- All junior doctors must consult with their respective consultant or consultant on call prior to prescribing any antipsychotic drugs above the BNF recommended doses.

---

[75] Or, for example, beta-blockers (BNF 2.4) for symptomatic relief of anxiety.

[76] Albeit only after the first three months of treatment. Provided that the SOAD system was adequately funded we would support the shortening of this period, and welcome the intention in the draft Mental Health Bill 2004 to reduce the equivalent of the three-month period to 28 days. For our further suggestion for the protection of patients see para 4.53 above

[77] The 'percentage method' requires the conversion of the dose of each medication into a percentage of its BNF maximum dose, and adding the percentages together – a cumulative dose of more than 100% is a high dose.

> **Recommendation 16:** All services should ensure that their policies provide similar safeguards to those outlined in paragraph 4.57 above for patients administered high-dose medication.

Section 61 reports to the MHAC

4.58   Section 61 directs the Responsible Medical Officer (RMO) of a detained patient to submit a report on the current treatment and progress of any patient for whom a Form 39 (or authority for neurosurgery under s.57) has been issued:

- when the detention power is renewed (or, for restricted patients, at the end of the first six months and then on subsequent occasions when a report is sent to the Secretary of State); and

- at any other time if so required by the MHAC.

The MHAC is empowered under s.61 to provide notice to any RMO that an extant Form 39 (or authority for neurosurgery) shall not apply to treatment after a certain date: if the RMO wishes to continue with the treatment, except in an emergency, a further authorisation would be required. These powers to review and withdraw certificates are the formal mechanism by which the Act ensures that SOAD certificates are not used indefinitely. In practice, SOADs may also time-limit their Forms 39 by simply writing an expiry date on the treatment plan that they describe, but where SOADs are prepared to leave the withdrawal of their authorisation to the discretion of the MHAC reviewers they may instead advise us to request a s.61 report after a certain period of treatment. We will also occasionally request a s.61 report without prompting by the SOAD, where we wish to keep a particular treatment under closer review for any particular reason (such as the use of high-dose medication, polypharmacy or off-label prescribing).

4.59   In our Tenth Biennial Report we noted that visiting Commissioners had identified that RMOs had failed to submit a s.61 report in a quarter of the 636 cases where Forms 39 had been issued and detention renewed[78]. Because the MHAC does not receive notifications of individual detentions or renewals, we are unable effectively to police this aspect of services' duties towards their patients and towards us as an organisation, but this could be corrected with arrangements for a future monitoring body or the Tribunal under the next Act.

> **Recommendation 17:** We suggest that powers and duties equivalent to s.61 of the 1983 Act should be established within the next legislative framework, whether these centre upon the Tribunal or the monitoring body, to allow for specific cases to be kept under review and for authorisations to be time-limited where appropriate.

---

[78]   MHAC (2003) *Tenth Biennial Report: Placed Amongst Strangers.* Chapter 10.28

Case management of judicial review challenges

4.60   In our last report we highlighted the administrative burden created by judicial review of SOAD authorisations[79]. In this two-year reporting period, we have dealt with eight such judicial review applications, and at least one letter before claim.   One administrative problem related to judicial review applications against SOAD decisions has been caused by our own historic expectations over the length of time that it is acceptable to 'hold' a SOAD authorisation for treatment in the absence of consent without implementing that treatment, or for a certificate to remain extant once treatment has commenced.   We are aware that there is no legal requirement in relation to either period, and therefore have not sought to establish an absolute rule.   Nevertheless, if a particular Form 39 is to be acted on at all[80], generally we do not expect there to be a gap of more than about three weeks between the issue of a Form 39 and the commencement of at least part of the treatment plan that it certifies 'should be given'. Where there is such a gap, we would usually expect that a new Second Opinion should be arranged to consider any further treatment proposals in case the circumstances of the patient have changed. We will also usually withdraw an extant Form 39 that is being implemented after between one and two years (depending on the complexity of treatment and other aspects of the individual case) to ensure regular review of treatment authority.   SOADs may choose to time-limit their certificates where they wish to ensure a review after a specified duration of treatment.

4.61   Where SOAD certification is subject to legal challenge to the High Court, the court usually allows an injunction against the commencement of treatment when granting permission to make an application for judicial review. In both *Wilkinson* and *N* cases discussed in our last report[81], the Forms 39 under challenge were unused but extant for over a year.   We felt bound to withdraw these forms during the legal proceedings to ensure a fresh consideration, if and when the treatment injunction was lifted, of whether the requirement that 'the treatment should be given' still held. In the *PS* and *B* cases discussed in this report (see Chapter 1.46 to 1.62), SOADs had time-limited their certificates to ensure review after three months, also therefore inadvertently rendering the challenges to them somewhat academic. We face a dilemma in this: where a SOAD authorises a contentious treatment, or treatment that may prove ineffective, he or she is all the more likely to wish to ensure a review of that authorisation. Similarly, whilst legal proceedings clearly must be cause to set aside our usual practice of withdrawing an unused authorisation after three weeks, it is more difficult to justify allowing such an authorisation, which is necessarily contentious, from remaining extant beyond our normal review periods. The issue of a fresh certificate during proceedings would not necessarily help, given that this would lead to a further application to challenge the new certificate[82].

---

[79]   *ibid.* Chapter 3.32 *et seq*

[80]   That is, we do not assume the issue of a SOAD certificate to create any legal or other duty upon an RMO to provide such treatment as it authorises. An RMO is of course responsible for the decision to administer any treatment, and may choose not to implement some or all of the treatment plan authorised.

[81]   MHAC (2003) *Tenth Biennial Report: Placed Amongst Strangers.* Chapter 3.32-7

[82]   *R (on the application of B) v (1) Dr SS, (2) Dr AC and The Secretary of State for the Department of Health* [2005] EWHC 86 (Admin), January 2005, appendix II, para 10.

4.62   In an appendix to his judgment in the *B* case discussed at Chapter 1.53 *et seq* above, Mr Justice Silber, with the support of the lead judge of the Administrative Court and the Head of the Administrative Court Office, proposed a framework to case-manage judicial challenges to SOAD authorised treatment. It was noted that this is necessary not only to address the problems of time-limited certificates, but also to avoid harmful delays in administering treatment that has been certified as required. Therefore it has been agreed that an oral case-management hearing will take place within two working days of any challenge application being brought, where timetables for proceedings would be agreed taking note of any time-limit on the Form and other relevant factors. All parties should attend an interim order hearing at which a timetable would be agreed for a substantive hearing, which would usually to be held as a rolled up hearing where the court considers the permission application and then proceeds to deal with the substantive application.

4.63   There was some confusion over the judge's earlier comments in the *PS* judgment, where he talked of a seven-month-old Form 39 being 'stale and out of date'[83]. Some commentators read this to imply that the judge had established a general time-limit for the review of Forms 39. Although Mr Justice Silber alluded to representation from the MHAC as to why we had used our powers under s. 61(3) to withdraw the Form 39 at the centre of the judicial review challenge, it was not apparent from the judgment itself that the Form was regarded as being 'stale and out of date' because an injunction granted against the treatment that it had authorised had precluded its implementation at all for over six months. We responded to a number of queries about this aspect of the judgment and issued guidance to Commissioners on timescales for Forms 39, which we published in a policy briefing for Commissioners and reproduce at figure 57.

MHAC advice on the timescales for treatment authorised on Forms 39

Delays in initiating treatment

1   The Commission would expect the plan of treatment authorised by a SOAD on Form 39 to commence within a reasonable time of that authorisation. In most cases, given that such treatment is by definition necessary, we would expect treatment to commence as soon as practicably possible. This expectation relates to the treatment plan as a whole, and not to each particular aspect of that treatment plan (i.e. every category of drug authorised). The Form 39 sets out a limit to authorised treatment and is not a prescription.

2   As a rule of thumb, we view a gap of three weeks between authorisation and commencement of treatment as cause to consider withdrawing the authorisation and requiring a further Second Opinion. However, this timescale is only a guide and individual circumstances should be taken into account.

---

83   *R (on the application of PS) v (1) Dr G and (2) Dr W* [2003] EWHC 2335 (Admin), para 24

3 Where a significant delay in initiating a treatment plan authorised by a SOAD is the result of an event that amounts to a change of circumstance in the patient's clinical condition (such as, for example, physical illness), we would expect RMOs to consider seeking a further Second Opinion before initiating that treatment. Where such circumstances are brought to our attention, the Commission will consider using its powers under section 61(3) to withdraw extant SOAD forms.

4 Where delays in initiating treatment under Form 39 are the result of ongoing legal action, the Commission will consider means of keeping the authority extant, but may use its powers to withdraw Forms 39 where it has no reasonable alternative.

Review of extant Forms 39

5 The procedure for review of extant Forms 39 is set out at section 61 of the Mental Health Act and Chapter 16.36 of the Code of Practice. It is the RMO's responsibility to submit an MHAC1 report form to the Commission upon the renewal of a patient's detention (or at equivalent points in a restricted patient's detention), and at any other time at the Commission's request. The Commission will thereafter take responsibility for determining whether a fresh Second Opinion is required due to the age of the extant form.

6 As a rule of thumb, the Commission will not usually allow Forms 39 to remain extant two years after their issue, and in many cases will seek a further review after a year.

Alerting the MHAC to Forms 39 in need of review.

7 RMOs or other professionals may, of course, approach the Commission directly if they encounter a Form 39 that they think should be considered for review, whether this is because of a gap in the commencement of the authorised treatment or because the Form has been extant for a particular period of time. Professionals should contact the Mental Health Act Commission office in such circumstances.

8 Commissioners on visits who encounter Forms 39 that should be considered *for review for any of the above reasons* should contact the Mental Health Act Commission office with details, rather than demanding action of the hospital administrator or RMO.

Fig 57: MHAC advice on timescales for treatment authorised on Form 39[84]

Second Opinion activity

4.64   Figure 59 below shows Second Opinion requests for medication and ECT over the lifetime of the 1983 Act, with percentage changes over the last seven years shown at Figure 60. Whilst the numbers of Second Opinions overall continue to rise, the numbers of referrals for ECT treatment may be showing a slight decline, perhaps as a consequence of NICE guidelines which imply that ECT is a treatment of last resort (see paragraph 4.68 *et seq* below). In our last report we suggested that a declining proportion of ECT referrals could skew the gender-balance of Second Opinion referrals, given that more men than women are referred for

---

[84]   From MHAC (2003) *Policy Briefing for Commissioners*, Issue 7; November 2003. www.mhac.org.uk

medication, and more women than men for ECT[85]. In this reporting period male patients have accounted for 59% of referrals, an increase of 4% from the last reporting period (figure 58).

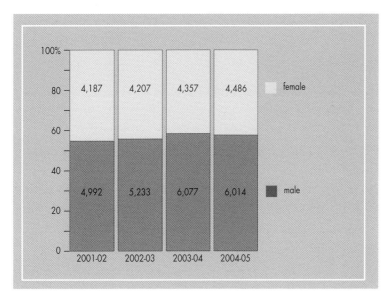

Fig 58: Second Opinion requests by gender of patients, 2001/02 to 2004/5

4.65 Perhaps more significantly, the biennially-grouped data shown at figure 59 below shows a steep and continuing rise in the number of Second Opinions for medication. The reasons for this may only be surmised, but the statistics *could* reflect:

- changing general clinical profiles of detained patients (i.e., an increasingly 'unwell' population who are less likely to be able or willing to consent to treatment); and/or

- a growing appreciation and care on the part of clinicians to consider whether apparent consent from a patient has a genuine basis, rather than being based upon inadequate understanding, capacity or freedom of choice; and/or

- an increasing desire on the part of clinicians to offset their accountability and liability in prescribing psychiatric medication to detained patients in view of a perceived increase in litigation in this area.

Over the last decade the volume of Second Opinion work has increased by about 250%, although the MHAC's staffing dedicated to Second Opinion work has remained at the same level. It is notable that if the trend of increase continues at the rate shown in our graphic at figure 59, the resources needed to fund the Second Opinion service (principally doctors' fees and travelling expenses) will also increase year upon year at a rate well above inflationary increases.

---

[85]   MHAC (2003) *Tenth Biennial Report: Placed Amongst Strangers*, Chapter 10.35.

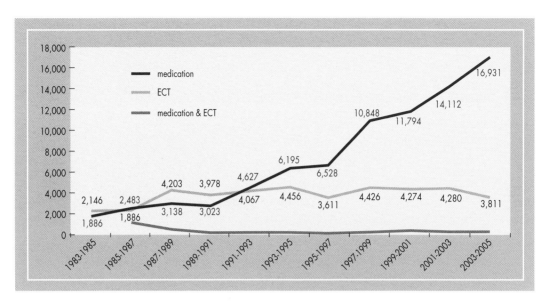

Fig 59: Second Opinion requests received by MHAC, England and Wales, 1985 – 2005[86]

	1998/99	% change	1999/00	% change	2000/01	% change	2001/02	% change	2002/03	% change	2003/04	% change	2004/05
Med	6,116	-5.8	5,761	4.7	6,033	12.4	6,781	8.1	7,331	12.4	8,373	2.2	8,558
ECT	2,229	-2.7	2,169	-3.0	2,105	3.5	2,179	-7.8	2,008	-2.5	1,958	-5.4	1,853
Med & ECT	79	27.8	101	-12.9	88	35.2	119	-15.1	101	1.9	103	-13.6	89
TOTAL	**8,424**	**-4.7**	**8,031**	**2.4**	**8,226**	**11.6**	**9,179**	**2.8**	**9,440**	**9.5**	**10,434**	**0.6**	**10,500**

Fig 60: Second Opinion requests 1998/99 to 2004/05, showing percentage changes

4.66   Ethnicity and age profiles of patients for whom Second Opinions were requested in this period are shown at figures 61 and 62 below.

Ethnic category	2003/04	% of Total	2004/05	% of Total
British (White)	6,120	58.7	7,179	68.0
Irish (White)	226	2.2	105	1.0
Any Other White Background (White)	567	5.4	385	4.0
White & Black Caribbean (Mixed)	79	0.8	122	1.0
White & Black African (Mixed)	59	0.6	17	0.2
White & Asian (Mixed)	49	0.5	30	0.3
Any Other Mixed Background (Mixed)	49	0.5	85	0.8
Indian (Asian or Asian British)	125	1.1	216	2.0
Pakistani (Asian or Asian British)	171	1.6	141	1.0
Bangladeshi (Asian or Asian British)	28	0.2	68	0.7
Any Other Asian Background (Asian or Asian British)	71	0.7	85	0.8

---

[86]   Source: MHAC Biennial Reports 1 to 10; MHAC data.

Ethnic category	2003/04	% of Total	2004/05	% of Total
Caribbean (Black or Black British)	490	4.7	706	7.0
African (Black or Black British)	243	2.3	322	3.0
Any other Black Background	93	0.9	91	0.8
Chinese (Other Ethnic Groups)	19	0.2	38	0.4
Any Other Ethnic Group	81	0.8	95	1.0
Not Stated 1,964	18.8	815	8.0	
Total 10,434	**100.0**	**10,500**	**100.0**	

Fig 61: Second Opinion requests: ethnicity of patients 2003/04 and 2004/05

Age Range	2003/04	% of Total	2004/05	% of Total
Under 16	19	0.2	30	0.3
16-18	256	2.5	226	2.1
19-59	7,682	73.6	7,597	72.3
60-74	1,452	13.9	1,573	15.0
Over 75	999	9.6	1,057	10.1
Not stated	26	0.2	17	0.2
Totals	**10,434**	**100.0**	**10,500**	**100.0**

Fig 62: Second Opinion requests: age of patients 2003/04 and 2004/05

4.67   Figure 63 below shows the outcomes of Second Opinions in this period (figure 56 on page 229 above shows outcomes in relation to proposed medication where dosages are in excess of BNF recommendations). As we highlighted in our last report, the proportions may be small but the absolute numbers are significant: at least 478 patients' proposed treatment was significantly altered as a result of a Second Opinion in the two years, an average of roughly one every working day; and nearly 2,000 treatment plans were slightly changed, amounting to between three and four patients on average each working day. We also have suggested that the value of the SOAD system's oversight of treatment plans cannot be measured simply by changes made, given that RMOs draw up treatment plans knowing that they will be subject to this system of scrutiny. It is important that the best elements of the SOAD system are preserved under the proposed legislative framework for the next Act, and we are pleased that Government is considering this aspect of their proposals in the light of our comments to the Joint Committee on the Draft Mental Health Bill 2004[87]. In particular, we urge Government to preserve the position whereby the Tribunal or its medical experts have the authority to certify treatment without a legal requirement that they secure the agreement of the patient's doctor to any limitation imposed upon the original treatment plan.

---

[87]   *The Government's response to the report of the Joint Committee on the Draft Mental Health Bill 2004.* Cm 6624, p.38-39.

	2003/04		2004-05	
	Number	% of Total	Number	% of Total
RMO's plan unchanged	7,802	74.8	8,404	80.0
Plan slightly changed	1,002	9.6	980	9.3
Plan significantly changed	252	2.4	226	2.2
Not recorded	1,378	13.2	890	8.5
Totals	**10,434**	**100.0**	**10,500**	**100.**

Fig 63: outcomes of completed Second Opinions

Electro-convulsive therapy (ECT)

NICE Guidelines

4.68   In our last report[88] we discussed the publication in 2003 of NICE guidelines for the use of ECT[89]. These sought to restrict the use of ECT to situations where all other alternatives had been exhausted and/or where the illness to be treated was life-threatening, and advised against 'maintenance' ECT treatment. NICE took this position having considered evidence from patients who had received ECT and reported cognitive impairment (usually in the form of memory loss) as an adverse effect[90], and in opposition to the statement of contemporary indications for ECT which it had requested from the Royal College of Psychiatrists[91]. It acknowledged that there was inadequate research-based information on the effects of ECT on memory, quality of life and other pertinent health outcomes. We noted then that the guidance had been unsuccessfully appealed by the Royal College of Psychiatrists. Clinicians using ECT have subsequently published research questioning assumptions made by NICE over the likely effect of ECT on quality of life or function[92].

4.69   In June 2005 a statement from the RCPsych Consensus Group was published as the first chapter of the College's revised ECT Handbook[93]. This notes that, whilst health professionals must take NICE guidelines into account, the latter cannot override the individual responsibility of doctors to make decisions appropriate to the circumstances of an

[88]   MHAC (2003) *Tenth Biennial Report: Placed Amongst Strangers.* Chapter 10.57- 58.

[89]   NICE (2003) *Guidance on the Use of Electroconvulsive Therapy.* Technology Appraisal 59. London: NICE.

[90]   NICE media briefing on Technology Appraisal 59.

[91]   For the background to the Royal College's statement to NICE, see Chapter 1 of RCPsych (2005) *ECT Handbook* Second edition. London, Gaskell.
See www.rcpsych.ac.uk/publications/gaskell/samplechaps/122_5.pdf

[92]   McCall, WV, Dunn A,& Rosenquist PB 'Quality of life and function after electroconvulsive therapy' *British Journal of Psychiatry* (2004) 185 405-9; Benbow SM & Crentsil J 'Subjective experience of electroconvulsive therapy' *Psychiatric Bulletin* (2004) 28 289-91. The latter study of 54 patient questionnaires found that it was more common for people to find ECT a little or a lot better than going to the dentist (27%) than to find it much or slightly worse (20%). 85% of patients rated themselves as a little or a lot better at the end of the course of treatment.

[93]   RCPsych (2005) *supra.*

individual patient. It envisages some circumstances when it might be considered in a patient's best interests to receive ECT treatment for depressive illness that is neither life-threatening nor severe, nor proven resistant to other treatments, or as a maintenance therapy. One such example might be where a patient has had the treatment in the past and indicates it as a preference against other interventions. In such circumstances, the Consensus Group recommends that clinical decision to depart from NICE guidelines should:

- have a fully documented assessment of the potential risks and benefits of treatment to which valid consent has been obtained;

- exercise particular circumspection in the use of ECT outside of NICE guidelines where patients have never had the treatment before, and in all cases ensure that discussions with patients about potential side-effects, such as retrograde amnesia for personal memories, are undertaken and recorded;

- obtain a second medical opinion; and

- use unilateral electrode placement and, where possible, avoid supra-threshold electrical doses for at least the initial treatment in a prescription[94].

4.70 We note that the RCPsych's Consensus Group assumes that departures from NICE guidelines will involve only consenting patients, and does not contemplate patients receiving ECT treatment outside of NICE guidelines under the powers of the Mental Health Act or, if incapacitated but informally admitted to hospital, under the common law. The use of the Act's powers to authorise ECT outside of NICE recommendations to a capacitated patient who refuses consent does seem unlikely, but there may be circumstances where treatment outside of NICE guidelines might be prescribed to patients who are incapable of giving consent through the incapacitating effects of their illness. We do not feel able to prejudge that, in the case of a detained patient, a SOAD would necessarily decline to authorise such treatment.

A capacity test for ECT imposition?

4.71 Government proposed in its 2004 draft Mental Health Bill a capacity-test in relation to the compulsory administration of ECT under the next Mental Health Act, so that clinicians cannot use the powers of that Act to override a capacitated refusal of consent to ECT treatment, except in an emergency[95]. We remain uneasy at what is arguably a rather selective if not arbitrary application of a capacity-test in relation to psychiatric compulsion. Other forms of compulsion that are not necessarily any less invasive than ECT (including detention and forcible maintenance treatment with medication) will still be applicable in the face of a capable patient's refusal of consent.

4.72 The Joint Committee on the draft Bill accepted the view of the Law Society that patients for whom compulsory ECT is indicated will be unlikely to have capacity to make a refusal of consent[96]. This is contrary to evidence of practice under the current Act. Figure 64 below

---

94 *ibid.* p.6-7

95 Draft Mental Health Bill 2004, clauses 178 – 9. See also *Explanatory Notes* (Cm 6305-II) paras 349-51.

96 Joint Committee on the Draft Mental Health Bill (2005) *Draft Mental Health Bill* . Vol 1, p.119 (from evidence of the Law Society).

shows that 36% of patients for whom a statutory Second Opinion to consider compulsory ECT is requested are deemed by their RMO to be capable of consent but refusing to give it. The Government takes the view that 'ethical standards, professional guidance and multi-disciplinary working would ensure that a consultant would not easily consider a patient [with capacity who refuses ECT] to lack capacity'[97]. We are not as confident that the concepts of mental capacity can or will be so objectively applied. We discuss at Chapter 3.27 above the problems of the danger of circularity of definition in determining mental incapacity (i.e. that a patient's decision to refuse treatment that appears self-evidently necessary is taken to imply a lack of capacity). As currently formulated and applied in practice, mental capacity in relation to treatment decisions appears to us to be too malleable a concept to provide any real safeguard to patients, especially when it is determined in individual cases by the treating clinician[98].

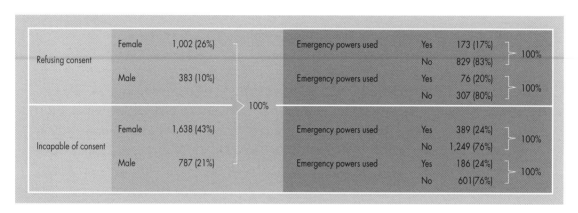

Fig 64: ECT SOAD data 2003/04 to 2004/05 by consent status, gender and use of emergency powers[99]

4.73 In our evidence to the Joint Committee on the draft Mental Health Bill we questioned why ECT and not other interventions should be subject to a capacity-test and observed, in relation to similar findings to those in figure 64 above relating to Second Opinion statistics for 2002/03[100], that:

> For each authorisation [of ECT to patients determined to be capacitated but refusing consent], two separate medical practitioners have concluded that ECT is in the patient's best interests[101]. Given this, and our concerns at the indeterminacy of the concept of capacity, we do have some doubts that the proposed change in the legal framework for administering ECT under formal powers would lead to all of these patients not receiving treatment. Although it is possible that there would be some reduction in the

---

[97] *ibid.* p.217

[98] See Chapter 3.27-40 above and also MHAC (2003) *Tenth Biennial Report: Placed Amongst Strangers.* Chapter 4.3 *et seq.*

[99] Data source: MHAC data collection

[100] It should be noted that the average percentage of ECT SOAD visits where emergency treatment has already been given appears to have increased from an average of 12% in 2002/03 to an average of 19% in 2003/04 and 25% in 2004/05. We cannot explain this increase, although it may be related to the effect of NICE guidelines promulgating ECT as a treatment only of last resort.

[101] The criteria for overriding a patient's refusal of consent under s58 of the MHA 1983 was dealt with in *R (on the application of PS) v (1) Dr G and (2) Dr W* [2003] EWHC 2335 (Admin). The Commission has issued a guidance note on this case (GN 2/04, January 2004).

numbers of patients treated overall, we therefore suggest two equally likely effects of the change:

(a) The apparent fluidity between categories of 'refusing' and 'incapable' patients in current practice suggests that, were the law to make mental capacity the determinant over whether ECT could be given, a number of patients currently considered to be 'refusing' would be classified as 'incapable'; and

(b) For those patients who could not be classified as incapable, the use of 'emergency' powers could increase as a means for practitioners to provide ECT where clinicians feel it is necessary for the patient's treatment. The invocation of emergency powers does, of course, deprive the patient of any safeguard over potential misuse of an intervention[102].

4.74 Based upon a literature review of academic studies and patient testimonies on issues of consent, information and perceived coercion in relation to ECT, Rose *et al* have suggested that approximately half of patients receiving ECT feel that they are given insufficient information about the procedure and is effects and a third perceive themselves into having been coerced into the treatment, even though most of the patients in the studies considered appeared to have been treated informally[103]. Of the two studies involving detained patients given ECT treatments (most of whom, incidentally, were deemed to have mental capacity) one reported overall satisfaction with the treatment except for uncertainties over information provision; the other reported that patients treated under formal powers were less knowledgeable about ECT than informal patients and more likely to be dissatisfied with the amount or quality of information given to them. Many patients' concerns centred upon not having possible side-effects, particularly regarding memory-loss, adequately explained. These findings are implicitly challenged by more recent clinician-led studies mentioned at paragraph 4.67 above, which were not considered in the literature review.

4.75 In the light of their findings of widespread perceptions of coercion, even amongst patients who had signed consent forms for ECT treatment, the researchers claim that 'neither current nor proposed safeguards are sufficient to ensure informed consent with respect to ECT, at least in England and Wales'. We agree with the researchers' view that

if the documenting of informed consent is designed to act as a safeguard for a controversial treatment such as ECT, it clearly fails in a significant proportion of cases

and we would argue that the reasons for this failure are inadequate provision of information or other forms of more or less hidden (or even unintended) coercive practices. However, as we have remarked above and in previous reports, we are more sceptical than the researchers appear to be that establishing a capacity-test in relation to overt coercion would provide any part of a solution to these problems[104]. It is difficult to see how the introduction of

---

[102] Joint Committee on the Draft Mental Health Bill (2005) *Draft Mental Health Bill.* Vol 2, Ev 34 (MHAC), para 6.12.

[103] Rose DS, Wykes TH, Bindman JP & Fleischmann PS 'Information, consent and perceived coercion: patients' perspectives on electroconvulsive therapy'. *British Journal of Psychiatry* (2005) 186; 54-59

[104] The researchers' claim that the Government has 'rejected the Richardson Committee's recommendation that compulsory treatment should be based upon the principle of lack of capacity' is not quite accurate with regard to the special measures proposed over ECT, as we discuss above at paragraph 4.70 above.

essentially unstable thresholds based upon mental capacity would prevent 'informed consent' being obtained from patients who in reality are too ill, too ill-informed, or too frightened to give it. Neither can we see how such thresholds would prevent patients who refuse treatment from having their refusal overridden on the grounds that they do not have mental capacity to determine what should be done to them. The solutions to these problems are not easily apparent, and would seem likely to rely upon attritional processes of training and developing multi-disciplinary teams to be alert to the issues; close and critical monitoring of practices; and developing a culture of user-involvement in care-planning and treatment decisions. The introduction of a capacity-test threshold for compulsion is unlikely to promote user-involvement for patients who are to some extent incapacitated by their illnesses.

The ECT Accreditation Service (ECTAS)

4.76   In our Ninth Biennial Report we reported our national audit of ECT practice, suggesting that about 20% of 230 ECT clinics were operating with substantial departures from best policy, practice or training[105]. In October 2003 the Royal College of Psychiatrists enrolled 21 clinics from the United Kingdom and Ireland as the first wave of clinics signed up for accreditation reviews under the ECT Accreditation Service (ECTAS)[106]. There are now more than 60 clinics signed up as member-clinics of the scheme, with 28 having completed accreditation. Ultimately it is hoped that all ECT clinics across the UK and Ireland will be involved. The scheme is based upon a set of standards for ECT practice, with accreditation requiring clinics to demonstrate through self/peer-review and audit that they provide safe, effective treatment and an acceptable and dignified experience for patients. The review process also involves patient questionnaires, and ECTAS is looking at ways to increase service-user involvement. The scheme also acts as peer support through members sharing information (including resources, such as leaflet information on ECT in languages other than English[107]) and discussion of topics through an e-mail discussion group.

4.77   Given the concerns expressed by patients and user-groups over ECT treatment we believe that the Department of Health should actively encourage NHS clinics to sign up for ECTAS approval. Whilst the Healthcare Commission has stated that ECTAS accreditation is one of the information sources that it will use to direct its inspection activities, it may be appropriate for it to consider whether membership of the scheme should be a condition of registration as an Independent Hospital if that hospital proposes to run an ECT suite.

Neurosurgery for Mental Disorder

4.78   Under s.57 of the 1983 Act, no patient (whether detained or informal) may be given Neurosurgery for Mental Disorder (NMD) without certified authorisation by a panel appointed by the MHAC. The numbers of referrals to the MHAC over the lifetime of the Act

---

[105] MHAC (2001) *Ninth Biennial Report.* Chapter 3.31-5

[106] Adrian Worrall 'Electric avenues' *Health Service Journal* 7 October 2004

[107] ECTAS have indicated that they intend to provide access to translated leaflets through their website. See www.rcpsych.ac.uk/cru/ECTAS.htm

[108] This data therefore represents referrals by clinicians. It does not show numbers of patients who may have been rejected at a clinical level prior to referral to the MHAC.

is shown below at figure 65 below[108]. Whereas, over the lifetime of the Act, the numbers of NMD operations peaked at 65 for the two-year period 1989-91, and has now dwindled to a few cases each year, in the years before the Act was passed far greater numbers of operations were taking place. For example, between 1974 and 1976 there were 431 neurosurgical operations for functional mental disorders in the United Kingdom, 8% (about 34) of which were operations (possibly amygdalectomies[109]) for conditions involving repeated violence[110]. It is barely conceivable today that patients exhibiting violent behaviour would be referred for neurosurgery.

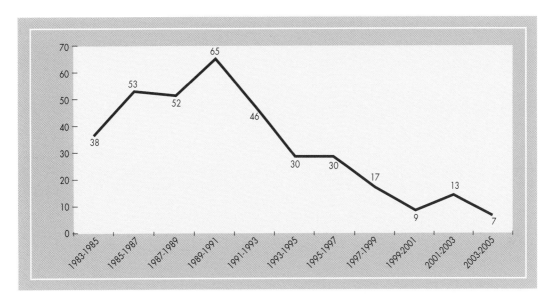

Fig 65: referrals for Neurosurgery for Mental Disorder, England and Wales, 1983/84 – 2004/05[111].

4.79 During this reporting period MHAC-appointed panels considered seven referrals for Neurosurgery for Mental Disorder: four in 2003/04 and three in 2004/05. All but one were authorised to go ahead, with the six operations (stereotactic bilateral anterior capsulotomy) taking place at the University Hospital of Wales, Cardiff. One case had originally been referred in 2002. There were four female and three male patients, with all patients (except one whose ethnicity was not stated) listed as White British. The six patients who proceeded to operations had either obsessive-compulsive disorders (three patients) or depressive disorders. Of the three patients with depression, one had unipolar depression, one bipolar depression, and one depression with general anxiety disorders and social phobia.

4.80 In the case where certification was withheld, the reasons given were linked to a need for a more intensive exposure to various forms of psychological therapies before NMD could be justified as a last resort; that the patient may have been misinformed about the effect of the

---

[109] Amygdalectomy (involving the removal of significant parts of the limbic system) was introduced as a means of treating intractable epilepsy but, as it appeared to also reduce aggression, was used on occasion to control aggression in patients without epilepsy. See Council for Science and Society (1981) *Treating the Troublesome* London: CSS, page 8-9. The operation is not in use for the treatment of mental disorder in the United Kingdom today.

[110] Council for Science and Society (1981) *supra*, using data from Barraclough BM & Mitchel-Heggs NA 'Use of neurosurgery for psychological disorder in British Isles during 1974-6' *BMJ* 9 December 1978, p.1591-3.

[111] Data source: MHAC Biennial Reports

procedures by misplaced assurances from nursing staff and therefore had impaired ability to give informed consent; and that the patient's changeable clinical presentation in different situations concerned the panel.

4.81   Since the end of this reporting period (31 March 2005), we have arranged two further panels to consider new cases, both of which refused to certify NMD treatment. One patient suffered from anxiety and depression with persistent and troubling obsessional thoughts, which the panel recommended should be addressed through a programme of cognitive behavioural therapy before NMD be reconsidered. The other patient blamed a change in medication for a worsening of her depression with obsessive compulsive elements. Whilst she retained mental capacity, she thought that it would take some months to 'get back to where she was' and was in the meantime frightened to have the operation. In none of the cases where certification was withheld did the panel rule out NMD treatment at some future point.

4.82   We welcome the following research initiatives into NMD treatment:

- Because of the relatively small numbers and highly specialised nature of the operations, a cooperative prospective clinical study is planned between the University of Dundee and Ninewells Hospital, Dundee and the University Hospital of Wales, Cardiff: the only two units in the UK currently undertaking this work. Planning meetings have already taken place.

- A prospective study which aims to refine the surgical target within the brain is currently underway at the University Hospital of Wales, Cardiff. Magnetic resonance imaging (MRI) is being used to relate the details of the operation in individual cases with their clinical outcome. Of 52 patients operated at the University Hospital of Wales since 1993, 10 have undergone a second operation. MR scans have been performed after 58 of the 62 operations, although not all cases will be suitable for inclusion in the study.

Deep brain stimulation

4.83   In our last report we drew attention to the advent of 'deep-brain stimulation' (DBS) for the treatment of mental disorder such as depression and obsessive-compulsive disorder[112]. Results from a pilot study into the use of the technique to treat depression were published in 2005[113]. The technique involves the implantation of electrodes into the brain for the suppression of activity in an area called the subgenual cingulate. Similar techniques, albeit with different anatomical targets, have previously been used in the treatment of a range of neurological conditions such as Parkinson's disease. Clinical researchers at the University of Toronto found that there was metabolic over-activity in the subgenual singulate of patients

---

[112] MHAC (2003) *Tenth Biennial Report: Placed Amongst Strangers.* Chapter 10.66-69.

[113] Mayberg HS, Lozano AM, Voon V, McNeely HE, Seminowicz D, Hamani C, Schwalb JM, Kennedy SH. 'Deep brain stimulation for treatment-resistant depression' Neuron Vol 45, 651-660, March 3 2005. See also Lisanby SH (ed) (2004) *Brain Stimulation in Psychiatric Treatment*, American Psychiatric Publishing, and the review of the same by Philpot M in the *British Journal of Psychiatry* (2005) 187:295-6: 'the technology is in its infancy... However, as ECT and psychosurgery are becoming more difficult to use in some parts of the world, these new methods may eventually offer practical alternatives for treating the most resistant disorders'. Alongside experiments with techniques involving electrical current between deep-brain implants, research is being undertaken into the use of magnetism and other non-invasive methods of stimulating neurological effects that could one day be used instead of ECT.

with treatment-resistant depression[114], and experimentally treated six such patients with the technique of chronic DBS. The treatment appeared to result in a striking and sustained remission of depression in four of the six patients[115]. Clinicians in Belgium have previously reported having achieved beneficial effects with chronic DBS for three of four patients with treatment-resistant obsessive-compulsive disorder, who might otherwise have undergone neurosurgery in the form of a bilateral capsulotomy[116].

4.84   At the time of going to press we were informed that a patient detained under s.3 of the Mental Health Act in the Oxford area was to undergo preliminary tests for the administration of DBS. The patient concerned was consenting to the treatment.

4.85   Insofar as it involves procedures that have strong similarities to techniques of Neurosurgery for Mental Disorder such as stereotactic subcaudate tractotomy (i.e. the introduction under local anaesthesia and with the aid of a stereotactic frame of an object through burr holes in the skull), some mental health practitioners and lay persons have assumed that the safeguards of s.57 of the Act do or should apply to its use. However, we do not take the view that DBS can fall within the description at s.57 of 'a surgical operation for destroying brain tissue or for destroying the function of brain tissue'. It would appear that the effects of the operation on brain function are reversible by discontinuance of electrical stimulation. We therefore concluded in our last report that the technique fell under neither s.57 nor s.58 of the Act, in which case the Act provided no safeguards in relation to its use. Indeed, in the case of a detained patient, the provisions of s.63 of the Act would theoretically allow the treatment to be given to a detained patient who was either incapable of consenting or had refused to consent to it, although we doubt either that the imposition of DBS to a refusing patient would be acceptable in terms of wider human-rights considerations, or that it would be likely to be proposed by any clinician.

4.86   We recommended in our last report that the Secretary of State should consider the regulation of deep-brain stimulation as a treatment for mental disorder by introducing safeguards for detained patients equivalent to those applicable for ECT[117]. Such regulations may be made under s.58(1)(a) of the Act after consultation with such bodies as appear to the Secretary of State to be concerned. Now that the treatment looks to be in use within the United Kingdom we strongly advise the Secretary of State to undertake the consultation that could lead to action upon our previous recommendation. We also recommend that consideration be given to establishing some form of specific accreditation over clinics carrying out this work.

---

[114] Patients were referred to the study by mood disorder specialists. All were considered resistant to all available therapeutic options, and had failed to respond to a minimum of four different classes of antidepressant medication at maximum tolerable dose. Five had previously undergone ECT treatment and all had attempted cognitive-behavioural therapy without clinical improvement.

[115] See also 'Deep Impact', the *Economist*, 3 March 2005. For a general account of DBS, see David Beresford 'Surgery that made me smile' and Laura Spinney 'As if a black cloud is being lifted', *The Guardian*, 9 June 2005.

[116] Nuttin B, Cosyns P, Demeulemeester H, Gybels J, Meyerson B 'Electrical stimulation in anterior limbs of internal capsules in patients with obsessive-compulsive disorder' *The Lancet* 1999; 354:1526

[117] MHAC (2003) *Tenth Biennial Report: Placed Amongst Strangers.* Recommendation 42.

> **Recommendation 18:** The Secretary of State should consider urgently the regulation of deep-brain stimulation for the treatment of mental disorder, providing safeguards *at least* equivalent to those applicable to ECT under the Mental Health Act 1983.

Physical healthcare

4.87 The physical health of seriously mentally disordered people is likely to be significantly worse than that of the general population, for a variety of factors, including: self-neglect; poor income; exclusion and stigma; lack of exercise or poor diet; damaging behaviours such as heavy smoking, drinking, or illicit drug use; the health-risks associated with some types of psychotropic medication[118]; the effects on the immune system of sustained stress or trauma[119]; a reduced likelihood of seeking medical help for physical problems[120]. Research has consistently found a high risk of premature death in people with mental illness from both natural and unnatural causes[121], with the mortality ratio in schizophrenia three times that for the general population for all causes, and high levels of morbidity of the circulatory, respiratory, digestive, endocrine and nervous systems[122]. Our own data on deaths from natural causes is outlined at chapter 4.282 *et seq.*

4.88 Long-stay hospital patients may be particularly at risk of poor health, although such patients also provide a stable population for strategic health-promoting interventions. A study of patients at Rampton Hospital in November 2000 found high levels of obesity and smoking[123]. Of the 250 patients studied (the 54% of the patient population that had consented to take part in the study), obesity levels in male patients (36%) were double that of the general male population, with three-quarters of male patients at least registering as overweight to some degree. Three-quarters of the women patients registered as obese or severely obese (roughly $3^1/_2$ times the average in the general UK women population), with a further 12% overweight. Eighty-two per cent of men and 71% of women smoked. The

---

[118] Cormac, I., Ferriter, M., Benning, R., & Saul, C. 'Physical health and health risk factors in a population of long-stay psychiatric patients'. *Psychiatric Bulletin* (2005) 29; 18-20. Cormac, I., Martin, D. & Ferriter, M. 'Improving the physical health of long-stay psychiatric in-patients'. *Advances in Psychiatric Treatment* (2004) 10; 107-115. Brown, S., Inskip, H., & Barraclough, B 'Causes of the excess mortality of schizophrenia' *British Journal of Psychiatry*, (2000) 177; 212-217. Mentality (2003) *Not all in the mind: the physical health of mental health service users.* Radical Mentalities - briefing paper 2. London: Mentality.

[119] Jenkins, R., McCulloch, A., Friedli, L & Parker, C. (2002) *Developing a National Mental Health Policy.* Maudsley Monographs no.43; Psychology Press, pp.78: 'Sustained stress or trauma increases susceptibility to viral infection and physical illness by damaging the immune system'.

[120] Phelan, M., Stradins, L. & Morrison, S 'Physical health of people with severe mental illness'. *BMJ* 2001:322; 443-444.

[121] Harris, E.C. & Barraclough, B. 'Excess mortality of mental disorder'. *British Journal of Psychiatry*, (1998) 137, 11-53. This research data is republished and discussed in Jenkins *et al* (2002) *supra*. pp.134. See also *Running on Empty; Building Momentum to Improve Well-Being in Severe Mental Illness*, June 2005. (Hafal; MDF; Primhe; Rethink; RCN; Sane); www.sane.org.uk.

[122] Brown, S., Inskip, H., & Barraclough, B (2000) 'Causes of the excess mortality of schizophrenia' *British Journal of Psychiatry*, 177; 212-217

[123] Cormac *et al* (2005) *supra*

majority of patients had significantly increased their body weight since their admission to the hospital. The reasons for this are likely to be complex, but it is known that some psychotropic medication leads to weight-gain, although low-levels of exercise amongst this seriously ill patient population are also likely to be a factor. More than a third of the patients reported breathlessness after climbing one flight of stairs. The study led to a number of new initiatives at the hospital to address patients' physical health, including the involvement of multi-disciplinary teams to review diet and activity levels; encourage and facilitate exercise and weight-loss; and reduce smoking.

4.89   It is a requirement of the National Service Framework for Mental Health that people with severe mental illness should have their physical needs addressed[124]. Despite this, the *Running on Empty* report published in June 2005 highlighted 'an urgent need to ensure that a holistic, supportive, choice-driven, approach is widely adopted into the everyday provision of care [of people with severe mental illness] and delivered by all healthcare professionals'[125].

4.90   Mentally disordered people in hospital settings should have access to physical health promotion services, including specifically targeted information and support on issues such as exercise; smoking; nutrition; housing; and safe sex. Where a patient has been admitted to hospital involuntarily, we believe that it is imperative that adequate means for healthy living (including diet, opportunity for exercise and fresh air, etc) are provided by the detaining authority. In many hospital wards this duty of care is not being met.

4.91   It has been suggested that there is often a gap between mental health service users and their professional and lay carers about physical health needs. A study by the charity *Mentality* found that a commonly held view of professionals was that mentally disordered persons 'have enough to worry about' whereas service users expressed a strong interest in and commitment to healthy living and achieving better physical health[126]. Whilst we believe that more can be done to promote physical health (and to address physical health problems) amongst detained patients, it is important that health-promotion and interventions designed to address specific healthcare problems do not undermine detained patients' right to make autonomous choices over their lifestyle where they have capacity to do so. Even patients who are to some extent incapacitated by their mental disorder should be engaged to the maximum extent in their care and treatment[127], so that coercion is used as a last resort for proportionate aims. Because the 1983 Act can be taken as authority to provide psychiatric 'nursing care, habilitation and rehabilitation' without a patient's consent[128], there is a potential for health promotion to involve further and unjustified infringements of detained patients' residual liberties. It would seem both ethically and practically more appropriate

---

[124] Department of Health (1999) *National Service Framework for Mental Health: modern standards and service models*; Welsh Assembly Government (2002) *A National Service Framework for Wales: Adult Mental Health Service.*

[125] *Running on Empty; Building Momentum to Improve Well-Being in Severe Mental Illness,* June 2005 (see n.121 above). See also Titmarsh S 'Lets get physical' *Progress in Neurology and Psychiatry* Vol 9 No 6, July/August 2005.

[126] Mentality (2003) *Not all in the mind* (*supra,* pp.24-5)

[127] Kennedy, I 'Patients are expert in their own field' *BMJ* (2003) 326:1276.

[128] MHA 1983 ss.63, 145 (definition of medical treatment)

that patients be empowered through dietary and lifestyle advice rather than coerced under the cloak of treatment for mental disorder[129]. We discuss this in more detail in relation to smoking at paragraph 4.92 below. The practice example given at figure 4.66 below shows how patients may be empowered through health promotion and how this can have positive effects on individual care and treatment and the milieu of psychiatric units.

Good practice in encouraging healthy lifestyles

The majority of patients in a new women's unit at the Berkshire-based Independent Hospital, Thornford Park, had been in hospital care for many years. Some were restricted patients, who had come from Broadmoor Hospital. Most were overweight and many were smokers.

The hospital introduced a healthy lifestyles group, entailing the following initiatives:

- patients received dietary advice, and the catering department produced healthier options on the hospital menu;

- the local GP practice's 'smoking cessation' team visited the hospital, offering advice and support to patients who wished to stop smoking. Patients who gave up smoking were offered free nicotine replacement therapy for an initial three months;

- patients who were allowed leave had enrolled at a local weight-watchers' group; other patients had asked whether the weight watchers' group would visit the hospital for those who were not allowed leave;

- some women who had escorted leave were using the time to take brisk walks around the hospital grounds; and one woman had started to use the hospital's running-track facility.

Not all the women on the unit were taking part in these initiatives, but what had started out with an initial involvement of just one or two patients had already grown at the time of the Commission's visit, as other patients recognised the benefits to those taking part. Women who were taking part in these initiatives were appreciative of their effects, stating that their confidence was increasing, and some ex-smokers showing some pride in their achievements.

Facilitating the opportunity for change and peer-support seemed to be the most effective way of promoting healthy lifestyles at this unit. We doubt that enforcement of a smoking ban or dietary regimes would have had similarly positive effects.

Fig 66: good practice in encouraging healthy lifestyles

Smoking

4.92   The Government has stated that the NHS will be generally 'smokefree' by the end of 2006, although its 2004 White Paper recognised that in some psychiatric hospitals which are patients' main place of residence and therefore their home, this may not be achievable[130].

[129] See, for example, Isaac M B & Isaac M T 'Should diet be a medical intervention?' *The Lancet* (correspondence), Vol 364, No 9451 11 December 2004, on dietary and lifestyle advice in Gresham Psychiatric Intensive Care Unit. On empowerment, see Ekpe H 'Empowerment for adults with chronic mental health problems and obesity'. *Nursing Standard*. (2001)15, 39, 37-42.

[130] Department of Heath (2004) *Choosing Health: making healthy choices easier.* CM 6374, Nov 2004.

Subsequent Health Development Agency guidance appeared to rule out 'blanket' exemptions from smoking bans in NHS buildings and grounds, although it conceded that case-by-case assessments could result in some long-stay patients retaining smoking privileges[131]. The guidance suggested that smokefree policies could be empowering for mental health patients and suggested that case studies have shown that NHS mental health care Trusts can become smokefree. It condoned the practice of one long-stay institution in phasing out smoking areas by making them unattractive, by limiting their use to two patients at a time, having no television or radio, and providing only basic seating[132]. In the Government's consultation on the smokefree elements of the Health Improvement and Protection Bill, launched in June 2005, it was proposed that regulations may exempt psychiatric hospitals and units, and long-stay adult residential care homes from the smokefree legislation, since they act as an individual's dwelling. The consultation suggested that exploratory work will be needed to see how psychiatric hospitals and units can move to become smokefree in the longer term. In Scotland it appears likely that *all* psychiatric facilities will be exempted 'on humanitarian grounds' from the smoking ban proposed for all public places[133].

4.93 Anti-smoking initiatives such as smoking bans in public spaces, although now under consideration or implemented across many European states, have already some history of implementation in the United States. In the USA hospitalised patients have generally been required to abstain from smoking since a national policy banning smoking in all hospitals, including psychiatric units, was introduced in 1992. A number of psychiatric units in the USA do, however, continue to provide some psychiatric patients with 'smoking passes'[134]. It seems likely, from what we have observed in the implementation of smoke-free policies in this country, that a similar pattern of special allowances for certain groups of patients is emerging as services seek to implement the Government commitment. There is a danger that the issue of 'passes' may become something of a reinforcing measure or reward for good behaviour, whether explicitly or by implication following risk-assessment procedures[135].

4.94 Psychiatric services across England and Wales, in implementing the extant Health Development Agency guidelines on case-by-case consideration of patients' facility to smoke, are faced with the dilemma of whether withholding tobacco from patients admitted under the Mental Health Act is justifiable as a consequence of their detention in hospital, or whether detained patients deserve special dispensation to smoke that will not be extended to others. We can see that there is a risk of smoking bans adding to the unintended anti-therapeutic consequences of admitting patients involuntarily to busy acute wards. Such patient's subjective experience of their care is likely to be highly coloured by the confiscation of their cigarettes, especially where the care regime may often appear limited to the administration of medication in a closed environment where there is little to do. Conversely, we

---

[131] Health Development Agency (2005) *Guidance for Smokefree Hospital Trusts*, p. 8 www.hda.nhs.uk/evidence

[132] *ibid.*, p.9

[133] Scottish Health Minister Andy Kerr quoted in Kirsty Scott 'Prison cells and care homes escape Scotland's smoking ban'. *The Guardian*, 11/03/05.

[134] Prochaska, J. Gill, O., Hall, S 'Treatment of Tobacco Use in an Inpatient Psychiatric Setting'. *Psychiatric Services* Nov 2004 Vol 55 No 11 1265-1270

[135] *ibid.*

accept that neither patients nor staff should be required to spend their days in an unhealthy environment where they are exposed to passive smoking. The Healthcare Commission's environmental audit of psychiatric facilities over this reporting period found over a quarter of all psychiatric units and wards either failed to provide non-smoking areas or did not have such areas adequately separated from smoking areas[136]. The danger of exemptions to a smoking ban (aside from the individual health risks and discomfort posed by passive smoking) is that psychiatric inpatients will be excluded by default from health promotion measures designed to help people stop smoking. It is important that psychiatric inpatients, who are proportionally greater users of tobacco products than the general population, are offered help in smoking cessation that continues after their discharge from hospital.

4.95   The percentage of people with mental disorder who smoke is higher than for the general population, although less striking disparities can be produced by comparing smoking rates of people with mental health problems with those of people from deprived socio-economic groups (where, incidentally, mental disorder is most prevalent)[137]. *Rethink* report that over 70% of persons with psychotic disorders who live in institutions smoke, with over 50% being 'heavy smokers'[138]. Both the reasons that people smoke and the neurophysiological effects of smoking are complex[139], but we would highlight the following as relevant to the situation of detained patients:

- Perhaps most importantly, smoking may be used by patients as a diversion or substitute activity in ward environments where there is little alternative to inactivity and boredom[140]. Such environments are likely to contribute to the heavy tobacco use of some patients. Patients may find that the smoking room in some wards, or a space outside designated for smokers, is a place where there is relative calm or opportunities to talk quietly with others, for want of better or quieter facilities elsewhere on the ward. Where 'going for a cigarette' becomes a legitimate means of respite from the general ward environment that is not otherwise available, services are unwittingly encouraging smoking amongst their patients.

- Psychiatric patients, especially those who have not entered a hospital environment voluntarily, may use smoking as a way of taking back or retaining some control of their patterns of behaviour and their environment.

- It is possible that some patients find their smoking reduces some positive and negative symptoms of their mental disorders. Smoking may have some antidepressant and anxiolytic effects, although in the long term it seems likely to exacerbate rather than relieve symptoms[141]. It may be experienced as improving cognition. It can reduce parkinsonian side-effects of antipsychotic medication (although it may also increase

---

[136] Healthcare Commission (2005) *National Audit of Violence*, p.15.

[137] *Rethink* 'Smoking and Mental Illness' from www.rethink.org/information/living/smoking.html.

[138] *ibid.*

[139] Wilhelm, K., Arnold, K., Niven, H. and Richmond, R. 'Grey Lungs and Blue Moods: smoking cessation in the context of lifetime depression history'. *Australian and New Zealand Journal of Psychiatry* 2004;38896-905

[140] Patients quoted in the *Radical Mentalities* briefing (*supra*, note 118, p.26) state: 'When I've been an in-patient in hospital, smoking seems to be the only thing to do. I initially started smoking because of mental health problems'; and 'It's the environment on the ward. You're bored stiff, you've got nothing to do, all you're doing is just killing time and the cigarettes are there one after the other, you just can't help yourself.'

[141] Wilhelm *et al* (2004) *supra.*

rates of akathisia and tardive dyskinsia)[142]. Smoking is known to effect the metabolism of some antipsychotic drugs (particularly Clozapine), so that stopping smoking without adjustment of dosage could bring out side-effects of the medication[143].

- It may be that many people with mental disorder find it harder to manage nicotine withdrawal symptoms of anxiety, depression or agitation, and therefore are less able to stop or reduce smoking once they are addicted.

- Many forms of mental disorder cause risk-taking behaviour, neglect of health, and general nihilistic outlook. This may make psychiatric patients disinclined towards health promotion and difficult to engage in smoking cessation programmes, although this is not to say that they should therefore be denied opportunities and encouragement to address their smoking.

- The number of cannabis users is increasing[144] and for a proportion of patients, particularly in the younger age groups, smoking cessation strategies must take account of concurrent cannabis use.

4.96 An Australian study has concluded that it is clinically inadvisable for persons with depression to stop smoking precipitously[145]. Nicotine withdrawal left unaddressed may also compromise psychiatric care in other ways: the nicotine withdrawal symptoms of irritability and agitation are also symptoms most likely to cause disruption on a psychiatric unit[146]. Some studies report that patients who smoke are more likely to disengage with inpatient services with unmet psychiatric needs[147]. These findings suggest that total smoking bans across hospital premises and grounds may be unsuitable for all types of psychiatric facilities, but that smoking cessation services need to adopt a planned approach involving education, nicotine replacement or other drug therapy[148] and the collaboration of patients.

---

[142] *ibid.*

[143] Leon, J de. 'Atypical Antipsychotic Dosing: the Effect of Smoking and Caffeine' *Psychiatric Services* May 2004 Vol 55 No 5 491- 493 found that smoking (tobacco or cannabis) decreased levels of Clozapine and Olanzapine metabolised, whilst caffeine increased the levels. Smoking appears not to affect risperidone, aripiprazole, or quetiapine. Smokers required higher doses of Clozapine or Olanzapine for therapeutic effect. Sudden cessation of smoking in a patient taking Clozapine could lead, within two to four weeks, to an increase in Clozapine plasma levels by a factor of 1.5 on average. Further changes to drug metabolisation can result from increases or decreases in a patient's caffeine intake (whether from coffee, canned drinks or other sources). If a patient stops smoking and increases caffeine intake there may be a particular danger of dramatic increases in their plasma concentrations of Clozapine. It is likely that similar effects occur in Olanzapine metabolism, but this is of less significance as its therapeutic window (and therefore the threshold of toxicity where side-effects are more serious) is broader than that for Clozapine.

[144] Smart R., Ogbourne A. 'Drug use and drinking among students in 36 countries'. *Addictive behaviours* 2000; 25: 455-460

[145] Wilhelm *et al* (2004) *supra* (n.139)

[146] Prochaska *et al* (2004) *supra* (n.134)

[147] *ibid.*

[148] See, for example, Williams, J., Ziedonis, D. Foulds, J (2004) 'A Case of Nicotine Nasal Spray in the Treatment of Tobacco Dependence Among Patients With Schizophrenia' *Psychiatric Services* Sept 2004 Vol 55 No 19 1064-1066; Hayford K., Patten, C., Rummans, T., Schroeder, D., Offord, K., Croghan, I., Glover, E., Sachs, D. & Hurt, R. (1999) 'Efficacy of bupropion for smoking cessation in smokers with a former history of major depression or alcoholism'. *British Journal of Psychiatry* (1999) 174, 173-178.

4.97   Patients who have been admitted to psychiatric facilities without their consent (and, being detained there, may also be prevented from leaving hospital premises even for short periods) may experience smoking bans as an additional and intolerable extension of the State's interference in their self-determination. It seems possible that enforcing a smoking ban on patients whose detention in hospital is justified for the purposes of psychiatric treatment would be found to be an unjustifiable interference in their human rights if this were subject to legal challenge. On the other hand, special allowance for detained patients who smoke may cause tensions where services have inpatient populations composed of both detained and informal patients. Whilst informal patients are, in law at least, free to leave hospital premises and grounds to smoke if they wish to do so[149], services should beware of establishing rules over smoking that have counterproductive effects. Smoking bans could, for example, discourage informal patients (and those detained patients who are allowed relative freedom of movement) from spending time in the ward environment or otherwise engaging with therapeutic services and activities. It is possible that the self-exclusion of some vulnerable patients who smoke from hospital grounds may pose greater dangers than the health risks of smoking.

4.98   At present, we encounter a number of small units that do not allow smoking in any indoor area, so that patients must go outside to garden or courtyard areas to smoke. Access to such areas can be limited by staff shortages.

4.99   The practice examples at figure 67 are all taken from the Cheshire area, although they are fairly typical of Commissioners' observations across England and Wales.

Poor Practice

- An NHS unit whose main lounge, where the only television in the unit was placed, was the designated smoking area. The non-smoking lounge was a side-room without television, where medical equipment was also stored;

- An NHS ward where the smoking room was left with its door open, and without the extractor fan switched on: the whole ward was permeated with smoke;

- Access to the designated smoking room in one mixed-sex NHS unit leading past the female dormitory: women reported feeling intimidated by male patients passing to and from the room;

- An NHS psychiatric intensive care unit, generally in a poor environmental state, where the smoking room was a bare unfurnished room, the sole object in which was an ashtray placed in the centre of the floor;

- An Independent Hospital whose main lounge, where most patient activity and sociali-sation was focused, was the designated smoking area. Commissioners reported a 'culture of smoking' in the unit that excluded non-smokers: the manager of the unit appeared to be constantly smoking during the Commission visit;

- A patient in a non-smoking Independent Hospital unit was allowed to smoke, but only in her own bedroom.

---

[149]   Our experience suggests that the reality of hospital life for many informal psychiatric patients is that they may be free to discharge themselves from hospital care, but they are not generally at liberty to come and go from wards to smoke in outside areas.

Good practice

- A well-designed NHS high dependency unit ensured through ward layout that activity was focused in the non-smoking lounge. Patients were actively encouraged to take responsibility for the upkeep of the environment, including checking and maintaining the smoking room. Community ward meetings were held involving patients and clinical and domestic staff. The ward had multi-disciplinary management: on the day of the MHAC visit the ward manager on duty was an occupational therapist. Staff seemed well-motivated and the culture of the ward seemed pleasant and therapeutic.

Fig 67: smoking arrangements in psychiatric hospitals visited by the MHAC in Cheshire

Diagnosis of physical health problems in psychiatric care

4.100   All psychiatric patients should receive a physical examination upon admission to hospital, with the intensity of that examination depending upon that patient's history and presenting symptoms[150]. NIMHE guidelines recommend a basic physical examination within 24 hours of hospital admission for all psychiatric patients[151]. A recent article by Dr Jayne Greening suggests that every patient with a long-term psychiatric disorder should undergo an annual physical examination with blood-monitoring, especially to cover variable such as blood-sugars; lipids and prolactin[152]. Psychiatric disorder may mask physical problems (not least because the patient may not volunteer information about experiencing physical problems, or may not be believed or understood when doing so). The following case shows that the level of examinations may be far from adequate in some psychiatric facilities.

'Poor physical healthcare locally - referrals slow. Regional Secure Unit - dentist, doctor, chiropody, massage, etc available readily within hospital'

Yasmin Jackson, ex-s.3 patient, Wales

'No one asks about physical health'.

Angela Williams, ex-s.3 patient, Somerset

4.101   In its report of November 2002[153], the Health Service Ombudsman outlined a finding in favour of a complainant whose wife (Mrs X) died of septicaemia (blood poisoning due to urinary tract infection) within two days of her admittance to a psychiatric assessment ward for elderly patients. Mrs X was admitted from a routine GP appointment: she had a known

---

[150]   Porter, I (1996) 'Is routine physical examination of psychiatric in-patients really necessary?' *Psychiatric Bulletin* 20, 218-220.

[151]   National Institute for Mental Health in England (2004) *Mental Health Policy Implementation Guide: Developing Positive Practice to Support the Safe and Therapeutic Management of Aggression and Violence in Mental Health In-patient Settings.* February 2004; Chapter 14. See also Garden G "Physical examination in psychiatric practice' *Advances in Psychiatric Treatment* (2005) 11; 142-9.

[152]   Greening J 'Physical health of patients in rehabilitation and recovery: a survey of case note records' *Psychiatric Bulletin* (2005) 29:210-212. See also correspondence from Drs Pitman & Phelan in *Psychiatric Bulletin* (2005) 29:354.

[153]   Health Service Ombudsman (2002) *Investigations Completed April-July 2002. 1st Report – Session 2002-2003.* HC 51-II. London; The Stationery Office. Case No. E.2390/00-01, p.56-64.

mental disorder managed with Lithium and had several previous hospital admissions. The Ombudsman's report was critical of the Trust for failing to perform basic observations of her temperature, pulse and respiration (TPR) and blood pressure, for failures in communication between staff members and with the complainant. Although the infection had been correctly diagnosed the failure to monitor vital signs (and to give sufficient notice to the husband's concerns) would have missed any opportunity to identify an appropriate medical response to Mrs X's septicaemia. The Trust accepted the recommendations of the Ombudsman's medical advisors, which we summarise at figure 68 below, and which we believe should be considered by all psychiatric services.

'Assessment wards should be able to isolate physical from psychological needs':

- Training should ensure that nursing staff are appropriately aware of the physical health problems which are likely to arise in older people with both functional and organic mental health problems;

- all such patients should have base line temperature, pulse and respiration (TPR) and blood pressure (BP) measures made and recorded as a matter of routine;

- monitoring of these parameters should be undertaken consistently and recorded appropriately when significant physical ill health problems arise; and

- nursing staff must report serious concerns raised by family members to the medical team and particularly the ward round, and should report back to family members that such concerns will be addressed.

Fig 68: summary of the Health Service Ombudsman's recommendations on physical assessment in psychiatric wards for elderly patients[154].

4.102 It is established that long-stay patients can benefit from the input of visits by a primary care doctor[155]. At Charing Cross hospital, a weekly three-hour primary care service is provided to the acute adult psychiatric wards (with a limited service for older persons' wards) by a GP. Patients may self-refer, or be referred by clinical staff, and appointments are made just as with any GP surgery (except appointment slots extend over a half-hour to acknowledge the complex needs and communication difficulties of many patients). Demands on the service are managed through priority being given to patients who are homeless, not registered with another GP (or had not seen that GP for more than six months), or had been in hospital for more than three months. A study of the service published in 2004 showed that this service filled a gap in health care provision and would seem to indicate that health benefits can be had from the extension of GP services into the acute sector as well as the long-stay wards. On a national scale, we doubt that either sector has sufficient input from primary care services to provide comprehensive physical health care to detained patients, although we see a number of other examples of good practice (see figure 69 below).

---

[154] Summarised from Health Service Ombudsman (2002) *supra*, p.63

[155] Fisher, N & Roberts, J 'Primary health care service for long-stay psychiatric patients'. *Psychiatric Bulletin* (1998) 22; 610-612.

In July 2004 Commissioners noted the consideration paid to the physical health needs of women patients at Heather Close, part of the South London and Maudsley NHS Trust. The Trust had noted in its clinical governance plans for 2004 that patients on this unit had no access to GPs, and therefore established a weekly 9 to 5 open clinic staffed by a dual general and mental health nurse, who would also review patients due to be seen on the following week's ward round. The review consisted of routine recording of patients' vital signs, with an Electrocardiogram (ECG) where required, as well as general consultation. Commissioners saw in patients' notes good evidence of physical health care from nursing care plans and evaluations, nurses and doctors' entries for ward rounds and correspondence with specialists, including dieticians, diabetic nurses and a gynaecological specialist registrar.

Fig 69: good practice example of women's physical health care

Recommendation 19: Service providers should audit their practice in providing physical health care (including initial physical examinations) to psychiatric inpatients and ensure that they are meeting NIMHE guidelines.

Physical health and diagnosis of mental disorder

4.103   Insufficiently thorough medical examinations of patients prior to or upon admission to hospital could risk misdiagnosis and indeed even attribution of symptoms to mental disorder where there is an underlying physical cause. In one complaint handled by the MHAC in this reporting period (and separate from the case reported at paragraph 4.100 above), the presentation of an elderly patient's urinary tract infection was misread as signs of dementia.

4.104   A study by Dr Dave Hambidge, a consultant psychiatrist who has been a Second Opinion Appointed Doctor and who provides independent reports for patients' MHRT applications, suggests that organic medical conditions are not routinely examined for when patients are diagnosed with schizophrenia, despite all current standard textbooks' exhortations that organic causative factors should be excluded in such a diagnosis[156]. In interviewing and reviewing the medical records of 56 detained adult patients who applied to the MHRT between 2000 and 2003 in the North-west of England, and who had been detained for less than a decade, Dr Hambidge found that:

- Blood tests results were recorded for 52 patients. Of these, 20 (38%) showed abnormal blood-test results (ABTR), including elevated glucose (6, or 12%) or white blood count (7, or 13%). Abnormal glucose levels could indicate diabetes or the side-effects of medication, although none of the patients evidencing these were undergoing further investigation. Elevated white blood count could be indicative of viral infections of the

---

[156] Hambidge, D 'Detection of organic causes of first episode psychosis' *Progress in Neurology and Psychiatry* Volume 9; No 4   May/June 2005

central nervous system, including neurosyphilis. Only two patients had received serological tests for syphilis (both negative). Given a reported rise in cases of syphilis in England in recent years, more widespread use of serological tests for syphilis perhaps should be reconsidered as a part of the differential diagnosis of any psychiatric patient. It is also possible that some cytomegalovirus (herpes) infection, which most adults will have had at some point and which can remain asymptomatic, may contribute to the symptoms of schizophrenia and that this contribution an be reduced with the administration of the antiviral agent[158].

- Urine drug screening had been undertaken in 23 (44%) patients, although surprisingly few first admissions, or those known or suspected of using illicit drugs, were tested. Of those who were tested, a third tested positively for cannabis. Lack of detection could lead to misdiagnosis, inappropriate medication or failure to use appropriate interventions[159].

- Of 49 patients whose documentation was indicative either way, 38 (77%) had neither EEG nor neuroimaging that could be of use in discounting temporal lobe epilepsy, brain tumour or Creutzfeld Jacob Disease (CJD) from their diagnosis.

- Of 41 patients whose documentation was indicative either way, 24 (42%) had clearly not been given any Electrocardiogram (ECG) tests. Two patients prescribed Clozaril (for which the risk of tachycardia indicates ECG recording before treatment is commenced) had no ECG records in their notes. Two further patients without ECG records were taking more than one antipsychotic drug simultaneously, and one was taking three different antispychotics (as part of a drug regime totalling six different psychotropic agents), which increased their vulnerability to cardiac abnormalities.

This study would seem to point to a widespread failing in diagnostic and ongoing tests for organic conditions which may underlie, or be a causation of, psychiatric illness and its treatment.

Arrangements for the care of physically disabled patients in psychiatric units

4.105   Commissioners continue to note poor provision made for patients with physical disabilities in psychiatric facilities (see figure 70).

4.106   The Healthcare Commission's environmental audit of psychiatric facilities over this reporting period found that only 42% of psychiatric facilities provided suitable access and facilities for people with special needs[160]. Only 36% of acute units, 42% of PICUs and 26% of forensic facilities met this standard. Surprisingly, only 55% of elderly wards provided adequate facilities and access for people with special needs.

---

[158]   Dickerson FB, Boronow JJ, Stallings CR, Origoni AE, Yalkin RH. 'Reduction of symptoms by valcyclovir in CMV seropositive individuals with schizophrenia'. *American Journal of Psychiatry* 2003; 160:2234-6.

[159]   Ley A, Jeffrey D, Ruiz J, McLaren S, Gillespie C. 'Under detection of comorbid drug use at acute psychiatric admission'. *Psychiatric Bulletin* 2002; 26:248-51.

[160]   Healthcare Commission (2005) National Audit of Violence, p.15.

Mr *F* had developed psychotic symptoms whilst undergoing treatment for Parkinson's Disease in hospital, and was transferred to psychiatric facility under s.2 of the Act. When a Commissioner visited him, she heard from him and his wife that his physical needs were not being met in the psychiatric ward. Although his condition varied from day to day, he was often immobilised and required help for the slightest movement, such as putting on his glasses. His bed was unsuitable, as it could not be adjusted to enable him to sit upright; and the wheelchair on loan from A&E was inappropriate and in poor condition: his wife said that she had found him left slumped in that chair. There was no disabled toilet on the ward and he required help to use the urine bottle with which he was supplied. He had been briefly transferred to an elderly ward, which had a disabled toilet, but they had been unable to cope with his disturbed behaviour. He was 'specialed' by an agency nurse who was stationed outside his room.

Mrs *V*, a woman in her 50s, had been detained under s.3 on an acute admission ward for three months when we met her. She raised with us the lack of facilities on the ward to meet her disability needs: she had significant problems with her back, hips and knees and walked with a frame. She received physiotherapy, but was unable to use the baths or the shower on the ward (consequently having to bathe on an adjacent elderly care ward when facilities and staff were available for her use, therefore preventing her from having a bath in the mornings as would be her choice), and was unable to use any of the ward toilets as they had neither grab-rails (which would have posed a risk to others as ligature points) nor raised toilet seats. She described using the toilets whilst standing, leaning on her frame, often soiling her clothing in the process. We asked the hospital to provide a raised toilet seat within seven days of our visit and contacted the Trust Chief Executive over their compliance with the Disability Discrimination Act.

Fig 70: examples of poor provision for physically disabled patients

Recommendation 20: Psychiatric service providers should audit their arrangements and facilities for caring for physically disabled patients to ensure that they meet the requirements of the Disability Discrimination Act and provide quality care in a humane environment.

The Mental Health Review Tribunal

4.107 The MHAC does not have a monitoring role in relation to the Mental Health Review Tribunal. In our Tenth Biennial Report we wrote that:

> because the Mental Health Review Tribunals come under the supervision of the Council of Tribunals and their hearings can be subject to legal appeal, the Commission has confined its observations about them over the years to the general. The Secretary of State has confirmed that it is not expected of the Commission to monitor the work of Tribunals under the present system[161].

We noted in our report that, under the proposed Mental Health Bill, where the Mental Health Tribunal would have a much broader involvement in the exercise of powers and discharge of duties (including sanctioning compulsion and reviewing its own decisions to do so), this position could be less tenable for the Commission's successors[162].

Problems in MHRT administration

4.108 In making our general comments about the Tribunal in this report, we are mindful that its functioning has been a matter of great concern in recent years to many mental health service professionals and to patients. The Institute of Mental Health Act Practitioners compiled a dossier of problems encountered by Mental Health Act Administrators and have submitted it to the Department of Health. These problems include communication problems; late cancellations; difficulties in listing cases; lack of Tribunal clerks; and breaches of patient confidentiality through administrative error. The following example of the Commission's own findings is taken from our visit report to a central London hospital in the summer of 2004:

> Commissioners were told of serious problems with the administration of and organisation of MHRT hearings, causing enormous distress to patients, considerable difficulties and inconvenience for staff and a great deal of additional work for Mental Health Act Administrators. The patient services manager described the problems as 'worse than ever before' and gave the following examples:
>
> - hearings being adjourned or rearranged at the last minute;
>
> - panel members being misinformed about the date or venue of the hearing, resulting in one or more members being absent;
>
> - panels turning up for hearings for patients who have been discharged, despite the MHRT office being notified of discharge;
>
> - hearings arranged on days when RMOs cannot be present; and

---

[161] Mental Health Act Commission (2003) *Tenth Biennial Report: Placed Amongst Strangers*, para 20.19. Some legal commentators argue that the 1983 Act does, in fact, place the Commission under a legal obligation to review the operation of the MHRTs as they relate to detained patients by virtue of the lack of specific exclusion (e.g. Jones, R (2004) *Mental Health Act Manual*, ninth edition, p.441).

[162] MHAC (2003) *Placed Amongst Strangers*, para 20.19.

- multiple bookings for hearings on one day with the result that at least one case cannot be heard[163].

Fig 71: extract from an MHAC visit report, June 2004 (central London hospital)

4.109 It is clear that the 2004 centralisation of the MHRT secretariat offices in London and Middlesex has created some difficulties which have yet to be resolved. Shortly before it was implemented, the centralisation was explained to Parliament as a rationalisation whose benefits would be consistency of approach in listing of cases; better and more flexible use of staff and resources; and assurance for the Secretary of State for Health that his or her statutory obligations are met[164]. Following centralisation the Southern Region MHRT told a Parliamentary Committee that it had had resulted in unsuitable accommodation for the London MHRT secretariat (where, for example, the telephone systems were inadequate for multiple use), and an exacerbation in staff turnover so that around 70% of London administrative staff had been with the Tribunal for less than a year, leading to staff training problems[165]. Government has recognised that there are problems with the English MHRT administration[166] and has instigated a programme of improvement work involving:

- investment to upgrade IT systems and train staff in its use;
- improvements to the handling of incoming telephone calls and to the use of other communication facilities including e-mail, fax, web-site etc;
- improvements in the advance booking system, with an aim to book Tribunal panels four weeks in advance of all hearings after April 2005;
- better staff induction, training and development; and
- a trial to test the viability of moving back to a more localised approach to case-management[167].

4.110 The data available from the MHRT (figure 72) shows some improvement in the numbers of 'postponed' hearings since their highest level in 2002. However, as the category of 'postponed hearings' encompasses all applications that did not reach a hearing for whatever reason, this improvement cannot be assumed to result from better administration[168].

---

[163] We note, however, comments from some MHRT members that the opposite of this problem also occurs – i.e. panels being convened (at daily fees) for a single hearing in some hospitals – and so it would seem that the correct balance between the requirements of justice and value for money are not always being met.

[164] *Hansard*, 20 November 2003, column 1393W (Ms Rosie Winterton)

[165] Joint Committee on the Draft Mental Health Bill (2005) *Draft Mental Health Bill*. Vol 3, p.440 (Supplementary Memorandum from MHRT Southern Region DMH 444).

[166] These problems are not shared by the MHRT administration in Wales, which is administered separately.

[167] Joint Committee on the Draft Mental Health Bill (2005) *Draft Mental Health Bill*. Vol 3, p.1177 (Memorandum from the Dept of Health, DMH 453).

[168] Some cancellations may be due to patients withdrawing applications, or to patients being discharged between the application and the hearing. It has been suggested that RMOs may discharge patients to avoid conflict and/or the administrative burden of preparing for the hearing: see Crimlisk, H. and Phelan, M. 'Mental Health Review Tribunals; Time for a change?' *British Journal of Psychiatry* (1996) 169, 678-681; Peay, J (1989) *Tribunals on Trial*, Oxford University Press.

Anecdotal reports from services would appear to indicate that there is still much improvement to be made. It would be helpful for the MHRT to report its activity with more specificity in its annual reports.

Recommendation 21: Government must give urgent attention to the concerns of users of the MHRT service and take remedial action over administrative problems with that service.

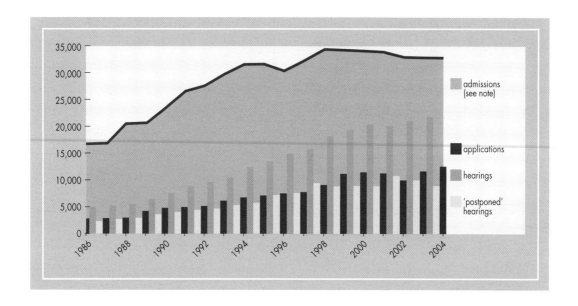

Fig 72: MHRT applications, hearings and 'postponed' hearings; England & Wales, 1986-2004[169]

Note: 'admissions' includes all formal admissions to NHS & Independent Hospitals, and changes from informal to ss.2 & 3 in NHS facilities; excludes some but not all short-term powers for which MHRT not applicable. Total unknown for 2004. 'Postponed hearings' includes all applications that did not reach a hearing, whether postponed, abortive or cancelled: December 2004 figure estimated from previous 11 months' data by DH.

4.111 Meanwhile patients continue to complain to Commissioners about their MHRT hearings having been cancelled at very short notice and then having to wait months for another date. The worst delays seem to be in relation to restricted patients, due to the required involvement of a legal member from an approved panel of circuit judges and Queen's Counsel, although short-notice cancellations have also been noted as a problem for all hearings. This is of great concern to us due to the distress and anxiety caused to patients; because it undermines the efforts of staff to ensure that patients are informed of their rights and can exercise those rights; and because cancellation of hearings creates a situation of detention without effective leave to appeal which is potentially in breach of ECHR requirements.

Recommendation 22: Government should focus resources and efforts into reducing cancellations of patients' MHRT hearings.

---

[169] Source: Joint Committee on the Draft Mental Health Bill (2005) *Draft Mental Health Bill.* Vol 2, p.504/5 (Further Memorandum from the Department of Health: Resources and the Regulatory Impact Assessment, DMH 404). Admission figures from DH Statistical Bulletins *Inpatients detained under the Mental Health Act and Other Legislation* issued between 1986 and 2004.

Patients' applications to the Tribunal

4.112 In 1995 it was reported that only one in four of all patients detained under s.2 exercised their right to apply to the Tribunal[170]. In 2005, the House of Lords' Appellate Committee considering the *MH* case was informed that 70% of s.2 patients made no application to the Tribunal. Whilst their Lordships were unable to tell the causes behind the recent statistic, the 1995 research did look for such causes in detail. Researchers analysed the available case notes of all patients detained under s.2 in the Oxfordshire Regional Health Authority during 1993 (384 patients) and interviewed 40 detained patients on the penultimate day before their right of appeal would expire[171]. They found that patients were more likely to appeal if they had previous admissions, and/or were educated to 'A' level standard, suggesting that legal rights were not explained in a way that all patients could understand. The research unsurprisingly found a strong link between cognitive impairment or loss of motivation through mental disorder and reduced likelihood of initiating an appeal in writing to the MHRT. The main reasons given for not appealing by interviewees (all of whom had sufficient mental capacity to consent to the research) was not being aware of rights and being deterred by having to apply in writing.

> 'Found out how to appeal by word of mouth. Daunting to go to panels & trying to put case across. Given list of solicitors – but no idea if need to pay or who is best one, etc'.
>
> *Yasmin Jackson, ex-s.3 patient, Wales*

4.113 The researchers concluded that 'the appeals procedure against detention under section 2 of the Mental Health Act is not a satisfactory way of protecting the civil liberties of patients. The procedure has two main flaws: firstly, the patient has to initiate the appeal and, secondly, there is an unsatisfactory method of informing patients of their right to appeal'. The Court of Appeal in *MH*[172] came to an essentially similar conclusion, declaring the lack of automatic review to be in breach of Article 5 of the European Convention, but this was overturned in October 2005 by the House of Lords following a Government appeal (see Chapter 1.89 *et seq*).

4.114 In our last Biennial Report we noted, in the wake of an out-of-court settlement of a similar case, that Tribunal acess for patients whose detentions under s.2 were extended pending displacement applications 'may... fail ECHR requirements of transparency and predictability'[173]. We recommended that Government could set an example of promoting a human rights culture in mental health services by providing a clear framework for such appeals through a policy statement allowing transparency and predictability in the use of

---

[170] Bradley, C., Marshall, M., Gath, D 'Why do so few patients appeal under section 2 of the Mental Health Act?' *BMJ* 1995; 310: 364-367 (11 February).

[171] Bradley *et al*, *supra*. Section 2 patients are detained for assessment and/or treatment for up to 28 days. They may appeal to the Tribunal within the first 14 days of their detention. The study interviewed patients as close to the deadline as to be sure that they would not, unprompted, have appealed their detention, but with a day to go so that patients who became aware of their right to appeal as a result of the researcher's visit should have an opportunity to do so.

[172] *R (on the application of MH) v Secretary of State for Health* [2004] EWCA Civ 1609

[173] MHAC (2003) *Tenth Biennial Report: Placed Amongst Strangers.* Chapter 3.15.

s.67(1)[174]. Although we were disappointed that that Government successfully challenged the Court of Appeal judgment in the *MH* case to the House of Lords, we hope that it will now consider what action can be taken to provide adequate safeguards to patients otherwise disadvantaged by their legal status or mental incapacity.

> **Recommendation 23:** Government should ensure that persons are not denied their Article 5 rights by reason of mental incapacity or legal status. We recommend that it publishes a policy statement on the use of the Secretary of State's discretion to refer cases to the Tribunal under s.67(1) of the 1983 Act, and directs hospital managers or social services authorities to notify the Secretary of State whenever an application is made under s.29 to displace a patient's Nearest Relative, so that the position can be considered.

4.115   The data shown at figure 72 (page 260) indicates that the numbers of applications to the MHRT have shown a slight rise even in the face of a (similarly slight) decline in the overall numbers of detentions. The explanation for this may be that more patients are aware of their rights to apply to the MHRT, or that hospital staff are being more proactive in helping patients make applications. We are far from confident that patients are given adequate information about their rights in hospital, but this may be an indication of some improvements.

4.116   In 1998 the courts found that a patient who exercised his or her right of appeal under s.2 did not have that right cancelled if their legal status changed to s.3 detention before the hearing took place[175]. At the time of writing, an application for judicial review had been lodged seeking to extend this principle to a s.3 patient for whom a supervised discharge application is accepted before their Tribunal hearing against s.3 detention can be heard. In correspondence with the applicant's solicitor we have written that we support such an extension of the principle, although we understand that it is MHRT policy at present to view acceptance of a supervised discharge application to cancel any outstanding appeal against s.3 detention. Part of our reasoning against this policy is simply that the acceptance of a supervised discharge application is in no way a guarantee that discharge from detention under s.3 is imminent.

Length of MHRT hearings

4.117   The average MHRT hearing time reported in a three-month pilot study in 2001 was one hour and thirty-nine minutes[176], although there are still examples (primarily relating to restricted patients) where a single hearing extends for more than a day[177]. Hearings are most likely to be extended where cross-examination of witnesses takes place, which the courts have suggested may be a requirement where such witnesses' hearsay evidence is crucial to

---

[174] *ibid*, recommendation 1

[175] *R v South Thames MHRT ex parte M* (1998) COD 83

[176] Source: Joint Committee on the Draft Mental Health Bill (2005) *Draft Mental Health Bill*, Vol 2, p.507.

[177] See, for example, our report on *R (on the application of DJ) v MHRT and others* [2005] at Chapter 1.94 *et seq* above; this hearing considering detention under s.37/41 lasted five days. In our *Tenth Biennial Report* (Chapter 7.24) we noted a three-day hearing of the Tribunal's fore-runner (the Lunacy Commission) from 1838: it is perhaps right and inevitable that difficult cases should have extended hearings.

the decision to be made[178]. This should perhaps sound a note of warning regarding the potential for lengthy adversarial hearings where the Tribunal is given the role of authorising compulsion under the Mental Health Bill proposals[179].

Patients' withdrawal of MHRT applications

4.118 Patients may request cancellation of their application for a Tribunal in writing at any time[180]. Any such request received before the hearing commences is granted automatically where it is accompanied by a letter from the patient's solicitor stating that the patient freely consents to the request and understands its implications; if there is no such accompanying letter the Tribunal chairman will exercise his or her discretion. Patients are most likely to withdraw applications when they feel that they have little chance of their appeal succeeding, and wish to reserve their right to appeal until later in their period of detention. In 2004 we were made aware of one Tribunal which was cancelled, at the patient's request, during the hearing itself. The Tribunal had sat for over two hours hearing all of the evidence when the patient requested, and was granted, leave for the hearing to be discontinued and the application withdrawn. We discussed this case with the Tribunal secretariat, who recognised a residual discretion in the Tribunal rules which allowed the sitting Tribunal to allow the application to be withdrawn, but suggested that once the Tribunal is seized of the matter and has entered into its judicial function it would usually be hesitant to abandon the hearing without good reason (for example, that the hearing was causing the patient emotional damage and discontinuation was the best means of addressing this). A patient who is given leave to withdraw their application in such circumstances will not have exercised their right to an MHRT hearing in that period of detention and will be able to apply again.

Outcomes of MHRT hearings

4.119 The outcomes of Tribunal hearings over the last five years are given at figure 73 below. Overall, about one in ten Tribunal hearings result in discharge of some description. We have suggested to the Tribunal that it should collate these figures categorised against the section of the Act under which the appellant was detained, as we believe that there are broad variations in this proportion depending on whether the patient is detained under, for example, Part II civil powers or Part III powers related to criminal justice. In depositions to the Administrative Court in December 2003, it was suggested that 22% of hearings of restricted patients result in conditional or absolute

'I have appealed three times in three years but have only used the Tribunals as reviews although the hospital and myself did not feel I was ready to be released. The people in my Tribunals were OK and told the truth to the best of their knowledge.'

Richard Holmes, s.37/41 patient, Yorkshire

---

[178] As in the *DJ* case itself (see note 177 preceding).

[179] Government has challenged the assumption (of, amongst others, his Honour Judge Sycamore at *Draft Mental Health Bill*, Vol 2, pp.440) that, under the Bill proposals, the length of Tribunal hearings will increase by 50%: 'this is based upon an untested assumption of the time required to consider a proposed care-plan, and needs to be balanced by other assumptions – for example it would be fair to assume that because Tribunals will be automatic, many will be uncontentious, and capable of being dealt with expeditiously' (Vol 2, p.178).

[180] MHRT Rules 1983, r.19: 'An application may be withdrawn at any time at the request of the applicant, provided that request is made in writing and the Tribunal agrees'.

discharge[181]. It seems likely that the Tribunal would discharge restricted patients at a higher rate than they would discharge other patients, given that other agencies are likely to discharge unrestricted patients when the conditions for compulsion are no longer met, and so fewer unrestricted cases who warrant discharge are likely to still be detained at the time of their hearing[182]. For restricted patients, the only other authority that has a power of discharge is the Home Secretary, and data shown at figure 162 (following Chapter 5.138 below) suggests that, whether intentionally or not, the Home Office has significantly passed over the responsibility for discharging restricted patients to the Tribunal during the lifetime of the 1983 Act.

Decision of MHRT	2000	2001	2002	2003	2004
Absolute Discharge	858	854	744	923	709
Delayed Discharge	342	334	427	518	317
Conditional Discharge	39	89	90	141	145
Deferred Conditional Discharge	97	74	101	265	180
Total Discharge	1,336	1,351	1,362	1,847	1,351
No Discharge	10,199	10,229	8,637	9,906	10,546
% of Discharges to Hearings	**12%**	**12%**	**14%**	**16%**	**11%**

Fig 73: Outcomes of Mental Health Review Tribunals, England, 2000 - 2004[183]

Conflicts of interest

4.120 In this reporting period the courts have considered the issue of conflicts of interest in Tribunal panel members. We discuss this at Chapter 1.101 *et seq*, where we summarise the current MHRT guidance on conflicts of interest. We were surprised to learn that the MHRT found no potential for conflict of interest or bias when a restricted patient found that the Tribunal chairman who was hearing his appeal was the judge who had originally ordered him to hospital under a restriction order. At the time of writing this matter was proceeding to judicial review, and we had made our views known to the parties concerned.

4.121 In our evidence to the Joint Committee on the Draft Mental Health Bill, we pointed to the potential for conflicts of interest or bias to arise from the proposed Mental Health Tribunal role in hearing patients' appeals against the imposition of formal powers when it had imposed those powers itself[184]. Other contributors made similar submissions, and the Committee recommended that, to avoid potential conflicts of interest or the appearance of bias in such a future system, any Tribunal member who was apart of the panel which authorised treatment in a particular patient's case should not sit on further panels hearing that patient's appeals against the continuance of such powers[185].

---

[181] *R (on the application of P) v Secretary of State for the Home Department* [2003] EWHC 2953 (Admin), para 20). See Chapter 1.175 *et seq* above for a discussion of the case.

[182] See note 168 above on RMO-instigated discharges prior to MHRT hearings.

[183] Data source: MHRT secretariat

[184] See Joint Committee on the Draft Mental Health Bill (2005) *Draft Mental Health Bill*, Vol 2, Ev 29. The MHAC put similar concerns to the Richardson Committee in 1998/9.

[185] Joint Committee on the Draft Mental Health Bill (2005) *Draft Mental Health Bill*, Vol 1, pp.101.

4.122   In the present legal framework for psychiatric detention, most patients enter compulsion through civil processes that have no judicial element. It is only in the case of patients detained consequent to court orders under Part III of the Act, or those detained under equivalent provisions of the Criminal Procedures Insanity Acts, where there will have been a judicial determination at the start of the patients' detention that their mental disorder warranted the imposition of compulsory treatment in hospital. In this sense, the position of patients admitted to hospital under court orders under the present legislative framework could be argued to be broadly analogous to patients who would be admitted to longer-term detention through a Tribunal determination under proposed powers.

4.123   Under the present Act, the question in law that the MHRT must consider for patients who appeal against their detention subsequent to court orders, whether they are restricted patients or not, is whether the Tribunal panel is satisfied by the evidence of the detaining authority that the patient is at that point suffering from any classified form of mental disorder of a nature or degree that makes detention in hospital for medical treatment necessary in the interests of his own health or safety or with a view to the protection of others[186]. Whilst, in practical terms, the question before most Tribunal hearings is therefore whether the patient's improvement or the passage of time means that conditions justifying formal powers are still met, rather than whether they were *ever* met, a patient should be able to appeal on the grounds that the imposition of powers was unjustified from the start, and such a patient must be confident that this would be considered impartially. We are concerned that the involvement of the patient's trial judge in his MHRT hearing damages that confidence.

> **Recommendation 24:** The MHRT secretariat should reconsider apparent or real conflicts of interest in having Tribunal members who have authorised compulsory treatment in any particular case considering appeals against such compulsion in that case. We recommend that regulations under the next Act prevent this situation from arising.

MHRT hearings and 'victims'

4.124   The Director of the Zito Trust, Michael Howlett, has been quoted in a number of newspapers calling for the overhaul of the Tribunal system, on the grounds that 'the Tribunals don't allow representations from victims or families of victims and none of their decisions can be appealed against'[187]. The Joint Committee on the Draft Mental Health Bill was sympathetic to the Zito Trust's call for victim representation and suggested that this should take the form of a written victim impact statement to help courts or the Tribunal assess risk[188]. We understand the general sympathy with victims of criminal behaviour, but we have grave concerns over these arrangements. Victim involvement must not be allowed

---

[186]   MHA 1983 s.72(1)(b)(i) and (ii). See s.73(1)(a) in relation to restricted patients.

[187]   *e.g.* 'Killer was freed to strike again by the authority of an outdated tribunal system' *The Times*, 16 Mar 2005

[188]   Joint Committee on the Draft Mental Health Bill (2005) *Draft Mental Health Bill.* Vol 1, p.96.

to distort the core function of either a court or the Tribunal under the 1983 Act in determining whether treatment under compulsion is warranted in a particular patient's case. We cannot see that this determination should be subject to appeal, by patients or any other party, except on 'technical' grounds of the Tribunal's exercise of its powers.

4.125 At Chapter 5.119 *et seq* below we discuss the requirements of the Domestic Violence, Crime and Victims Act 2004 regarding duties towards victims of sexual or violent offences. We are pleased to note that the MHRT has issued guidance on how it will perform the duties placed upon it from July 2005 to provide such victims with the opportunity to maker representations to the Tribunal and be informed of its determinations[189]. The duties are not retrospective, being applicable only where the sexual or violent offence was committed subsequent to the 1 July 2005, but the MHRT has indicated that it will normally use its existing powers under the Mental Health Tribunal Rules 1983 to provide equivalent access to victims of sexual or violent crimes committed before that date.

> **Recommendation 25:** Victim involvement must not be allowed to distort the core function of either a court or the Tribunal under the 1983 Act in determining whether treatment under compulsion is warranted in a particular patient's case.

Media presentations of the MHRT

4.126 While mental health services complain of shortcomings in the administration of the Tribunal, parts of the media resent the Tribunal's existence at all. In the traditionally 'tabloid' press, the very existence of a Tribunal system (and the public funding of appellants) has been attacked[190]. The high-profile convictions of Peter Bryan and John Barrett in this reporting period[191] also provoked some ill-informed media comment on the functions of the Tribunal from traditionally 'broadsheet' organs of the press, with the *Times* newspaper describing the MHRT as 'outdated' and 'a hangover from the days of the Victorian Asylums' where

> proceedings are closed and patients have no right of appeal. Their secrecy has long frustrated mental health campaigners and the Home Office. The Tribunals can override Home Office advice and the Home Secretary can appeal only on technicalities.[192]

---

[189] MHRT (2005) 'New procedures concerning the rights of access to MHRT hearings of victims of certain criminal offences committed by patients'. July 29 2005 Available from the MHRT website www.mhrt.org.uk

[190] e.g. Phil Nettleton 'Psycho Killed 2: You pay for release bid' *Sunday People*, 12 June 2005

[191] Peter Bryan had been convicted of manslaughter in 1994 and sent to a secure hospital. In 2002 he was conditionally discharged by the MHRT. In February 2004 he killed an acquaintance, dismembering and eating part of the body. Having been subsequently detained in Broadmoor Hospital, he then killed a fellow-patient there in April 2004. In a heavily-publicised case, Bryan pleaded guilty to two counts of manslaughter on grounds of diminished responsibility and was sentenced to two life sentences. He was returned to Broadmoor hospital. John Barrett, who had a diagnosis of paranoid schizophrenia, killed a cyclist in Richmond Park in September 2004 after discharging himself from hospital where he was an informal patient. We understand that a previous inpatient admission under the Act he was released by a Tribunal decision.

[192] *The Times*, 16 March 2005

We regret that the culture of human rights has not penetrated across all aspects of the media, and we are saddened by the ignorance of legal and human rights requirements shown in these reports. We urge spokesmen for mental health agencies to be mindful of this when briefing journalists on Tribunals, or the workings of mental health compulsion generally, so that they might try to redress such ignorance where they encounter it. Had the rudiments of the Tribunal system not been established in the nineteenth century, it would be necessary to establish them now to address the very contemporary concern with human rights.

The current and potential role of the Tribunal system in mental health services

4.127   In 1994 Sir John Wood told the Royal College of Psychiatrists' annual conference that 'happily' the Tribunal had adopted a constructive role, and had not limited its approach to a sterile 'safeguard against wrongful detention':

> …that constructive role involves … enabling those who resist help to be treated as humanely as possible, and checking that such treatment and care is not concealing over-zealous control… a dialogue between the patient and the patient's representative and the doctors and social workers concerned has been encouraged at Tribunal hearings. It is rarely resented, and most patients expect that level of interest to be taken in their problems. As mental health legislation ages and reform is considered, and as the provision of resources adequate for need becomes more and more difficult, it is important that the constructive role of the Mental Health Tribunals is recognised. A patient's rights, however that concept is interpreted, are best protected by periodic constructive review, so that needs can be identified and pressure exerted to meet them.[193]

In common with a number of other stakeholder organisations, we do have a number of concerns over the practical implementation of the Mental Health Tribunal role under the Mental Health Bill. Nevertheless, it is important to recognise the potential that this role, if it is not constrained by maladministration, under-resourcing, restricted powers or lack of discretion, could build upon the current system and play a significant and constructive part in the delivery of mental health services.

Managers' reviews

4.128   Under proposals in the draft Mental Health Bills of 2002 and 2004, the legal authority for detention or compulsion will rest primarily with the Tribunal rather than the health service providing medical care and treatment[194]. This has wide-ranging implications for any

---

[193] Wood, J 'The Challenge of Individual Rights; Mental Health Review Tribunals' *British Journal of Psychiatry* (1995) 166, 417-420. We hope that the proposed power to review (and accept or reject) care-plans may finally provide the Tribunals with power to influence quality of treatment (Crimlisk, H. and Phelan, M. 'Mental Health Review Tribunals; Time for a change?' *British Journal of Psychiatry* (1996) 169, 678-681) or to order transfers between levels of security (see Taylor, P., Goldberg, E., Leese, M., Butwell, M., Reed, A 'Limits to the value of Mental Health Review Tribunals for offender patients; suggestions for reform'. *British Journal of Psychiatry* (1999) 174, 164-169).

[194] Joint Committee on the Draft Mental Health Bill (2005) *Draft Mental Health Bill.* Vol 1, p.194 (Government response to consultation).

equivalent in the new legal framework to 'hospital managers' under the current Act, and in particular will abolish their role in hearing patients' appeals against detention[195]. Many organisations have concerns at the loss of this appeal mechanism which, as the quote on this page from a service user shows, can be perform a valuable function for patients. However, we accept that there is a potential for duplication of effort, waste of resources and consequent confusion of patients and staff in having two parallel systems of appeal.

> 'Never felt I would get anywhere before and after the MHRT appeal. Found managers' meeting more beneficial ... gave me more confidence. '
>
> *male s.3 patient, Yorkshire*

4.129   In the preface to the ninth edition of his *Mental Health Act Manual*, Richard Jones advises hospitals to ensure, in the interests of efficient use of resources, that Managers' hearings are only convened when there is a legal requirement to do so[196]. The practice of holding Managers' hearings for s.2 appeals in close proximity to MHRT hearings is particularly criticised, and the Manual advises that there is no express or implicit requirement to hold a Managers' hearing for a s.2 patient who has also appealed to the MHRT, as the latter will satisfy the Article 5 requirements for review. We accept this contention, although we would add that a patient who has not made an appeal to the MHRT should be made aware that the option of a Managers' hearing is available to them as an alternative appeal mechanism.

4.130   Hospital Managers' role under the Act extend beyond the hearing of appeals against detention. In their general role of overseeing that the powers and duties of detention are exercised appropriately and lawfully, Managers scrutinise legal documentation, and should play a role in the audit and/or oversight of practice and administration in relation to aspects of patient care such as the Care Programme Approach; consent to treatment issues; the use of leave; visiting arrangements; ward environments and patient activities, etc. Hospital Managers can play a role (in the absence of more formal advocacy arrangements) in ensuring that patients' general welfare (including housing, benefit needs and any general worries that patients may have) are brought to the attention of someone who is able to intervene on the patient's behalf. It is unclear to what extent this aspect of the role of the Hospital Managers will survive the abolition of their power to discharge patients under the next Mental Health Act.

Recommendation 26: We urge Government to seek to retain local oversight of hospital services for detained patients by non-executive Managers' committees under the new legal framework.

---

[195]   The Department of Health announced an intention to abolish managers' hearings in 1996 on the grounds that the two systems of managers' hearings and MHRTs caused confusion for patients and duplication of effort (Department of Health press release 17/9/96, quoted in Gregory P 'Who can best protect patients' rights?' *Psychiatric Bulletin* (2000) 24; 366-7), but it did so in the wake of 'a media outcry' over 'a widely publicised disaster that occurred following the discharge of a patient by managers' (Kennedy H 'Managers' hearings: dialectic and maternalism' *Psychiatric Bulletin* (2000) 24; 361-2).

[196]   Jones R (2004) *Mental Health Act Manual*, ninth edition, preface.

Humber Mental Health Teaching NHS Trust have issued a *Hospital Managers' Handbook* which seeks to explain to Hospital Managers, patients, their advisers and clinical staff the role, duties and guiding principles of Hospital Managers under the 1983 Act. The handbook, which was collated in part from other Trusts' similar publications, contains a job description for Hospital Managers, with discussion of the tasks and delegated responsibilities of the role, including substantial guidance on the conduct of managers' reviews of detention.

Electronic copies of the guidance which could be adapted for local use are available from the Trust's Mental Health Legislation Manager, who produced the booklet.

Contact: Mike Hood, Mental Health Legislation Manager mike.hood@humber.nhs.uk

Fig 74: good practice example; guidance for hospital managers

Aftercare

4.131 Under s.117 of the Mental Health Act, health and local authorities have a combined duty to assess the requirement for, and then provide, after-care services for patients upon their discharge from detention under sections 3, 37, 45A, 47 or 48. Case-law relating to the operation of these duties is discussed at Chapter 1.145-8 above.

4.132 In our last Biennial Report we discussed at length the House of Lord's judicial ruling in *Stennett* that rejected charging for such services[197]. Their Lordships rejected arguments that the provisions of s.117 created an anomaly between detained patients, who cannot be charged for aftercare service provided under s.117, and informal patients, who can be charged for some aftercare services. Lord Steyn suggested in *Stennett* that the anomaly argument was 'simplistic' and that detained patients covered by s.117 were an 'identifiable and exceptionally vulnerable class'[198]. This assessment has been questioned by academic commentators[199] and by Richard Jones, whose writing about the anomaly in the *Mental Health Act Manual* was raised in the Court. These commentators question whether there is any objective difference between the needs of detained and informal psychiatric patients upon discharge from hospital: Richard Jones points to Lords Steyn's own statement in the House of Lords' *Bournewood* judgment that mentally incapable compliant patients were 'diagnostically indistinguishable from compulsory patients'[200]. This argument does not take account of Lord Steyn's further statement that 'to their inherent vulnerability [compulsory patients] add the burden, and the responsibility for the medical and social services, of

---

[197] *R v Manchester City Council, ex p. Stennett and two other actions* [2002] UKHL 34. See MHAC (2003) *Tenth Biennial Report: Placed Amongst Strangers.* Chapter 9.62 *et seq.*

[198] *Stennett*, para 13.

[199] see Priaulx N 'Charging for Aftercare service under Section 117 of the Mental Health Act 1983 – the final word?' *Journal of Mental Health Law* (2002) 8 313-322; Fennell P All E.R. Rev 2002 paras 18.57-8. See also Jones R (2004) *Mental Health Act Manual*, ninth edition, p.430.

[200] *ibid.*

having been compulsorily detained'[201]. In this, his Lordship appears to be arguing something like a duty of reciprocity for authorities who have deprived a patient of liberty[202].

4.133 Such a duty could, of course, create a disincentive for authorities to use formal powers, as we discussed in our previous report[203]. Conversely, whilst authorities as budget holders may wish to avoid incurring the liability to fund aftercare subsequent to the use of formal powers, the charging position may create a perverse incentive for patients' families, or individual mental health workers sympathetic to patients or families who are worried about charges, to implement formal powers when alternatives might have been considered. We hope that the Government's response to the European Court's ruling in *HL v United Kingdom* (see Chapters 1.1 & 3.1 *et seq* above) will create greater certainty over the thresholds for compulsory and informal care that may make the grounds for using or not using compulsion clearer.

4.134 In its response to the Joint Committee, Government has finally stated clearly that it intends to limit the waiver on charging to the first six weeks of aftercare for patients subject to the next Mental Health Act[204]. In its rationale for this move it accepts the argument about inequity that was rejected by the House of Lords. Thus patients who are released from compulsion will be entitled to six week's free care, of which accommodation costs may only be included if they are provided as part of an intermediate care package and are not related to a patient's ordinary residence[205]. This does put patients subject to compulsion on basically similar terms as any other patient released from hospital to whom s.15 of the Community Care (Delayed Discharges) Act 2003 might apply. We are disappointed that this assumes six weeks' free care to be adequate 'reciprocity' where the State has deprived a patient of liberty on health grounds. We also see some risk of this creating a perverse incentive for patients (or families, or sympathetic mental health workers) to extend powers of compulsion (especially those that may be applied in the community) to avoid patients' liability for charging (see Chapter 3.71 above). Such perverse incentives would not be countered by the eventual extension of penalty systems in Part I of the Community Care (Delayed Discharges) Act 2003, from which mental health services are currently exempt[206].

4.135 It is of great concern that Government proposals under the next Act would remove all statutory duties towards aftercare planning, leaving such duties to be implied (and not legally binding) through a combination of the implementation of the Care-Programme Approach and the oversight of care-plans by the Tribunal. At Chapter 2.75 above we have

---

[201] *Stennett*, para 14.

[202] That there has been an 'indefensible gap in mental health law' allowing incapable compliant patients to be deprived of their liberty with neither the formal processes nor safeguards of the Act does not refute this as a point of principle. Nor does the fact that other patients, through misapplication of the legal framework, may be similarly and unlawfully deprived of their liberty within mental health services (see Chapter 3.17 *et seq* above)

[203] MHAC (2003) *Tenth Biennial Report: Placed Amongst Strangers.* Chapter 9.65 *et seq.*

[204] *The Government's response to the report of the Joint Committee on the Draft Mental Health Bill 2004.* Cm 6624, p.35.

[205] Draft Mental Health Bill 2004, clause 68.

[206] Indeed it remains our view that such penalties are not appropriate to mental health services, and would have the unintentional consequence of encouraging premature discharge and creating the 'revolving door' patients that much of the draft Mental Health Bill seeks to provide for.

discussed the still patchy implementation of the Care Programme Approach. It may be unrealistic to expect the Tribunal system to police care-planning whilst it performs its primary task of determining whether detention or compulsion is a justifiable intervention for a patient's current care, particularly without the leverage of statutory requirements to plan aftercare services. The case-law discussed at chapter 1.145 above shows that the duties assumed to be provided by the 1983 Act are under constant attritional pressure from authorities mindful of their limited resources: removal of all legal duties to assess and provide aftercare is unlikely to be to the benefit of patients or to help the policy aim of tackling social exclusion.

> **Recommendation 27:** We urge Government to seek to reconsider how aftercare arrangements may be assured through duties established in primary legislation, taking into account the concerns expressed in this report.

The Mental Health Act and the Police

4.136   The MHAC has long been concerned at the adequacy of arrangements between the police and health and social services regarding the use of Mental Health Act powers. We welcome the efforts made in some police authority areas to improve these arrangements, such as the minimum standard protocols for section 136 assessments, returning AWOL patients and carrying out assessments on private premises agreed between the London Development Centre for Mental Health, the Metropolitan Police and other agencies[207]. We would welcome the promotion of similar protocols, or of agreements modelled upon their example, on a national basis.

> 'I was picked up by the police once – they were kind, worked with my advocate and did not take me to the police station. But I do think the police need more training in mental health'
>
> *Angela Williams, ex-s.3 patient, Somerset*

4.137   Anecdotal evidence provided to the Government's Social Exclusion Unit[208] suggested that police officers can lack understanding of mental health problems and not know how best to help in a crisis situation. Police officers are often the first to be called to any incident of a person experiencing a mental health crisis, and may spend significant amounts of time interacting with people with mental health problems, but currently receive very little training in mental health awareness and recognition. Most initiatives aimed at improving interagency working and the treatment of the mentally disordered by all authorities recognise the need for enhanced police training. Pilot mental health awareness training courses for police officers have taken place in Northumbria with contributions from service users and experienced personnel supplied by local health bodies. The Home Office and National Institute for Mental Health in England have jointly identified up to £155,000 to

---

[207]   See www.londondevelopmentcentre.org for details

[208]   Social Exclusion Unit (2004) *Mental Health and Social Exclusion.* London, Office of the Deputy Prime Minister, June 2004, p.29.

strengthen police training for the financial year 2004/05[209]. This is a good start, but it is a budget of little more than one pound per officer employed nationally[210], and will clearly need to be built upon in coming years rather than regarded as a one-off investment.

Recommendation 28: We understand that the Association of Chief Police Officers (ACPO) may recommend enhanced mental health training as a part of a national training programme: we urge them to do so.

New officers from British Transport Police and City of London Police have a half-day training on mental health after they have been working with the public for ten weeks alongside a mentor. By this time approximately 50% of the students will have had some experience of dealing with someone who has a mental health problem. Both forces employ Janey Antoniou, a mental health service user with experience of being in police custody under s.136 of the Act, to deliver the training. It covers behaviour shown by people with mental health problems; personal experiences; what it is like to hear voices; good practice suggestions; and how to look after their own mental health.

Fig 75: good practice in police training

The role of police in the management of patients on wards

4.138   In 1993 we expressed our concern at police involvement in clinical situations, following reports of police being called to assist in giving forcible medication[211]. Mental health services' ward policies should set out when it is appropriate to request the help of police and should generally discourage requests for police involvement in the day to day clinical management of patients. We have heard of some hospitals requesting police assistance on a regular basis for the administration of psychiatric medication to refusing patients. This is an inappropriate use of police resources, and may raise questions of law (we understand that some police authorities are concerned as to their legal powers in such circumstances). At all events, inappropriate use of police services is an indictment of staffing and staff-training levels on the hospital wards concerned. Mental health facilities that detain patients should be staffed sufficiently and appropriately so that they are capable of ensuring the safe management of such patients without outside help.

4.139   However, it is conceivable that situations may arise where nursing staff require the help of the police to control or resolve incidents in hospital environments. In general terms, we would expect such incidents to involve serious disturbances involving dangerous behaviour that nursing staff are unable to manage and that poses a risk to patients and others if not

---

[209] *ibid.* p.7.

[210] Linda Van den Velde 'New Thinking For Policing Mental Health Issues' presentation at *Policing and Mental Health; Risks and Realities* Independent Police Complaints Commission conference, Birmingham, 20 January 2005. There were 142,795 full-time equivalent police officers in England and Wales as at 31 March 2005.

[211] MHAC (1993) *Fifth Biennial Report* 1991-3. London: Stationery Office, Chapter 3.5(f)

brought under control. We understand that such situations will not always be containable by nursing staff, and that the expertise of police may be required. We think that the use of such expertise is legitimate.

4.140 Over-reliance on the police to manage patients in hospital environments may be a result of inadequate training of hospital staff in patient management techniques and the legal framework in which they can be applied. In part, the police may have been partly responsible for encouraging some mental health units' over-reliance on police intervention, by explaining the police role in dealings with the mentally ill as if it were unique in having a potential for the use of legitimate force. In this reporting period we have suggested to the Metropolitan Police that their policy documents[212] should be amended to acknowledge that, particularly in respect of inpatients detained in hospital under the powers of the Mental Health Act 1983, nursing staff may exercise powers of control and management that extend to physical interventions. Guidance on the appropriate management of aggression and violence in inpatient units has been published by NIMHE in this reporting period[213].

Reporting patient behaviour to the police

4.141 Hospital staff should be cautious of involving the police in relatively minor incidents, where the police may resent being asked to take charge of a situation where nursing skills could suffice. However, this should not mean that criminal behaviour by patients should go unreported to the police. It is likely that psychiatric patients who are victims of assault, including sexual assault and rape, are denied access to the criminal justice system[214]. The Commission advises hospitals that they should have readily available policies, agreed with the police, setting out the expectations of both police and health bodies on police involvement in incidents where crime is concerned[215]. Such policies should provide advice on the need to consider reporting incidents to the police, with a view to investigation and possible prosecution. Whilst some criminal behaviour is so serious that there should never be any question of not reporting it[216], the policy should allow a certain amount of discretion over reporting. Matters to take account of may include the needs and wishes of victims (including requirements of, for example, potential criminal

'I was punched to the ground by a male patient in the middle of the day room and in front of several patients and staff. Nobody took any notice at all, even when I appealed to the staff in utter amazement, asking if they would really allow this to happen with no response.'

Emma Laughton, ex-s.3 patient, Somerset

---

[212] see Metropolitan Police Service Policy Document, 28/12/94, final paragraph.

[213] National Institute for Mental Health in England (2004) *Mental Health Policy Implementation Guide Developing Positive Practice to Support the Safe and Therapeutic Management of Aggression and Violence in Mental Health In-patient Settings.* December 2004. www.nimhe.org.uk

[214] In a MIND survey in 2000, three-quarters of professionals questioned considered that there were problems of access to the criminal justice system for people with mental health problems. See Pedlar M (2000) *Silenced witnesses* (snapshot survey). London, MIND.

[215] A specimen prosecution policy has been produced by Len Bowers at the City University London (St Barts) and is available from www.staff.city.ac.uk/~ra917/psychiatric-nursing/threds/prosec_policy.

[216] i.e. homicide or attempted homicide; rape or serious sexual assault; arson endangering life; or physical assaults resulting in serious harm.

injuries compensation); the need for special investigative expertise in relation to areas such as drugs concealment; and the making of an effective record of any incident for legal and future risk-assessment purposes. It may also be the case that excusing offending may not be in the patient's interests: the legal process itself may be useful for a patient's reality-testing, and a presumption that prosecution of violent behaviour is routine rather than exceptional may help patients take responsibility for their behaviour and instil a sense of justice amongst patients and staff. In cases of serious allegations, where the allegation may colour future care planning or even instigate a move to higher security care, the criminal justice system provides an opportunity for justice for the accused offender, including testing of the allegation and culpability for the actions constituting the alleged offence[217].

4.142   There are likely to be strong links between illicit drug-use and disturbed behaviour on wards, and some wards adopt robust policies regarding illicit drugs, including searches and drug-testing of patients returning from leave. *The Report of the Independent Inquiry into the Care and Treatment of Mark Harrington* recommended that the police should be requested to consider issuing formal warnings to patients found in possession of drugs as part of a zero-tolerance approach to illicit drug-use in inpatient units.[218]

4.143   Originally as a part of the Department of Health 'zero-tolerance' approach towards violence against NHS staff, and now in directions in support of the NHS Security Management Service[219] (see paragraph 4.198 below), the Secretary of State requires that the police must be informed of any physical assault upon an NHS staff member, and should always be called in non-physical assaults that are racially or religiously aggravated[220]. We support the contention of Dr Kevin Murray, Associate Medical Director of Broadmoor Hospital, that there should be no lesser standards applied to physical assaults on patients[221], although to our knowledge no such extension of the Department of Health's Directions or guidance has taken place.

4.144   A common and sometimes accurate assumption may be that the Crown Prosecution Service is unlikely to welcome legal action regarding low-level violence or other unlawful behaviour perpetrated by inpatients with psychiatric disorder[222]. Assumptions may also be made by the police regarding patients' legal culpability, and these may lead to investigations being discontinued or left unresolved unless staff are willing to discuss these issues and put themselves forward as witnesses. Police involvement that is discontinued without resolution may be damaging to staff and patient morale; to the unit's relation with the police; and to

---

[217]   Page M and Meiklejohn C (2004) 'Psychiatric inpatients who commit criminal offences: the legal, ethical and therapeutic challenges'. *Mental Health Practice* June 2004 Vol 7 No 9.

[218]   Blackburn & Darwen Primary Care NHS Trust (2003) *Report of the Independent Inquiry into the Care and Treatment of Mark Harrington.* November 2003, recommendation 10.

[219]   *Secretary of State directions on work to tackle violence against staff and professionals who work or provide services to the NHS,* issued 20 November 2003 under the powers of the NHS Act 1977.

[220]   *ibid.*

[221]   We are grateful to Dr Murray for copying us into his January 2004 correspondence with the Director of Security Management at the Department of Health on this issue.

[222]   Davison S 'The Management of Violence in General Psychiatry' *Advances in Psychiatric Treatment* (2005) vol II; 362-70

the likelihood of the offending patient confronting and addressing his or her own behaviour. Previous NHS Directives have suggested that, in the absence of public prosecution, NHS Trusts should consider taking private criminal or civil action, seeking civil injunctions (such as ASBOs) or taking administrative action under guidance on withdrawal of treatment in secondary care[223]. NHS Trusts now have the support of the NHS Security Management Service in determining what interventions may be appropriate where the police do not prosecute. However, few if any of the interventions discussed above - and certainly not those that remove treatment from patients or bar patients from hospitals - are likely to be appropriate against a patient detained in hospital under Mental Health Act powers. We are pleased that the NHS Security Management Service has appointed experienced mental health practitioners[224] and is currently working on a policy covering appropriate responses to violence in psychiatric settings.

4.145 Mary Cole has written in the context of sexual assaults that 'any patient who has been frightened, injured or is at risk from infection or impregnation should be encouraged to report the assault to the police', and has also pointed to inconsistencies in the management of sexual assault allegations[225]. At the very least, an incident of sexual assault (such as inappropriate touching or other harassment) should be recorded on an adverse incident form, giving the time, location and description of the incident; the names of the assailant and any witnesses; who has been informed; and what further action has been taken. The incident should be mentioned in discharge summaries for the alleged assailant. Incident forms should be regularly audited so that lessons can be considered, not only about the wards staff's response to incidents, but whether there are lessons to be learned about ward routines or design.

4.146 An article by the consultant psychiatrists Richard Bayney and George Ikkos in this reporting period has emphasised that regular liaison with the police is central to the management of violent inpatients, whom they classify as 'in many respects, the most complex inpatient group'[226]. Underpinning this should be an agreed local protocol on expectations of police involvement, with liaison officers from both the police and mental health service, and joint training initiatives involving discussions of realistic complex cases. Bayney and Ikkos also point to the important role of prevention of violence through well-controlled environments and ample clinical treatment programmes, use of the Care Programme Approach, and joint positive approaches to co-morbid substance misuse. We endorse these suggestions and recommend their article to services who are establishing or reviewing protocols with the police.

> **Recommendation 29:** Mental health services should establish police liaison arrangements, joint training, and protocols for police interventions on inpatient units.

---

[223] HSC 2001/18.

[224] NHS Security Management Service (2005) Secure newsletter, issue 1, June 2005, p.3. www.cfsms.nhs.uk

[225] Cole M (2003) 'Sexual assaults in psychiatric in-patient units'. *Psychiatric Bulletin* 27, 25-28.

[226] Bayney R & Ikkos G (2003) 'Managing criminal acts on the psychiatric ward: understanding the police view'. *Advances in Psychiatric Treatment* Vol 9; 359-367.

Reporting crimes against psychiatric patients to the police

4.147 People with mental disorder are more likely to be the victims of crime than people within the general population. Indeed, research consistently shows that mentally disordered people are more likely to be the victims of crime than perpetrators, and that much of this crime goes unreported or unpunished[227].

4.148 Unfortunately the inpatient environment does not protect patients against being victims of crime. Patients should be given access to lockers or other means of securing property, and where theft occurs staff should support patients in making a complaint to the police. It is important that staff and the police recognise the value for patients, and the requirements of justice, that police actions over reported crimes in hospitals are commensurate with their actions in the community. It can be especially disempowering for patient-victims of crime where police actions imply that criminal behaviour that is unrelated to mental disorder (such as theft of property) is a matter for the self-regulation of the hospital as an institution.

> **Recommendation 30:** Psychiatric inpatients should be protected from crime through security measures in their physical environments (including lockable storage for belongings, and, where necessary, adequate security staff to prevent intruders); and such patients who are victims of crime must not receive a lesser service from the police or any other agency than they would expect in the community.

Information sharing between mental health services and the police

4.149 Under s.325(4) of the Criminal Justice Act 2003 (CJA), parties to Multi-Agency Public Protection Arrangements (MAPPA) should draw up memoranda setting out ways in which they co-operate. In our view, such memoranda should set out carefully the expectations and arrangements for co-operation between health services and the police, particularly given that disclosure of patients' confidential medical information will have to be justified within the terms of the Data Protection Act 1998. Information applicable to health bodies on the implementation of the CJA has now been included in the Home Office's *MAPPA Guidance*[228].

4.150 It is of course the case that MAPPA arrangements only apply to persons who have been convicted of offences, and can provide no mechanism for the rather more controversial

---

[227] Mentally ill people living in the community are more than twice as likely to be victims of violence as other members of the public (Littlechild, B & Fearns D (2005) *Mental Disorder and Criminal Justice. Policy, Provision & Practice.* Russell House Publishing Ltd). See also Mencap (1999) *Living in Fear.* For a resumé of U.S. research findings see Consensus Project (a U.S. initiative co-ordinated by the Council of State Governments) *Fact Sheet: Criminal Victimization of People with Mental Illness*; and Sorensen, D (2002) *The Invisible Victims* (www.consensusproject.org). See also Teplin L, McClelland G, Abram K, Weiner D 'Crime victimisation in adults with severe mental illness; comparison with the national crime victimization survey' *Arch Gen Psychiatry* 2005;62: 911-921. A study published in Australia in 2005 found patients with schizophrenia spectrum disorders living in an outer metropolitan suburb of Melbourne were at increased risk of victimisation, both of violent and non-violent crime (Fitzgerald, P, Castella, A R de, Filia, S L, Benitez, J & Kulkarni, J 'Victimization of patients with schizophrenia and related disorders' *Australian and New Zealand Journal of Psychiatry* Vol 39, issue 3 p.169).

[228] http://www.probation.homeoffice.gov.uk/output/page30.asp; see paras 210 -214 on information disclosure

aspects of information-sharing about other persons who may be considered to present a risk of violence. In April 2004, the Home Office issued guidance to inform local protocols between the police and health services on handling *potentially* violent individuals[229]. The guidance advocated that there should be an inter-agency management steering group at a senior level to monitor the operation of local protocols and to identify and disseminate best practice lessons. In its response to the Joint Committee on Human Rights, Government gave as an example of good practice in information sharing the Risk Data Sharing Project managed by the London Development Centre for Mental Health, which 'should enable the police to exchange information with health bodies on individuals with

> 'When my laptop and my phone were stolen from a staff office, I contacted the police. The minute they heard I was a psychiatric patient they seemed dismissive and phoned the ward office. They did not seem to think it appropriate to investigate crimes that took place in hospital, but seemed to feel that the hospital should deal with this internally. This upset me deeply because theft in hospital should be treated as seriously as theft that occurs in the community.'
>
> *Gul Davis, ex-s.3 patient, Birmingham*

mental health problems'[230]. This pilot project ran across three London boroughs in 2004, aiming to establish a mechanism for information-sharing between mental health, police, ambulance and probation services. It was intended to pool data on individuals, that would be accessible to professionals through a single telephone contact point staffed by mental health professionals and based in the London Ambulance Service control room. Community Mental Health Teams provided information to the database on such patients as they assessed to be at risk to themselves or others (amounting to 2.5% of their caseload). Independent evaluation of the project found that it could be useful and there is an agreement in principle that it will be rolled out across London[231], although we understand that funding problems in establishing a 24-hour service have stalled its development.

4.151 Service users interviewed as part of the evaluation of the Risk Data Sharing Project were not supportive of the scheme, having particular concerns about stigma resulting from 'the association made between mental health and violence and the potential for discriminatory practice by police, ambulance crews and others if mental health status is shared'[232]. Given the gaps in training on mental health issues in the police and other agencies, sharing information on service users' clinical backgrounds does involve a risk of inappropriate responses to that information, particularly if the information is given by telephone to professionals who are operating without the support of mental health colleagues. Because of the nature of medical confidentiality, information passed into the system by health professionals may be exclusively that which can be justified under GMC guidelines relating to a patient's risk to others. There is a danger that such information, viewed out of the context of other aspects of a service user's medical history and coping strategies, could (but

---

[229] Home Office (2004) *General Principles To Inform Local Protocols Between The Police And Health Services On Handling Potentially Violent Individuals* Circular 17/2004

[230] *Government Response to the Third Report from the Committee: Deaths in Custody* HL 69/HC 416

[231] Risk Data Sharing Pilot: Presentation to Metropolitan Police Authority Mental Health Review Project Board, 13 April 2005.

[232] Quoted in Hugh Muir & Mary O'Hara 'Risk strategy' *The Guardian*, 9 March 2005.

perhaps need not necessarily) have a distorting effect on the weight given to incidences relating to an individual's risk behaviour.

4.152 It is important that the principle of medical confidentiality is preserved, so that seeking medical help for mental disorder cannot open the way for dissemination of details that may constitute an unwarranted interference with privacy. This is not to say, of course, that medical confidentiality requirements should override the need to pool such information as is necessary to aid the police and other agencies in their work of public protection. It may be, however, that the police expectations of the benefits of such pooled data in their day-to-day dealings with mentally disordered persons are unrealistic. One senior officer is reported to have said that by withholding information, health professionals were shifting risk onto others: "we end up having to arrest the person, but you look at the incident afterwards and think 'hang on, that was preventable'"[233]. We do not see how police access to patient data can prevent incidents to which they might be called, or to prevent their needing to take appropriate action in response to such incidents. The criteria for use of police powers under s.136 of the Act do not require any objective information about the mental state or history of the person to whom they are applied, as a police officer is entitled to use such powers upon his or her subjective view that a person appears to be mentally disordered and in need of care or control. As such, where an arrest may have been 'preventable', perhaps it was because s.136 could have been used in its place.

4.153 These matters require careful consideration in the management of any system of information sharing, particularly if patients are not to be dissuaded from contact with medical help if they fear that their confidences may be broken to their overall detriment.

The role of police in the transportation of patients

4.154 In our Tenth Biennial Report we expressed serious concern at the methods used by some private security firms who were contracted to transport mental health patients by some NHS Trusts[234]. We are aware of some detained patients having been conveyed between hospitals, sometimes for considerable distances, by untrained personnel, inside vans fitted with security cages and barely adequate seating. There were clear risks to the patients' lives in some of these examples. We recommended that all authorities check that their arrangements for the conveyance of patients meet the standards suggested by Chapter 11 of the Mental Health Act Code of Practice.

4.155 The Commission advises all authorities that are responsible for detaining patients to be wary of delegating transport arrangements to other bodies without careful oversight of the procedures and practical means employed. Where the police are required to help with the transport of patients, the officers involved will usually consider handcuffing the

'I have found my dealings with the police on several occasions not very pleasant. They have been rough, uncaring and not understanding mental health. Being handcuffed for eight hours while awaiting transfer I thought was completely uncalled for.'

Deborah Hickman, ex-s.3 patient, Lancashire

[233] *ibid.*

[234] MHAC (2003) *Tenth Biennial Report: Placed Amongst Strangers.* Chapter 11.45

patient if there is considered to be a risk of violence, and indeed a number of police vans are caged and are no better for the transportation of mentally disordered people than the private security firm arrangements that we criticised in our last report. We recommend that mental health services take this into account when requesting police assistance, if possible through a clinical risk-assessment prior to the request being made. We do, however, recognise that some mental health services may need assistance in the transportation of patients where there is a risk of dangerous behaviour. Where police resources can provide safe and appropriate means of transport, and their use can be justified according to risk-assessment, we would be loath to see such resources withdrawn, particularly where this might lead to proliferation of arrangements with the unregulated private sector.

> **Recommendation 31:** Mental health services should be wary of using ill-suited police resources for the transport of vulnerable patients, but police resources must remain available to transport patients at risk of violence or absconding where appropriate.

4.156   We understand that in London a system is under negotiation whereby, in the event of a police vehicle being used to transport a patient to hospital, a member of the ambulance team will travel with the patient in the police vehicle and an ambulance will follow behind. The current policy of the Metropolitan Police is to refuse any request for police transport to convey a patient from one hospital to another or from a hospital to a court (see Chapter 5.80 *et seq* below), although police escorts may be given to patients conveyed in a properly equipped ambulance under the care of qualified staff.

Police restraint and deaths

4.157   The death in police custody of Roger Sylvester continued to cast a shadow over this reporting period[235]. Roger Sylvester died in 1999 following prolonged restraint by police, during which he suffered cardiac arrest. He was detained under s.136 at the time of his restraint, and was naked throughout the episode. In November 2004 the inquest jury's verdict that he had been unlawfully killed as a result of police restraint was overruled in the High Court. We share the concerns expressed by Mind over this action: whilst the judge may have had questions around the consistency of the reasons given for verdict returned, in disallowing another inquest he effectively denied Mr Sylvester's family the chance to pursue the question of accountability for his death[236]. We are aware of how deeply this reversal has affected the Sylvester family, who feel that justice has been denied to them.

4.158   Following the original jury verdict, the Deputy Commissioner ordered a review to be carried out of Metropolitan Police safety training regarding restraint and the police procedures for dealing with people suffering from mental illness. This review focussed on the Coroner's recommendations. The Metropolitan Police Service issued guidance to its officers in 2002 on 'policing acute behavioural disturbance' and this document was amended in the light of the review.

---

[235] See MHAC (2003) *Tenth Biennial Report: Placed Amongst Strangers* Chapters 11.30.

[236] See *Mind comments on Roger Sylvester inquest jury ruling* (Mind press release, 26 November 2004).

4.159	Although neither Government nor the police have accepted the Bennett inquiry[237] recommendation that face-down restraint should last for no more than three minutes (arguing, quite understandably, that where such restraint is a proportionate response to risk it cannot be abandoned at an arbitrary point before that risk is manageable by other means), police training will stress the dangers of prone restraint and the need to reposition patients under such restraint as soon as possible. We understand that the Metropolitan Police are to adopt the method used in the prison service, where one of the officers involved in the restraint episode will, wherever practically possible, take no active part in the restraint but instead act as a safety officer in supervising his or her colleagues, monitoring the health of the person under restraint and actively controlling the restraints being applied (see also recommendation 40, following paragraph 4.218 below).

Searching and conveyance

4.160	During this reporting period we were approached for an opinion on the police role in searching patients whom they assist in conveying to hospital. The police had attended a Mental Health Act assessment on Mr Y, who had a history of carrying knives when unwell and was subject to paranoid delusions. The police transported Mr Y to hospital to be admitted under the Act, but it was not until he had been admitted and was searched by hospital staff that he was found to have hidden two knives on his person. The police had taken the view that, as their searching powers were circumscribed under s.32 of the Police and Criminal Evidence Act 1984 (PACE), they had no powers to search the patient as he had at no time been under arrest.

4.161	We disputed this interpretation of the law. We argued that police searching powers are not confined to s.32 of PACE, and indeed are not confined to persons who are under arrest. The power to search a suspect is also contained in a number of statutes[238], including (in relation to knives) the Criminal Justice and Public Order Act 1995[239]. When the police convey a patient to hospital for admission under the Act they retain all their powers as police officers[240], and may lawfully search the patient in the manner and to the extent that any relevant statutory power allows.

4.162	Even if there is no relevant criminal law power to search a person under conveyance, it is possible that the Mental Health Act 1983 itself implies such a power. In *R v Broadmoor Special Hospital Authority and the Secretary of State for Health, ex parte S, H and D*[241], Auld LJ said that the express power of detention must carry with it a power of control and discipline, including, where necessary, of searching (p.17) and Judge LJ held that:

> [...] where an admission to [hospital] is made under section 3 of [MHA 1983], an essential ground for the application and admission is that it is 'necessary for the health or safety of the patient or for the protection of other persons that he should receive such

---

[237]	David Bennett died under restraint by mental health staff in a medium secure unit in 1998. In January 2005 the Government published *Delivering race equality in mental health care: An action plan for reform inside and outside services and the Government's response to the Independent inquiry into the death of David Bennett*.

[238]	See Annex A of Code of Practice A to the PACE Act 1984

[239]	Criminal Justice and Public Order Act 1995, s.60 (as amended by s.8 of the Knives Act 1997)

[240]	MHA 1983 s.137(2)

[241]	*R v Broadmoor Special Hospital Authority and the Secretary of State for Health, ex parte S, H and D*, Court of Appeal, 5 February 1998, CO/2284/97

treatment'. It would be absurd if having been admitted on the basis that either of these two requirements had been established prior to his admission, the criteria of the health and safety of the patient himself or the protection of other persons were minimised during detention. (p.23)

At the time of his conveyance, Mr *Y* was not (yet) detained in hospital, and even after he had been admitted to hospital his position could be distinguished from the restricted patients in a 'Special Hospital'[242] that were the subject of the above judgment. However, it seems to us that many of the key issues involved in the two situations override these differences. Both cases concerned the operation of a key function or duty under the Act – detention in hospital or conveyance to hospital – and in both cases some degree of control and discipline was necessary in order for that function/duty to be performed properly and safely. It is arguable (to say the least) that those conveying a patient to hospital under the Act have the implied power to search the patient for items that might make that task – as distinct from the task of detaining him/her when s/he reaches hospital – more difficult or perilous. If our interpretation is correct, that power would in theory be available not just to police officers, but (because of the provisions of s.137(2)) to anyone else who was lawfully conveying the patient, including the ASW or ambulance staff.

4.163 Where the police 'remove' a patient to a place of safety under ss.135 or 136 of MHA 1983 the situation is much clearer. The common law allows the police to search an arrested person for a weapon[243], but the fact that removal under ss.135 or 136 counts as an arrest for the purposes of PACE[244] suggests that the searching powers in s.32 of PACE apply, so that detainees may lawfully be searched provided there are reasonable grounds for believing that they may present a danger to themselves or others.

The use of section 136

4.164 There are no reliable statistics on the use of section 136. The limited statistical data that is available is of questionable value because of its incompleteness, and because of marked regional variations in practice which make generalisation difficult[245].

> 'I have been picked up in a public place in the past also escorted and transported from hospital to hospital. The police were generally OK especially as they knew me - I have no complaints'.
>
> *Richard Holmes, s.37/41 patient, Yorkshire*

4.165 In this reporting period we attempted to collate such statistics as are known from each local authority in England and Wales. We have had a disappointing level of response, with only 30% of the 118 authorities contacted supplying us with any data. We set out that data at figure 4.46 below. It is particularly disappointing that this data is not apparently easily available, given that the Code of Practice (10.4) requires all agencies involved to have a joint policy that provides for the monitoring of the use of s.136 of the Act so that 'a check can be made of how and in what circumstances it is being used, including its use in relation to ethnic

---

[242] In law the three High Security Hospitals are designated 'special hospitals' by virtue of s.4 of the NHS Act 1977. We called for emendation of the language of this section in MHAC (2003) *Placed Amongst Strangers: Tenth Biennial Report*, para 12.8 and recommendation 52.

[243] *Dillon v O'Brien and David* (1887) 16 cox C.C.245

[244] Mental Health Act Code of Practice para 10.09

[245] Bartlett P & Sandland R (2004) *Mental Health Law; Policy and Practice* 2nd edition. Oxford University Press, pp.161.

minorities; and the parties to the policy can consider any changes in the mental health services that might result in a reduction of its use'. This requirement does not appear generally to have been met.

type of place of safety:	Number of times used			Number of patients detained following assessment			Number of patients taken into hospital under informal basis			Number of patients needing any other follow up care			Number of patients released without further action		
	London	rest of UK [246]	total	London	rest of UK	total	London	rest of UK	total	London	rest of UK	total	London	rest of UK	total
hospital	952	2,174	3,126	333	465	798	307	563	870	52	180	232	121	300	421
police station	3	1,309	1,312	3	416	419	-	202	202	-	186	186	-	388	388
Total use[247]	**956**	**3,494**	**4,450**	**336**	**887**	**1,217**	**307**	**765**	**1,077**	**52**	**366**	**418**	**121**	**688**	**809**

Fig 76: MHAC data on use of s.136, 2002/03 – 2003/04

4.166 The scale of underreporting in the above data is evident from Department of Health statistics collated from the use of psychiatric hospital premises as places of safety under s.136 (figure 77). This shows more than double the number of hospital-based detentions than are given in the figure above. Of course, Department of Health statistics do not show any use of s.136 where a police station or venue other than a psychiatric hospital was the place of safety.

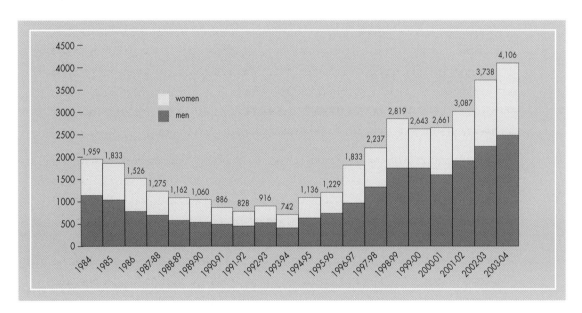

Fig 77: the use of s.136 places of safety in hospitals, 1984 – 2003/04[248]

---

[246] i.e. England and Wales, excluding parts of UK where MHA 1983 is not in force.

[247] Includes 12 reported uses of places of safety classed neither as hospital premises not police stations (one in London). Not all of these were clearly identified, but examples listed included community mental health team premises and general practice clinics. At least two were domestic environments of patients or their families.

[248] Data source: Department of Health *Inpatients Formally Detained in Hospitals Under the Mental Health Act 1983 and Other Legislation*, 1984 – 2004

4.167 Department of Health statistics on hospital-based use of s.136[249] can give some indication of the regional variations in the use of the power, although the picture given of such variations is inevitably distorted by the absence of data on detention in police-stations. Authorities whose s.136 usage takes place largely or entirely in police cells do not register in the Department's data, and there are still some authorities – such as Portsmouth – who have made no provision for places of safety outside police cells in their area even though we have raised the issue with them over a long period.

Data collection and monitoring bodies: lessons for the next Act

The MHAC is entrusted on behalf of the Secretary of State, to keep under the review the exercise of powers and duties of the 1983 Act as these relate to the detention of patients, and is empowered to require the production of any records relating to the treatment of any person for this purpose (ss.120, 121). Failure to produce documents or records without reasonable cause may constitute an offence under s.129.

Despite this general legal authority, we have great difficulty in obtaining generalised information on the use of the Act from responsible authorities. We do not expect authorities to be burdened by such requests (and indeed information 'gateway' mechanisms would generally frustrate any attempt by us to request burdensome information), and so we limit our requests to information that should be being monitored by authorities and therefore easily retrievable by their administrators.

In the case of data on the use of s.136 of the Act, the Code of Practice requires all agencies to have a joint policy that provides for the monitoring of the power as described at paragraph 4.165 above. It is clear that this general requirement, extant for over a decade, has not led to widespread monitoring, even across the London metropolitan area where the use of s.136 is at its highest. The 'good practice' requirement of the Code has not been effective in its aim, perhaps because it is a shared accountability between different authorities. We believe that stronger requirements are needed to ensure that monitoring takes place.

Under the proposals for the next Mental Health Act, the monitoring body that takes over MHAC responsibilities will be given specific duties to gather information that is to be prescribed by regulation (clause 259 of the 2004 draft). It is not helpful that the only legal duty thus created would be on the monitoring body collecting the information, rather than on the authority providing that information. Our experience suggests that effective data collection across a range of authorities would be best ensured by relatively prescriptive regulation, requiring information in particular formats, and that such requirements should extend across any area where good practice suggests that monitoring and audit should take place.

Recommendation 32: We recommend that future data collection on the use of core powers of a Mental Health Act are specified in statutory regulations, with a duty paced upon services to submit data to a monitoring body.

Fig 78: Data collection and monitoring: lessons for the next Act

---

[249] Department of Health (2005) *Inpatients Formally Detained in Hospitals Under the Mental Health Act 1983 and Other Legislation; NHS Trusts, Care Trusts, Primary Care Trusts and Independent Hospitals: 2003-04.* Table 7a-c

4.168   The greatest numerical use of s.136 over 2003/04 was unsurprisingly in the London area, which accounted for over a third of reported uses (1,488 of 4,106). The counties bordering the London area[250] account for a further third. Use was high in the North-East, with Manchester (360 uses) and Cheshire/Merseyside (331) making up the bulk of uses, but significant numbers in Lancashire (69) and Cumbria (115). Elsewhere, Doncaster (111) and Derbyshire (110) stand out as having a relatively high use. These results can, however, be misleading. It is notable that high-density areas such as Birmingham and Leicester show hardly any uses, although in the case of Leicester this is almost certainly because the first-choice of place of safety is a police station[251]. The marked difference between North Staffordshire (3 uses) and South Staffordshire (62 uses) shows how such issues of service provision can affect the use of s.136.

4.169   Perhaps more significantly, there is a considerable variation in the results of detention under s.136 across different regions. Forty per cent of patients detained under s.136 in London hospital premises in 2003/04 were assessed to require further detention under ss.2 or 3 of the Act, and almost all the remainder became informal psychiatric patients (only one half of one per cent were released from a London hospital place of safety with neither formal nor informal psychiatric patient status). Admission to hospital under s.136 carried only half the likelihood of further detention in surrounding Government office regions, such as East of England[252] (20%) or South East England[253] (22%). In some areas the likelihood of further detention was lower still; in the South West region[254], only 12% of persons taken to hospital under s.136 were detained under a further section after assessment, and 20% were released without entering into either formal or informal psychiatric care. We do not know the reasons for these variations, but it seems possible that:

- the pressure on London beds may create a form of triage in the acceptance of patients under s.136, so that only those most likely to need further detention may be taken to hospital in the first place (although it is noted that London has a far higher rate of detention per population than other parts of the country[255]);

- the tolerance of unusual behaviour or apparent distress may be higher in the London metropolitan area than in other parts of the country, leading to a higher operational threshold for police intervention under s.136;

- police constables in areas where s.136 use is infrequent, or who have little training in mental health issues, may be more inclined to use s.136 to bring in people who are under the influence of drink or drugs, or otherwise not mentally disordered within the meaning of the Act; and

- charging practices may vary for different police forces.

---

[250] i.e. Essex, Kent, Surrey, Berkshire, Bucks, Herts.

[251] Although we are pleased to note plans for a 136 suite on the Glenfield Hospital site which should be open by the publication of this report.

[252] Bedfordshire, Hertfordshire, Essex, Norfolk, Suffolk & Cambridgeshire.

[253] Hampshire & Isle of Wight, Kent & Medway, Surrey & Sussex, Thames Valley.

[254] Avon, Gloucestershire & Wiltshire, Dorset & Somerset.

[255] See, for example, Kings Fund (2003) *Mental Health Service Activity in London: Recent Developments.* Working Paper, Nov 2003, p.6.

It is important, however, that we do not assume that the use of s.136 is valid only if it results in further detention or even informal psychiatric care. The justification for s.136 is simply that a police considers that a patient appears to be mentally disordered and is in need of care or control. Where this is well understood, the police response is most likely to be humane and effective. By contrast, some police officers appear to resent their role under s.136, taking the view that the police service is being left to manage people who have been failed or ignored by health or social services authorities. We do not share this view, which is often predicated upon the incorrect assumption that every use of s.136 powers indicates a failure of community services. We encourage all police authorities to promote police intervention under ss.135 and 136 as an integral part of modern policing that is complementary to other authorities' duties towards mentally disordered people.

Data on the use of police powers under the Mental Health Act

The lack of data on the use of police powers in dealing with mentally disordered persons prevents adequate assessment of service needs and trends in the use of the Act. The lack of centrally collated and audited data with regard to ethnic monitoring cannot but set an obstacle to fulfilment of police authority duties under the Race Relations (Amendment) Act 2000 (RR(A)A). We accept that some elements of recording the use of Mental Health Act holding powers could fall to social services and NHS authorities, and urge social service and police authorities to co-ordinate efforts to address the lack of monitoring in this area. However, not all uses of police powers under ss.135 or 136 can be captured through data collections by other agencies, as on occasion the use of a power may be terminated or aborted before their involvement. We consider it to be self-evident that until police services can access and audit complete data on their exercise of legal powers in relation to mentally disordered persons, they cannot meet their legal obligations under the RR(A)A and may similarly fail to meet their legal obligations to promote equality of opportunity for disabled people[256].

Recommendation 33: We recommend that ACPO should consider issuing guidance on data collection and audit of the use of police powers under the Mental Health Act.

Fig 79: data on the use of police powers under the MHA

Identifying places of Safety

Use of police stations as places of safety

4.170   The Commission has always called for priority to be given to the establishment and use of hospital-based facilities for the reception of persons detained under s.136[257]. We believe

---

[256] The Disability Discrimination Act 2005 places a duty on public bodies to promote equality of opportunity for disabled people. See Office of the Deputy Prime Minister Social Exclusion Unit Report *Mental Health and Social Exclusion*, June 2004, p32.

[257] See MHAC (1997) *Seventh Biennial Report* 1995-97, p.49; (1999) *Eighth Biennial Report 1997-99, para 4.77 et seq*, (2001) *Ninth Biennial Report* 1999-2001, chapter 4.4 *et seq*.

that it is now established that, ideally, police stations should be used only where necessary (usually because of issues of the containment of seriously disturbed behaviour), and not as a first choice[258]. In this reporting period the Parliamentary Joint Committee on Human Rights, in the context of inquiring into deaths in custody, stated that

> People requiring detention under the Mental Health Act should not be held in police cells. Police custody suites, however well resourced and staffed they may be, will not be suitable or safe for this purpose, and their use for this purpose may lead to breaches of Convention rights. In our view, there should be a statutory obligation on healthcare trusts to provide places of safety, accompanied by provision of sufficient resources for this by the Government[259].

4.171 The use of police stations as places of safety has been long abjured in theory but accepted in practice, often for want of better accommodation elsewhere:

- Between 1992 and 1994, 69% of persons arrested under s.136 by the Hammersmith, Paddington or Holloway Metropolitan Police divisions were taken to a police cell, despite the recognised place of safety being a hospital[260]

- Data analysed from Metropolitan Police records of uses of s.136 over the two calendar years 1996 and 1997 suggested that, in London at that time, about 15% (204 of 1,354) of the records available on s.136 detentions showed the use of a police cell as a place of safety[261]. It seems likely that there was significant underreporting of the overall use of s.136 in this study, as it relied on police data that was not, and is still not, systematically collated.

- MHAC data at figure 76 above (page 282), which is also significantly incomplete, suggests that the proportionate use of Metropolitan Police cells as places of safety may have considerably reduced since the 1990s, although it is likely the effect of missing data in our survey is to exaggerate the rarity of the use of police stations for this purpose.

- In April 2004 the Under-Secretary for Correctional Services, Paul Goggins MP, reported to the Parliamentary Joint Committee on Human Rights upon a national survey undertaken by the Home Office trying to establish 'the scale of the problem' of the use of police cells as places of safety. The Home Office survey (including late responses after the report to the JCHR) elicited responses from 27 out of 43 police forces across England and Wales, of which 20 routinely used police cells as paces of safety because no other accommodation could be found. Over the calendar year 2003, the total number of individuals held in police cells under s.136 across the 27 forces was 5,726, with an average of 286 cases per year across the 20 force areas without effective s.136 protocols with health authorities[262]. This suggests that the results of our survey (figure 76) may have greatly underrepresented the use of police cells nationally[263].

---

[258] See Mental Health Act Code of Practice, chapter 10.5; Royal College of Psychiatrists (1997) *Standards of Places of Safety under Section 136 of the Mental Health Act* (1983). Council Report CR61

[259] Joint Committee on Human Rights *Deaths in Custody* Third Report of Session 2004-05

[260] Revolving Doors Agency (1995) *The Use of Section 136 Mental Health Act in Three Inner London Police Divisions.* This ten-year old data is perhaps unlikely to reflect current practice, but we have no more recent data for comparison.

[261] Lelliott, P., Audini, B., Bindman, J., Eastman, N., Peay, J., Quirk, A. & Thornicroft, G. (2000) *Research into the Mental Health Act 1983 (Parts II and X). Final Report to the Department of Health.* London: Royal College of Psychiatrists' Research Unit. Chapter 4.

[262] Home Office Police Leadership and Powers Unit, personal communication.

[263] The Home office, having surveyed about 60% of police authorities for 2003, found 5,726 uses of police cells for s.136. The MHAC, surveying 30% of local authorities, found about 650 such uses over one year (1,312 over 2003-4 to 2004/5). Even allowing for the widespread variation in practice across England and Wales these figures are markedly disparate.

4.172 Government has indicated that the issue of provision of appropriate places of safety and whether there should be a statutory obligation on healthcare Trusts to provide places of safety is being considered as a part of a general review of s.136 policy by the Cross Government Group on the Management of Violence[264]. This body includes representation from the Department of Health (mental health and prison health care), the Home Office, the Police and the MHAC. As this report went to press funding for the establishment of more hospital-based places of safety was announced by the Department of Health.

4.173 In our Ninth Biennial Report we emphasised that places of safety need not be confined to hospital premises, and called for a more imaginative approach to identifying appropriate facilities to avoid unnecessary use of police cells[265]. One particularly stark example of the dangers inherent in having too limited choices for places of safety was the admittance during this period of a child to a police cell due to concerns at the appropriateness of the

> 'In East Sussex, the only place of safety is in Brighton and Crawley Police Stations. Individuals are transported quite long distances and often past the hospitals where they end up as inpatients'.
>
> *MHA Commissioner, July 2005*

available adult psychiatric facility. It could be that children's services, in particular, could usefully be approached as alternative venues for appropriate cases. We have heard anecdotally of at least two examples of the detention of young children (aged eight and twelve) under s.136 in the last two years.

4.174 The Independent Police Complaints Commission (IPCC) concluded in June 2005 that a woman's eight-hour detention in the Queens Road Police Station in Birmingham could have amounted to a breach of ECHR Article 3's prohibition on degrading treatment. Before being admitted to hospital under the powers of s.2 of the Act, the woman (who had been arrested on a public order offence in her home after police responded to a call from her relative) attempted to commit suicide on a number of occasions whilst in police custody. She spent some of the time in the police cell naked after her clothes were removed as ligature hazards. The IPCC stated that 'this case illustrates the inappropriateness of a police station as a safe or satisfactory environment for vulnerable people experiencing acute mental illness'[266].

4.175 We recognise, of course, that problems in identifying places of safety other than police stations cannot be the fault of the police alone: often the police have great difficulty in handing-over apparently mentally disordered people into the care of medical authorities. When health authorities refuse to accept such patients, the police appear to retain responsible for them by default, even where they are clearly not the best agency to deal with a problem. It is vital that police and other agencies build strong collaborative working partnerships to ensure appropriate and safe care is provided.

---

[264] *Government Response to the Third Report from the Committee: Deaths in Custody* HL 69/HC 416

[265] MHAC (2001) *Ninth Biennial Report* 1999-2001, chapter 4.4 *et seq.*

[266] IPCC press release, *IPCC concludes West Midlands mental health case*, 9 June 2005. As a result of the investigation, discussions with senior officials from the police, local NHS Trusts and social services were undertaken to address the questions of inter-agency working raised by the case, and the IPCC formally invited the Chief Constable and West Midlands Police Authority to review the implications of the legal advice provided to the IPCC that the circumstances arising in this case could amount to a breach of a person's human rights and to set out the specific actions to be taken to avoid any repetition in similar circumstances in the future.

4.176 In some areas of the country it would seem that there are not only too few hospital-based places of safety, but also great difficulties in finding hospital beds for persons assessed as requiring inpatient treatment subsequent to detention under s.136. We are aware of one case in Somerset where a patient was held in a police station for seven days before a bed could be located. Whilst seven days is no doubt an extreme delay, we understand that many patients are held for some time post-assessment in police stations whilst mental health professionals struggle to identify an available bed. In its submission to the Joint Committee on the Draft Mental Health Bill, the IPCC recognised that police cells my be required as last resort places of safety, but suggested that the next Act provide a duty upon health authorities to provide alternative facilities, and that any use of holding powers at a police station should be limited to 12 hours rather than 72 hours, with the presumption that any holding power running over 12 hours should be continued following transfer to health facilities[267]. We support these proposals.

> **Recommendation 34:** Holding powers relevant to police stations under the next Act should be limited in duration to 12 hours

4.177 In December 2004 the media reported that an 80 year old woman from Hastings, having been found sitting on the ground 'in an unkempt state', was detained in a police cell for six hours under the powers of s.136[268]. In cases where there is little chance of danger to others from violent behaviour, or need for secure custody arrangements, we would expect flexibility in the identification of facilities to hold the patient in whilst assessments are made. Authorities should take a flexible approach as to whether or not the designated s.136 place of safety, if it is a place of secure custody, is really required in individual circumstances, or whether any other local facility (such as a GP clinic, for example) might not serve the purpose in a more humane manner.

4.178 In general we prefer places of safety in hospitals to be a designated room or suite of rooms. Admitting a person under s.136 directly to an acute admission ward can be disruptive to that ward and its patients, disturbing for the person concerned and could lead to an assumption that the patient should be formally admitted. Wherever possible we would recommend that the place of safety is a designated assessment unit within or linked to a psychiatric facility. In our Ninth Biennial Report we reported arrangements at Enfield as a good practice example in this respect[269]. We understand that the Metropolitan Police are considering the development of 'safe-havens' for the reception of apparently mentally disordered people as well as people apparently under the influence of drink or drugs, or exhibiting problem behaviour. We will follow these developments with interest.

---

[267] Joint Committee on the Draft Mental Health Bill (2005) *Draft Mental Health Bill.* Vol 3. Memorandum from the IPCC (DMH 206) para 7, p.912.

[268] BBC News,13 December 2004 *Police Cell Pensioner Complains*

[269] MHAC (2001) *Ninth Biennial Report* 1999-2001, p.34

Recommendation 35: Section 136 assessment facilities should:

- preferably be in a quiet area of the facility used;

- offer privacy from persons not concerned with the assessment;

- facilitate appropriate and frequent observation by staff;

- be safe for use (with attention paid to ensuring that furniture and fittings do not provide ligature points or other potential hazards);

- be accessible to staff (i.e. with outwards opening doors); and

- have washing / toilet facilities en suite or within easy and safe reach of the room under escort (i.e. avoiding physical obstacles such as staircases, and in preference not passing through ward areas etc).

Accident and Emergency departments

4.179 It has been suggested that Accident and Emergency (A&E) departments may be the most frequently used settings for urgent mental health assessments (including of persons presenting themselves for treatment) in central London[270]. Substantial guidance on the provision of psychiatric services to A&E departments was issued by the Royal College of Psychiatrists in February 2004[271]. This recommends that all A&E departments include facilities and resources for the assessment of patients with mental health problems, including an interview room with adequate safety features, but it recognises that A&E departments are often ill-equipped for use as a place of safety. They may be unsuited to receive people with severe mental disturbance, and their use for that purpose may put others at great risk.

4.180 In any locality, the places of safety that may be used under s.136 should be agreed between NHS Trusts responsible for general non-psychiatric hospitals, those that provide psychiatric services, and the police. In addition, the police should be invited to state in what circumstances they would assist in the removal of dangerous persons, and what they would do to assist hospital staff in circumstances where they have brought a dangerous person to a general hospital for medical assessment and/or care that is not possible elsewhere. Police should use the A&E department for the patient if they believe that this is necessary for medical reasons (e.g. the patient is bleeding profusely)[272].

4.181 A&E services are increasingly called upon for s.136 assessments in London, although many are not the locally agreed Place of Safety. The *Metropolitan Police Pan-London Guidance* requires that where 'acute behavioural disturbance' is observed in the detainee, s/he should be treated as in need of emergency medical treatment and taken by ambulance to an A&E

---

[270] Cassar S, Hodgkiss A, Ramirez A & Williams D (2002) 'Mental health presentation to an inner city accident and emergency department'. *Psychiatric Bulletin* 26;134-136

[271] Royal College of Psychiatrists (2004) *Psychiatric services to accident and emergency departments.* Council Report CR118, February 2004, p.7.

[272] *ibid.*, p.81

department. Acute Behavioural Disturbance (which has previously been called 'excited delirium') was defined by the Police Complaints Authority as an extreme form of behavioural disturbance which goes far beyond the 'distressed' state often encountered by the police, having the main features of a period of agitation, excitability, perhaps paranoia, coupled with great strength, aggression or non-pain compliance, which may result in sudden collapse and death[273]. The Metropolitan Police are issued with a check-list of features to identify this state, although of course such features are largely distinguishable from more common presentations of s.136 detainees only by degree, leading to a broadly subjective element in the use of this guideline. The protocol does allow that ambulance crews, who will generally not recognise 'acute behavioural disturbance' as a specific entity as it is not a part of medical training, may determine that a detainee thought to be at risk by the police constable does not in fact require A&E attendance, in which case the constable should determine which other place of safety is appropriate.

4.182   The experience of London A&E departments in receiving patients brought in by police has not always been very positive, as indicated by the following three vignettes from St Thomas' Hospital:

- A patient found wandering on railway tracks was brought by the police in handcuffs (neither under arrest nor under s.136). The police left promptly, after which the man produced a Stanley Knife and threatened a nurse.

- A patient brought by ambulance having smashed up her flat was 'forced into A&E' by police, who left promptly, after which she assaulted the psychiatrist.

- A patient who was brought to A&E 'under unclear powers' (after which the police left promptly) immediately set fire to his clothes and tried to leave. Different police officers answered the call for assistance from A&E staff[274].

4.183   However, the Metropolitan Police have also had difficulty in gaining access to A&E departments when they feel that a patient is in need of emergency medical intervention. In two separate incidents over a weekend in March 2005, patients conveyed by police to A&E departments were turned away on the grounds that the A&E was not a place of safety. In one of these cases, the patient had been detained by police following a violent incident outside the A&E department itself. In both cases police reluctantly started to drive the patients to the locally-agreed assessment suite, but in both cases the patients stopped breathing during the journey and had to be returned to A&E as an acute medical emergency. We understand that one patient subsequently required the use of a life-support machine.

4.184   Police also report being turned away from A&E departments and agreed places of safety on the basis that the patient whom they have detained appears to be drunk or under the influence of drugs, or even where the patient only smells of alcohol. We have heard of examples of 'doorstep triage' where detainees are breathalysed outside of medical facilities by medical staff, and refused access if signs of alcohol are present.

---

[273] Police Complaints Authority (2002) *Policing Acute Behavioural Disturbance*, revised edition.

[274] Dr Andrew Hodgkiss (Consultant Liaison Psychiatrist, SLAM) Policing and Mental Health Joint Review presentation: Liaison Psychiatry. 13 April 2005. These examples are likely to have involved other forces than just the Metropolitan Police, such as the City of London or Transport Police.

Recommendation 36: Mental health services should be flexible in response to s.136 patients, and ensure that policies do not result in patients who are in need of assessment being turned away on spurious or unnecessary grounds, such as because staff detect a smell of alcohol on the patient.

4.185 We commend the establishment of local protocols with accident and emergency units to ensure that they have an understanding of the procedures for s.136 admissions; how they might be expected to play a role in caring for a person detained under such powers; and what expectations they may have of other agencies. We recommend that similar protocols are undertaken nationally. It is important to stress in protocols that the law provides no mechanism for transfers from one place of safety to another, and that a patient brought to A&E as a place of safety may therefore have to remain there for the purposes of the mental health assessment as well as any emergency physical intervention. We support the proposal in the draft Mental Health Bill 2004 to allow for transfers between places of safety so as to remove this artificial barrier to appropriate patient care. We understand that this proposal is viewed warily by the police, who are concerned over the potential for this to increase demand upon their resources in conveying patients, but we believe that effective protocols and working practices can counter such problems.

Assessments on private premises and the use of section 135

Police attendance at Mental Health Act assessments

4.186 We have received a number of accounts of difficulties arising out of the roles or expectations of the police or social services in relation to assessments. A significant proportion of Mental Health Act assessments are carried out with the assistance of police officers, either because of the need for obtaining entry to a property or because of anticipated violence or physical resistance from the person being assessed.

4.187 The Commission has expressed concern at some police forces' apparent heavy-handedness in assisting Mental Health Act assessments. In our Fifth Biennial Report we warned that sending a number of police officers in riot-gear in response to requests for assistance may worsen rather than help any situation likely to arise[275]. It is important that protocols regarding contact with the police set out what kind of assistance may be requested and expected, and it may be that lack of clarity in requests is a factor in seemingly inappropriate responses. But we urge that, alongside flexibility in determining when it is appropriate to respond to social services' requests for assistance, police services allow for flexibility in the type of assistance that is provided. We are pleased to note the London Development Centre for Mental Health's joint risk assessment process for requests for police intervention goes some way to address these concerns, by ensuring that the faxed request for police assistance provides a detailed risk assessment and that the police fax back to social services details of the police resources to be deployed[276].

---

[275] MHAC (1993) *Fifth Biennial Report* 1991-1993. London: Stationery Office, Chapter 3.5f

[276] London Development Centre for Mental Health (2005) *Draft risk assessment document.* In *Review of assessments on private premises report and recommendations,* June 2005, app.3.

4.188 We are concerned that an unintended consequence of police authorities' perceptions of the obligations and demands of the Human Rights Act may make them withdraw from co-operation in assessments. We do, of course, applaud the police for their concern not to act in any way that is contrary to the requirements of the European Convention on Human Rights. The Metropolitan Police Service trains its officers to consider the human rights implications of their policing duties according to the acronym 'PLAN B' (Proportionality; Legality; Accountability; Necessity; Best Information). When considered against these principles, the Metropolitan Police Service questions whether customary policing roles in mental health assessments (i.e. where a police officer accompanies an ASW on a 'just in case' basis without being assured of the necessity of his/her involvement) meets the criteria of a risk of violence that is established in Pan-London Protocols. Individual social workers are often more cynical over the police motivation, questioning whether it is resource-driven rather than a result of human rights concerns, although the police deny that this is the motivating factor[277]. There has consequently been something of a cultural conflict across services in London, where social workers may expect the police to play a supportive or reassuring role in assessments, but the police view their involvement as only legitimate if there is a risk of violence or disorder. Although both health and police services appear generally to accept that interventions should be based upon risk-assessment (and the police quite understandably refuse to respond to requests that are not based upon a risk-assessment[278]), it is not clear that each authority has been applying the same theoretical or practical definitions of 'risk' or 'risk-assessment'. We note that the joint risk assessment process developed by the London Development Centre for Mental Health may address these disparities of approach.

4.189 We have no reason to question the good faith of the police in regarding the issues at stake as being fundamental questions of police powers and the Human Rights Act, but we think that the analysis behind this, which can appear to equates the legitimacy of police involvement with a risk of violent disorder, is flawed. We take the view that there is nothing intrinsically contrary to human rights requirements in having a police presence at a Mental Health Act assessment, whether or not there is a risk of violent disorder. We understand the general role of the police not to be limited solely to dealing with violence or disorder, and cannot therefore see why it should be so restricted when dealing with the exercise of important civil powers relating to possible detention. This is not to say that it would be appropriate for the police to always accompany ASWs and doctors to assessments, or even to do so routinely.

4.190 In our view, a police officer's presence at a Mental Health Act assessment, alongside other legitimately present professionals, cannot itself be a breach of human rights or make such a breach more likely in general terms than would be the case without a police presence. Similarly, whilst the assessment or its resolution may involve actions that are interferences with human rights (such as, for example, picking up and carrying a passively resisting patient to an ambulance), the assessment process and outcome can provide legal authority

---

[277] Inspector Bruce Frenchum 'Appropriate Involvement of the Police' presentation at *Policing and Mental Health; Risks and Realities* Independent Police Complaints Commission conference, Birmingham, 20 January 2005

[278] The Dixon Inquiry (1999) was critical of mental health and social services' care of a patient with paranoid schizophrenia who stabbed and killed PC Nina Mackay in 1997. PC Mackay and colleagues from the Armed Territorial Support Group forced entry into his flat to arrest him for breaching bail conditions. The report was also critical of the Metropolitan Police Service for not obtaining a risk-assessment before turning out to make the arrest, and questioned whether the police approach had been heavy-handed. PC McKay had also removed her protective vest before entering the property. See Amelia Gentleman 'Serious failings led to PC death' *The Guardian* 20 April 1999.

for such interferences where they are themselves proportionate and necessary. The process of assessment under the Act therefore provides any professional, including a police constable if so directed by the ASW responsible for co-ordinating the actions of professionals, with the authority to undertake actions that would normally be an unwarranted interference with human rights.

4.191   This is not to presuppose that carrying a passively resisting patient to an ambulance is a legitimate role only for the police. The police understandably question the assumption that such matters are 'police business', when the police have no more legal authority to pick up and carry a patient than ambulance staff or other professionals present. We are sympathetic to this concern, but not to it being misrecognised as a question of law when it is actually a legitimate question of appropriate use of resources. The ultimate resolution of the question of whether a police officer's presence at a particular assessment was justifiable is not a legal question relating to human rights, but a practical (if fundamental) question of what the police role should be at such assessments, given the competing claims on police time and the legitimate expectations that should rest on each party to the assessment. In assuming that the police role is only legitimated in response to violent resistance or threats to other professionals, the Metropolitan Police Service appears to have assumed a narrower remit for police work than that which we understand.

4.192   In December 2004 the Metropolitan Police Service announced that, following legal advice, it intended to require that a warrant under s.135 was obtained as a condition of its officers accompanying ASWs on Mental Health Act assessments. As a result of serious concern from health and social services authorities, the implementation of this requirement was postponed whilst the policy was reconsidered.

4.193   The police concern was that, in order 'to ensure that any potential interference by a police officer with a person's right to respect for privacy, a family life and their home is demonstrably proportionate, legal and necessary to manage the identified risks... the best way ... is for the assessment to be carried out under the protection of a s.135(1) Mental Health Act warrant'[279]. Against anticipated objections to this policy, the police suggested that:

- whilst some magistrates had required previous evidence of a refusal of entry before granting a warrant under s.135[280], such a stipulation is not a requirement of the Act, so that 'where an ASW had sufficient evidence to demonstrate to the local police that their involvement would be proportionate and necessary, that risk assessment will be very strong evidence in support of an application to the court'; and

- to avoid raising tensions or causing anxiety through the production of a warrant on the doorstep of the person to be assessed, 'where in the planning stage the ASW and police consider it appropriate to first of all obtain consent to entry, it would be proportionate and legal to keep the warrant undeclared during the assessment process. If circumstances dictate it could then be executed, providing the legal protection necessary to enable police officers to act'.

4.194   We note that the Metropolitan Police Service has now accepted that the current statutory grounds for requesting a warrant may not cover all the circumstances in which police may

---

[279]   Metropolitan Police Service letter to all Directors of Social Services in London, 17 December 2004.

[280]   See MHAC (2003) *Tenth Biennial Report: Placed Amongst Strangers*, Chapter 8.55

be requested to attend assessments on private premises, and that police may therefore attend assessments without such warrants (but will leave the premises if consent to their entry is withdrawn before the social worker has completed any application for admission under the Act). In particular, of course, there are many circumstances where entry to private premises is given by someone other than the person who is to be assessed, whether this person is a carer, family member or landlord who is legally empowered to grant such access. But the Metropolitan Police Service view appears to remain that the police and other agencies involved in assessments are best protected by the issue of a warrant when attending private premises. There may be some pressure on Parliament to accommodate this view in establishing the thresholds for warrants under the next Mental Health Act, the proposals for which would already widen police powers under the draft Mental Health Bill of 2004[281]. This causes us some concern. We would consider it a great irony that a consequence of authorities' concerns not to violate human rights principles should lead to a considerable extension of State power over the mentally disordered through the routine issue of warrants of entry to private premises. It does not seem to be in the spirit of human rights law for domestic law to be reinterpreted so that warrants of entry are issued as a matter of course for any mental health assessment where a police officer may be present[282].

Recommendation 37: We urge police services to be flexible in their response to requests for help and support from social services in mental health assessments.

Data on the use of s.135

4.195   Data collected from social services authorities on the use of s.135 is set out at figure 80 below. We discussed the limitations of the data at paragraph 4.164 *et seq* above.

type of place of safety:	Number of times used			Number of patients detained following assessment			Number of patients taken into hospital under informal basis			Number of patients needing any other follow up care			Number of patients released without further action		
	London	rest of UK[283]	total	London	rest of UK	total	London	rest of UK	total	London	rest of UK	total	London	rest of UK	total
hospital	126	186	312	105	132	237	14	38	52	3	23	26	4	32	36
police station	-	6	6	-	5	5	-	-	-	-	1	1	-	-	-
other[284]	-	16	16	-	9	9	-	4	4	-	-	-	-	1	1
Total use	**126**	**208**	**334**	**105**	**146**	**251**	**12**	**42**	**56**	**3**	**24**	**27**	**4**	**33**	**37**

Fig 80: MHAC data on use of s.135 by place of safety and outcome, 2002/03 – 2003/04.

---

[281] See *Draft Mental Health Bill 2004*, clauses 226 and 228, and paragraph 4.199 *et seq* below.

[282] We also doubt the soundness of the police's original legal advice that authorities should enter a property without revealing that a legal warrant of entry has been granted, or otherwise conceal the existence of such a warrant whilst undertaking the warranted action.

[283] i.e. England and Wales, excluding parts of UK where MHA 1983 is not in force.

[284] The place of safety under s.135 can be anywhere, including a private residence provided that the 'occupier' is prepared to receive the patient (MHA s.135(6)).

4.196 Our data indicates that the use of police cells as places of safety is much less of an issue in relation to detentions under s.135 than s.136. This is to be expected, as the former require planning in advance, and such planning should include the identification of the holding facility most likely to be appropriate. When considering applications for warrants under s.135, it may be impractical for magistrates to require *specific* evidence relating to the criteria for applying s.135 (i.e. whether there is reasonable cause to suspect a person believed to be suffering from mental disorder is unable to care for themselves or is being neglected, etc), but they could usefully enquire of the ASW whether alternatives to executing a s.135 warrant had be considered, and whether suitable plans were in place once access had been gained, including arranging a suitable place of safety or alternate places of safety depending on the situation that arises upon entry to the property.[285]

4.197 Because there is likely to be less use of police cells as places of safety for s.135 detentions than for detentions under s.136, it is possible that the Department of Health statistics on the use of s.135 (figure 81 below) may be a relatively accurate reflection of the extent of the use of the power, even though these statistics only include the use of the power to take patients to hospitals.

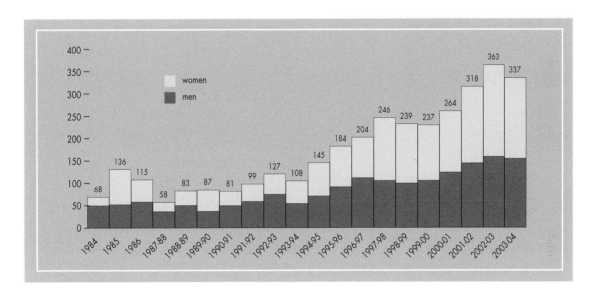

Fig 81: the use of s.135 places of safety in hospitals, 1984 – 2003/04[286]

4.198 In response to some magistrates' uncertainty over their powers in issuing warrants (see Chapter 1.80), we have placed placed on the MHAC website a precedent warrant for use by magistrates[287].

[285] Carr L 'Magistrates and Mental Health Act Warrants' *the Magistrate*, October 2002 p.283 www.magistrates-association.org.uk/documents/magistrate_archive/2002/mag_oct_2002.pdf

[286] Data source: Department of Health *Inpatients Formally Detained in Hospitals Under the Mental Health Act 1983 and Other Legislation*, 1984 – 2004

[287] We are grateful to Andrew Parsons of RadcliffesLeBrasseur, solicitors, for drawing up the precedent warrant for this purpose.

The proposed extension of police powers under the draft Mental Health Bill of 2004

4.199   The draft Mental Health Bill 2004 restates the powers of ss.135 and 136 in its provisions with little change: indeed we were disappointed that no attempt was made to update the language used in those provisions, so that the Bill continued to speak of mentally disordered persons 'being kept otherwise than under proper control'[288], etc. Alongside the retention of such language, which can be dated back at least to the Lunacy Acts of the nineteenth century, the draft Bill also proposed additional emergency powers that echo provisions of s.20 of the Lunacy Act 1890 which were specifically removed with the passing of the Mental Health Act 1959. The proposed clause 228 of the 2004 draft Bill would extend police powers of entry to private premises, so that where 'urgency' precludes a warrant from being obtained, a police officer accompanied by and acting on information from an Approved Mental Health Professional may force entry to private premises without such a warrant and remove the occupant to a place of safety.

4.200   The British Association of Social Workers strongly objected to this extension of police powers (although the proposed 'police power' is, of course, in fact only likely to be used at the behest of an Approved Mental Health Professional), pointing out that the safeguard of the need for a warrant under s.135 was introduced because of widespread misuse of previous powers had led them to become the main route for compulsory admission[289]. Arguing that there is no less a risk of malpractice today than there was prior to 1959[290], BASW indicated that it would advise its members against making use of such a power were it enacted, and suggested that a warrant (and the presence of a doctor as well as an AMHP and police constable) should be the minimum requirement for forcible entry into private premises under mental health powers.

4.201   There is certainly a danger that the criterion of 'urgency' which would justify the use of the emergency powers, and which was not further defined in the draft Bill of 2004, could be open to broad interpretation. The forced entry into a prospective patient's home is always necessitated, to some extent, by an 'urgent' need to help that person, and it is a small step from recognising the need to make such an entry to assuming that it is not practicable to obtain a warrant and a doctor's presence before acting on that need. Whilst the advice of professional bodies such as BASW may restrict overuse to some extent, not all AMHPs will be social workers, and not all practitioners follow the advice of their professional bodies. We believe that there is a need for a more considered debate on the extension of these powers, and that closer definition may be required in the statute to prevent their abuse. We doubt that either the general requirement on public authorities to act within the requirements of the European Convention, or guidance in the Code of Practice, would be sufficient safeguards against the misuse of the extended powers proposed.

---

[288]   *Draft Mental Health Bill* 2004, clause 227(1)

[289]   Joint Committee on the Draft Mental Health Bill (2005) *Draft Mental Health Bill*, Vol 2, p.578.

[290]   Although there was arguably more incentive to misuse emergency admission powers under the Lunacy Acts, given the lack of an equivalent to the Mental Health Bill's 28-day assessment order prior to the need for complex certification proceedings.

Recommendation 38: The extension of police powers to enter private property under emergency mental health provisions should be carefully considered by Parliament and, if enacted, should be carefully defined to prevent misuse or expansion beyond Parliament's intention.

Managing patient behaviour

'My senior clinical manager told me 'if you want safe, go and work in Safeways"

nurse quoted in Healthcare Commission (2005) The National Audit of Violence[291].

4.202   During this reporting period we have seen the development of mental health posts within the NHS Security Management Service, the special health authority established in 2003. Although the primary focus of the NHS Security Management Service is tackling violence against NHS staff, in the context of mental health care this focus inevitably broadens to all aspects of control and restraint operated by staff in the management of violent behaviour. The Secretary of State has issued directions requiring NHS bodies to co-operate with the new special health authority; identify Board-level responsibility for security matters; and appoint at least one local security management specialist to whom incidents must be reported and who will record the incident, co-ordinate local actions and liaise with the Security Management Service[292]. The new special health authority is tasked with implementing the Government's announcement of a national strategy on tackling violence and abuse that will ensure all staff working in mental health and learning disability units are trained in preventing and managing violence[293] (see paragraph 4.212 below).

4.203   At present, there appears to be significant under-reporting of incidents of violence and threatening behaviour in mental health units (figure 82).

---

[291]   Healthcare Commission (2005) *National Audit of Violence (2003-2005) Final Report.* Royal College of Psychiatrists' Research Unit / Healthcare Commission. p.21. www.healthcarecommission.org.uk.

[292]   *Secretary of State directions on work to tackle violence against staff and professionals who work or provide services to the NHS*, issued 20 November 2003, annex 2.

[293]   'NHS responds to violence survey' *Mental Health Today* July/Aug 2005 p.6. See also Department of Health (2005) *Delivering Race Equality in Mental Health Care; an action plan for reform inside and outside services and the Government's response to the independent inquiry into the death of David Bennett.* Jan 2005, p.27-9.

	acute		PICU		forensic		all units[294]	
	Y	N	Y	N	Y	N	Y	N
are *all* incidents of threatening behaviour or violence reported and recorded?	69	23	76	21	77	19	71	22

all figures are percentages[295]

Fig 82: Healthcare Commission findings on nurses' perceptions of the reporting and recording of threatening or violent behaviour, by service sector, 2003-2005[296].

4.204 We are encouraged by an evident focus on prevention in guidance issued to date, including recognition of the environmental and situational triggers of difficult behaviour in patients[297]. We have summarised the Healthcare Commission's findings over the common causes of violent behaviour at figure 14 (following Chapter 2.41 above). The most common trigger for violent behaviour on wards was identified by the Healthcare Commission as being substance abuse by patients, with alcohol playing a particularly important role[298].

4.205 There is a great deal to be done to make both patients and staff feel safe in many units. The national audit on violence, published by the Healthcare Commission in May 2005, found that fourteen per cent (15) of acute units were marked as unsafe in the opinion of the mental health staff respondents[299].

4.206 In previous Biennial Reports we have stressed the need for service to implement Code of Practice requirements over establishing policies and guidelines on restraint (Code of Practice Chapter 19.14) and seclusion (19.17). In our last report we noted that even self-assessments by hospitals and Trusts showed that not all had met these basic requirements[300]. The Healthcare Commission Audit of Violence showed a continuing failure to implement the Code's guidance on policies for a significant minority of services (figure 83).

---

[294] 'All units' includes acute, PICU, forensic, rehabilitation, elderly, learning disability (short stay, long stay and challenging behaviour) units and small group homes.

[295] Only responses clearly identified as 'yes' or 'no' are shown in the data: answers categorised as 'other' by the researchers account for the shortfall when 'yes' and 'no' in each category do not amount to 100%.

[296] Healthcare Commission (2005) *National Audit of Violence.* p.59.

[297] National Institute for Mental Health in England (2004) *Mental Health Policy Implementation Guide: Developing Positive Practice to Support the Safe and Therapeutic Management of Aggression and Violence in Mental Health In-patient Settings.* February 2004

[298] Healthcare Commission (2005) *National Audit of Violence*, p.7.

[299] *ibid.*, p.47.

[300] MHAC (2003) *Tenth Biennial Report: Placed Amongst Strangers*, Figures 30 and 32 (pages 170, 175).

	acute		PICU		forensic		elderly		all units[301]	
	Y	N	Y	N	Y	N	Y	N	Y	N
Do you have a policy on using/ recording restraints?	86	10	100	-	95	5	33	47	87	9
Do you have a policy on using/ recording seclusion?	77	13	94	6	68	21	80	13	67	24

all figures are percentages[302]

Fig 83: Healthcare Commission findings on seclusion and restraint policies, by service sector, 2003-2005[303].

Physical Restraint

4.207   We have no doubt that the best modern mental health nursing practice aims towards the empowerment of patients in a supportive and caring environment. In many cases this is what we encounter on our visits. But certain aspects of nursing practice - or perhaps the limitations placed upon such practices by environmental and other constraints - can easily result in a dysfunctional process in which interventions become limiting and controlling rather than empowering and caring[304]. For example, the lack of nurse/patient interaction on a busy acute ward with a high level of agency workers may fail to create a therapeutic environment or to engage with patients who are at risk of self-harm or aggressive behaviour. A resulting 'custodial' atmosphere on wards may distort or corrupt therapeutic aims so that nursing interventions tend to be reactive to problem behaviour, involving forms of restraint, which are then perceived as controlling or even punitive by patients. This can also have the effect of unintentionally encouraging patients to 'act out' to get nursing attention.

4.208   Even in well-managed therapeutic environments, mental health nurses may have to face hostile and aggressive patients; may be required to intervene to prevent patient upon patient violence; and of course, rather uniquely in the nursing profession, may be called upon to enforce the administration of treatment against a patient's active resistance. All of these situations may involve physical restraint.

4.209   Patients have reported that 'more positive attention and open communication, especially before the conflict that led to restraint had climaxed, could have reduced the chance of the patient becoming so aggressive that restraint was needed'[305]. In our last report we stressed

[301] 'All units' includes acute, PICU, forensic, rehabilitation, elderly, learning disability (short stay, long stay and challenging behaviour) units and small group homes.

[302] Only responses clearly identified as 'yes' or 'no' are shown in the data: answers categorised as 'other' by the researchers account for the shortfall when 'yes' and 'no' in each category do not amount to 100%.

[303] Healthcare Commission (2005) *National Audit of Violence* p.47.

[304] See Sullivan P 'Care and control in mental health nursing' *Nursing Standard* 16; 13-15, 42-45. December 1998.

[305] Wynn R 'Psychiatric inpatients' experiences with restraint' *Journal of Forensic Psychiatry & Psychology* Vol 15 No 1 March 2004 124-144

that patients should also be told as much as possible of the reasons for the restraint during the intervention itself: de-escalation need not stop just because physical intervention has started[306].

4.210 Physical restraint can bring back memories of prior sexual assault, and patients may experience delusions or hallucinations during restraint[307]. While it is common for staff members involved in restraint episodes to be debriefed, it is as important that patients are given an opportunity after their restraint episode to discuss it with staff. Such discussions would provide an opportunity for establishing the patient's preferences in handling any similar occurrence. Even if it is not appropriate to have such discussions immediately after an intervention, some form of care and support should be provided to all patients in the period immediately after they have been subject to restraint.

> 'I think the way I was restrained … was diabolical. I weighed probably then 8¹/2 stone and to be pinned down by four or five staff – some males – and have one or two needle jabs in my bottom was uncalled for, I have never posed a threat to anyone other than myself, so I did not see the need for such hard restraint, then to be put in a room all by myself was just not the way of doing it'
>
> *Deborah Hickman, ex-s.3 patient, Lancs*

4.211 In this reporting period important practice guidance has emerged on managing disturbed or violent behaviour in psychiatric hospitals. We are pleased that positive practice standards for the management of aggression and violence have now been made available by NIMHE[308] and we commend these to services. We were pleased to contribute to the consultation over the National Institute of Clinical Excellence's guidance on the short-term management of violence in inpatient psychiatric settings, which was published in final form in February 2005[309]. All services should be working within these guidelines, and should have copies on wards (including in 'quick reference guide' form[310]) and in use for staff training. Services should also have copies of the 'information for the public' booklet on the NICE guidelines[311] readily available for patients and their families.

> **Recommendation 39:** Restraint policies should reflect the emphasis placed by NICE and NIMHE guidance on prediction and prevention rather than dealing solely with the interventions themselves.

---

[306] MHAC (2003) *Tenth Biennial Report: Placed Amongst Strangers*, Chapter 11.31.

[307] Wynn R (2004) *supra*.

[308] National Institute for Mental Health in England (2004) *Mental Health Policy Implementation Guide: Developing Positive Practice to Support the Safe and Therapeutic Management of Aggression and Violence in Mental Health In-patient Settings*. February 2004

[309] National Institute for Clinical Excellence (2005) *Violence: the short-term management of disturbed/ violent behaviour in inpatient psychiatric settings and emergency departments*. Clinical Guidelines 25. February 2005.

[310] The NICE *quick reference guide* on clinical guideline 25 is available by telephoning 0870 1555 455 (ref N020828) or from www.nice.org.uk/CG025quickrefguide.

[311] Information about NICE clinical guideline 25 ('*Violence: managing disturbed/violent behaviour. Understanding NICE guidance – in formation for service users, their advocates, families and carers, and the public*' available from 0870 1555 455 (ref N0829 for English version, N0830 for English and Welsh).

4.212 At the time of writing, the NHS Security Management Service (see paragraph 4.202 above) had completed pilots of its training programme *promoting safer and therapeutic services*, and should launch this formally in September 2005. The training covers aspects of the NICE guidelines and David Bennett Inquiry recommendations (see paragraph 2.215 below), and focuses on prevention rather than crisis management, with modules on values; communication; engagement and de-escalation; understanding service-user experience; legal rights and professional responsibilities[312].

The prevalence of restraint

4.213 Eight per cent (2,703) of all informal and detained psychiatric patients in hospital at the time of the 2005 National Census on Mental Health and Ethnicity had experienced one or more episodes of control and restraint during their current hospitalisation, or within the last three months if they had been in hospital for a longer period. Of these, 511 patients (1.5% of all inpatients) had experienced more than five control and restraint episodes; and 224 (0.7%) more than ten episodes.

4.214 Mental Health Act Commissioners look at restraint records and discuss patients' experiences on our visits. The example below describes serious concerns over practice raised as a result of one visit.

Poor practice example

On a visit to an independent secure psychiatric unit for women in October 2004, we noted a high incidence of restraint in the incident book and heard concerns over the use of restraint in private meetings with patients. We noted 24 incidents of restraint over the ten days before our visit, which did not appear to be an untypical frequency, and were alarmed to see records of restraint justified solely in response to 'verbal aggression'. Patients described what they perceived as unnecessary use of restraint, stated that 'some staff enjoy it' and described use of thumb-hold techniques causing pain during restraint. This group of women patients were very vulnerable, having almost all (if not all) experienced past physical and/or sexual abuse. In response to our concerns we received reassuring letters from the hospital and its C&R training provider, the former indicating that staff meetings had discussed our concerns; that the need to accurately and fully record C&R rationale (with documentation of attempts at de-escalation prior to C&R) had been stressed; that audits would take place; and that the patient's advocate would be acting as a conduit for patient concerns. We suggested that these measures could be supplemented with 'post-incident' discussions with patients. The C&R trainer's letter contained reassurances over the company's credentials, and summarised how staff were trained by them and what that training consisted of.

---

[312] See www.cfsms.nhs.uk

At our next visit in spring 2005, we did not find that practices seemed to be living up to the identified standards. Of 51 recorded incidents of C&R over the month prior to our visit, only 21 were recorded clearly as responses to assault or physical aggression. Even in records that did indicate physical aggression as the cause of C&R, details were often missing so that the level of risk was implied rather than recorded. We are in discussion with the hospital over our concerns as we go to press.

Fig 84: practice example of high-use of control and restraint

Restraint practices after the David Bennett Inquiry

4.215 The restraint that led to David Bennett's death in 1998 involved, for at least some its duration, nursing staff lying across him whilst he was face-down on the floor. At other times he was reported to be on his back, but at some point a nurse had a hand on his throat[313].

4.216 The David Bennett Inquiry recommended that 'under no circumstances should any patient by restrained in a prone position for a period longer than three minutes'[314]. It noted views of witnesses to the inquiry that any time-limit for such intervention was bound to be arbitrary, but no witness was reported to oppose a time limit, and the suggestion gained the support of Professor Appleby, the National Director for Mental Health[315]. The inquiry was shown the prison service control and restraint manual which stated that the maximum time face-down restraint should be used continuously was five minutes[316].

4.217 In its response to the Inquiry in January 2005, Government did not accept this recommendation[317]. It gave no specific reason for this, but in its response referred to the NICE guidelines on the management of violence, which were in preparation, and acknowledged that restraint was only to be used as a last resort, in the safest way and for the shortest possible time. The NICE guideline (see figure 85 below) appearing the following month, made no mention of face-down or prone restraint but simply referred generically to 'physical interventions'[318]. This response in the face of the inquiry recommendation disappointed many mental health campaigners.

---

[313] Norfolk, Suffolk and Cambridgeshire Health Authority (2003) *Independent Inquiry into the Death of David Bennett.* December 2003, p.19-22.

[314] *ibid.* p.52

[315] *ibid.* p.52-3

[316] *ibid.* p.52.

[317] Department of Health (2005) *Delivering race equality in mental health care: An action plan for reform inside and outside services and the Government's response to the Independent inquiry into the death of David Bennett,* pages 26-7.

[318] National Institute for Clinical Excellence (2005) *Violence: the short-term management of disturbed/ violent behaviour in inpatient psychiatric settings and emergency departments.* Clinical Guidelines 25. February 2005, see section 1.8.2.

Nice Guidance

NICE recommendations on interventions for the management of disturbed or violent behaviour include:

- rapid tranquilisation, restraint or seclusion should only be considered when de-escalation and similar strategies have failed;

- de-escalation techniques should continue during restraint;

- a crash bag should be available within three minutes in healthcare settings where restraint, rapid tranquilisaton or seclusion might be used;

- a doctor should be available to be on site within 30 minutes when such interventions are used;

- one member of staff should assume leadership and control throughout the process of restraint, and be responsible for protecting the patient's head and neck; ensuring that the patient's breathing is not obstructed; and that vital signs are monitored;

- the infliction of pain has no therapeutic value and may only be used for the immediate rescue of staff, service users or others.

Fig 85: NICE guidance on restraint[319]

4.218 It remains the case that there is a dearth of research regarding the positive and negative effects of any restrictive physical interventions on patients[320]. In their report *Physical Interventions and the Law* Christina Lyon and Alexandra Pimor suggest that 'it may be that further much-needed research would demonstrate that the use of restrictive physical interventions may, with many service users, be completely counter-productive'[321]. The lack of research extends to physical dangers of particular measures, and was bound to limit the extent to which the methodology of NICE would produce strong guidelines over details of practice. We believe that it is uncontroversial that all restraint that involves making a patient kneel or lie down is dangerous and may, in certain circumstances, result in death. Patients may be asphyxiated or subject to other physical trauma lying face-up as well as face-down, and it is therefore vital that staff adhere to the NICE guidelines that prohibit the application of direct pressure to the neck, thorax, abdomen, back or pelvic region under any circumstances. In addition, however, we believe that policies on restraint should reflect the views of witnesses to the Bennett Inquiry on prone restraint.

---

[319] *ibid.* See also *NICE Guideline: quick reference guide – Violence*, pages 14-16

[320] Lyon C and Pimor A (2004) *Physical Interventions and the Law. Legal issues arising from the use of physical interventions in supporting children, young people and adults with learning disabilities and severe challenging behaviour.* para 2.4.3, British Institute of Learning Disabilities www.bild.org.uk

[321] National Institute for Clinical Excellence (2005) *Violence* (see n.318 above)

Recommendation 40: Hospital policies on restraint should recognise that the placing of a patient in 'prone' (face-down) restraint should be:

- an absolute last resort intervention, not normally countenanced as acceptable practice in a psychiatric setting;

- undertaken, if at all, on the assumption that it should last for seconds, not minutes, and only for such time as is necessary to move the patient to a less dangerous position;

- never continued to the point where a patient is exhausted from struggling or has gone limp;

- considered to require the immediate attendance of a medical practitioner as a medical emergency[322].

Mechanical restraint

4.219　In our last report we pointed to the various forms of mechanical restraint in use in mental health services, and suggested that the patient groups most likely to encounter mechanical restraint were probably learning disabled and frail elderly patients rather than acutely disturbed or violent patients with mental illness[323]. We were disturbed that this area of mental health provision is not openly discussed or acknowledged. We suggested that Government should consider extending the remit of future monitoring arrangements (which would restricted neither by our limited remit nor resources) to cover the use of mechanical restraint in all mental health services.

4.220　We are pleased that the Department of Health has now approached us with the suggestion that we introduce a system of notifications on the use of mechanical restraint to inform future Government actions. We are keen to do this but have suggested that the Minister must use her powers under the Act to extend our remit to do this; should direct NHS hospitals to comply with notifications; and should fund the project so that its cost is not at the expense of the Commission's core activities in meeting detained patients. We hope that discussions over these terms can be concluded quickly and that notifications will begin shortly after this report is published.

4.221　It appears from the Department of Health's discussions with us that it is minded to use the Code of Practice as the regulatory mechanism in this important area of human-rights practice. We are concerned as to whether non-mandatory guidance in a Code of Practice will be sufficient safeguard against the broad potential for abuse raised by the use of mechanical restraints (see *Regulation of seclusion and other means of restraint* at paragraph 4.237 below), but it may be appropriate to have this debate based upon evidence collated from the notification system.

---

[322] See *Independent Inquiry into the Death of David Bennett*, p. 52 (particularly evidence of Mr Tucker and Drs Shepherd and Carey).

[323] MHAC (2003) *Tenth Biennial Report: Placed Amongst Strangers*. Chapter 11.35-41, recommendation 46.

4.222 We understand that professional advisors to the Department of Health have suggested that there should be no place in elderly patient services for such forms of restraint discussed briefly in our last report (i.e. chairs with harness-type straps to prevent falls)[324]. There is, to our knowledge, no official guidance on this matter[325]. Reported deaths of elderly patients in the U.S. due to forms of mechanical restraint have appeared to involve entanglement in garments designed for restraint purposes or in straps meant to prevent patients from slipping from a bed or chair[326]. In 1995 a woman with learning disabilities died in Staffordshire in similar but grotesque circumstances, having slipped from a toilet to which a 'bib' she was wearing had been tied as a form of mechanical restraint[327].

4.223 During this reporting period the Commission has been involved in the decision to use mechanical restraint on *X*, a learning-disabled minor. We outline the particulars of the case below. We view this case (in common with a previous case mentioned in our last Biennial Report[328]) as a justifiable use of mechanical restraint. Where the alternative may be to have a patient constantly held by two or more members of staff, the use of mechanical restraint lessen the restrictions placed upon a patient. Even where mechanical restraint is the least restrictive option available to the clinical and management team, the discontinuance of the restraint (and indeed all restraint) should be an aim that is kept in clear focus during clinical discussions and reviews of treatment. The case below appeared to us to have been a responsible and well-managed intervention.

> ### Practice example: mechanical restraint
>
> Because of severe self-injurious and assaultative behaviour, upon *X*'s admission to hospital constant 4:1 observations with minimum-force physical restraint by staff was deemed necessary. This involved a member of staff holding each arm at all times, with others prepared to hold his legs when necessary. The holds were released only when the patient was asleep, although staff remained with him and gently reapplied holds whenever he awoke. After considerable consultation the decision was taken to employ mechanical restraint in the form of an 'emergency response belt' made of reinforced fabric with 'velcro' type fasteners, with the sole aim of supporting an improvement in *X*'s quality of life. The use of such a device when necessary was declared to be in *X*'s best interests by the High Court in May 2005, when he was made a ward of court[329].

---

[324] *ibid.*, chapter 11.39-40

[325] National Institute for Clinical Excellence clinical guidelines regarding fall-prevention in older people (*The assessment and prevention of falls in older people.* Clinical Guideline 21. November 2004) extend only to people in the community or 'extended care settings', and not to hospitalised patients, and do not discuss this aspect of practice.

[326] Myles S H & Irvine P (1992) 'Deaths caused by physical restraints' *The Gerontologist* 32, 6 762-6. See also Paterson B, Bradley P, Stark C, Sadler D, Leadbetter D, Allen D 'Restraint-related deaths in health and social care in the UK: learning the lessons' *Mental Health Practice* June 2003 vol 6 no 9 p.10-17.

[327] Paterson B *et al* (2003) *supra*, p.12.

[328] MHAC (2003) *Tenth Biennial Report: Placed Amongst Strangers.* Chapter 11.37

[329] The High Court also ruled that no-one may publish any particulars that might lead to X's identification, after the *Sun* newspaper ran a distorted and unpleasant account of his care by the journalist Andy Russell under the headline " 'Hell' lad must be pinned to bed".

> Following the introduction of the device X was able to walk and sit outside without being held, and was pleased at the prospect of travelling in a car and engaging in activities. The device does not seem to have been used for extended periods, and now appears to be rarely used, if at all. X has now been transferred to a learning disabilities unit, where he is making encouraging progress: he can now indicate to staff when he wants his arms to be held and is spending increasing amounts of time free from physical holds.

Fig 86: practice example of the use of mechanical restraint

Seclusion and isolation of patients

> The glory of the modern system is repression by mildness and coaxing, and solitary confinement.
>
> *John Perceval, 1845*[330]

> Seclusion is the most awful experience: the hopelessness and despair one feels locked in a cell with no knowledge of when one can get out, the powerlessness one feels, the sense of being punished, is overwhelming. Even after relatively short periods – hours, let alone the days of weeks that it can go on for – one finds it having traumatising effects on the mind.
>
> *Gul Davis, s.3 patient, Birmingham, 2005*

4.224 Seclusion has been a concern in psychiatry for over 150 years. Throughout this time a number of clinicians, reformers and commentators have proselytised or predicted its demise as a practice, and others have insisted on its place as a tool for the management or even treatment of patients.

4.225 Seclusion or solitary confinement was noted to be 'getting into general use in the treatment of the insane' by the Lunacy Commission in 1843: this was most likely as a result of the widespread reduction in use of mechanical restraints[331]. In 1858 the Lunacy Commission considered as seclusion any amount of compulsory isolation in the daytime whereby the patient was confined in a room and separated from all associates[332]. In 1901 the Commission's definition was 'the enforced isolation by day, between the hours of 7am and 7pm, by the closing, by any means whatsoever, of the door of the room in which the patient is'[333]. Variations of this definition

> 'I've found people are secluded for punishment / management reasons – I've been given 'time-out' (open seclusion) several times for trivial matters'.
>
> *Trevor Howard, s.37/41 patient, Notts*

---

[330] Peceval J (1846) *Letters to Sir James Graham … upon the Reform of the Law affecting the Treatment of Persons Alleged to be of Unsound Mind*, London, 1846. Letter dated 1 August 1845 quoted in Hervey N 'The Lunacy Commission 1845-60 with special reference to the implementation of policy in Kent and Surrey' PhD dissertation, Bristol University 1987: see Scull A (1989) *Social Order / Mental Disorder: Anglo-American Psychiatry in Historical Perspective* p.17n & 82.

[331] Fennell P (1996) *Treatment Without Consent: Law, Psychiatry and the Treatment of Mentally Disordered People since 1845.* Routledge. p.20.

[332] *ibid.* p.33. C19th and early C20th regulation did not recognise seclusion outside of daytime hours, given that patients were locked up at night anyway. The 1983 Act's Codes of Practice deliberately reversed this, although today direction of the Secretary of State requires some HSH patients to be locked up at night without their status being recognised as seclusion.

[333] *ibid.* (1996) p.59

seem to have remained in use as a basis for regulation throughout much of the twentieth century[334], although perhaps subject to the ebb and flow of 'legalism' and 'clinicalism[335]'. For example, in 1925 the Lunacy Commission's successor, the Board of Control, allowed that seclusion could be 'a valuable form of treatment' and redefined it to exclude holding a patient alone in a room where only the bottom half of a stable-style door was shut[336].

4.226 In friendly settlement of an ECtHR challenge to seclusion practice in Broadmoor hospital[337], by 1980 the Government had introduced a seclusion policy to the hospital which specified that the criterion for seclusion was the patient's safety and the safety of others, thus underlining the impermissibility of using seclusion as a disciplinary or punitive measure.

The definition of seclusion

4.227 In common with its predecessor, the 1983 Act provides neither statutory definition nor regulation of seclusion. However, attempts have been made throughout the lifetime of the Act to define and control the use of seclusion through the Code of Practice.

4.228 The Code of Practice (chapter 19.16) currently defines seclusion as 'the supervised confinement of a patient in a room, which may be locked to protect others from significant harm'[338]. The Code's definition of seclusion is particularised with the following:

'Its sole aim is to contain severely disturbed behaviour which is likely to cause harm to others.

Seclusion should be used;

- as a last resort
- or the shortest possible time

Seclusion should not be used;

- as a punishment or threat
- as part of a treatment programme
- because of shortage of staff
- where there is any risk of suicide or self-harm'[339]

---

[334] Although regulation of seclusion did not continue after the passing of the Mental Health Act 1959, practitioners from that time recall that the pre-1959 definitions of seclusion (in particular in not recognising night-time seclusion) continued to be generally recognised for the purposes of hospital policies etc. It seems likely that some practices established by pre-1959 regulation continued without the support of statutory obligation, at least in some establishments.

[335] The disputed model of mental health regulatory practice as a scale with legal intervention at one end and clinical discretion at the other, with the scales tipping according to the mores of society at the time, originates with the work of Kathleen Jones (see Jones K (1960) *Mental Health and Social Policy* 1845-1959, Routledge & Kegan Paul).

[336] See Fennell (1996) *supra* p.159. This definition was codified in the Mental Deficiency Regulations 1948, Regulation 34(2) and Mental Treatment Rules 1948, Rule 57(2).

[337] *A v United Kingdom* EctHR Application no.6840/74

[338] The punctuation of the Code's definition appears to have been inserted in error at the last revision. The comma implies, falsely, that the justification 'to protect others from significant harm' relates only to a decision to lock a seclusion room door, whereas it is, of course, the justification for the use of seclusion as a whole. Previous editions did not carry this error.

[339] Mental Health Act Code of Practice, chapter 19.16

4.229 In the Court of Appeal judgment for *Munjaz*[340], Lady Justice Hale sought to differentiate between seclusion as practised according to the Code's definition and the locking of certain high security patients in their rooms at night in accordance with HSH security directions:

> Seclusion is keeping a person under regular, frequent observation, while he is prevented from having contact with anyone in the world outside the room where he is confined.

4.230 The Court's judgment did not provide any greater clarity to the core definition of seclusion. It is probably axiomatic that 'supervision' in this context amounts to 'regular frequent observation'. As a criterion for defining seclusion, prevention of contact with 'anyone in the world outside of the room' cannot be taken literally, as this could disqualify most seclusion practice (including that considered as seclusion by the court in this case) from being recognised as seclusion at all[341]. In any case, the Court of Appeal was here making a point of distinction rather than attempting a core definition. A similar point of distinction is provided by Taylor and Gunn's *Forensic Psychiatry*:

> In the special (maximum security) hospitals of England, patients are locked in their rooms at night without possibility of egress, a practice not treated as seclusion, and without the attendant recording and monitoring[342].

That is, insofar as seclusion might be defined by its rationale (i.e. as a last resort means of containing dangerous behaviour), or by its attendant procedural requirements, then locking HSH patients into their bedrooms falls without the definition. This is clearly Government's will, however much the objective distinction between seclusion and the forcible locking of a patient in a bedroom overnight is open to question. The practice example at figure 91 (pages 317-8 below) shows the potential for arbitrariness or illogicality in such distinctions. In the case discussed, a patient was secluded in the room that was intended to serve as his bedroom that night because of his resistance to acts preparatory to locking him into that room under the security direction rules. Because that seclusion episode had not ended by the time that patients would normally be locked in on the unit, he was deemed to be in overnight seclusion after this time even though his objective situation (i.e. being locked in his 'bedroom') was no different to what had been intended under the guise of security directions. There is a danger that arbitrary distinctions or rules imposed from outside the hospital by Government directive may be damaging to staff and patient morale and reinforce 'institutionalisation'.

---

[340] *R (on the application of Colonel Munjaz) v Mersey Care NHS Trust and (i) Secretary of State for Health and (ii) Mind; S v Airedale NHS Trust and (i) Secretary of State for Health and (ii) Mind* [2003] EWCA Civ 1036. para 75.

[341] Patients who are kept in seclusion rooms may and sometimes must be visited or contacted by medical and nursing staff, doctors, solicitors, MHA Commissioners and even, perhaps, friends or relatives, or may contact any of the above, and yet still be confined within a room and deprived of association amongst other patients within the ward milieu. It would be counter-productive to exclude patients who have such contact from the regulations regarding seclusion. The ability to *instigate* contact with persons (other than such persons such as solicitors or MHA Commissioners to whom there is something of a right of access) could, however, be more useful as a defining criterion for seclusion.

[342] Taylor P and Gunn J (ed) (1993) *Forensic Psychiatry: Clinical Legal and Ethical Issues.* Butterworth Heinmann, p.659. This was published before the introduction of '24 hour care' in the HSHs (c.1995) ended the practice of locking patients' rooms at night.

4.231   Some difficulties arise from a literal reading of the established Code of Practice definition:

- If *confinement in a room* is the key defining criteria, should escorted trips to nearby toilet or washing facilities (commonly facilitated in hospitals without *en suite* facilities in seclusion rooms) be seen to terminate periods of seclusion, even if the patient is immediately returned to seclusion conditions?

- If confinement in a [single] room is the defining characteristic of seclusion, then are patients confined within seclusion suites of rooms (for instance seclusion rooms with *en suite* facilities) excluded from the definition?

Most hospitals, and the MHAC, take a pragmatic rather than literalist approach to defining seclusion with regard to questions such as these, allowing that confinement in a suite of rooms is still seclusion, and that a period of seclusion is not terminated if the patient is allowed to go to a nearby toilet under escort before being returned to the room[343].

4.232   The Code of Practice distinguishes seclusion from 'time out', the latter described as a technique used in behaviour modification programmes where a patient is removed from an activity or environment for no more than 15 minutes. In 'time out' locked doors should not be used. In practice, the main distinction between seclusion and time out would seem to be the intention behind each intervention: for seclusion the putative intention is always simply to control aggressive or dangerous behaviour; for time out the intention is more therapeutic and forms a part of a planned treatment programme.

4.233   Alongside definitional problems, there are organisational incentives to understating the use of seclusion:

- Service providers are keen to present themselves are forward-thinking and humane, by abandoning the use of practices seen by many mental health professionals as regressive and old-fashioned.

- The Code of Practice places on service providers an onerous review and recording requirement. If a service provider can effect the same outcome without triggering the Code obligation, there is a clear saving in staff time and paperwork.

- The Code of Practice demands a four-hourly medical review of all patients in seclusion without any reference to special night time circumstances. Managing and supporting night time reviews of patients has always been a challenge for those staffing junior doctor

---

[343] There is less consensus over whether brief respites from conditions of seclusion, such as occasions where secluded patients are given the chance to emerge from seclusion and socialise on the ward under supervision for a specified trial period, at the end of which they may be returned to the seclusion room, should be considered to terminate seclusion or merely suspend it. On the one hand, the ability to give a form of 'trial leave' from seclusion could be justified in the same terms as the law allows detained patients trial leave from hospital: it is a means of testing a patient's ability to manage without relinquishing power to intervene or requiring a repeat of the formal procedures of initiating such control. In this way it allows clinical teams to take a measured risk and can help in the earlier termination of seclusion. On the other hand, some hospitals continue the formal seclusion of such patients over long periods (weeks or even months) whilst allowing them limited or controlled periods of socialisation, thus effectively reducing the threshold for reinitiating actual seclusion and bypassing the safeguards of the Code. The MHAC in the *Munjaz* case in the Court of Appeal (and the SHSA in 1993) criticised Ashworth Hospital's practice in this respect, but there is a body of opinion within the MHAC that would accept the need for specific rules and safeguards for high security patients nursed in long-term isolation.

rotas. This situation has become even more difficult following the implementation of the Working Time Directive. In our last report we suggested that Government should consider guidance to units whose staffing precludes authorisation or review of emergency interventions according to the expectations of the Act and Code of Practice[344]. We regret that we have had no response to this recommendation and do not believe that it has been taken up.

> **Recommendation 41:** Government should consider guidance to units whose staffing precludes authorisation or review of emergency interventions according to the expectations of the Act and Code of Practice.

4.234　We frequently encounter interventions that look to us like seclusion but are not recognised as such by the authorities who use them (see figure 87 below). For example, one Independent Hospital told us (as well as the Healthcare Commission, who were responsible for its registration) that it did not use seclusion, and its policy stated clearly that the rationale for this was because of the potential negative effects of seclusion for patients, including reduced self-esteem; feelings of vulnerability and powerlessness; worsening of anger, delusions or hallucinations; and a possible increased risk of self-harm or suicide. However, as our report of the visit explained:

> … practice in managing disturbed behaviour is to remove the patient to the quiet room under conditions of control and restraint and continue the control and restraint until the patient is fit to return to association. The completion of the control and restraint operation is defined by the moment when the C&R team feel it is safe to leave the room having completed the de-escalation phase. Thus there is a period of time when the patient is not being physically restrained but is being kept in the room as they are too volatile to be permitted association with other patients. This phase can last anything between five minutes and one hour.

Seclusion by another name

As long ago as 1997 we drew attention to the confusion surrounding the definition of seclusion[345]. Despite this, examples continue to prevail where the practice of seclusion may be referred to as:

- 'removal from the environment'
- 'therapeutic isolation'
- 'open-door seclusion'
- 'de-stimulation rooms'
- 'de-escalation rooms'
- 'single-person wards'

- 'enforced segregation'
- 'restriction of movement'
- 'de facto seclusion'
- 'removal to a "calming room" '
- 'placed in a quiet room'

Fig 87: euphemisms for seclusion

---

[344] MHAC (2003) *Tenth Biennial Report: Placed Amongst Strangers*, Recommendation 44, p.172.

[345] MHAC (1997) *Seventh Biennial Report*, Chapter 10.1.3

4.235   We also encounter situations where patients have been found to be spending long periods in isolation while not being formally secluded. A common factor among them was that they were all extremely challenging patients causing enormous problems for those employed to care for them. The quality of care being delivered varied from the very good to the dangerously substandard.

> **Patient 1**   This learning disabled patient was nursed in isolation in a special unit set aside for him alone, to reduce the severity of risks to him apparent when he was nursed on a ward with other patients, and because other patients were at risk from his behaviour. He had free movement of the special unit which had no unsafe areas (for example furniture was bolted to the floor so he could no longer move it around or lift it up rendering it hazardous), ending the need for staff to constantly thwart him. Incidents of confrontation and aggression reduced as a result. Whilst this environment ensured his safety, he still required one-to-one nursing care from staff with specialist skills in managing him. Nursing staff were increased to two staff per shift to ensure his safety whilst meeting his care needs.

> **Patient 2**   After high-dosage medication was reduced to counter side-effects, this patient's behaviour became a significant and persistent risk to others, and he was segregated for some time. The patient was kept in a secure area separate from other patients, with a bedroom, bathroom, living room with TV and a small dining area. There was access to a garden. He was under 24 hour surveillance and had a team of four nurses attending. He was taken on a regular basis to on-site day services, between the hours of 10 a.m. and 3 p.m., but did not always choose to stay and sometimes opted out. The Trust managers showed great concern over their arrangements and consulted widely about whether seclusion procedures should be invoked.

> **Patient 3**   This informal patient was nursed on his own in a locked environment. Commissioners found the patient to be in effective isolation from patients and staff, despite a risk assessment recommending that he receive 2:1 nursing care. The area in which he spent his time was without furniture or apparent means of stimulation or activity: the patient appeared to have been given a makeshift 'rattle' for diversion. Deficiencies in relation to the safety, privacy and dignity of the patient that were apparent to Commissioners were an open drain, the absence of a toilet seat, soap, towels and door to the toilet area, and the patient's bathroom and bedroom area were cold and smelt of urine and faeces despite, according to the ward manager, regular cleaning. The Service Manager reported being unaware of the situation until we brought it to his attention.

4.236   We are disappointed the Department of Health policy documents contribute to the confusion of terminology and to the weakening of patient safeguards regarding seclusion. The Department's *National Minimum Standards for Psychiatric Intensive Care Units (PICU) and Low-secure Environments* proposes:

- 'Extra Care Areas' (ECA) as 'an alternative to seclusion', defined as 'a closely supervised living space away from the main clinical area in which a single patient may be nursed away from [the] rest of the patients'; and

- as an alternative to seclusion rooms, a 'de-escalation room in which staff remain with the patient, rather than the patient being locked in'.[346]

---

[346] Department of Health (2002) *Mental Health Policy Implementation Guide: National Minimum Standards for General Adult Services in Psychiatric Intensive Care Units (PICU) and Low-secure Environments.* April 2002, p.49

We do not see how or why nursing in an 'Extra-Care Area' should be distinguished from seclusion as defined in the Code of Practice; and if there is a distinction to be made, the Departmental guidance should establish what it is. The Guidance's apparent distinction between de-escalation (where staff remain with the patient) and seclusion (where staff retreat outside of a locked room) has no basis in the Mental Health Act Code of Practice and may be challenged as a matter of law. The Code of Practice definition of seclusion clearly encompasses situations where nursing staff enter or remain in the seclusion room.

Recommendation 42: Regulations under the next Act should ensure that the definition of seclusion extends to all incidents of isolation and solitary confinement so that neither confusion nor obfuscation over definitions deprives patients of safeguards established for its use.

Regulation of seclusion and other means of restraint

4.237   In our previous reports we have repeatedly called for the regulation of seclusion and other means of restraint. We were pleased that this call has been supported by the Joint Committee on Human Rights[347] following our representation to them.   The Joint Committee on the Draft Mental Health Bill acknowledged our argument that issues of seclusion and restraint were key areas of the law having a human rights dimension, and criticised Government for not publishing the provisions of a Code of Practice that would deal with such issues[348]. That the latter Committee did not consider whether the relevant merits of primary or secondary legislation and Codes of Practice in relation to these issues may have been because they were deliberating as the issues were to be considered by the House of Lords in the *Munjaz* appeal (see introduction to this report), or it may have been because they did not think the issue of any importance. As our submission to the House of Lords in *Munjaz* made clear, we do still find the question important, not least because of the widespread failure of services to meet the Code's requirements when secluding or otherwise restraining patients.

4.238   In our submission to the House of Lords in the *Munjaz* case we emphasised our view that disparity of practice and uncertainty in relation to the practice of seclusion is contrary to the interests patients (and for that matter also of healthcare professionals) and contrary to a mental health system that recognises and promotes respect for the system of rights provided for by the Human Rights Act. Given that seclusion has the potential to infringe Articles 3 and 8 of the ECHR, it is essential to meet the obligations of Government and service providers that its implementation is premised upon consistent and predictable standards and that all hospitals apply the same approach (at the least as a starting point).

4.239   The practical consequence of radically different practices from hospital to hospital were demonstrated by the treatment afforded to one patient referred to as '*WL*' in evidence

---

[347] Joint Committee on Human Rights (2004) *Deaths in Custody: Third Report of Session 2004/5*. HL Paper 15-I, HC 137-I. Para 245.

[348] Joint Committee on the Draft Mental Health Bill (2005) *Draft Mental Health Bill*. Vol 1, p.5.

submitted to the House of Lords for Mersey Care NHS Trust in the *Munjaz* case. The circumstances of this patient are well-known to the Commission. The Trust's evidence indicated that *WL* had been in seclusion for 3,280 days (i.e. the best part of 10 years) in Ashworth Hospital. In October 2002 *WL* was transferred from Ashworth Hospital to Rampton Hospital, whereupon his long-term seclusion ceased. At Rampton, *WL* has on occasion been subject to seclusion but for much shorter periods, and never long enough to trigger Rampton's independent review process (which applies if any patient is placed in seclusion on any one occasion for 8 hours, or for a total of 12 hours within any 48 hour period). It is possible that the startling difference in approach between Ashworth Hospital and Rampton Hospital may be explained in part by the fact that Ashworth Hospital's policy adopts a wholly different notion of seclusion from that appearing within the Code of Practice. However, this point simply underlines the potential for arbitrariness if each hospital is able to disregard the provisions of the Code of Practice as a matter of routine. Psychiatric patients are a vulnerable group. These vulnerabilities can mean that they are more susceptible to harm as a result of seclusion. This requires a heightened sensitivity to the requirements of Convention rights where compulsion is used.

4.240   The Government has informed us that it intends to pursue the statutory regulation of seclusion through the mechanisms of a new Mental Health Bill concerned with medical treatment. We discuss this general approach below. A potential model for the establishment of secondary legislation specifically concerned with seclusion and restraint that does not rely on treatment powers is provided by the Irish Mental Health Act 2001. This includes in its 'miscellaneous' provisions a requirement that seclusion or mechanical restraint must be used in accordance with rules established by the Irish Mental Health Commission[349]. The Irish Commission is currently in the process of drafting these rules. Whilst we are not looking for an equivalent role for the Mental Health Act Commission or its successor body in drawing up rules, we do prefer this legislative solution to the apparent course to be taken in English and Welsh law.

The perils of medicalisation

4.241   In 1843 the Lunacy Commission allowed that seclusion was 'a valuable remedy' for 'the tranquillisation and subduing those who are under temporary excitement or paroxysms of violent insanity', but also suggested that its use should only be permitted for short periods and never for the permanently violent and dangerous patient. In 1925 the Lunacy Commission stated that seclusion could be a valuable form of medical treatment. There is a long and fairly ignominious history of regulatory bodies blurring (explicitly or implicitly) the distinctions between medical and managerial aspects of the confinement of mentally disordered people. It is perhaps the case that the distinction between clinical and non-clinical interventions in this context is always artificial, given the roots of modern psychiatry in 'moral treatment' and the continuing, indeed structural, requirements of 'order' in mental hospitals. But, even though the legal definition of treatment has become so stretched so as to encompass any activity that takes place within a hospital (and was recognised as such by the judiciary in the *Munjaz* case), it is extremely important that we start from and maintain a position that seclusion itself is not treatment in any accepted medical sense, but

---

[349]   Mental Health Act 2001 (Eire), s.69

is a managerial response to contain violent behaviour[350]. In 1981, the Council for Science and Society wrote in its policy report *Treating the Troublesome* that

> the clearest possible line of separation should be drawn, and maintained, between what is thought by an independent clinician to be in the best interests of the patient, and what is thought by administrators to be in the best interests of their institutions. The clinician's task is to develop and use the best techniques for curing or alleviating his patients' disorders; the administrator's task is to develop and use the best techniques for maintaining order within their institutions. These tasks are wholly distinct, and should never be confused. In the long run, the greatest risk is that one day, for what may appear to be the best of motives, they will be[351].

4.242   There is a great danger in adopting strategies for regulating seclusion that rely upon its legal status as 'treatment', such as using emergency treatment powers and safeguards as the regulatory framework around seclusion practice, or using safeguards around the authorisation of care plans by a Tribunal or its medical advisers for this purpose. The danger of these 'medical' approaches is not only that they may entrench seclusion as an accepted practice for the 'treatment' of certain patients, but also that they could remove seclusion further from any regulatory body's grasp by providing the excuse of 'clinical discretion' for any departures from regulatory guidelines. In this way regulation of seclusion could be entirely counter-productive. Phil Fennell has argued that 'the method which the [Lunacy] Commission adopted to regulate seclusion, bathing and restraint was to place them under medical control, creating the paradoxical result that whilst intended to limit their use it also legitimised them as medical interventions'[352]. We appear to be in danger of repeating mistakes that we should have learned from our history.

> **Recommendation 43:** Regulations on seclusion should identify it as a managerial intervention rather than an aspect of clinical treatment.

The prevalence of seclusion

4.243   In the 2005 census we found that 3% (1,014) of all psychiatric inpatients resident on the 31 March 2005 had experienced one or more episodes of seclusion in their period of admission (or in the previous three months, whichever was shorter). 112 patients had experienced at least five periods of seclusion in this period, and 42 had experienced at least ten such periods. The maximum number of periods of seclusion was over 100.

---

[350] Maden T 'Seclusion' *Journal of Forensic Psychiatry* Vol 10 No 2 September 1999 242-244.

[351] Council for Science and Society (1981) *Treating the Troublesome* London: CSS, page 51. The CSS was a charity established in 1973 with the object of promoting study and research of the social effects of science and technology. It established *ad hoc* working parties to report on issues identified for its attention. The *Treating the Troublesome* report was intended to investigate the ethical problems of compulsory medical treatment for socially unacceptable behaviour and was produced by a working party chaired by David Sullivan QC with membership including Professors John Gunn and Malcolm Lader of the Institute of Psychiatry and representatives of the parole board, Mind, and Justice.

[352] Fennell P (1996) *Treatment Without Consent.* p.35.

4.244   The census showed high rates of seclusion for Black patients. The following example of seclusion encountered on an MHAC visit involved a young Black patient.

> On a recent visit to a medium secure unit we encountered a young Black man who had been secluded for an extended period of time following an incident of restraint where a member of staff was injured. The conditions of seclusion appeared punitive and the long-term nature of the seclusion inappropriate. This was exacerbated when the RMO went on leave as it appeared the only reason for continuing seclusion was the RMO's absence. The Commission carried out two visits in a short period of time, raised a number of concerns with the Chief Executive and the Regional Director liaised with the young man's family. Seclusion was ended but MHAC are continuing to take an interest in this case due to outstanding complaints and issues regarding assessment.

Fig 88:   practice example of a seclusion incident, 2005.

4.245   The Healthcare Commission's national audit of psychiatric facilities over this reporting period found that approximately one third of all 239 units audited claimed to use seclusion[353]. Figure 89 below shows these findings broken down by sector, and compares them to reported use of intensive nursing care. Whilst 'intensive nursing care' is not necessarily a euphemism for seclusion, many practices that the MHAC might classify as seclusion may be contained within this category. The correlation between services that claim not to seclude patients and those that report use of 'intensive care areas' is striking. Even if this correlation is coincidental, it should be remembered that even those units who genuinely do not seclude patients are likely, as a last resort, to transfer patients who cannot be managed by other means to hospitals that do operate seclusion[354].

	acute		PICU		forensic		all units[355]	
	Y	N	Y	N	Y	N	Y	N
Do you use seclusion?	37	63	47	53	63	37	32	68
Do you have access to a PICU / intensive care area?	62	38	n/a		81	6	49	50

all figures are percentages[356]

Fig 89:   Healthcare Commission findings on use of seclusion and intensive care nursing, by service sector, 2003-2005[357]

[353]   Healthcare Commission (2005) *National Audit of Violence* p.48.

[354]   Maden T 'Seclusion' *supra.*

[355]   'All units' includes acute, PICU, forensic, rehabilitation, elderly, learning disability (short stay, long stay and challenging behaviour) units and small group homes.

[356]   Only responses clearly identified as 'yes' or 'no' are shown in the data: answers categorised as 'other' by the researchers account for the shortfall when 'yes' and 'no' in each category do not amount to 100%.

[357]   Healthcare Commission (2005) *National Audit of Violence* p.37-8, 62.

Conditions of seclusion

4.246   In our last report we published a checklist of physical aspects of seclusion facilities based upon our monitoring work[358]. Commissioners continue to see examples of poorly-designed or constructed seclusion facilities. An article in *Hospital Design* magazine in January 2005 provided detailed suggestions for the design and build of seclusion facilities[359]. It makes the point that it is essential the practice of seclusion takes place in a designated seclusion room or suite. However, taking into account the negligible amount of design and construction information available to clinicians, architects and managers, most hospitals have to design a seclusion facility based on limited information, anecdotal evidence and personal experience. Considering that a 'secluded patient' is further deprived of their liberty and freedom of movement within the ward area of the mental health hospital and its potential for abuse[360], it is surprising that there appear to be no Government regulations and little or no quality standards in respect of designing and building a safe and secure seclusion facility.

4.247   We have been very concerned to note examples of patients being transported to seclusion facilities in ways which may be hazardous or distressing. It is inadvisable, for example, for patients to have to be taken up or down staircases to reach seclusion rooms. Consideration should also be given to whether access to seclusion rooms requires the patient to be taken through relatively public or populous areas of the hospital, such as reception areas, dayrooms or other wards to the one in which the patient resides. In one hospital, we have encountered 'temporary' arrangements (lasting many months) where patients were transported across the hospital campus in a van to reach seclusion facilities. In Ashford, Kent, patients requiring seclusion have been taken 12 miles by ambulance to a seclusion room in Canterbury. These practices are not acceptable. Patients being taken to seclusion are likely to be extremely distressed and the distance involved in moving them should be kept to an absolute minimum.

> ### Practice example
>
> The following quotes are from our interview with a patient shortly after an episode of seclusion lasting over 48 hours. The seclusion room used was not *en-suite*, but was provided with a paper chamber pot and the patient could be escorted to the bathroom. She was allowed to wash in the morning and evening; was not allowed to smoke for the first twelve hours (afterwards on request); and had no access to reading, music or other recreational material whilst in seclusion. She had been – and indeed still was – dressed in protective clothing. On our visit we helped her to raise her concerns as a complaint.
>
> 'Seclusion is humiliating. They even watch you go to the toilet. They say I have to wait until the ward team meeting to come out of protective bedding and clothing ('strips'), even though I'm out of seclusion. I'm supposed to be in strips for three days after seclusion, a

---

[358]   MHAC (2003) *Tenth Biennial Report: Placed Amongst Strangers*, Fig. 31, p.171.

[359]   Curran C, Adnett C, Zigmond T 'Seclusion: factors to consider when designing and using a seclusion suite in a mental health hospital' *Hospital Development* January 2005 19-26. www.hdmagazine.co.uk

[360]   See for example the 1973 *Report of the Committee of Inquiry into South Ockenden Hospital*, or the 1990 *Report of the Committee of Inquiry into Complaints about Ashworth Hospital*, (Vol I, p 203): both The Stationery Office, London

nurse says. I hate my body being touched - I kick off if touched so new search policy is horrible for me. Nurses are reasonably sensitive, but patients stroke me inappropriately. You can guarantee they'll seclude me all the time if I get involved in an incident (not all other girls get that). I feel I'm getting treated differently'.

Female s.37/41 patient, Broadmoor Hospital

We were concerned to note that in answer to 'what does the patient have to achieve for seclusion to be ended?', staff replied that the patient 'has to be settled *and show remorse*'. This calls into question whether seclusion is being used solely to contain dangerous behaviour and gives credence to the patient's sense of being punished through seclusion.

Fig 90: practice example of seclusion use over 48 hours duration

4.248 Many seclusion rooms do not have easy access to toilet or washing facilities. Where there are no *en-suite* facilities, patients may be reliant on staff being available and able to escort them to facilities elsewhere on the ward, or else they may be provided with chamber pots or urine bottles, etc. This is a serious concern to us, especially when seclusion rooms may be in use for relatively long periods. On a visit to Rampton Hospital in January 2004, we found a secluded patient supplied with a chamber pot in old seclusion facility on the main corridor of one ward, whilst a new seclusion room in a quiet area of the ward was not in use. We were told that staffing levels precluded the use of the new facility, and that this was not an isolated incident. It seems possible that requiring patients to use chamber-pots in such circumstances could leave services open to legal challenge on the basis of potential breaches of human rights (see Chapter 1.200 *et seq* above). The following case (figure 91) gives a further example of seclusion conditions that may be challenged on the grounds that they breach Article 3 of the European Convention.

Seclusion incident at Rampton Hospital

All patients detained in Rampton Hospital's purpose-built DSPD unit are required by the Safety and Security Directions be locked in their rooms at night. One challenging patient with a history of serious self-harm (patient X) was assessed to be at risk in his own room and required to sleep in a seclusion room. As neither beds nor mattresses initially supplied to the new-build unit were fit for purpose (both having been damaged by patient X in attempts to self-harm) they had been removed: no seclusion facility on the Unit had a bed installed at the time of the incident described. As the seclusion room on his own ward was occupied, Patient X had spent one night sleeping on two strong blankets on the floor of the Intensive Care Unit in another ward. X was unhappy at the prospect of spending another night in the ICU of another ward. At around 17.00 hours on the following evening, he refused to co-operate with his move to that ward in preparation for locking him down for the night. He was restrained and carried to the ward where he was placed in seclusion.

In seclusion X had both his blankets and clothing removed to prevent him from self-harming after he had shredded the strong bedding and was observed to attempt to legate himself with it. He was provided with food and drink in seclusion, but had no pot or urine receptacle in the room. He took his medications but was refused his asthma inhaler because (according to an entry made by staff in his seclusion record) the 'hole in door was too small' for it to be passed through. Whilst reportedly settled for most of the time, X told us later that he had, unsurprisingly, been uncomfortable and cold sleeping naked on the floor that night. The seclusion record was neither consistent with the requirements of the Code of Practice, nor with the objectives of X's care plan, which had suggested two-hourly reviews of the decision to withhold bedding and clothing. The computerised nursing records report that a risk assessment had been conducted at 20.45 as X was complaining about being denied strong bedding or shorts and, after consultation with the senior nurse manager, a decision taken to continue nursing him naked. Other nurse managers reviewed the situation at 10.30 the next morning, and immediately determined that it was safe to give the patient his shorts. It would appear that his shorts were again taken from him when he was secluded a day later.

X complained to the MHAC about his treatment and we visited him as a result. He reported his experience as humiliating and degrading, which echoed his experiences as the victim of childhood sexual abuse. He reported serious psychological consequences of his experience. The nurse manager who had reviewed the seclusion episode and returned X's shorts to him indicated that he was shocked at the withholding of the asthma inhaler. A clinical management team discussion of the incidents that week concluded that although there was no doubt that staff were acting in what they believed to be X's best interests to prevent him from serious self-harming, his dignity had not been maintained and the staff's actions had damaged the patient's trust in his clinical team. Staff training would be undertaken as a result.

At paragraph 4.174 above we note a similar case where a female detainee was held naked in a police cell as a precaution against self-harm. Legal advice to the Independent Police Complaints Commission suggested that such treatment could breach the requirements of Article 3 of the European Convention. At the time of our going to press X's solicitor was preparing to litigate on the basis of a violation of his client's rights under that Article to protection from degrading treatment.

Fig 91: practice example of seclusion use in Rampton Hospital

Recommendation 44: Services using seclusion or isolation should review their facilities and procedures, and audit incidents, to ensure that patients' rights to privacy and dignity are not compromised unnecessarily.

(see also recommendation 46 below)

MHAC data on isolation episodes lasting more than 48 hours

4.249 Over six month periods during 2004/05 we asked hospitals in the acute sector and medium/high secure sector to notify us when they had held a patient in isolation for more than 48 hours. We defined isolation as 'any incident where a detained patient is isolated from all other patients whether behind a locked or unlocked door or in their own bedrooms'.

4.250 Units were asked to complete a form giving basic patient details; details of recent risk assessments; a description of the type of environment that the patient used; the duration of the isolation; and the details of any post–incident review. The notification was usually followed up by a visit from a Mental Health Act Commissioner who completed a structured questionnaire comprising a document check, and interviews with staff. The patient was interviewed if he or she was willing and able to take part. As some patients were isolated on a number of occasions during the reporting period, not every notification was followed by a visit.

4.251 We were notified of 74 isolation episodes lasting more than 48 hours in the acute sector, and of 156 such episodes in the medium or high secure sector (figure 92). It seems likely that some episodes will have gone unreported to us during the exercise.

Quantity of Notifications	Acute	MSU / HSH
Number of incidents reported	74	156
Number of patients involved in incidents	59	121
Number of patients with multiple incidents	6[361]	25
Number of facilities reporting incidents	27	24
Number of facilities reporting multiple incidents	25	17
Number of Independent Hospitals reporting incidents	2	11

Fig 92: incidence of isolation over 48 hours reported to MHAC over six months during 2004/05

4.252 It is evident that isolation episodes lasting over two days are relatively frequent events (figure 93). The results of our study indicate a monthly average of 12 such episodes in the acute sector, and 28 in the medium and high security sectors. We suspect that there was widespread under-reporting, perhaps especially in the acute sector, although we would expect the acute sector to use long-term seclusion more rarely, and for shorter periods, than facilities in higher security sectors (not least because patients requiring longer-term isolation in the acute sector may consequently be transferred into a higher level of secure care).

---

[361] 23 questionnaires were received from one acute hospital, which may significantly distort the perception of seclusion use in the acute sector.

4.253   In the acute sector, about one third of reported episodes lasting more than 48 hours in fact lasted over 10 days[362]. Taking an average figure from the absolute minimum number of days spent in isolation according to this data suggests that, on any given day in mental health services across England and Wales, at least five patients have been in conditions of seclusion or isolation for more than 48 hours. The actual figure is likely to be considerably higher.

Duration	Numbers	
	Acute	MSU / HSH
Less than 5 days	13	28
5 to 9 days	28	5
10 to 19 days	14	3
20 to 49 days	6	1
49 to 299 days	-	2
300 days plus	2	1
Ongoing	2	63
Unknown	9	52
Total	**74**	**155**

Fig 93: duration of isolation episodes reported

4.254   It is extremely significant that the patient was described as formally secluded in only nine of the 31 acute sector episodes and 52 of the 74 medium/high secure sector episodes described in the qualitative exercise. As discussed above, the process of secluding a patient brings with it a higher level of external scrutiny, observation and recording. By failing to define the episode as seclusion, the patient is deprived of this higher level of protection, which the Code of Practice defines as necessary.   Patients who are isolated in the High Security Hospitals are generally recognised as secluded, even when the isolation is ongoing or effectively permanent, although the guidance of the Code of Practice concerning the intensity and type of review of seclusion, etc, is rarely if ever followed for 'permanently' secluded patients in the High Security Hospitals (see paragraph 4.239 above).

Findings from MHAC interviews with patients and staff

4.255   Interview records were at least partially completed in relation to 38 patients in the acute sector and 74 in the medium or high security sector. However, as a number of patients were still very ill or distressed by their experience, a smaller number agreed to be interviewed: 18 patients from the acute sector and 48 medium/high secure patients answered at least some of the questions. As a consequence the analyses that follow do not pretend to statistical validity. Rather, we aim to give a flavour of the isolation experience and raise a set of policy questions for those managing or regulating services

---

[362]   The high number of 'ongoing' (which means only that the isolation had not stopped after a minimum of 48 hours, when the MHAC would have been notified) and 'unknown' returns in the medium and high security sectors precludes a comparative calculation.

4.256 The questions covered a wide range of the patients' experience before, during and after their period of isolation. Unsurprisingly staff and patients viewed this almost-shared reality very differently. As the same questions were asked of both patients and staff, the responses are set alongside each other for comparison.

Contributory Factors

4.257 An episode of disturbed behaviour has many causes, although ward-based analyses of events leading to seclusion or isolation may be likely to concentrate on the mental state of the individual involved to the exclusion of social, environmental and organisational factors that can all combine to trigger problem behaviour. We asked staff and patients to consider the relevance of various contributory factors in the seclusion episode. In acute services the patient's illness was almost always given by staff as a significant factor in an incident, and recognised as such by 80% of high and medium secure services staff. Patients were much less likely to attribute their mental state as a contributory factor in events leading to the seclusion incident. Although of course not all patients have insight into their condition and the way it may influence what they do, patients do complain that many aspects of their behaviour may be pathologised in the hospital environment, and one service user in a medium-secure unit recently told us that in his view

> 90% of violent incidents in a hospital setting are not related to mental illness, but are normal reactions to an abnormal situation. If you feel incarcerated against your will, humiliated, powerless, treated like a child, subject to arbitrary decision, voiceless and badly treated – especially if you come from a background where conflict is generally resolved through fights and self-esteem is built around being tough – then it is no surprise that violence occurs.

factor	acute hospital				medium/high secure hospital			
	staff		patient		staff		patient	
	yes	no	yes	no	yes	no	yes	no
Patient illness	30	1	8	10	52	13	20	14
Boredom and lack of stimulation	7	17	4	12	11	47	10	22
Too much stimulation, noise and disruption	13	14	2	13	18	38	13	20
Overcrowding	3	18	7	6	7	50	7	25
Antagonism, aggression and provocation by others	7	16	4	11	21	37	27	13
Influence of alcohol and substance abuse	6	18	3	12	2	55	3	28
Unsuitable patient mix	2	19	7	6	14	42	13	22
The rewarding of undesirable behaviour with attention	8	16	2	12	16	40	9	23
Insufficient staff	2	19	7	6	10	46	9	23
Change in medication	5	16	3	12	9	46	8	24

Fig 94: contributory factors in incidents leading to seclusion viewed by patients and staff

4.258 Almost half of all staff who expressed a view felt that an atmosphere of over-stimulation, noise and disruption contributed to the episode. This has significant implications for ward design and management. At one PICU, for example, patients had no access to their rooms all day and no other opportunity to withdraw from the noise of a very busy ward. Staff reported that patients frequently asked to go into the seclusion room in order to get some peace and quiet. This should be seen in the context of our past recommendation and comments that

> patients should have access to quiet space and opportunity to be alone without seclusion procedures being instigated, as there should be no need for them to be locked into or in any way 'confined' in a room. In our Sixth Biennial Report we reported the policy decision to terminate the need for 'self-seclusion' in high secure hospitals, as patients' rights to privacy and opportunity for time alone was to be respected, for instance by the installation of privacy locks on patients' rooms. The recognition of patients' right to privacy and time alone has been slow to spread across all psychiatric services.[363]

4.259 Alongside reports of over-stimulation through irritant noise or the disruptive behaviour of others, a considerable proportion of service users and staff recognised boredom and lack of stimulation as a contributory factor to incidents leading to seclusion.

4.260 The patient profile describes a very troubled group (figure 95). With a history of treatment resistance and verbal and physical violence to people and property, most were on routine medication, but few appeared to be on any other form of formal treatment. Only nine of the 31 acute patients took part in any off-ward activities, and only five were receiving any form of formal psychotherapy.

Previous history of the patient	acute hospital		medium / high secure hospital	
	staff	patient	staff	patient
Self harm	13	12	33	28
Prolonged verbal abuse	22	8	46	18
Physical violence to others	25	4	64	3
Attempted escape/absconding	15	15	8	44
Treatment resistance	23	8	34	24
Damage to property	19	9	35	27
Sexually inappropriate behaviour	6	19	26	27
On routine prescribed medication	25	6	68	2
Consenting to medication	7	18	26	35

Fig 95: previous clinical history of the isolated patient

---

[363] MHAC (2003) *Tenth Biennial Report: Placed Amongst Strangers.* Chapter 11.22

The issue of self harm

4.261 The Code of Practice states that 'seclusion should not be used ... where there is any risk of suicide or self-harm'[364]. Nevertheless, considerable numbers of staff reports acknowledged that the isolated patient was at risk of self-harm (figure 95). When the matter was discussed with the patients, eight of 21 acute sector patients and 15 of 35 medium or high security sector patients who responded to this question felt that the staff were worried that they might harm themselves.

4.262 A literal application of the Code's prohibition would have peculiar consequences, such as patients who have been secluded to prevent harm to others being released from seclusion on the grounds of having made gestures towards self-harm, irrespective of the fact that their risk to others remains unchanged and that seclusion had been properly used as a last resort. The prohibition on seclusion of persons at risk of self-harm perhaps needs to be more carefully worded in future editions of the Code. We recommend that the Code should read that 'seclusion should not be used where it will exacerbate the risk of suicide or as a method of controlling self-harming behaviour'.

4.263 In the meantime, evidence from this study and from our general experience suggests that the current restrictions on the use of seclusion where there is a risk of self harm are not tenable, and that service providers cannot and do not respect the Code's guidance in this area.

Recommendation 45: The Code of Practice guidance on secluding patients at risk of self-harm should be revised. Service providers who cannot avoid secluding patients at risk of self-harm should ensure that seclusion is not used where it will exacerbate the risk of suicide or as a method of controlling self-harming behaviour.

The purpose of isolation

4.264 The rationale for isolating the patient according to staff questionnaires is given at figure 96.

Rationale for isolation	acute hospital	medium / high secure hospital
To protect patient	2	16
To protect others	14	54
To calm patient / decrease arousal / reduce stimulus	3	10
To review treatment	1	2

Fig 96: rationale for isolation / seclusion episodes in MHAC study

---

[364] Mental Health Act Code of Practice, Chapter 19.16

4.265 Other reasons given for isolation in the medium and high secure sector included 'self-isolation'; 'to deal with sexually inappropriate behaviour and reduce incidents of restraint'; to 'minimise the risk of damage' and 'to prevent recurrence' (we are uncertain of what).

Learning from what happened

4.266 The analysis shows that acute sector hospital thinking about an episode of isolation almost entirely focused on the problems of the individual in the short-term. Acute sector staff answers to the question 'what changes were put in place to ensure that the episode will not be repeated?' were typically 'received medication, referred to Rampton for transfer' or 'high level of supervision and observation'. In the medium and high security sector there was more indication of seclusion triggering wider reviews of treatment plans, including reviews of medication levels but also referral to psychology services. A number of high/medium secure sector notifications referred to debriefings where the causes of seclusion were discussed with the patient resulting in changes to the management of the patient (such as improving access to quiet space or meaningful activity during the day, or to increase staff contact with the patient). Some of these reports indicated that patients had recognised triggers to their behaviour leading to seclusion (e.g. 'flashbacks'; 'saying goodbye to mum' after visits; 'abandonment') that allowed management strategies to be considered. One High Security Hospital patient was returned to prison after seclusion.

4.267 There was reported to be a debrief for the patient in 23 of the 31 acute sector episodes and in 29 of the 31 cases the matter was reported as having been discussed in the multi-disciplinary team. Fifty-three reports of debriefings involving the patient, and 63 reports of discussions in the multi-disciplinary team were recorded in the 74 detailed responses from the medium / high security sector. However, it was less clear how the patient's views were represented at these discussions. On one occasion a solicitor was invited, but advocacy services were not mentioned by anyone in the acute sector. The most common response in the acute sector was that the key worker said that they represented the patient's views at the meeting, and in the medium and high secure sector nurses similarly reported 'representing' the patients views in some examples. Indeed, in another context, a nurse recently reported to a Commissioner 'we nurses feel we are the patients' advocates'. Such a view appears naïve and denies the power differential between staff and detained patients.

Care plans

4.268 An event as significant as the isolation of a patient should have a significant effect on the care planning process. Nevertheless, an examination of the care-plans of patients showed little evidence of strategic thinking or action (figure 97). When staff were asked what links there were between the episode and the patient's care plan, a considerable number thought that there was none. Major reviews of treatment were rare.

Effect of incident on care plan	acute hospital	medium / high secure hospital
wrote new care plan	2	8
adjusted medication	2	12
specific care plan whilst isolated	4	4
transferred to another ward / unit	1	9

Fig 97: recorded effects on care-plans incidents leading to isolation

4.269 Patients were asked what they needed to achieve in order for the isolation to stop. For those patients in the acute sector who had a sense of what was required of them, the typical answer was 'I have to stop hitting people'. Patient involvement in their care-planning was reported patchily (figure 98). We found risk-assessments a majority of cases (29 of the 31 cases in the acute sector and 66 of 74 in the medium/high security sector), most of which showed multi-disciplinary input, but only two of which were signed by the patient.

Patient involvement with care-plan	acute hospital	medium / high secure hospital
Agreed with care plan	7	35
Disagreed with care plan	6	11
Denies knowledge of a care plan	9	16

Fig 98: patient involvement in their care-planning

Facilities

4.270 We found the following with regard to seclusion or isolation facilities:

- *Smoking* - Staff reports indicated that in only one case was there no facility for the isolated patient to smoke. Most staff reported that the patient could smoke as often as s/he wished, with a minority reporting limitations on smoking (i.e. the patient being allowed three or four smoking opportunities per day). Only one patient (in the acute sector) complained that the access was inadequate.

- *En-suite toilet* - In 9 of the 30 acute sector staff reports, and 30 of the 74 medium or high sector reports, it was acknowledged that patients did not have *en-suite* toilet facilities. For some patients, this meant that had to be a staff-intensive escort arrangement to enable the patient safely to use the ward toilet. More worryingly the Commission has been informed of a number of sites where cardboard urine bottles or bedpans are used all or part of the time (see paragraph 4.248 above)

- *Washing facilities* - In nine of the 30 episodes investigated in the acute sector, and 41 of the 74 episodes in the medium or high sectors, patients did not have *en-suite* washing facilities. However, patients generally reported that they had adequate access to washing facilities.

Activity

4.271   Insofar as seclusion or isolation should be used only for the shortest possible time to control dangerous behaviour, we would not expect patients reporting extended periods of boredom or deprivation of constructive activity. However, Commissioners frequently hear complaints from patients who have been secluded that one problem with seclusion is a lack of ways to pass the time.

4.272   When asked what there was for them to do in seclusion, more than two-thirds of patients who responded indicated 'nothing or sleep'[365]. One patient reported, 'I get bored. The main problem is it is difficult to sleep at night if I have slept during day'.

4.273   The activities mentioned by the remaining third of patients included reading, drawing, playing games, listening to music, chatting and smoking. A small number of patients in high secure units indicated that they were allowed to do whatever they wanted in seclusion, where they had access to personal possessions, and others indicated that they had access to activities 'outside of the seclusion room' whilst still formally secluded. These cases would seem to be indicative of the different use of seclusion as a long-term nursing strategy for some patients in high secure care.

4.274   In 25 of the 31 acute sector episodes, and 46 of the 74 high or medium secure episodes, staff reported that patients had access to music or reading materials or another occupation. Some patients reported being able to listen to the 'hospital radio' and have access to papers, books or magazines: other responses appeared to indicate (as we would expect in some cases) that patients had been too disturbed to be allowed access to even basic diversions such as papers or magazines.

Staff Contact

4.275   Staff reported in 29 of 33 acute sector episodes of isolation they were close enough to talk with the patient at all times. Patient reports confirmed this availability. In the medium and high security sector, 64 of 74 reports from staff indicated that they could talk with the patient at all times, but only 37 patients told us that they thought this was the case[366].

Clothing

4.276   All the patients interviewed in the acute sector were in their own clothes during seclusion. According to staff interviewed in the medium or high secure sector, there were ten episodes of seclusion where special or protective clothing was used, although one patient told us that special clothing had been used in an additional case where this had not been mentioned by staff.

---

[365] This accounted for six out of eight responses from the acute sector and eleven out of sixteen in the medium and high secure sector.

[366] This discrepancy in findings cannot be simplified to state that 27 patients specifically disagreed with staff perceptions, as patients were not told what staff had reported (and vice-versa), and some patients declined to comment or commented ambiguously in response to this question.

Patients' views on the management of the incident leading to seclusion / isolation.

4.277   We asked patients and staff to evaluate how well the isolation process was managed. Staff consistently evaluated their practice as good with only one of the respondents saying that there were 'a lot of lessons to be learned for both staff and other agencies'.

4.278   A limited number of answers were given by patients (figure 99), many of whom found the exercise difficult:

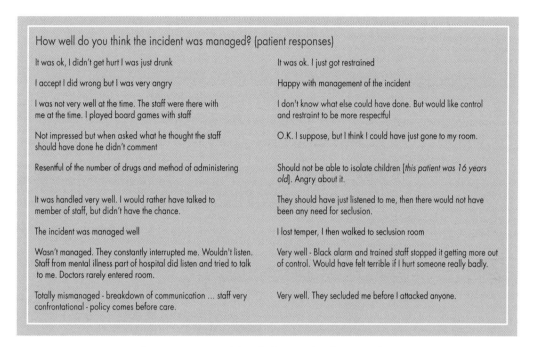

Fig 99: patient views on the management of their behaviour leading to seclusion

Recommendation 46: MHAC findings (discussed at paragraphs 2.49-78) on seclusion practice should inform reviews of facilities and practices by service managers.

(see recommendation 44 above)

Deaths of detained patients

4.279   The Commission asks to be notified of any death of a patient who is detained under the 1983 Act. The primary purpose of such notification is to ensure that we take appropriate monitoring action in response to individual cases: we will often attend inquests, for example, either to observe or as a 'properly interested person'. In February 2001 we published a report summarising data obtained from notifications between the years 1997 to 2000[367]. In the following chapter we present similar information taken from notifications received from the 1 January 2000 to the 31 December 2004.

---

[367] MHAC (2001) *Deaths of Detained Patients in England and Wales. A report by the Mental Health Act Commission on Information Collected from 1 February 1997 to 31 January 2000.* Nottingham, MHAC, Feb 2001.

Total deaths recorded 2000 – 2004

4.280 Over the four year period 2000 – 2004, we were notified of 1,672 deaths of detained patients. More than three-quarters of these (1,277) were ascribed to natural causes[368]. Of deaths due to unnatural causes, 16% (261) were determined to be suicide at inquest, with the remainder being largely ascribed to accidental death or misadventure.

Gender

4.281 At figure 100 below we show the gender split between natural and unnatural deaths for each year collected. The gender split for all natural deaths is probably not significant: in this study 52% of natural deaths were of male patients; our 1997 study found that for the previous three years male patients accounted for 46% of natural deaths. However, male patients are clearly more likely to die unnatural deaths than female patients: the data set out below shows that 63% of unnatural deaths were of male patients, and our 1997 study found this proportion to be 72%.

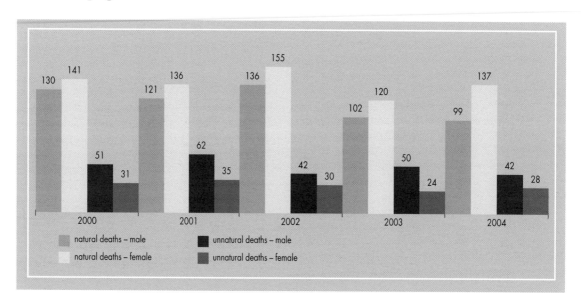

Fig 100: deaths of detained patients recorded by the MHAC, 2000-2004; gender and natural / unnatural causes

Age

4.282 At figure 101 we show the ages of detained patients at the time of death by natural and unnatural causes. Whilst most patients dying of natural causes are, as we would expect, in the older age ranges, two-thirds of patients whose deaths are by unnatural causes are aged between 26 and 55. In our 2001 study, we found a median age of 34 for all detained patients whose deaths subsequently received a suicide or open inquest verdict and suggested that this showed that younger people were most at risk from this form of death[369].

---

[368] Deaths are categorised administratively into 'natural' and 'unnatural' causes within the MHAC secretariat, although all 'natural' death classifications are reviewed by a clinician to consider whether there are aspects of care (such as levels of prescribed medication) that may undermine the validity of such categorisation.

[369] MHAC (2001) *supra*, para 125

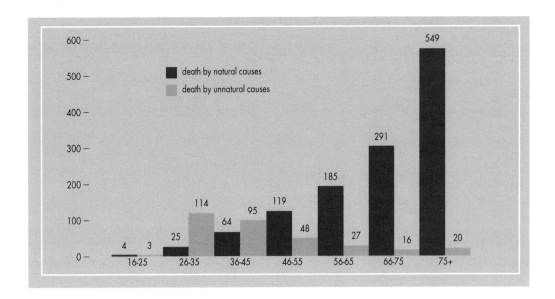

Fig 101: deaths of detained patients recorded by the MHAC, 2000-2004; age and natural / unnatural causes

Ethnicity

4.283 In our Seventh Biennial Report (1997) we called for rationalisation and reinforcing of ethnic monitoring across all mental health services. We are pleased to note progress in this reporting period, and especially the introduction of ethnic categories for NHS data collection that match census data. Because of the change in categories, we have set out data on ethnicity in a split table at figure 102 below. The data appears to show a higher proportion of Black and minority ethnic patients in the 'unnatural death' category. This can be accounted for, in part at least, as a reflection of the relative ages of the ethnic populations in England and Wales. The Black and minority ethnic population is proportionately younger than the white population, and it is younger patients who are most at risk of suicide or other unnatural death, with mainly older people dying of natural causes whilst detained under the Act.

Ethnic category	Total no. natural deaths	Total % natural deaths	Total no. unnatural deaths	Total % nnatural deaths
Data collected under pre-2003 categories				
White	877	89.8	256	83.1
Black - Caribbean	20	2.0	15	4.9
Black - African	6	0.6	7	2.3
Black - Other	6	0.6	5	1.6
Indian	11	1.1	3	1.0
Pakistani	2	0.2	1	0.3
Bangladeshi	.	.	1	0.3
Chinese	1	0.1	2	0.6
Other	30	3.1	11	3.6
Not Stated	24	2.5	7	2.3
Total	**977**		**308**	

Table A

Ethnic category	Total no. natural deaths	Total % natural deaths	Total no. unnatural deaths	Total % nnatural deaths
Data collected under post-2003 categories				
British (White)	229	76.3	50	57.5
Irish (White)	6	2.0	1	1.1
Any Other White Background (White)	33	11.0	15	17.2
White & Black Caribbean (Mixed)	1	0.3	.	.
White & Black African (Mixed)	1	0.3	.	.
White & Asian (Mixed)	1	0.3	.	.
Any Other Mixed Background (Mixed)	.	.	.	.
Indian (Asian or Asian British)	3	1.0	2	2.3
Pakistani (Asian or Asian British)	1	0.3	2	2.3
Bangladeshi (Asian or Asian British)	.	.	1	1.1
Any Other Asian Background (Asian or Asian British)	2	0.7	1	1.1
Caribbean (Black or Black British)	1	0.3	.	.
African (Black or Black British)	1	0.3	2	2.3
Any other Black Background	.	.	1	1.1
Chinese (Other Ethnic Groups)	.	.	0	.
Any Other Ethnic Group	2	0.7	1	1.1
Not Stated	9	3.0	10	11.5
Any other White Background (Wales)	10	3.3	1	1.1
Total	**300**		**87**	

Table B

Fig 102: deaths of detained patients recorded by the MHAC, 2000-2004; ethnicity

Note: table A shows data collected up to the change in ethnic categorisation in 2003, with data collected under the second category shown in table B.

Deaths by natural causes

Time of death after admission

4.284 In a 1995 study of MHAC data on deaths of detained patients[370], it was suggested that three main groups of detained patients die of natural causes whilst still under the powers of the Act:

- Long-term patients who have grown old and become physically ill whilst in hospital;

- People who die fairly soon after admission under the Act (probably related to acute delirium or physical disorder that had been an associated cause of their admission); and

- An intermediate group of patients who die from incidental physical disorder or organic psychosis.

4.285 Our recent data continues to provide general support this finding. Around 40% of deaths by natural causes occur within the first four weeks of admission, and 34% after ten weeks have passed since admission (figure 103).

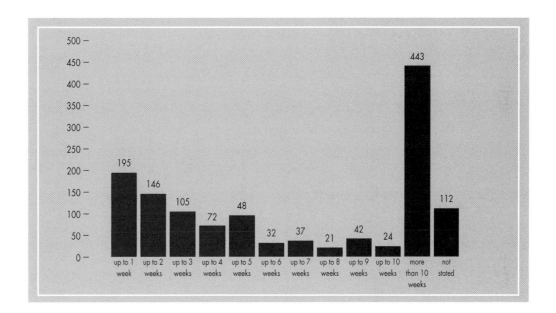

Fig 103: deaths by natural causes - time between admission and death

Age at time of death

4.286 As might be expected, the majority of deaths by natural causes are of patients from the older age groups (figure 104). The table overleaf shows more detailed breakdown of age ranges by year.

---

[370] Bannerjee S, Bingley W, Murphy E (1995) *Deaths of detained patients – a review of reports to the Mental Health Act Commission.* London, the Mental Health Foundation.

	16-25	26-35	36-45	46-55	56-65	66-75	75+	not stated
2000	0	2	18	19	32	63	135	2
2001	0	5	13	31	39	58	104	7
2002	2	6	13	26	44	55	132	13
2003	0	5	8	26	35	54	82	12
2004	2	7	12	17	35	61	96	6
Total	4	25	64	119	185	291	549	40
(Total %)	-	(2%)	(5%)	(9%)	(14%)	(23%)	(43%)	(31%)

Fig 104: deaths by natural causes – age at time of death

Section at time of death

4.287 More than 90% of the patients died whilst detained under ss.2 or 3 of the 1983 Act (figure 105). Over 5% were detained under s.37 hospital orders, with or without restrictions. In our 2001 study we found a similarly small proportion (3.6%) subject to s.37 hospital orders; this is significantly less than the 20% of such patients found in the 1995 study. This may indicate that patients are less likely now than a decade ago to continue to be detained under hospital orders when age or ill-health makes them infirm (we discuss the rise in conditional discharges of patients at Chapter 5.135 below).

	2000	2001	2002	2003	2004	Total	Total %
2	89	69	91	70	73	392	30.7
3	157	160	172	134	138	761	59.6
4	1	0	2	0	0	3	0.2
5/2	5	2	0	0	2	9	0.7
35	0	0	0	0	1	1	0.1
37	2	4	2	3	4	15	1.2
37/41	13	12	15	8	10	58	4.5
47, 47/49	1	3	2	1	2	9	0.7
48/49	0	0	0	2	1	3	0.2
CPIA	0	0	1	1	2	4	0.3
Not stated / other	3	7	5	3	3	21	1.6
Total	**271**	**257**	**291**	**222**	**236**	**1277**	

Fig 105: natural deaths - section of Mental Health Act at time of death

Place of death

4.288 Forty-eight percent of all these deaths occurred on a psychiatric ward, with 43% occurring in a medical or surgical unit. Six percent took place in the hospital grounds[371], and less than 2% at the patient's home or in another household. Although the number of patients dying in a domestic environment is very low, this is perhaps to be expected: it is perhaps likely that any patient who returns home in the terminal stage of an illness will be discharged from detention and not show in our statistics.

Cause of death

4.289 The most common causes of death are set out at figure 106 below, alongside findings from previous studies of MHAC data. We discuss relations between physical morbidity and mental disorder at paragraph 4.87 *et seq* above.

Cause of Death	2000- 2004 %	1997-2000[372] %	1992-1994[373] %
Pneumonia / respiratory	34 %	38 %	33 %
Cardiac	31 %	27 %	25 %
Pulmonary embolus	7 %	9 %	15 %
Malignancy	7 %	5 %	5 %
Cerebrovascular accident	4 %	6 %	5 %
Gastrointestinal haemorrhage	4 %	1 %	5 %

Fig 106: natural deaths – most common causes of death

Deaths by unnatural causes

Cause of death

4.290 The most common recorded form of unnatural death for detained patients is by hanging. We show the causes of death, where known, at figure 107 overleaf. A comparison with research on methods of unnatural death in prisons does not show any essentially dissimilar patterns, when the different circumstances of patients and prisoners are taken into account. Detained patients may be held in a wide range of facilities with a number of opportunities to leave custody; prisoners are denied these opportunities but probably have better means at hand for suicide (more than 90% of prison suicides between 1999-2000 were hanging or self-strangulation, with around half of these involving a ligature of bedclothes attached to window bars[374]).

---

[371] We urge caution over assuming that this category has been universally interpreted as being restricted to the space outside of buildings on the NHS estate. Some hospitals may have interpreted this to mean any place within the NHS estate that is not the psychiatric ward where the patient resided.

[372] Data from MHAC (2001) *supra.*

[373] Data from Bannerjee S, Bingley W, Murphy E (1995) *supra.*

[374] Shaw J, Baker D, Hunt IM, Moloney A, Appleby L 'Suicide by Prisoners' *British Journal of Psychiatry* (2004) 184;263-67.

	2000	2001	2002	2003	2004	Total	Total %
Hanging	22	25	17	24	18	106	26.8
Jumped before train	9	8	5	9	1	32	8.1
Jumped off tall building	7	9	4	4	5	29	7.3
Unsure suicide/accident	6	2	2	6	5	21	5.3
Self poisoning by drug overdose	6	4	6	3	1	20	5.1
Self suffocation	7	3	3	.	4	17	4.3
Drowning	2	6	2	1	1	12	3.0
Accidental	7	1	1	.	.	9	2.3
Jumped before vehicle	1	3	2	1	.	7	1.8
Fire	2	.	2	1	2	7	1.8
Self strangulation	1	2	1	1	1	6	1.5
Iatrogenic	1	.	.	2	1	4	1.0
Death caused by another person	2	.	1	.	1	4	1.0
Hosepipe to car exhaust	0	2	.	.	1	3	0.8
Not known / not stated	9	32	26	22	29	118	29.9
Total	**82**	**97**	**72**	**74**	**70**	**395**	

Fig 107: all unnatural deaths: cause of death

Diagnosis at time of death

4.291 At least 40% of these patients had a diagnosis that involved psychotic illness. It is not necessarily the case, however, that positive symptoms of psychosis would have been evident at the point of death, and we urge caution over assuming any causative link between suicidal ideation and diagnosis as shown at figure 108 below (see also paragraph 4.303 below). There is also likely to be extensive co-morbidity between the primary diagnoses shown in this table and other forms of mental disorder experienced by the patients who died (see Chapter 1.63 above).

Diagnosis	number	%
Schizophrenia & related disorders	139	35.2
Depression & related disorders	43	10.9
Personality disorder	31	7.8
Psychotic episode	20	5.1
Bipolar disorders	19	4.8
Other	31	7.8
Not stated	112	28.4
Total	**395**	

Fig 108: all unnatural deaths - diagnosis

Place of death and leave status

4.292 Over a third of all deaths of unnatural causes involved patients who were on leave (73 patients; 18% of all unnatural deaths) or absent without leave (70 patients; also 18% of the total unnatural deaths). A further quarter occurred either in the hospital grounds (6%) or in another health unit (19%), the latter probably after having being taken there for medical treatment following the incident which led to death (figure 109).

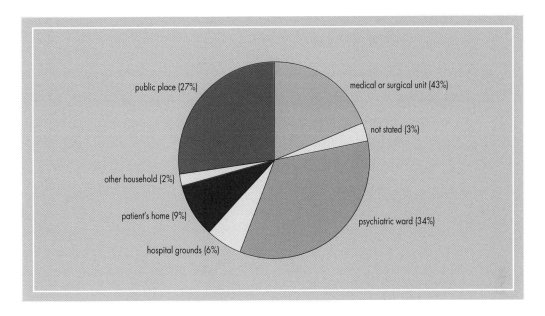

Fig 109: all unnatural deaths – place of death

4.293 The following example of our concerns following the drug-related death of a patient in a Psychiatric Intensive Care Unit shows the need for assessments of patients' physical state and adequate CPR resuscitation training for psychiatric nursing staff.

In June 2003, *X*, a young male with hypomania and a history of drug and alcohol abuse, died in a psychiatric intensive care unit (PICU) whilst under five-minute observations and subject to section 5(2) of the Act. The cause of death was methadone and olanzapine toxicity, with the terminal event the inhalation of vomit due to the failure of the gag reflex and respiratory depression due to prescribed medication.

X had become an informal patient shortly after release from prison. On the day before his admission the Drugs Dependency Service had issued an unusually high daily prescription of methadone: upon admission to hospital he was also prescribed antipsychotic, antimuscarinic and hypnotic medication. He had been detained under a 5(2) when he asked to leave the ward.

The last recorded observation of *X* was made through a window into his room, where he was in bed and was recorded as 'scratching his leg'. The next observation was delayed, but within the next ten minutes *X* was observed by the staff nurse on duty to be blue and not breathing. The staff nurse examined *X* and checked his pulse, at which point the ward manager arrived in the room and was told that *X* was dead and that resuscitation was not appropriate. The

Senior House Officer (SHO) arrived within ten minutes of being bleeped and pronounced X to be dead.

We attended the inquest with properly interested person status, and highlighted, *inter alia*, our concerns that:

- No physical examination (not even a urine test) took place during X's admission to hospital;

- X was prescribed an unusual mix of anti-psychotic drugs;

- The level of observations and record keeping was inadequate in the circumstances; and

- Cardio-Pulmonary Resuscitation was not administered to the patient despite him being observed making voluntary movements ten minutes before nursing staff noted that he had stopped breathing. We understand that staff were CPR trained but may not have had refresher training in the last year prior to the death. The SHO did not appear to have been told of the patient's recent signs of life and purposeful movement, but was given to understand that he had died in his sleep.

The jury returned a narrative verdict in September 2005, describing the methadone prescription as inappropriate without a full medical examination taking place and not in accordance with set guidelines. The jury also concluded that the level of observations given his unknown physical state and the use of sedation was also inadequate.

Recommendation 47: Adequate CPR training and refresher training should be provided to psychiatric nursing staff.

Fig 110: example of a drug-related death in a PICU, 2003

Suicide

4.294   Those unnatural deaths recorded as suicide at inquest are shown at figure 111 below.

4.295   Suicide rates in the general population have shown a downward trend since the early 1980s. According to the National Confidential Inquiry into suicide and homicide by people with mental illness, the total numbers of inpatient suicides in England (i.e. including informal patients) in the years shown above was 195 in 2000, 180 in 2001, and 156 in 2002 (data was unavailable for 2003 and 2004 at the time of our going to press)[377].

4.296   Hanging remains the predominant method of suicide recorded in our data (figure 112). If both hanging and self-strangulation are considered together (see paragraph 4.308 *et seq* below on why they should be so considered), these account for 43% of all suicides of detained patients.

---

[377] National Institute for Mental Health in England *National Suicide Prevention strategy for England Annual Report on Progress 2004*, p.5. See also Department of Health (2004) *The National Service Framework for Mental Health – Five Years On*, p.34-5

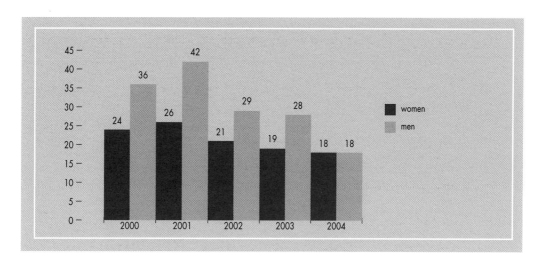

Fig 111: unnatural deaths recorded as suicide at inquest, 2000- 2004

	2000	2001	2002	2003	2004[378]	Total	Total %
Hanging	22	25	17	24	18	106	40.6
(self-strangulation)	(1)	(2)	(1)	(1)	(1)	(6)	(2.3)
Jumped before train	9	8	5	9	1	32	12.3
Jumped off tall building	7	9	4	4	5	29	11.1
Self poisoning by drug overdose	6	4	6	3	1	20	7.7
Self suffocation	7	3	3	0	4	17	6.5
Drowning	2	6	2	1	1	12	4.6
Fire	2	0	2	1	2	7	2.7
Jumped before vehicle	1	3	2	1	0	7	2.7
Hosepipe to car exhaust	0	2	0	0	1	3	1.1
Method unclear/other	3	6	8	3	2	22	8.4
Total	**60**	**68**	**50**	**47**	**36**	**261**	

Fig 112: Suicide – cause of death

4.297 The North-West Wales comparison of contemporary service utilisation with that of a century ago[379], which we discussed at Chapter 2.14 above, scrutinised 2,892 asylum records between 1875 and 1915, and found only three inpatient suicides and two suicides of patients soon after discharge. A comparison with suicide rates shown by the 1999 *National Confidential Inquiry into Suicide and Homicide by People with Mental Illness* suggested that by the standards of the late 1990s a similar volume of admissions would yield 10 inpatient suicides and 240 suicides in the year following discharge. The old asylum system may

---

[378] See n.375 above.

[379] Healy, D., Harris, M., Michael, P., Cattell, D., Savage, M., Chalasani, P. & Hirst, D (2005) 'Service Utilisation in 1896 and 1996: morbidity and mortality data from North Wales'. *History of Psychiatry* 16(1) 27-41

therefore be argued to have been better at preventing suicide than modern mental health practice; but if so it was better at a considerable cost, characterised by considerably longer first admissions in much more regimented conditions. Mental health services today must balance more demanding legal constraints and concerns for personal autonomy against the requirements of protective care.

Place of death

4.298 At least a third of all suicides of detained patients take place on the hospital ward (figure 113); the true proportion could be up to half of all suicides, given that deaths recorded as taking place in medical or surgical units could have been the result of suicide attempts on psychiatric wards. Only 41% of patients committing suicide are acknowledged to be on leave or AWOL at the time, and so 59% should physically have been somewhere within the hospital at the time of their suicide.

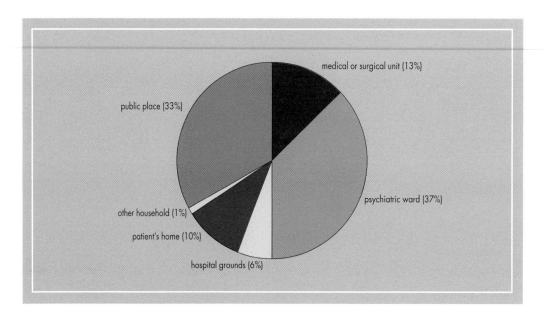

Fig 113: suicide – place of death

4.299 The following practice example (figure 114) highlights the particular danger of allowing rooms or spaces within the ward to become unused and unmonitored spaces.

Practice example

In June 2003 the body of a patient who had cut his throat with a razor lay undiscovered in a shower-room of a Yorkshire psychiatric unit for four days. It was assumed that the patient, who had been brought into hospital as a result of a suicide attempt, had left the hospital when he went missing. Suspicions were not aroused by the locked shower-room door as the shower was often out of order. The body was discovered when another patient complained of a bad smell. The coroner said that the shower-room appeared to be the ideal location for anyone contemplating self-harm because there was little chance of being disturbed.

Recommendation 48: Ward managers should be careful not to allow rooms or areas within the ward, such as store-rooms or disused facilities, to provide undisturbed or unchecked spaces that could pose a risk to vulnerable patients. Private and quiet spaces on the ward should be regularly monitored by staff.

Fig 114: patient suicide – case study 1

4.300   Over the last five years, nearly one in five suicides of detained patients took place whilst the patient concerned was under at least 15-minute observations (figure 115). If patients who are not physically on the ward (whether they are AWOL or on authorised leave) are discounted, this proportion rises to nearly one in three. The figures do appear to show, however, that suicides of patients who are under observation are becoming rarer.

	2000	2001	2002	2003	2004	Total	Total %
Continuous	8	4	4	1	-	17	6.5
Up to 15 mins	5	12	3	8	5	33	12.6
Other / not stated	47	52	43	38	31	211	80.9
Total	**60**	**68**	**50**	**47**	**36**	**261**	**100**

Fig 115: suicide – observation level at time of death

	2000	2001	2002	2003	2004	Total	Total %
On leave (s.17)	15	11	12	9	4	51	19.5
AWOL (s.18)	21	17	10	5	3	56	21.5
Other	24	40	28	33	29	154	59.0
Total	**60**	**68**	**50**	**47**	**36**	**261**	**100**

Fig 116: suicide – leave status at time of death

Age at time of death and gender

4.301   It is notable that suicides are predominant in the younger adult age groups (figure 117). In 2001 we found that almost 80% were aged under 45 years: in this study the proportion is 76%.

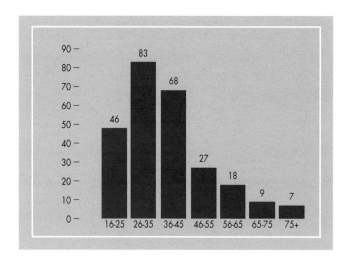

Fig 117: suicide - age at time of death

4.302   Of all suicides, 41% were women: this is a considerably larger proportion than we found in 2001 (24%) or 1995 (32%).

Diagnosis at time of death

4.303   The primary diagnoses of detained patients who committed suicide are shown at figure 118 below. In showing this data we do not assume a causative link between the suicidal ideation and positive symptoms of the mental disorders diagnosed in each case. It is probably the case that, even amongst those patients diagnosed with psychotic disorders who committed suicide, few did so as a direct consequence of delusory beliefs or distortions of perception or cognition[381]. Many will have killed themselves during remission of their illness, and indeed the initial period of remission in such illnesses is considered by many clinicians as a time of increased risk of suicide. It is notable that a significant proportion (10% in this study, 11% in our 2001 study[382]) of such suicides are by patients with a primary diagnosis of personality disorder.

---

[381]   See, for example, Jamison K R (2000) *Night Falls Fast: Understanding Suicide.* London; Picador, pages 81-97, 255 *et seq.* Whilst many suicides may be liked to mental disorders, it is not necessarily the case that suicides result from symptoms of incoherent or delusional thinking consequent upon mental disorder (although a patient's feelings of shame, despair, worthlessness or guilt over living with a mental disorder may have arguably delusional origins in, or be sharpened in their effect by, the symptomology of mental disorder). Virginia Woolf famously wrote in her suicide note, in which she sought to reassure her husband that he was not to blame for her despair, that insofar as there was a cause, 'it is this madness', although she was at the time anticipating rather than suffering the full effects of her bipolar disorder (see Jamison p.84-5).

[382]   MHAC (2001) *supra,* chart 19

Diagnosis	number	%
Schizophrenia & related disorders	80	30.7
Depression & related disorders	33	12.6
Psychotic episode	30	11.5
Personality disorder	25	9.6
Bipolar disorders	12	4.6
Other	14	5.4
Not stated	67	25.7
Total	**261**	

Fig 118: suicide – diagnosis at time of death

Deaths by Hanging

4.304 Patients who kill themselves within psychiatric units frequently use hanging as their method. There are proportionally fewer patients who are on leave or absent without leave in this category than for the general category of suicides (figure 119 below) and over 60% of deaths of detained patients by hanging take place on the psychiatric ward where the patient is detained (figure 120). Overall, somewhere between 70 and 80% of detained patient deaths by hanging take place on hospital premises[383]. The proportion of men to women who hanged themselves whilst detained under the Act over the four years was roughly 3:2[384].

	2000	2001	2002	2003	2004	Total	Total %
On leave (s.17)	4	1	6	3	2	16	15.1
AWOL (s.18)	2	2	1	1	1	7	6.6
Other	16	22	10	20	15	83	78.3
Total	**22**	**25**	**17**	**24**	**18**	**106**	**100**

Fig 119: hanging – leave status at time of death

[383] It is impossible to be accurate within this 10% margin as the data does not show what proportion of those patients who die in 'other medical or surgical units' were transferred there after the hanging attempt, and where such hanging attempts took place. In our 2001 report we found, including such 'other medical and surgical units as well as hospital grounds, that 78% of all hangings took place on hospital premises. See MHAC (2001) *supra*, para 86.

[384] Our previous report found the proportion for 1997-2000 to be 3:4. See MHAC (2001) *supra*, para 81.

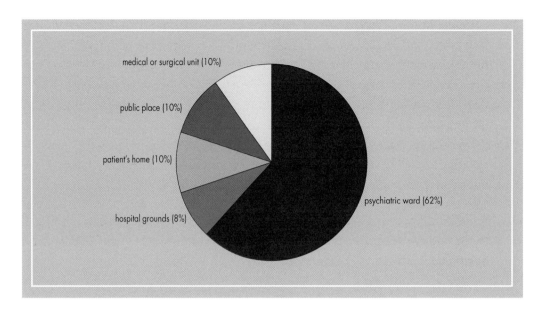

Fig 120: hanging – place of death

Reducing hanging risks in hospital environments

4.305   In March 2004, NHS Estates issued a safety warning notice to all NHS Trusts in England on the dangers posed by suspended ceilings in mental health units. A warning had been given on this subject by the authorities in Northern Ireland and Scotland in 2001, but communications sent from those authorities appears not to have been received by the English authorities. Tragically, in September 2003 an informal patient who was on observation as a suicide risk in an English psychiatric unit located a ligature point behind such a ceiling and used it to commit suicide. In response to the concerns of that patient's parents, NHS Estates issued a letter which stated that 'each individual body is responsible for carrying out its own risk assessment and deciding what action it needs to take in the light of that assessment to minimise and… eliminate risk. Each Trust has the responsibility for ensuring a safe environment'. Insofar as this response might be read to shift the burden of ensuring patient safety away from the Department of Health and its executive agencies, we consider this approach highly unsatisfactory. We were pleased to note the Minister of State's implied refutation of this approach in her response in a Parliamentary debate secured by the Member of Parliament for the patient and his family[385]. The Minister indicated that the protocols for NHS Estates were to be reviewed to ensure that such communication breakdown does not re-occur. The Minister also pointed to work being initiated by the National Patient Safety Agency (NPSA), which had been created in July 2001 'as part of [Government's] wider commitment to ensuring patient safety', and which was reported to have identified patient safety in acute mental health care settings as a priority area in its mental health programme. We strongly support the need for co-ordinated action over this issue, as we have found that too many units remain unsafe environments for vulnerable patients despite our repeated warnings in past years.

---

[385]   *Hansard*, 22 April 2004, Column 525-8, *Acute Mental Health Units.* Mr Oliver Heald MP secured the debate, and was answered in the House by the Minister of State Ms Rosie Winterton MP.

[386]   MHAC (2001) *supra*, paras 134–144.

4.306 Since the Minister's response to the House, NHS Estates has been abolished as part of the Department of Health's review of arm's length bodies, with some of its function returning to the Department itself. Whilst, as signatories to the concordat between inspection bodies that includes the Health and Safety Executive and the Healthcare Commission, we recognise that alternative structures can be put in place to monitor progress and disseminate information, it is important that any initial impetus to improving patient safety is not lost in the various re-organisations of the Department of Health and its executive or arm's-length agencies. It is vital that safety measures are taken uniformly and effectively across psychiatric units that detain patients on behalf of the State.

4.307 A significant proportion of patients hang themselves whilst under observation (figure 121). In the last two years no patient has managed to do so whilst officially under 'continuous' observation, although this is not unknown.

	2000	2001	2002	2003	2004	Total	Total %
Continuous	4	1	2	-	-	7	6.6
Up to 15 mins	3	9	1	8	3	24	22.6
Other / not stated	15	15	14	16	15	75	70.8
Total	**22**	**25**	**17**	**24**	**18**	**106**	**100**

Fig 121 hanging – observation level at time of death

4.308 In our 2001 report we hypothesised that many deaths by 'hanging' may not in fact involve suspension from a high point, with the resulting 'hangman's fracture' of a displaced second cervical vertebra caused by the full body-weight exerting a substantial force on the neck. Rather, we suggested that a number were likely to be caused by strangulation, where a ligature pulled around the neck (perhaps also using a load-bearing support, but not necessarily one placed high above floor-level) caused asphyxiation; cardiac inhibition leading to arrest; or failure of blood supply to the brain[386].

4.309 If our supposition is correct (and it would seem to be supported by the common types of ligature and support used in the deaths in our study, detailed at figure 122 overleaf), it is important that services do not concentrate exclusively on eradicating load-bearing supports that are above head-height, but also pay attention to the dangers of low pipework; heavy furniture (particularly where this has exposed 'legs' or other easily-exploited ligature points); door-handles and other low fixtures, etc. Particular attention should be paid to ensuring that rails and fixture supports for disabled people are of a suitable design to prevent them being used as ligature points.

---

[386] MHAC (2001) *supra*, paras 134 –144.

Most common type of ligature	Most common load bearing support
Belt	Window
Sheet	Door/Door Frame
Rope/Cord	Beam/Ceiling Frame
Dressing Gown Belt/Cord	Wardrobe
Electric Cable	Bed
Scarf	Bathroom Fixtures (shower/towel rail)
Shoe Laces	Tree

Fig 122: hanging – most common ligatures and load-bearing support

4.310 The case study below (figure 123) shows that care should be taken against assumptions that ligature points can be too high to pose a risk. We continue to draw attention to ligature points seen on our visits to hospitals.

4.311 The case study outlines a truly stark picture of care in a busy London acute unit. It gives us some reassurance that the events described are evident from an excellent internal inquiry report commissioned by the NHS Trust responsible for the ward, which appeared to us to have managed both an honest and objective account of failings in practice, without needlessly apportioning blame on staff who did their best in the circumstances, and also a sensible set of recommendations to influence future practice.

4.312 Unfortunately a number of the points arising from this death occur all too often amongst the deaths that we encounter. We particularly draw attention to the issues around observations (including staff training in and understanding of what constitutes 'observation'); staffing levels and the adequacy of training and experience; and contact with and support to the family.

Case study of a patient suicide

D was a young male patient diagnosed with schizophrenia who was known to services. He was an asylum-seeker. He had been discharged from his previous two admissions without any fixed abode; with no GP registration; and with sufficient medication for only 28 days. He lost contact with psychiatric services. His final admission in May 2003 was a referral from the refugee and asylum team. He was floridly psychotic and had possibly aggravated his condition through cannabis use.

D was cared for on a busy acute admission ward where staffing levels and a large number of acutely unwell patients probably precluded much meaningful one-to-one work with clinical staff. He appealed to the MHRT but his hearing was postponed within 24 hours of the arranged date. D was noted to be upset about this, absconded and was brought back from his sister's house by police. His urine tested positive for cannabis. On his return he was put on enhanced observations.

On the day of his death, which was a Saturday, *D* was one of eight patients on a 22-bedded ward who were on 15-minute observations. The observation duties were divided during the night-shift between a nurse and a nursing assistant. For the seven hours before the night-shift commenced, no records of observations had been made for *D* or three other patients on the ward. After a shift changeover at 9pm, records of 15 minute observations were made by a nursing assistant, but the record for 9.45 was completed without sight of him, on the assumption that he was using the toilet. Shortly before 10.30 he was discovered suspended by his belt from a 14ft-high ceiling pipe in the bathroom. He had placed a linen-skip onto a free-standing rubbish bin to climb access the pipe. The pipes had not been considered a risk in a ligature-assessment conducted by the hospital.

The duty doctor who was called was unable to find a pulse in *D*'s foot and pronounced him to be dead. No attempt was made to resuscitate. Staff could not reach the ligature point, and were unsure as to whether they should take down the body, and so this was not done until the arrival of the undertakers, to whom the body was signed over. There was later some dispute over what possessions were with the body at this time. Staff who dealt with the body were not relieved from their shift that night. The duty manager requested that police inform *D*'s mother, giving some contact details. No-one contacted *D*'s mother, who learnt of his death upon being telephoned by the coroner on the following Monday morning.

(see paragraphs 4.310 et seq above)

Fig 123: patient suicide – case study 2

Recommendation 49: Government should ensure co-ordinated action across all mental health sectors to reduce and remove environmental hazards such as ligature points in inpatient environments.

5

Mental health legislation and the criminal justice system

5.1 Whilst the following sections of this report focus upon the mentally disordered as offenders, with a particular focus on serious offending, we preface our comments with a reminder that detention of convicted offenders accounts for only a fraction (perhaps 6%[1]) of uses of the Mental Health Act to admit people to hospital.

5.2 People with mental disorder are often themselves victims of crime. Research consistently finds that mentally disordered people suffer from violent and other major crimes at rates many times higher than the general population and that much of this crime goes unreported or unprosecuted[2].

5.3 Furthermore, although our focus is inevitably with the population of mentally disordered offenders who are detained under the 1983 Act in hospital (figure 124), this group is only a small subset of a much broader range of persons, the majority of whom are based in the community. It is arguable that the attention given to the smaller group of patients who are detained following contact with the criminal justice system distracts attention from this wider group, who are widely underserved by mainstream and forensic services[3].

---

[1] Department of Health (2005) *Inpatients formally detained in hospitals under the Mental Health Act 1983 and other legislation, NHS trusts, care trusts and primary care trusts and independent hospitals*: 2003-04, para 4.6

[2] Mentally ill people living in the community are more than twice as likely to be victims of violence as other members of the public (Littlechild, B & Fearns D (2005) *Mental Disorder and Criminal Justice. Policy, Provision & Practice*. Russell House Publishing Ltd). See also Mencap (1999) *Living in Fear*. For a resumé of U.S. research findings see Consensus Project (a U.S. initiative co-ordinated by the Council of State Governments) *Fact Sheet: Criminal Victimization of People with Mental Illness*; and Sorensen, D (2002) *The Invisible Victims* (www.consensusproject.org). A study published in Australia in 2005 found patients with schizophrenia spectrum disorders living in an outer metropolitan suburb of Melbourne were at increased risk of victimisation, both of violent and non-violent crime (Fitzgerald, P, Castella, A R de, Filia, S L, Benitez, J & Kulkarni, J 'Victimization of patients with schizophrenia and related disorders' *Australian and New Zealand Journal of Psychiatry* Vol 39, issue 3 p.169).

[3] Roskes, E 'Offenders with mental disorders: a call to action' *Psychiatric Services*, 50:12, December 1999; Vaughan, P J 'Mentally disordered offenders: everyone's responsibility'. *British Journal of Forensic Practice*, 3(4), December 2001, pp16-21.

	Number of times used in 2003	Resident population as at 31/12/03
Hospital Order, unrestricted[4]	559	n/a
Hospital Order, restricted[5]	196	1909
Transfers from prison[6]	721	663
Unfit to Plead[7]	39	180
Not Guilty by Reason of Insanity[8]	2	37
Hospital and Limitation Direction[9]	4	11

Fig 124: hospital-based supervision of mentally disordered offenders

Court diversion

5.4   The Department of Health's *Offender Mental Health Care Pathway*, a best practice template for dealing with mentally disordered offenders, was published in January 2005[10]. It aims to provide for the realisation of two aims:

- that no-one with acute severe mental illness should be in prison, and

- that prisons should be safe places for other people with mental health problems, with a particular focus on the creation of in-reach services and suicide prevention.

5.5   Nacro's Mental Health Unit, who annually survey court diversion schemes on behalf of the Home Office, have pointed out that the pathway:

is written on the premise that areas have a Criminal Justice Liaison Team with inputs from an Approved Social Worker (ASW), Registered Mental Nurse (RMN), psychiatrist, psychologist and learning disability specialist. In reality, Nacro has found that, thirteen years on from the Reed report[11], the national picture is far from that ideal. Many areas have no provision at all. Many others rely on one lone worker, most often a community psychiatric nurse (CPN). There is no advice in the document for those areas that do not have a Criminal Justice Liaison Team either on how to set one up or on what alternative

---

[4]   S.37 MHA 1983. Data source: Home Office *Statistics of Mentally Disordered Offenders* 2003, Bulletin 16/04, table 18 (provisional figure).

[5]   S.37/41 MHA 1983. Data source: Home Office Bulletin 16/04, tables 3 & 6.

[6]   Data source: Home Office Bulletin 16/04, tables 3 & 6.

[7]   Criminal Procedure (Insanity) Act 1964 s.4 as substituted by the Criminal Procedure (Insanity and Unfitness to Plead) Act 1991 s.2. Data source: Home Office Bulletin 16/04, tables 3 & 6.

[8]   Trial of Lunatics Act 1883 s.2 as amended by the Criminal Procedure (Insanity and Unfitness to Plead) Act 1991. Data source: Home Office Bulletin 16/04, tables 3 & 6.

[9]   MHA 1983 s.45A. Data source: Home Office Bulletin 16/04, tables 3 & 6.

[10]   Department of Health (2005) *Offender Mental Health Care Pathway.* January 2005.

[11]   The Reed Report (Department of Health & Home Office (1992) *Review of health and social services for mentally disordered offenders and those requiring similar services* recommended *inter alia* that 'there should be nationwide provision of properly resourced court assessment and diversion schemes'.

arrangements may be in place to effect a mental health assessment. Lack of, or poor quality, guidance in this area can all too often lead to serious failures in service provision.[12]

5.6   The key findings of Nacro's latest survey on court diversion schemes for mentally disordered offenders is given at figure 125 below. In Nacro's view,

> Court diversion has been a much-neglected area over the last few years when compared to the focus placed on other recent initiatives such as prison mental health in-reach and Crisis/Assertive Outreach teams.

5.7   We support the recommendations of the Nacro report, and in particular adopt and highlight the following two recommendations:

Recommendation 50:

- The Department of Health should effect an increase in the number of psychiatric beds available and not simply leave it to the discretion of NHS Trusts;

- Money should be ring-fenced for the creation and maintenance of court diversion/criminal justice liaison schemes and where possible joint funding between criminal justice and healthcare/social services should be encouraged, with the intention of creating robust multi-disciplinary teams. This funding should not be time limited[13].

Key findings of Nacro's survey of court diversion in 2004

- All schemes surveyed felt confident that the courts followed their recommendations to divert people to hospital, but some said courts were less likely to follow recommendations to treat in the community.

- 25% of schemes surveyed said they had seen a decrease in staffing levels in the last year. 30% of schemes cited staffing issues as a barrier to their scheme operating. Despite this, operational hours for most schemes had remained unchanged from the previous year. A third of schemes were operating with only one member of staff.

- 50% of schemes had no sessional input from either a psychiatrist or a psychologist and, unsurprisingly, 41% of schemes reported difficulties in obtaining psychiatric reports

- 72% of schemes cited lack of beds as a barrier to their scheme operating successfully.

- Almost a quarter of schemes felt that mentally disordered offenders were a low priority for agencies in their area.

---

[12]   Nacro (2005) *Findings of the 2004 survey of Court Diversion/Criminal Justice Mental Health Liaison Schemes for mentally disordered offenders in England and Wales.* Nacro, March 2005, p14. www.nacromentalhealth.org.uk

[13]   *ibid.*

- 34% of schemes said their area was using the police station as the sole 'place of safety' for s.136. Of these 40% had no jointly agreed policy on s.136.

- 78% of schemes collected statistics. 50% of schemes that were collecting statistics did not collect data on ethnicity and 42% did not collect data on gender.

- 36% of schemes did not have a policy on information sharing.

Fig 125: key findings of Nacro's court diversion survey[14]

The Criminal Procedure (Insanity) Acts

5.8 The Criminal Procedure (Insanity) Acts (CPIA) provide a form of diversion at the point of a Crown Court hearing for mentally disordered offenders. The CPIA provides a framework for such diversion where an offender is either found unfit to plead at trial or found to have lacked criminal responsibility for an offence. In this reporting period the CPIA has been partially revised through Government amendments made to the Domestic Violence, Crime and Victims Act 2004. We discuss these amendments, which came into force on the 31 March 2005, at paragraph 5.25 *et seq* below. A consequence of the choice of legislative vehicle for these amendments is that they were not widely debated amongst mental health professionals, and many professionals are unaware of the changes that have been made. We note below that the Scottish Law Commission's detailed consideration of parallel areas of law in Scotland has resulted in their recommendation for a more fundamental reform than the 2004 amendments achieve, and suggest that similar reconsideration of the law in England and Wales is appropriate.

Use of Criminal Procedure (Insanity) Acts over the lifetime of the Mental Health Act 1983

5.9 In our last report we pointed to the rising if still rare use of the Criminal Procedure (Insanity) Acts to admit restricted patients to hospital under formal powers. In 2003 the number dropped slightly (figure 126 below), although the numbers involved are too small (and, as discussed below, the data is too incomplete) to allow for meaningful generalisation.

5.10 The number of restricted patients resident in hospital subsequent to CPIA findings (figure 127) has continued its gradual increase. On the 31 December 2003, there were 217 such patients who were subject to restriction orders, 37 of whom had been found by a jury to be 'not guilty by reason of insanity', with the remaining 180 having been found unfit to plead[15].

---

[14] *ibid.*

[15] The *Count Me In* National Mental Health and Ethnicity Census 2005 identified only 131 resident patients detained subsequent to findings under the Criminal Procedures (Insanity) Act, although this total excludes all learning disability patients.

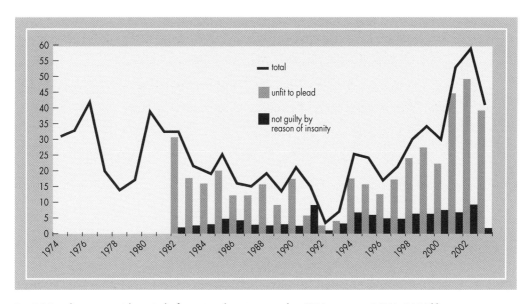

Fig 126: admissions to hospital of restricted patients under CPIA powers, 1974–2003[16]

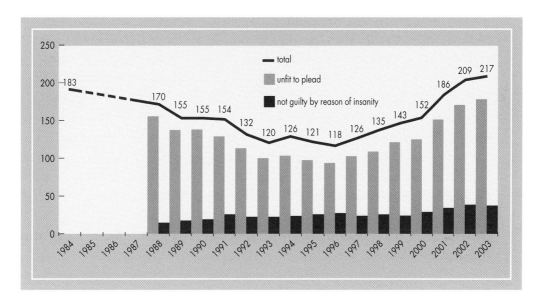

Fig 127: restricted inpatient population subsequent to CPIA disposals, 1984- 2003[17]

5.11 Home Office statistics provide only a partial indication of the extent of resident patient populations or court disposals under the CPIA, as only those CPIA disposals where the court imposes the equivalent of a restriction order are collated and analysed. After 1991, when the courts were enabled by a change in legislation to make alternative disposals (including the equivalent of an unrestricted hospital order), the overall use of the CPIA

---

[16]   Data from Home Office *Statistics of Mentally Disordered Offenders, England and Wales,* Bulletins from 1984 – 2003. A breakdown of data by categories of unfit to plead/ not guilty by reason of insanity is not available prior to 1982

[17]   Data as for fig 126. Data from 1985-87 inclusive (shown as dotted trendline) is estimated based upon the previous and subsequent years' data. Breakdown of CPIA categories not available prior to 1988.

increased and the courts adopted a wider range of disposals. The use of CPIA disposals has been researched by Professor R D Mackay and his colleagues at De Montfort University, although at the time of our writing published results from this research were only available up to 1996[18]. Over the five years 1992 to 1996, this research noted 35 unrestricted hospital orders subsequent to findings of unfitness to plead[19], and three unrestricted hospital orders subsequent to a finding of not guilty by reason of insanity[20]. The research findings are set out in tabular form at figure 128 below.

Disposal	unfit to plead		not guilty by reason of insanity	
	Number	%	Number	%
restricted hospital order without limit of time	48	43.7%	17	38.6%
restricted hospital order with limit of time	2	1.8%	1	2.3%
unrestricted hospital order	35	31.9%	3	6.8%
guardianship order	6	5.4%	-	-
supervision and treatment orders – 2 years	2	11.8%	18	40.9%
supervision and treatment orders – less than 2 years	4	1.8%	3	6.8%
absolute discharge	4	3.6%	2	4.5%
Total	**110**		**44**	

Fig 128: disposals under the Criminal Procedure (Insanity) Acts, 1992-1996[21]

5.12 Official statistics provide little corroboration of the full extent of the use of CPIA powers. Data published by the Department of Constitutional Affairs on Crown Court trials 'cracked'[22] due to the defendant's unfitness to plead can account for no more than three quarters of hospital admissions listed subsequent to such a finding since 1999 by the Home Office[23]. We cannot account for this discrepancy. Statistical returns given by the Department of Health on hospital admissions subsequent to CPIA findings are presented in financial rather than calendar years, and perhaps more significantly collate CPIA admissions under a general category of 'previous legislation and other Acts', which also counts admissions to hospital under, for example, the powers of the Children Act (see figure 129). Department of

---

18   We understand that at the time of going to press, research on the use of CPIA disposals between 1997 and 2001 is in preparation by Professor Mackay, funded by the Nuffield Foundation.

19   Mackay R D and Kearns G 'An upturn in Unfitness to Plead? Disability in Relation to the Trial under the 1991 Act' *Criminal Law Review* [2000] 532-543, table 9.

20   Mackay R D and Kearns G 'More Facts(s) about the Insanity Defence' *Criminal Law Review* [1999] 714-715, table 6.

21   Adapted from Mackay R D and Kearns G (1999, 2000) *supra*.

22   i.e. listed as a contested trial by jury but disposed of in some other way on the day of the trial.

23   Department of Constitutional Affairs (1999- 2003) *Judicial Statistics*. According to these figures, 143 trials were cracked between 1999-2003 due to either the death or the unfitness to plead of the defendant. Home Office statistics at fig 125 above record 185 restricted hospital orders over this period.

Health statisticians cannot break this category down into its component parts, and can therefore neither account for its components nor for its dramatic fall in the mid-1990s.

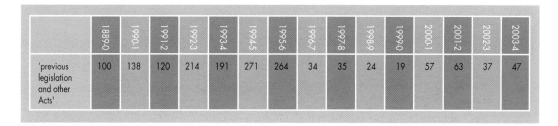

	1989-0	1990-1	1991-2	1992-3	1993-4	1994-5	1995-6	1996-7	1997-8	1998-9	1999-0	2000-1	2001-2	2002-3	2003-4
'previous legislation and other Acts'	100	138	120	214	191	271	264	34	35	24	19	57	63	37	47

Fig 129: formal admissions to psychiatric hospital under legislation other than Mental Health Act 1983, 1989-2004[24]

5.13 Research on Scottish disposals between 1 April 1996 and 31 August 1998 found that hospital orders with restrictions accounted for only 12 of a total of 30 hospital orders under the equivalent of the CPIA[25]. In addition to these hospital orders, findings of unfitness to plead or insanity resulted in six supervision and treatment orders, one civil detention under the Mental Health (Scotland) Act, and no action in a further seven cases. Restriction orders were applied to nearly a quarter of hospital orders subsequent to a finding of unfitness to plead, and to nearly three-quarters of hospital orders subsequent to a finding of insanity.

5.14 Although CPIA disposals are available only to a Crown Court, the Mental Health Act 1983 provides a similar diversionary tool to magistrates' courts under s.37(3). No statistics are available on the use of this power, although it is said to be used very rarely[26].

> **Recommendation 51:** We recommend that centralised data collection is undertaken and published on an annual basis by Government on the use of Criminal Procedure (Insanity) legislation and its practical effect as a diversionary mechanism.

Unfitness to Plead

5.15 The most common CPIA use appears to be the finding of unfitness to plead under s.2 of the Trial of Lunatics Act 1883 as amended by the CPIA legislation of 1964 and 1991.

---

[24] Department of Health Statistical Bulletins 1996 - 2004 *Inpatients formally detained in hospitals under the Mental Health Act 1983 and other legislation, England.*

[25] Research based upon proceedings under the Criminal Procedure (Scotland) Act 1995, published in Scottish Law Commission (2003) *Discussion Paper on Insanity and Diminished Responsibility.* (Discussion paper 122). Edinburgh, Stationery Office, Annex C. Data originally produced by Michele Burman and Clare Connelly (1999) *Mentally Disordered Offenders and Criminal Proceedings* (Scottish Office Central Research Unit, 1999).

[26] *R v Lincoln (Kevesten) Justices ex parte O'Connor [1983]* 1 WLR 335 DC. See Bartlett, P. & Sandland, R (2003) *Mental Health Law Policy and Practice* second ed. Oxford, p.284.

5.16   For courts in England and Wales, the test of disability for fitness to plead still relies upon the 1836 case *R v Pritchard* [27]. The burden of proof differs depending on who raises the issue in court. The defence have to prove unfitness on a balance of probabilities, but the prosecution must prove it beyond reasonable doubt. The test in practice is whether the accused can:

- understand the nature of the charge against him;
- distinguish between a plea of guilty and not guilty;
- instruct a lawyer;
- follow the evidence in court; and
- challenge a juror to whom he might object.

5.17   This test has been said to be silent about the mental state of the defendant except in relation to intellectual ability, so that it takes little account of 'decisional competence' (i.e. a notion of capacity similar to that forming the basis of the Mental Capacity Act 2005) [28]. Professor R D Mackay has pointed out that the Mental Capacity Act is 'part of a continuing trend to protect the decision-making process of the mentally vulnerable within the civil law' which has been extended in part to criminal law (for example in s.30 of the Sexual Offences Act 2003, which protects persons 'with a mental disorder impeding choice' from sexual interference), but as yet continues to be ignored in the context of fitness to plead: 'the criminal law fails to protect equally vulnerable persons who cannot make true choices about the trial process, including in particular the decision about whether or not to plead guilty' [29]. In the Jersey courts, the test for fitness to plead has been recently formulated around 'capacity to participate effectively in the criminal process' after the bailiff declined to adopt 'the test laid down in England more than one hundred and sixty years ago' preferring the 'new road which has been essentially engineered by the intellectual efforts of many specialists in this field [as presented in the Scottish Law Commission on insanity and diminished responsibility report]' [30]. In his judgment the bailiff explained his preference for a test encompassing decisional competence as follows:

> Social conditions have changed, and the importance of protecting human rights and the dignity of those effected by mental… incapacity is nowadays more widely appreciated. In my judgment I should adopt a test which is consonant with the European Convention of Human Rights, conscious of developments in medical science in the last one hundred years or more, and appropriate to the needs of this jurisdiction in the twenty-first century.

---

[27]   *R v Pritchard* (1836) 7 C & P 303.

[28]   Bartlett, P. & Sandland, R. (2003) *Mental Health Law Policy and Practice*, p 268. However, *dicta* of Otton LJ in *R v Friend* [1997] EWCA Crim 816 1, WLR 1433 acknowledged that whether the accused 'could understand *and reply rationally* to the indictment is obviously a relevant factor' (our emphasis). For the statutory definitions of mental incapacity in relation to decision-making, see Mental Capacity Act 2005, ss.2, 3. See also Chapter 3.30 *et seq* above for a discussion of capacity and 'appreciation'.

[29]   Mackay R D 'On being Insane in Jersey Part Three – the Case of Attorney-General v. O'Driscoll' *Criminal Law Review* [2004] 291-296.

[30]   *ibid. Attorney –General v Neil Liam O'Driscoll*, July 9 2003, JRC 117/2003

5.18   The Scottish Law Commission proposals are that the criteria for the Scottish equivalent of unfitness to plead (which Scots law already extends beyond a purely cognitive test[31]) should be that a person 'is incapable, by reason of mental or physical condition, of participating effectively in a trial'. In determining this question the court would have regard to the accused's ability to understand the nature of the charge, the requirement to plea to the charge and the effect of that plea, and the evidence; to instruct and communicate with a lawyer and any other factor considered relevant by the court[32].

5.19   If the *Pritchard* test applicable in the courts of England and Wales is interpreted literally as a test of cognition, it is possible that persons without mental capacity to participate effectively in criminal proceedings could still progress to trial, which could lead to a breach of ECHR Article 6[33]. As such there may have been some protection in having juries consider this matter prior to March 2005. Lord Diplock, on a separate but related matter, saw the benefit of matters being decided not 'by a judge trained in logical reasoning but …by a jury drawing on their experience of how ordinary human beings behave in real life'[34]. As we note at paragraph 5.32 below, the question of whether a person is unfit to plead under the terms of the CPIA has from March 2005 been decided by a judge rather than a jury, which makes reappraisal of the criteria for such decision all the more pressing.

> **Recommendation 52:** We recommend that Government reconsider the criteria for unfitness to plead in the light of the above.

Verdicts of not guilty by reason of insanity

5.20   The legal test (the 'M'Naghten rules') for the special verdict that is now described as 'not guilty by reason of insanity' was established in the House of Lords in 1843. The test remains extant today, despite a number of changes to the legislative framework that surrounds it and

---

[31] In Scotland a broader interpretation of the criteria (linked to the undefined concept of 'insanity') has in past years resulted in much more frequent findings of unfitness to plead than in England or Wales. See Chiswick, D., McIsaac, M. W., & McClintock, F.H. (1984) *Prosecution of the Mentally Disturbed*. Aberdeen University Press: p12: 'findings of unfitness to plead are returned ten times more frequently in Scotland than in England [and Wales]. …the verdict …accounts for nearly half of those mental hospital admissions which are ordered by the court each year'. We have not located current statistics.

[32] Scottish Law Commission (2004) *Report on Insanity and Diminished Responsibility*. Edinburgh, Stationery Office, Annex A: draft Criminal Responsibility and Unfitness for Trial (Scotland) Bill, clause 4.

[33] See *T v United Kingdom and V v United Kingdom* (2000) 30 EHRR 121.

[34] *Camplin* [1978] A.C.705 p718A. Lord Diplock was specifically referring to juries' application of the tests pertinent to the defence of provocation: see 5.47 below. Examination of psychiatric reports from Unfitness to Plead cases suggests that evidence on criteria other than those relevant in law are frequently available to the court's proceedings (Mackay R D and Kearns G 'An upturn in Unfitness to Plead? Disability in Relation to the Trial under the 1991 Act' *Criminal Law Review* [2000] 532-543).

despite its interpretation over the years in specific cases[35]. The M'Naghten rules state that an offender may be excused legal responsibility for an act where, at the time of committing that act

> ...the party accused was labouring under such a defect of reason, from disease of the mind, as not to know the nature and quality of the act he was doing or, if he did know it, that he did not know he was doing what was wrong[36].

5.21 The term 'insanity' has been described as 'something of a legal relic which has ceased to convey any clear psychiatric meaning'[37]. It is certainly neither congruent with the definitions of mental disorder under the Mental Health Acts nor the test as established in *Pritchard* relating to unfitness to stand trial[38]. Although it can be argued that the term is used simply to denote a legal concept of a total lack of responsibility for any criminal act, it is not easy to see why a term which is offensive, and no longer meaningful in either a clinical or common language context, serves this purpose adequately. The Scottish Law Commission, whilst acknowledging that the approaches of law and medicine towards the insanity defence are not identical, argued in 2004 that

> ...it is also the case that they are not in conflict with each other. For the law to determine acceptable boundaries of criminal responsibility it must refer to medical concepts. The effect of the present law is to create difficulties for expert witnesses in providing the courts with the medical information needed to give effect to the legal test in individual cases. The Millan Committee expressed this point as follows[39]: 'It seems wrong to us that such an important issue as determining the responsibility of an individual for a serious criminal charge should depend on terms and definitions which are largely meaningless to those with the responsibility of giving expert evidence to the court'.[40]

5.22 The *M'Naghten* rules themselves are open to the same criticism that may be applied to the *Pritchard* test, which reveals their common basis in a rather outdated psychology. Applied literally, the rules are limited to cognitive factors, making no allowance for conative issues of volition (i.e. the 'irresistible impulse'), and thus excluding many instances where mental

---

[35] The vicissitudes of the special verdict of insanity in statute law are illustrative of this point. In 1800 the first Trials of Lunatics Act provided a verdict of 'not guilty on grounds of insanity', and required subjects so found to be held at His Majesty's pleasure. The 1883 Trial of Lunatics Act altered the verdict's wording to 'guilty but insane' at the behest of Queen Victoria (Walker, N. (1968) *Crime and Insanity in England*, Vol. 1, p190). The verdict's wording was returned to its 1800 origins by the Criminal Procedure (Insanity) Act 1964, after calls for reform over the previous 40 years. Before the 1964 Act there had been, generally, no right of appeal against the special verdict (a 1907 Court of appeal decision to the contrary was quickly qualified, and then reversed in the House of Lords in 1914). After 1964, the verdict has been subject to appeal and can be asked for by the prosecution: 'thus one Gilbertian situation was replaced by another. Instead of a verdict which sounded like a conviction but was treated as an acquittal, we now have a verdict which sounds like an acquittal but is treated as a conviction' (Walker, N. (1968), p.192). Only since 1991 has the law allowed that a judge may actually choose to impose no sanction on a person found not guilty under these provisions, and only in 2005 has the law extended this flexibility to all indictments (including, where hospitalisation cannot be justified, murder).

[36] *M'Naghten's Case* (1843) 10 C & F 200, para 210.

[37] Chiswick, D., McIsaac, M. W., & McClintock, F.H. (1984) *Prosecution of the Mentally Disturbed*. Aberdeen University Press, p7.

[38] Bartlett, P. & Sandland, R (2003) *supra*, p 285.

[39] Millan Report, para 29.43

[40] Scottish Law Commission (2004) *Report on Insanity and Diminished Responsibility*. July 2004, para 2.10

disorder should prove a defence (and does so under diminished responsibility law for murder charges)[41]. The incongruity between the 'all or nothing' nature of the *M'Naghten* defence and the more flexible concepts of criminal responsibility available as defences against murder indictments may well become more acute now that mandatory sentencing requirements have reducing judicial discretion in sentencing for many other offences than murder (see paragraphs 5.33 *et seq* below).

5.23 In the mid-1950s the American Law Institute proposed a model penal code that included a concept of insanity that, unlike the *M'Naghten* rule, had two components: one grounded in cognition, but also relating to the *appreciation* of wrongfulness (which encompasses both knowing the factual wrongfulness of an act and being aware personally and emotionally that the act is wrong for that person in that context), and one grounded in volition, relating to capacity to conform behaviour. This model has been influential in many US state and other legislatures[42]. The Butler Committee on Mentally Abnormal Offenders recommended in 1975 that a new verdict of 'not guilty by reason of mental disorder' should be introduced, which could be returned either where the defendant was unable to form the requisite *mens rea*[43] due to mental disorder; or where the defendant was aware of his actions but was at the time suffering from severe mental disorder. The Law Commission drafted the following clauses of a Criminal Code Bill based upon this recommendation:

35   (1) A mental disorder verdict shall be returned if the defendant is proved to have committed an offence but it is proved on the balance of probabilities (whether by the prosecution of the defendant) that he was at the time suffering from severe mental illness or severe mental handicap.

      (2) Subsection (1) does not apply if the court or jury is satisfied beyond reasonable doubt that the offence is not attributable to the severe mental illness or severe mental handicap

36   A mental disorder verdict shall be returned if

      (a) the defendant is acquitted of an offence only because, by reason of evidence of mental disorder or a combination of mental disorder and intoxication, it is found that he acted or may have acted in such a state of automatism, or without the fault required for the offence, or believing that an exempting circumstance existed; and

      (b) it is proved on the balance of probabilities (whether by the prosecution of the defendant) that he was suffering from mental disorder at the time of the Act. [44]

---

[41] In 2001 the courts in Jersey, faced with a defence of not guilty by reason of insanity based upon volitional impairment resulting from mental illness, applied Professor R D Mackay's proposed test for 'insanity' (where unsoundness of mind affected the defendant's criminal behaviour to such a substantial degree that the jury consider that he ought not to be found criminally responsible) to interpret Article 2 of the Criminal Justice (Insane Persons) (Jersey) Law 1964. The bailiff concluding that this test 'will…cater for defects of volition' (see Mackay R D & Gearty C A 'On being Insane in Jersey – the case of Attorney General v. Jason Prior' *Criminal Law Review* [2001] 560-563). An appeal cast some doubt on the bailiff's approach in departing from the *M'Naghten* Rules (see [2002] Crim.L.R. 728).

[42] Guthell, T G (1999) 'A confusion of tongues; Competence, Insanity, Psychiatry and the Law' *Psychiatric Services* Vol. 50, No.6; 767-773.

[43] *Mens rea*, or 'guilty mind', is used in criminal law to describe criminal intent.

[44] Law Commission (1989) *Draft Criminal Code*, Law Com No 177.

5.24 In their report *Insanity and Diminished Responsibility*, the Scottish Law Commission points out that the return of a special verdict has never placed persons beyond the reach of the court in making a disposal that effects social control over persons who have committed criminal acts[45], although it does of course prevent a court from passing a sentence of imprisonment. Until relatively recently (1991 in England and Wales), an insanity verdict required hospitalisation of the accused, whether or not this was merited. We note at paragraph 5.26 below the important amendments made to the law in 2005 to address remaining human rights concerns over compulsory hospitalisation. As a result, the insanity verdict, where it is applicable, should result in the most appropriate disposal of the case in the interests of the accused and of wider society. There should no longer be a danger of the verdict leading to the compulsory hospitalisation of persons whose conditions do not warrant such a drastic measure. The remaining task must be to ensure that the defence is applicable where it is warranted and where it can act as a means to divert the mentally disordered from custodial sentences.

> **Recommendation 53:** We recommend that Government consider whether the title and criteria for the special verdict of not guilty by reason of insanity should be reformulated in the light of the above.

Changes to the Criminal Procedure (Insanity) Acts in 2004

5.25 Government first announced its intention to amend the Criminal Procedure (Insanity) legislation in 2002[46]. The amendment proposed in outline was to remove from the CPIA the power (and in the case of offences of murder, the duty) to make the equivalent to a hospital order under s.37 of the Mental Health Act irrespective of whether the offender suffers from a mental disorder or would otherwise meet the normal criteria for a Mental Health Act disposal. The Mental Health Bill was to be the legislative vehicle, but the change has now been effected through Government amendments to the Domestic Violence, Crime and Disorder Bill, which was enacted in October 2004. The changes discussed below – which extend further than Government's originally announced intention – came into force on the 31 March 2005[47].

Criteria for hospital orders

5.26 Prior to the amendment of the CPIA in March 2005, courts were required to make a hospital order where the CPIA finding related to a murder charge, and had the power to do so in relation to any other charge, irrespective of medical opinion or recommendations as to appropriate placements. It is questionable whether the detention in hospital of persons who

---

[45] Scottish Law Commission (2004) *Report on Insanity and Diminished Responsibility*. July 2004, para 1.10 *et seq.*

[46] Department of Health (2002) *Mental Health Bill Consultation Document*. Cmnd 5538-III, para 4.3.

[47] The Domestic Violence, Crime and Victims Act 2004 (Commencement No.1) Order 2005 (SI 2005 No.579 (C.26))

are neither convicted offenders nor in need of medical treatment warranting compulsion could be justifiable under human rights requirements[48].

5.27 In a small number of cases the Criminal Procedure (Insanity) Acts have resulted in the compulsory admission of offenders to hospital without clear medical justification, and even in the face of medical opposition. Two recent cases known to the Commission where there are at least questions as to the clinical need for a hospital order are outlined below.

- In our last report[49] we highlighted one case from 2002 where a consultant was asked by the court to provide a bed for an offender as a disposal under s.4 of the CPIA. At the time of this request the offender, Ms S, was in Holloway Prison whilst a hospital placement was being sought. We are unaware of any medical view that supported compulsory psychiatric treatment of Ms S's alcohol dependence, social phobia and possible other personality disorders, and we know of no evidence that, if the criteria of the 1983 Act were applied, such compulsion would have been lawful. Neither of these matters were relevant to the lawfulness of compulsory hospitalisation under Schedule 1 of the Criminal Procedure (Insanity) Act 1991 as it stood at that time. Ms S was eventually admitted under compulsion to the care of a second consultant psychiatrist, who specialised in the treatment of substance misuse. She was regraded as an informal patient within two months and discharged uneventfully within three.

- In March 2005 a hospital order was made in respect of a man found by a jury at Manchester Crown Court to be not guilty by reason of insanity to the charge of having murdered his elderly father. Mr L beat his father to death whilst sleepwalking following heavy drinking, and claimed to have been unaware of his actions. The judge had explained to the jury that the defence case of automatism 'did not mean the defendant was insane in the normal sense of the word'[50]. Nevertheless, upon the jury's verdict the judge had no legal alternative but to send Mr L to hospital under a restriction order. Mr L was initially sent to the hospital wing of Strangeways Prison whilst a hospital bed was found. At the time of writing he had been transferred to an NHS medium secure unit.

5.28 The use of the CPIA was described by the first consultant in Ms S's case as a 'back door to detention under the Mental Health Act without supporting medical recommendations'[51]. Although it is usually some weeks or months before an appeal may be made to or heard by the Mental Health Review Tribunal[52], the law provides the Tribunal with no criteria specific to CPIA orders and as such a Tribunal, applying the tests applicable to patients' detention under the Mental Health Act 1983, would appear bound to discharge a patient from compulsion that is not justified by his or her medical condition. The Government's consultation document described the result of disposals that are not justified by the person's

---

[48] In *Winterwerp v Netherlands* (1979) 2 EHRR 387 it was determined that there must be objective medical evidence justifying the 'lawful detention of persons of unsound mind' as provided for under ECHR Article 5(1)(e). See, further, Mackay R D & Gearty C A 'On being Insane in Jersey – the case of Attorney General v. Jason Prior' *Criminal Law Review* [2001] 560-563, s.1: The McNaghten Rules and the Human Rights Act.

[49] MHAC (2003) *Placed Amongst Strangers; Tenth Biennial Report*. Chapter 13.14.

[50] Jane Perrone 'Sleepwalker cleared of murdering father' *The Guardian*, March 19 2005.

[51] Personal correspondence to the MHAC.

[52] An unrestricted patient detained subsequent to an order of the Criminal Procedure (Insanity) Acts may apply to the MHRT within the first six months of the order, and then annually; a restricted patient may apply only in the second six months of detention, and then annually.

medical condition as 'likely to be immediate discharge from hospital without any benefit to the person concerned, or added protection to others'[53].

5.29   Under the amended provisions of s.5 of the Criminal Procedure (Insanity) Act 1964[54], the hospital order available to the court as a disposal is no longer a free-standing power established within CPIA legislation, but is the disposal provided by s.37 of the Mental Health Act 1983. The requirement on the court to make a hospital order where a murder charge results in a CPIA finding or special verdict, and the court's discretion to make hospital orders in relation to other offences, is now subject to the conditions for a hospital order as established under s.37 of the Mental Health Act being met[55].

Criteria for restriction orders

5.30   The amendments to CPIA similarly abolish any 'free-standing' CPIA power to make restriction orders, so that where a court does so in respect of a hospital order made subsequent to a CPIA finding or special verdict, it does so under the powers of s.41 of the Mental Health Act. However, the new legal framework continues to require the court to impose a restriction order in addition to any hospital order it makes subsequent to a CPIA finding or special verdict relating to a murder charge[56]. In this way a court will be prevented from using the discretion or applying the criteria established under s.41 of the 1983 Act[57]. Although, of course, no *convicted* murderers receive hospital orders from the court[58], persons who are arraigned for murder but convicted of manslaughter on the grounds of diminished responsibility (or other grounds) may do so, and courts retain discretion over placing restrictions on any hospital order in such circumstances. This raises a potential anomaly in the way in which restriction orders are applied to mentally disordered persons involved in homicide cases.

Powers of remand

5.31   The Domestic Violence, Crime and Disorder Act 2004 amendments allow that a person found unfit or insane under the CPIA may be remanded by the court to hospital using the powers of ss.35, 36 or 38 of the Mental Health Act 1983, provided that the 1983 Act's conditions for such remand (i.e. written or oral medical evidence) are met. This introduces

---

[53]   Department of Health (2002) *Mental Health Bill Consultation Document.* Cmnd 5538-III, para 4.3.

[54]   As amended by the Domestic Violence, Crime and Disorder Act 2004, s.24.

[55]   To make a hospital order under s.37 of the 1983 Act, courts require medical evidence (written or oral) from two doctors to the effect that the accused is suffering from one or more of the four classifications of mental disorder listed in the 1983 Act (i.e. mental illness, mental impairment, severe mental impairment or psychopathic disorder) to a nature or degree that makes detention in hospital for treatment appropriate and, if the classification is psychopathic disorder or severe mental impairment, that such treatment is likely to alleviate or prevent a deterioration in the condition.

[56]   Criminal Procedure (Insanity) Act 1964, s.5(3) (as amended by the Domestic Violence, Crime and Disorder Act 2004, s.24).

[57]   Section 41 provides courts with discretionary powers to impose restrictions on court orders where 'it appears to the court, having regard to the nature of the offence, the antecedents of the offender and the risk of his committing serious offences if set at large, that [such restrictions are] necessary for the protection of the public from serious harm'.

[58]   Persons convicted of murder must be sentenced to life imprisonment (Murder (Abolition of the Death Penalty) Act 1965, s.1(1)).

powers of remand for the first time into the range of CPIA disposals. We are aware that the lack of such powers has been felt as a gap by courts in the past:

- In the 2002 case described above, a doctor was erroneously informed by one legal counsel involved in the case that the court was seeking a remand to hospital for assessment.

- In the automatism case described above, the defendant had to be brought back to court immediately after the initial disposal, as the judge had mistakenly assumed a power to remand.

Removal of jury involvement in determinations of fitness to plead

5.32   Lord Justice Auld's Review of the Criminal Courts of England and Wales 2001 recommended that a judge, rather than a jury, should determine the issue of fitness to plead:

> In the majority of cases the jury's role on the issue of unfitness to plead is little more than a formality because there is usually no dispute between the prosecution and the defence that the defendant is unfit to plead[59]. However, the procedure is still cumbrous, especially when the issue is raised, as it mostly is, on the arraignment, because it can then require the empanelling of two juries. More importantly, it is difficult to see what a jury can bring to the determination of the issue that a judge cannot. He decides similar questions determinative of whether there should be a trial, for example, whether a defendant is physically or mentally fit to stand or continue trial in applications to stay the prosecution or for discharge of the defendant. The consequences of a finding of unfitness to plead are now much more flexible than they were, ranging from a hospital order with restrictions to an absolute discharge; and the judge is entrusted with the often very difficult task of what to do with the defendant, with the assistance of medical evidence. In my view, he, not the jury, should determine the issue of fitness to plead at whatever stage it is raised, leaving, where it arises, the jury to determine whether the defendant did the act or made the omission charged.[60]

Section 22 of the Domestic Violence, Crime and Disorder Act 2004 amends the Criminal Procedure (Insanity) Act 1964 to effect this change. Had there been an opportunity for debate amongst mental health professionals over the amendment to the law, we would have suggested that the removal of jury involvement in determining whether the *Pritchard* test is met could have been taken as an opportunity to revise that test to ensure that its literal application does not exclude mentally disordered persons from its scope[61] (see paragraphs 5.16 *et seq* and recommendation 52 above).

---

59   R D Mackay and Gerry Kearns, 'An Upturn in Unfitness to Plead? Disability in Relation to the Trial under the 1991 Act' [2000] *Crim L R* 532, at 536

60   Auld LJ, *Review of the Criminal Courts of England and Wales* 2001, para 213.

61   We note that Auld LJ, in making his recommendation, is clear that the test being applied is an essentially cognitive one: 'The test … is broadly whether the defendant has sufficient intellect to instruct his advocate, to plead to the indictment, to follow and understand the evidence and to give evidence' (*ibid*, para 212).

Mental health disposals and sentencing powers

Mandatory sentencing

5.33 In this report we give some space to an examination of the use of psychiatric defences in murder trials. The way in which the courts deal with mentally disordered persons who are arraigned upon murder charges has long been of special significance, not because such persons are more likely to commit murder than other people (see paragraph 5.1 above), but because the mandatory penalties for murder prevent diversion at sentencing stage if guilt is established.

5.34 The original mandatory sentence was death. In the early years of the formulation of formal insanity defences, a number of doctors argued that

> the difficulties with which administrators of justice have to contend in distinguishing crimes from the result of insane impulse will never be entirely removed, but they will be rendered much less important when the good sense of the community shall have produced the effect of abolishing all capital punishments   *J.C. Prichard, 1835* [62]

or, as Henry Maudsley put it 40 years later, 'abolish capital punishment, and the dispute between doctors and lawyers ceases to be of practical importance'[63]. Today, 170 years after Maudsley's statement, and 40 years since the abolition of the death penalty, the Royal College of Psychiatrists takes the view that

> at least as far as psychiatric evidence is concerned, the vast majority of problems that arise in homicide cases could, and would, be abolished with the abolition of the mandatory life sentence on conviction of murder. Once psychiatry [is] placed solely within sentence hearings, rather than within hearings directed towards jury decisions about verdict, the effect of the mismatch between medical and legal thinking is all but abolished[64].

5.35 In June 2003 the Home Secretary requested a review by the Law Commission of the provocation and diminished responsibility 'partial defences' to murder (we discuss these defences below at paragraph 5.47 *et seq*). The resulting Law Commission report noted the origin of such partial defences in 'the mandatory death/life sentence for murder'[65] and called for a further review that would extend to the issue of mandatory sentencing. Responses to the Law Commission's consultation (including the views of 21 judges) provided what its final report described as a 'compelling' view that 'the application of a mandatory life sentence to every case of murder was indefensible and should cease'[66].

5.36 Insofar as there is a dispute, it is therefore no longer between the legal and medical professions, but between both professions and Government. In October 2004 the then Home

---

[62] From Prichard's *A Treatise on Insanity and other Disorders Effecting the Mind*, 1835, quoted in Smith (1981) *Trial by Medicine; insanity and responsibility in Victorian trials*. Edinburgh University Press, p.25.

[63] Quoted in Smith, R. (1981) *supra*, p.25.

[64] RCPsych response to Law Com consultation paper 173 of Oct 2003, quoted in Law Commission (2004) *Partial Defences to Murder* Final Report, para 5.44

[65] Law Commission (2004) *Partial Defences to Murder* Final Report, August 2004, para 2.59

[66] *ibid.*, para 2.15

Secretary, the Rt. Hon David Blunkett MP, announced that he accepted the need for a review of the law of murder but that such a review would not extend to consideration of mandatory sentencing[67]. Despite the outgoing Lord Chief Justice's indication that he would support a review of mandatory sentencing and that he is 'not in favour of mandatory sentences, full stop'[68], the Home Office announcement of the first review of murder laws for more than fifty years will stop short of reconsidering mandatory sentencing at policy level[69].

5.37   The scope of mandatory sentencing has increased significantly from the Crime (Sentences) Act 1997, which introduced mandatory life sentences for a second serious offence, to the passing into law of the Criminal Justice Act 2003, which extends mandatory sentencing to persons defined in that Act as 'dangerous offenders' and to sexual and violent crimes other than murder[70]. Although the real effect of these changes is to remove discretion from the courts in exercising powers that they already had, at least with regard to persons exhibiting some forms of abnormality of mind (see paragraphs 5.38-42 below), the changes introduced in the 2003 Act could be approached positively as an extension into criminal law mechanisms for preventive detention that have previously been the preserve of mental health law. This may therefore reduce the pressures on mental health law to provide for public safety in respect of convicted persons[71]. On the other hand, it is clear that mandatory sentencing creates 'a pressure to accommodate "hard" or "deserving" cases'[72] through, for example, the various forms of 'psychiatric' and other defences, and that this can have a distorting effect on such defences[73]. It seems as though these fault-lines between mental health and criminal law will continue to be active for some time to come.

The role of indeterminate sentencing

5.38   The Joint Committee on the Draft Mental Health Bill recognised that a consequence of the more rigorous criteria that it suggested for future legislation would be that a small group of people with dangerous and severe personality disorder (DSPD) may not meet the conditions for the use of compulsory powers. The Committee did not believe that this group should be dealt with by mental health legislation, but suggested that separate legislation should be introduced to manage individuals with DSPD[74].

---

[67]   Home Office Press Release 332-04, 27 Oct 2004. The murder review was announced by the Home Secretary during that day's debate on the Domestic Violence, Crime and Victims Bill in the House of Commons.

[68]   Clare Dyer ' Woolf supports murder law reform' *The Guardian*, 24 June 2005.

[69]   Home Office Press Release 110-05, 21 July 2005. *Fundamental Review of Murder Law.*

[70]   Criminal Justice Act 2003, s.225. The sentencing expert Dr David Thomas has expressed concern that 'the definition of who is a dangerous offender [in the CJA 2003] is so broad that all manner of people will fall within it and we'll see – or in theory should see – some bizarre sentences which judges will be very reluctant to pass' Clare Dyer, 'Judges speak out against erosion of independence by government' *The Guardian*, 26/04/05. This article also quotes an anonymous Appeal court judge stating that judges are likely to interpret 'the wriggle room' around such mandatory sentencing 'a bit more widely than government would like'.

[71]   See Chapter 5.71 below.

[72]   Law Commission (2004) *Partial Defences to Murder* Final Report, para 2.8

[73]   The Law Commission has noted (*ibid*, para 2.8) that the law regarding provocation has developed in ways unintended at the time of its enactment as the result of such pressures. We discuss this at para 5.47 below.

[74]   Joint Committee on the Draft Mental Health Bill *Draft Mental Health Bill*, Vol 1, p.5.

5.39   For convicted offenders, sufficient sentencing powers already exist. The Criminal Justice Act 2003 introduced, from April 2005, new powers for indeterminate and extended sentencing on the grounds of the risk to the public posed by an offender:

- An *indeterminate sentence for public protection* must be imposed if a sexual or violent offender is assessed by the court as posing a significant risk to the public and the offence committed carries a maximum penalty of ten years or over. (A discretionary life sentence may be awarded where the maximum penalty is life and the seriousness of the offence warrants it). The indeterminate sentence is similar to a life sentence in that the court will set a tariff period, after which release is at the discretion of the Parole Board on grounds of public safety. On release the offender will be subject to supervision on licence for at least ten years, after which time the licence may be revoked by the Parole Board if it considers it safe to do so.

- An *extended sentence for public protection* is required in the same circumstances as the indeterminate public protection sentence, but where the sexual or violent offence committed carries a maximum penalty of less than ten years, and where the sentence imposed is at least 12 months. The court must set a custodial period and an extended licence period. The offender may be released on the Parole Board's recommendation at any time between the halfway point and the completion of the custodial period. The extended licence period may be up to five years for violent offenders and up to eight years for sexual offenders[75].

5.40   Criteria for imposing discretionary indeterminate sentences were established at common law in *R v Hodgson*[76] (1968) as:

(i)   the offence or offences are in themselves grave enough to require a very long sentence;

(ii)   it appears from the nature of the defendant's history that he is a person of unstable character likely to commit such offences in the future; and

(iii) the consequences to others of such future offences would be likely to be especially injurious, as in the case of sexual offences or crimes of violence[77].

Subsequent caselaw has determined that the criterion of 'unstable character' should be established through medical evidence in all but exceptional cases[78]. In *R v Wilkinson and others* (1983) it was stated that discretionary life imprisonment should be reserved for offenders who cannot be detained under the Mental Health Act, and yet whose mental state makes them a danger to the public[79].

---

[75]   Home Office / National Probation Service (2003) *Criminal Justice Act* 2003 National Probation Service Briefing 16, December 2003, p.3

[76]   *R v Hodgson* (1968) 52 CR App R (s) 113

[77]   Summarised in Smith, A (1998) 'Psychiatric evidence and discretionary life sentences' in *The Journal of Forensic Psychiatry*, Vol 9 No 1 May 1998 p.17-38. We have used this article extensively in the following paragraphs.

[78]   i.e. *R v De Havilland* (1983) 5 Cr App R (s) 109; *R v Dempster* (1987) 9 Cr App R (s) 176

[79]   *R v Wilkinson and others* (1983) Cr App R (s) 105. Some mentally disordered persons given life sentences at the discretion of the court have appealed successfully and had their disposal varied to a hospital order with restrictions (*R v Mbatha* (1985) 7 Cr App R (s) 373; *R v Howell* (1985) 7 Cr App R (s) 360). However, in *R v Fleming* (1993) 14 Cr App R (s) 151, the court imposed a life sentence on conviction of two counts of manslaughter, although the defendant had schizophrenia and was, until discharged prior to the killings by the MHRT, a patient in Broadmoor Hospital. This approach was not followed in *R v Fairhurst* (1996) 1 Cr App R (s) 242, where the court noted that it was incorrect to impose life imprisonment simply to prevent premature release by the MHRT. Subsequent to *Fairhurst*, of course, Parliament has added powers to the Mental Health Act (s.45A, discussed at 5.89 *et seq* below) which provide a statutory mechanism for doing just that.

5.41   Discretionary life sentences have been used in cases where the defendant suffers from a personality disorder whose treatability, and therefore relevance to the detention criteria under the Mental Health Act, was disputed[80]. Defendants exhibiting sexually deviancy (e.g. paedophilia or sadistic sexual fantasy) in the absence of other mental abnormality have also been given discretionary life terms[81].

5.42   Insofar as courts are provided with the option of hospital orders or discretionary sentencing powers where appropriate, they have all the means necessary to ensure public safety from convicted offenders. Extensions to mandatory sentencing requirements may serve only to limit the courts' discretion to use these means appropriately in the case of mentally disordered offenders. For such offenders who are classified with psychopathic disorder the danger of inappropriate custodial sentences is offset in part by the creation of 'hybrid' hospital and sentencing disposals (see paragraph 5.89 *et seq* below), but offenders with other classified mental disorders have no such protection and, as the cases of *Newman* and *Drew* have shown, such offenders may be reluctantly imprisoned by the sentencing court (see Chapter 1.208 *et seq* above).

The use of CPIA disposals and diminished responsibility verdicts in homicide trials

Psychiatric defences in murder trials; rates of use

5.43   Although findings and special verdicts under the CPIA are relatively rare today (see paragraph 5.9 *et seq* above), the wider statutory framework concerning criminal responsibility and mental disorder continues to play an important part in criminal proceedings for murder indictments in England and Wales overall. We provide an historical survey at figure 130 overleaf.

5.44   This 'wider statutory framework' regarding criminal responsibility and mental disorder was established under the Homicide Act 1957, which formalised in statute existing common-law means to convict persons charged with murder of a lesser crime in recognition of diminished responsibility or other extenuating circumstances. Section 2 of the 1957 Act created the statutory defence of 'diminished responsibility' specifically designed for mentally disordered offenders.

5.45   Figure 130 shows that during the twentieth century, up to the abolition of capital punishment in 1965, approximately 40% of all persons indicted for murder were found either to be unfit to plead under the *Pritchard* test; or to have diminished criminal responsibility under s.2 of the 1957 Act; or to have no criminal responsibility at all under the *M'Naghten* rules. Technically, the effect of such findings for what amounts to roughly eighteen hundred persons between 1900 and 1965 was diversion from the death penalty, although in practice not all persons convicted of the capital charge of murder were

---

[80]   i.e. *R v Sanderson* (1994) 15 Cr App R (s) 263; *R v Waller* (1995) 16 Cr App R (s) 251; *R v Hann* (1996) 1 Cr App R (s) 267; *R v Vale* (1996) 1 Cr App R (s) 405.

[81]   *R v Stevenson* (1993) 14 Cr App R (s) 22; *Attorney-General's Reference* (no 34 of 1992) (1994) 15 Cr App R (s) 167

executed, sometimes because of a less formal recognition of the presence of mental disorder[82]. From the abolition of the death penalty, the proportion of these findings in murder indictments has been decreasing, and now appears to involve fewer than 10% of cases[83]. We must, however, strike a note of caution against drawing hasty conclusions from this observation. It is not possible to quantify the proportion of cases falling outside of our calculation where a defence (or a guilty plea to a lesser charge) was founded upon the presence of mental disorder, but where the formal mechanisms of the 'psychiatric defences' that we have focussed on were not invoked. We look briefly at this in relation to the defence of provocation at paragraph 5.47 below.

Diminished Responsibility

5.46   Insofar as the special verdict of *not guilty by reason of insanity* functions to divert mentally disordered persons who have committed homicide from the mandatory custodial sentence and into suitable treatment, its purpose could be argued to have been superseded in 1957 by the establishment of a defence of *diminished responsibility* under s.2 of the Homicide Act[84]. In terms of practical effect (providing that the desired effect was a hospital order[85]), there is no real difference between the two verdicts. However, even if the two verdicts have the same practical effect, they theoretically derive from quite distinct conclusions as to the culpability of the offender. Where a jury passes a *special verdict* it declares the offender to be 'not guilty' by reason of insanity, implying that the degree of the mental disorder or its effect was such that it negates criminal responsibility. In contrast, a verdict of manslaughter under s.2 of the Homicide Act is a 'guilty' verdict, albeit one that recognises the effect of an abnormality of mind in reducing, but not negating, criminal responsibility for the offence. The difference between the two defences may therefore be crudely drawn as a matter of degree, although a defence counsel would seem to be forced to choose strategically between one or other plea, given that the defendant must plead not guilty to achieve an insanity verdict but guilty for a

---

[82]   From the 19th century Home Secretaries had in practice reprieved persons from the death penalty (Smith, R. (1981), *supra* p.170). According to health records obtained by lawyers acting for John Straffen, Britain's longest serving prisoner, it was accepted (if not public) policy in the early 1950s that 'if a prisoner is "insane", sentence of death is never carried out but the prisoner is reprieved and detained indefinitely, usually as a Broadmoor patient'. In Straffen's case the reprieve unusually led to imprisonment rather than hospitalisation. Straffen's case is instructive of the potential for illogicality in the application of the insanity defences. Considered unfit to plead as a 'mental defective' for killing two girls, Straffen was sent to Broadmoor Hospital in 1951, from whence he absconded for four hours in 1952. He was subsequently convicted of capital murder for a further killing that took place whilst he was AWOL from Broadmoor. The second trial was allowed to go ahead after doctors asserted that he was fit to plead, partly on the basis that he understood four of the ten commandments (i.e. using a cognitive test) although all agreed that he had a mental age of below 10 years old and, according to his Broadmoor doctor, would know the nature of the act of killing 'but not as a normal person'. Straffen's high-profile case (the Crown was represented by the attorney-general, and the Director of Public Prosecutions and two chief constables were in attendance) was also unusual for the fact that, having never been convicted of the first murders due to unfitness to plead, these were admissible evidence for the jury, whereas previous convictions would not have been at that time. See Bob Woffinden 'Historic murder case may reopen', 'Insane, guilty or neither?' *The Guardian* 26/05/01.

[83]   Although the actual figure for 2003/04 is 3%, this may be subject to upwards revision as more cases are completed and known to statisticians. The 2002/03 rate was 10%.

[84]   Bartlett, P. & Sandland, R (2003) *supra*, p.265.

[85]   Until April 2005, a special verdict in relation to a murder charge would have automatically led to a restricted hospital order, whereas a manslaughter verdict could lead to a range of disposals. It is now the case that a special verdict must only result in a restricted hospital order where the conditions for imposing such an order under s.37 of the Mental Health Act 1983 are met (see paragraph 5.26 above).

diminished responsibility verdict. Of course, if one defence is pleaded by the defendant, the Crown may argue the other.

Provocation

5.47 Section 3 of the Homicide Act 1957 introduced into statute the ancient common-law defence plea of 'provocation'. As enacted, the plea takes account of whether the person charged with homicide was provoked sufficiently 'to make a reasonable man do as he did' in losing control, and should therefore be liable to conviction of manslaughter rather than murder. Prior to the 1957 Act, judges had increasingly directed that the 'reasonable man' test was not to take account of any individual mental infirmity of the defendant, effectively excluding provocation as a workable psychiatric defence. The 1957 Act removed a judge's power to direct the jury over this matter, and case law from that time up to the judgment of the Privy Council in June 2005 (see below) had broadened the use of the power. *R v Camplin* [1978][86] determined that a person's age could be taken into account in applying the 'reasonable man' test, and a number of cases, culminating in the House of Lords judgment *R v Smith* [2000][87], extended this to allow juries to consider whatever personal characteristics they consider relevant (including mental disorder) in coming to a view as to whether the defence of provocation should be allowed. In *R v Rowland* [2003][88] the court underlined that a judge's summing up to the jury in any case involving the provocation defence must be careful to include all potentially relevant factors, especially in '…difficult borderline cases … between mere bad temper or excitability on the one hand and identifiable mental conditions and personality traits on the other'. However, in *Jersey v Holley* [2005][89], the Privy Council (by majority) stated that the majority view in *Smith* – i.e. that the standard of self-control required by the statute is flexible rather than the constant standard of a person with ordinary self-control – was erroneous.

5.48 In *Smith*, Lord Slynn had argued that notwithstanding any philosophical distinction between a defence of diminished responsibility under s.2 of the Homicide Act (where the defendant claims the mental abnormality preventing him from behaving normally) and provocation under s.3 of that Act (where the defence is that the act is at least partially excused as normal behaviour in response to external circumstances), 'in many cases the two forms of claim are inextricably muddled up with each other'[90]. In *Jersey v Holley* the majority of the Privy Council[91] viewed the approach of *Smith* to have departed from the law as established by Parliament in the 1957 Homicide Act, and stated that s.2 of that Act should not be distorted to accommodate the types of case for which s.3 (diminished responsibility) was specifically enacted[92]. Whether the Privy Council's judgment (especially, perhaps,

---

[86] *R v Camplin* [1978] A.C. 705

[87] *R v Smith (Morgan)* [2000] UKHL 49

[88] *R v Rowland* [2003] EWCA Crim 3636

[89] *Attorney-General for Jersey v Dennis Peter Holley (Jersey)* [2005] UKPC 23 (15 June 2005) 3 All ER 371

[90] Slynn LJ in *R v Smith* [2000] UKHL 49, para 8

[91] Majority judgment by Baroness Hale and Lords Nicholls, Craighead, Foscote, Earlsferry, and Gestingthorpe. Lords Bingham, Hoffman and Carswell dissenting.

[92] *Jersey v Holley* paras 15-16.

taking into account the dissenting opinions in that judgment) leaves any of the *Smith* approach to judges in their direction of future cases remains to be seen, but it would appear that Lord Slynn's reading of the defence of provocation as a type of second-level psychiatric defence, which may succeed in obtaining a manslaughter verdict even though a defendant is unable to convince the court that his mental disorder is of a nature or degree warranting a finding of diminished responsibility, may no longer be tenable. Although defence counsels may still be likely to advise their clients to claim both diminished responsibility and provocation defences wherever possible, to increase their chances of a successful manslaughter plea, it would seem that the use of both as alternate *psychiatric* defences may now have ended[93].

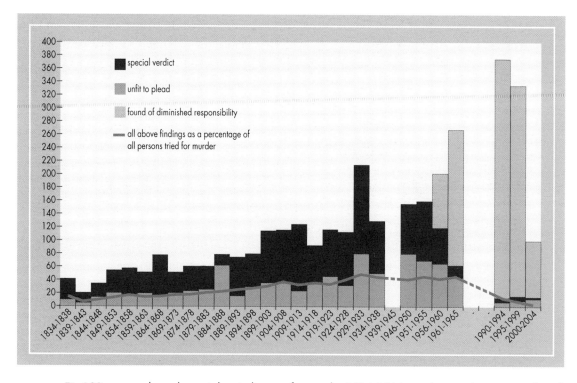

Fig 130: persons brought to trial on indictment for murder 1834-2004; numbers and percentage found unfit to plead / insane / of diminished responsibility[94]

---

[93] It appears that an unusual plea of self-defence was made in the January 2005 trial of Jason Canns, a patient at Springfield Hospital in Tooting who, in June 2003, attacked and killed nurse Mamade 'Eshan' Chatun whilst undergoing treatment for paranoid schizophrenia. Mr Cann's lawyers argued that he had acted in self-defence under the delusion that the nurse was about to attack him. This defence claim argued that the question of 'reasonable force' in self-defence should be determined relative to a patient's mental state. Canns was instead found guilty of manslaughter. The Criminal Appeal Court refused leave to appeal the conviction in July 2005.

[94] Data for 1834-1965 from Walker, N (1968) *Crime and Insanity in England* Volume 1, Appendix A. Data not collected 1939-45. 1990-2004 data from Home Office (2001) *Criminal Statistics* Cmnd 5312 (for 1990-2); Home Office (2005) *Crime in England and Wales 2003/04:Supplementary Volume 1: Homicide and Gun Crime* (for 1993 –2003/4). There were 478 incomplete court proceedings (out of a total of 3,264) in the data available for 2004. Diminished responsibility finding only applicable subsequent to Homicide Act 1957: see para 5.545 *et seq* above for discussion.

The decline of diminished responsibility verdicts

5.49 It is not possible from published figures to identify verdicts of manslaughter based upon the defence of provocation. However, at figure 131 below we show that the number of diminished responsibility verdicts peaked about 25 years ago and has been tailing away since that time, whilst the number of other manslaughter verdicts has been increasing steadily over that time (it is not clear whether the 2004 total is a reflection of incomplete data returns or a fall in number). Figure 132 shows the decline of diminished responsibility verdicts as a proportion of all homicide indictments.

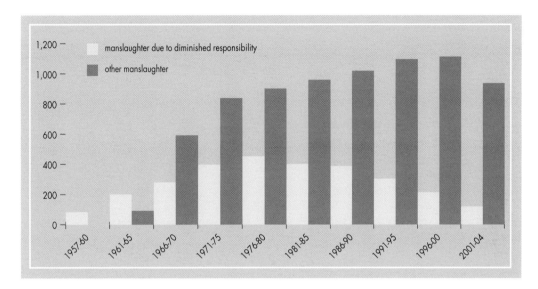

Fig 131: persons found guilty of manslaughter, 1957-2004[95]

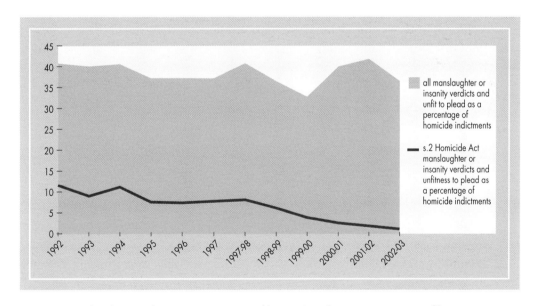

Fig 132: manslaughter verdicts as a percentage of homicide indictments, 1992-2003[96]

---

[95] Data for 1957 – 1995 from House of Commons Research Paper 99/56 *Homicide Statistics* (Patsy Richards, May 1999). 1996-2004 from Home Office (2005) *Crime in England and Wales 2003/04:Supplementary Volume 1: Homicide and Gun Crime.* Note that periods 1957-60 and 2001-04 are four-year periods rather than full five-year periods, and that data for 2003/04 is likely to be substantially incomplete.

[96] Data as for Fig 130.

5.50 What makes these figures especially significant in our view is the surprising fact that diminished responsibility verdicts no longer account for the majority of Mental Health Act hospital orders subsequent to a manslaughter verdict (see figure 133). After 1999/2000 manslaughter verdicts other than diminished responsibility account for over 80% of all such hospital orders recorded.

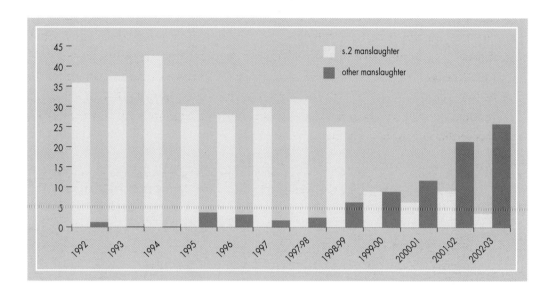

Fig 133: Mental Health Act hospital orders subsequent to manslaughter verdicts, 1992-2003[97]

5.51 It is not possible to state from available data the precise nature of the 'other' manslaughter verdicts represented at figure 131 (page 369). We suggest that the changes in law relating to provocation may, however, have made that an 'easier' defence to submit than a diminished responsibility plea, and that defence counsel will be likely to advise their clients to plead both defences. This can lead to complicated directions having to be given to juries, given that the pleas have differences in the nature of the psychiatric evidence needed and the burden of proof required. The Law Commission has reported no general support, however, for reform which would merge these two defences together in law, stating that the majority view is that each rests on a different moral basis[98]. We also note that some examples given in the Law Commission's *Partial Defences to Murder* report suggest that a plea of 'common-law' manslaughter was accepted by Courts[99].

5.52 At figure 134 below we aggregate data known about outcomes of homicide indictments that resulted in a verdict under the CPIA or a verdict of manslaughter. The average ratio of Mental Health Act hospital orders against other sentences for manslaughter with diminished responsibility verdicts is comparable for men and women: 51% and 48% respectively since 1990. Men are much more likely than women to receive a custodial rather than probationary sentence if a hospital order is not given. For homicide indictments generally, women are less likely than men to be convicted generally, and more likely when

---

[97] Data source: as for fig 131

[98] Law Commission (2004) *Partial Defences to Murder*, pp.107.

[99] Law Commission *supra*; see for example case 149, p.178

convicted for the verdict to be manslaughter with diminished responsibility (i.e. men are more likely to be convicted of murder)[100]. This is as likely (or perhaps more likely) to be a reflection of differences in type and context of offence than any inherent bias in court judgments.

5.53   It should be noted that our table does not include the alternative verdict of 'infanticide'. This defence rests on the balance of mind being disturbed in a mother by the act of birth or lactation, in which case the killing of her infant is classed as manslaughter rather than murder. As a common-law defence it has a long history[101], but it was first named and set out in statute law in 1922, and was re-enacted in the 1957 Homicide Act. It accounted for three or four additional verdicts each year in the period shown at figure 134, of which only two resulted in court orders under the Mental Health Act (both in 1998/9). Most sentences for this verdict consist of probation or supervision.

year	gender	unfit to plead	not guilty by reason of insanity	manslaughter due to diminished responsibility (1957 Act s.2)				other manslaughter	
				restricted court order	unrestricted court order	probation / supervision	prison sentence	restricted court order	unrestricted court order
1990	M	-	1	25	10	3	34	-	-
	F	-	-	5	-	2	1	-	-
1991	M	-	2	26	3	5	28	-	1
	F	-	-	5	-	7	2	-	-
1992	M	2	2	28	2	5	33	1	-
	F	-	1	4	2	1	3	-	-
1993	M	-	1	26	3	4	12	-	-
	F	-	-	7	2	3	1	-	-
1994	M	4	-	35	3	2	21	-	-
	F	-	-	3	1	2	3	-	2
1995	M	1	-	17	8	1	16	1	1
	F	-	1	2	3	3	1	-	-
1996	M	-	-	16	5	-	20	2	2
	F	1	-	7	-	1	1	-	-
1997	M	1	3	22	2	1	10	1	1
	F	-	-	5	1	4	1	-	-
1997/98	M	2	4	24	1	1	12	1	2
	F	-	-	6	1	3	1	-	-
1998/99	M	-	3	22	1	2	9	5	1
	F	3	-	2	-	2	2	1	-

[100] See table 7 of House of Commons research paper 99/56 (p.24) and table 1.09 of Home Office (2005) *Crime in England and Wales 2003/04:Supplementary Volume 1: Homicide and Gun Crime*

[101] See Walker, N (1968) *Crime & Insanity in England* vol. 1, Chapter 7.

year	gender	unfit to plead	not guilty by reason of insanity	manslaughter due to diminished responsibility (1957 Act s.2)				other manslaughter	
				restricted court order	unrestricted court order	probation / supervision	prison sentence	restricted court order	unrestricted court order
1999/00	M	2	2	7	1	2	9	6	2
	F	1	·	·	1	3	2	1	·
2000/01	M	4	1	4	3	1	9	3	5
	F	1	·	·	·	1	3	1	3
2001/02	M	2	·	3	5	·	4	6	13
	F	·	·	·	1	·	3	·	3
2002/03	M	1	1	·	4	·	7	9	13
	F	·	·	·	·	1	·	2	2
2003/04	M	1	·	·	1	·	9	3	6
	F	·	2	·	·	·	·	·	·

Fig 134: persons indicted for homicide offences 1990-2004. CPIA finding or special verdicts leading to hospital admission orders with restrictions; verdicts of manslaughter leading to hospital orders and other disposals[102]

5.54 In reaching a verdict of diminished responsibility, a jury attends only to the question of the guilt or otherwise of a defendant, and its is impossible to generalise from this determination as to what the appropriate disposal would have been in any particular case. Certainly diminished responsibility verdicts do not necessarily imply the presence of a treatable mental disorder at the time of disposal. Because of this, the verdict itself cannot properly be regarded as part of the State's apparatus to divert mentally disordered persons from criminal justice disposals.

5.55 Nevertheless, there has long been interest in the incidence of hospital orders subsequent to verdicts of diminished responsibility. Research undertaken by Dell and Smith twenty years ago recognised that there had been a change in the disposal of men convicted of the verdict, where the predominance of hospital orders had given way to prison sentences[103]. The cause was identified to be changes neither in the make-up of the offender population, nor the willingness of judges to make hospital orders, but the pattern of treatment recommendations made by the examining doctors in their court reports. Professor Mackay's study of 126 diminished responsibility verdicts between 1997 and 2001 found that 62 (49%) resulted in restricted hospital orders, with six resulting in unrestricted hospital orders[104]. The reduced

---

[102] Data source: as for fig 131.

[103] Dell, S. and Smith, A. (1983) 'Changes in the sentencing of diminished responsibility homicides' *British Journal of Psychiatry* 142:20-34

[104] Mackay R D 'The Diminished Responsibility Plea in Operation- an Empirical Study' published as Annex B to the Law Commission (2004) *Partial Defences to Murder* Final Report.

incidence of the verdict itself over the last twenty years (see figure 131) makes comparison problematic, as there are too few verdicts to reliably identify trends, but from available data (figure 135) it would appear that over the likelihood of a court order disposal continues to fall and has done so at a proportionally greater rate than other types of available disposal. This is true for women as well as men, although the numbers involved for women are very small[105].

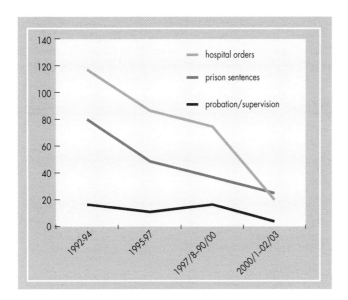

Fig 135: outcomes of manslaughter with diminished responsibility (Homicide Act 1957, s.2) verdicts, 1992-2003[106].

5.56 The data in figure 135 gives a more detailed indication as to how the verdict of diminished responsibility operates in practice as a diversionary system. This shows the disposals following that verdict that result in hospital orders or probation/supervision, against those leading to prison sentences. According to this data, which admittedly is dealing with very small numbers, even as the frequency of diminished responsibility verdicts is falling, the likelihood of such a verdict leading to prison rather than hospital or probation is on the rise:

- Over the twelve years from 1992 to 2002/03[107], just over a third of diminished responsibility verdicts (182 of 515, or 35%) resulted in prison sentences rather than hospital or

---

[105] Data for diminished responsibility verdicts, females, from figure 135:

	1992-1994	1995-1997	1997/8 – 1999/0	2000/1 – 2002/3
hospital order	19	18	10	1
probation	6	8	8	2
prison	7	3	5	6

[106] Data source: as for fig 131.

[107] We have disregarded data available from 2003/04 (shown at fig 134 above) from this comparison as it is likely to be incomplete and subject to revision in future statistical releases. Our comparison (and fig 134 above) excludes from the period studied (1992- 2003) eight verdicts of diminished responsibility leading to a suspended custodial sentence, and two resulting in 'other sentences' impossible to classify from available information.

probation disposals. Of these prison sentences, 49 (27%) were life-sentences; one was another sentence of over ten years' duration; 83 (45%) were sentences of between 4 and 10 years; and 49 (27%) were sentences of less than four years' duration.

- Of the 72 recorded diminished responsibility verdicts between 1999/00 and 2002/3[108], 35 (i.e. 49%) of these resulted in a prison sentence (7 life sentences, 1 other sentence of over 10 years duration, 15 sentences between 4 and 10 years, and 12 of less than 4 years, and two suspended sentences)[109].

Transfers of prisoners under the Mental Health Act 1983

'The real stigma of my mental health problems was when I was in prison, because of my self-harming scars and constant stitches. I was labelled a freak and tortured by other inmates and so had to spend all my time on the health care wing until I was transferred to an MSU'

Dawn Cutler, service user, Cheshire

5.57 Convicted prisoners who are suffering from mental disorder to a nature or degree that makes hospital treatment appropriate may be transferred to hospital under s.47 of the Mental Health Act 1983 and detained there as if subject to a hospital order imposed by a court (see 5.82 *et seq* below). Unsentenced prisoners, whether they are on remand, awaiting sentence, civil prisoners or immigration detainees (or, during this reporting period, anti-terrorism detainees) may be transferred under powers set out at s.48 of the Act. Although, particularly in the case of s.47, the criteria for admission to hospital under these transfer orders is similar to that set out at s.3 of the Act[110], in practice the threshold is lower as the prisoner has already been deprived of his or her liberty by the criminal law, and community-treatment is not an alternative option that must be weighed when determining the most appropriate placement.

5.58 Figure 136 shows Home Office statistics for the transfer of restricted prisoners to hospital under the powers of the Mental Health Act 1983 over the last twenty years. This data does not give a complete picture of transfers, in that it does not include any *unrestricted* patient transfers. It is usually assumed that such transfers are relatively rare, given that:

- In relation to transfers of unsentenced or untried prisoners, the discretion to transfer without restrictions under s.48 applies only in a fraction of cases (i.e. civil prisoners or immigration detainees)[111];

---

[108] Excludes two verdicts of diminished responsibility leading to a suspended custodial sentence; see note above.

[109] Data source: as for fig 131 above

[110] Whilst the criteria for transfer under s.47 is essentially similar to that for s.3 detention, s.48 criteria limit the transfer of unsentenced prisoners to those suffering from mental illness or severe mental impairment (thereby excluding psychopathic disorder or mental impairment) where there is urgent need of psychiatric treatment. Nevertheless we would maintain that the effective threshold for hospital treatment is lower than for non-prisoners, given the fact that fundamental questions of liberty are not engaged.

[111] MHA 1983 s.49(1)

- In the case of transfers of sentenced prisoners under s.47, where the Home Secretary retains complete discretion over the imposition of restrictions, the Home Office has maintained for the lifetime of the Act that its normal policy is always to impose restrictions, unless the prisoner is transferred 'within days of his release date and the nature of the offence suggests that restrictions are unnecessary for the protection of the public from serious harm over that short period'[112].

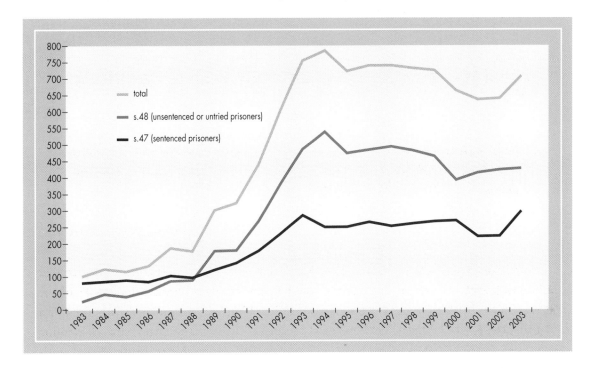

Fig 136: transfers of restricted prisoners to hospital under the Mental Health Act, 1983–2003[113]

5.59 Department of Health data given at figure 137 suggests quite significant numbers of unrestricted transfers, not included in figure 136 above[114].

---

[112] See *R (on the application of T) v Secretary of State for the Home Department* [2003] EWHC Admin 538; (see Chapter 1.182 *et seq*). In the 1978 White Paper *Review of the Mental Health Act* 1959 (Cmnd 7320, para 5.43) the Government stated that 'the Home Secretary's current practice is almost invariably to impose restrictions on the transfer of a prisoner under section 72 [the predecessor of section 47 of the 1983 Act], the only exception being prisoners transferred a month or less before their earliest date of release (EDR) from prison (though in exceptional cases some of these are also transferred with restrictions)'

[113] Data source : 1983 – 1993: Home Office *Statistics of Mentally Disordered Offenders England & Wales* Statistical Bulletin 01/95 Table 1; 1993-2003: Bulletin 16/04 Table 3.

[114] Home Office statistical bulletins did publish data on unrestricted transfers prior to 1993, but a comparison with Department of Health Bulletins shows a wide discrepancy between the data collected by the two arms of Government. According to the Home Office, in the first six years of the 1983 Act, on average 20% of all prison transfers were of unrestricted patients. This figure rapidly decreases over the next five years: 8% in 1989; 7% in 1990; and 6% in 1991. No unrestricted transfers were reported for the years 1992 and 1993. After 1993 the Home Office refrained from publishing statistics on unrestricted transfers. By comparison, Department of Health statistics partly shown at figure 137 below suggest that 57% of transfers from prison in the first six years' of the Act were unrestricted (390 transfers), with 26% (51 transfers) unrestricted in 1989/90; 22% (55) in 1990/91; 26% (93) in 1991/2, 21% (229) over the two years 1992/3 and 1993/4; and 10% (562) over the decade between 1994/5 and 2003/4.

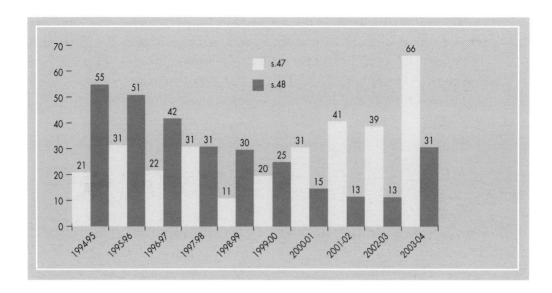

Fig 137: unrestricted transfers of prisoners to hospitals 1994/5 to 2003/4 (DH stats)[115]

5.60   We doubt the accuracy of the Department of Health data on restricted transfers. Overall, the Department of Health's statistics show significantly less restricted transfers than are accounted for by the Home Office. Some idea of this difference may be given by a trend-line comparison of the two sets of statistics at figure 138, although the comparison is not exact as the Department of Health uses financial years after 1996, whilst the Home Office figures are based upon calendar years throughout.

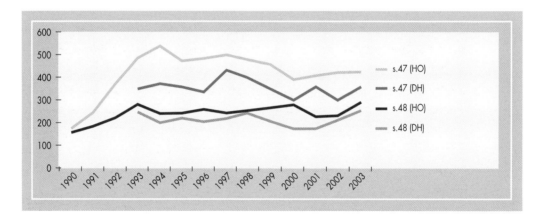

Fig 138: data on restricted MHA transfers from prison 1990-2003; a comparison of statistics published by the Home Office and Department of Health[116]

5.61   It seems likely that the Home Office figures are the more accurate as these are collected from Home Office computer databases and case-files, whereas the Department of Health statistics rely upon returns from hospitals. Nemitz and Bean have previously pointed to the

---

[115] Data source: Department of Health Statistical Bulletins 1996 - 2004 *Inpatients formally detained in hospitals under the Mental Health Act 1983 and other legislation, England.*

[116] Data source: as for figures 135 & 136 above.

discrepancies and inaccuracies in the latter form of data collection[117]. However, all statistical collations from either source should be viewed with some caution: we have heard from practitioners that Home Office officials have on occasion appeared to be unaware of court orders with restrictions passed by the courts until (and presumably unless) the RMO of such a patient contacts them regarding leave or some other variation in the condition of their detention.

	1994	1995	1996	1997	1998	1999	2000	2001	2002	2003	total
HO s.47 restricted	249	250	264	251	258	267	270	222	223	296	2,514
DHa s.47 restricted (+ unrestricted)	202 (223)	222 (253)	208 (230)	216 (247)	236 (247)	211 (231)	184 (215)	185 (226)	220 (259)	252 (318)	2,136 (2,449)
Difference	-47 (-23)	-28 (+3)	-56 (-34)	-35 (-4)	-22 (-9)	-56 (-36)	-86 (-55)	-37 (+4)	-3 (+36)	-44 (+22)	-378 (-65)
HO s.48	536	473	481	495	481	464	392	413	421	425	4,581
DH* s.48 restricted (+ unrestricted)	367 (422)	359 (410)	342 (384)	429 (460)	405 (435)	353 (378)	296 (311)	349 (362)	297 (310)	349 (380)	3,546 (3,852)
Difference	-169 (-114)	-114 (-63)	-139 (-97)	-66 (-35)	-76 (-46)	-111 (-86)	-96 (-81)	-64 (-51)	-124 (-111)	-76 (-45)	-1,035 (-729)

Fig 139: data on transfers under s 47 and 48, comparison of Department of Health and Home Office statistics, 1994-2003[118]

* DH statistics collated by calendar year, so, for example, '1993' = 1993/4

5.62   The relevant figures are tabulated at figure 139 above. Because of the mismatch of financial and calendar years, the discrepancies within each individual column are not meaningful. The table therefore shows the total use of each section of the Act over the last decade according to each statistical source, and the total divergence over that time between the two sources. For 'restricted' transfers under s.47 the Department of Health figures count 414 less transfers than the Home Office: a variance of around 15%. This variance reduces to 2.5% if all Department of Health totals (restricted and unrestricted) are counted against the Home Office figures. For s.48, the Department of Health counts 1,166 less transfers: a variance of more than a quarter, although this can be reduced to 16% if distinctions between restricted and unrestricted patients are ignored. One possible reason for the mismatch in figures, therefore, may be due to hospitals returning statistics to the Department of Health that fail to recognise patients' restricted status.

5.63   Statistics from both the Home Office and Department of Health show similar overall trends in transfer usage. Both show that the numbers of transfers fell sharply at the turn of this decade, but that the numbers of transfers has since risen again, albeit not to an overall level that it has reached in the past (figures 136, 138). However, the number of transfers of *sentenced* prisoners is higher than ever before, by a small margin. This data must be viewed in the context of a huge rise in the prisoner population over the last decade: the prison

---

[117] Nemitz T and Bean P (1995) 'Discrepancies and Inaccuracies in Statistics for Detained Patients'. *Psychiatric Bulletin* (1995) 19, 28 – 32. See also House of Commons Health Committee Fifth Report of Session 1992-93, *Community Supervision Orders* Vol 1, HC 667-1, p.ix-x; where Department of Health's written evidence to the committee expressed 'some concerns about the accuracy' of MHA statistics on admissions.

[118] data source: as for fig 138.

population is currently at its highest ever, with a prison population of over 75,000, 17% of whom are untried or unconvicted. Since 1993, when the number of transfers from prison under the Act was at its peak, the prison population has increased by over 70% (figure 140), and so the rate of transfers against that population total has in fact fallen considerably. Although it is a crude measure, in 1993 it could be said that one in every 86 prisoners was transferred to hospital under the Mental Health Act: in 2003, this ratio was one in every 113 prisoners; it is now likely to be an even smaller ratio of prisoners who are transferred.

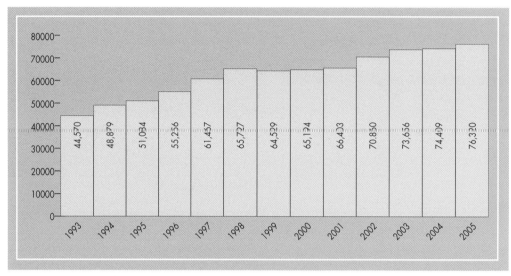

Fig 140: prison population 1993 - 2005[119]

5.64 At figure 141 below we show the population of restricted patients who had been transferred from prison between 1988 and 2003.

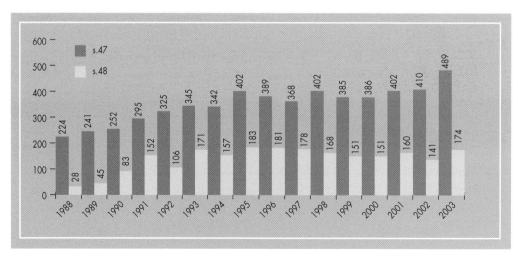

Fig 141: hospital population of restricted transferred prisoners 1989 – 2003[120]

---

[119] data source: For 1993 to 2002, Home Office *Statistics on Race and the Criminal Justice System*, published under section 95 of the Criminal Justice Act 1991 (average monthly population over the year). Data for 2002 from *Prison Statistics 2002* (CM 5996). Data for 2003-05 from Home Office quarterly prison statistics (www.homeoffice.gov.uk/rds). Data for 2005 is a provisional figure averaged from the first two quarterly returns and the prison population as of 1 Sept 2005 (77,807).

[120] data source: Home Office *Statistics of Mentally Disordered Offenders*, 1985 – 2004

5.65   As we show in figures 142 and 143, the net increase in the hospital population of patients who have been transferred from prison is much less than the number transferred when discharges or the return of patients to prison is taken into account. For obvious reasons, the population of prisoners transferred on remand will be much more transient than the sentenced prisoner population[121].

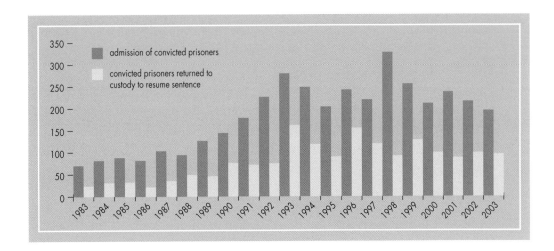

Fig 142: transfer to hospital (s.47 MHA 1983) and return to custody of convicted prisoners, 1983-2003[122]

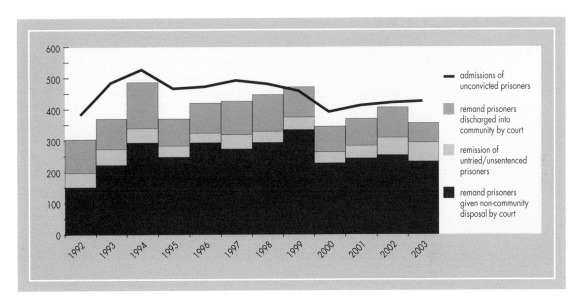

Fig 143: transfer to hospital (s.48 MHA 1983) of unconvicted prisoners with main outcomes, 1992 - 2003[123]

---

[121] The most thorough study of s.48 to date is MacKay R D & Machin D 'An Empirical Study of the Transfer of Remand Prisoners to Hospital' *British Journal of Criminology* (2000) 40; 727-745, summarised in *Transfers from Prison to Hospital – The Operation of Section 48 of the Mental Health Act 1983*, Home Office Research Findings No. 84, Home Office Research, Development and Statistics Directorate, 1998.

[122] Data source: Home Office Statistics of Mentally Disordered Offenders, 1985 – 2004

[123] Data source: as fig 142 above

'Notional section 37'

5.66 We are frequently asked the meaning of the administrative term 'notional section 37'[124], particularly as the term is now used in some computerised record software.

5.67 A 'notional s.37' is an administrative term for the power of detention and treatment provided under s.47 when it is used without an accompanying restriction order to transfer a prisoner to hospital, or where the accompanying restriction order on such a prison transfer expires as the date that the prison sentence would have ended had no transfer taken place is reached[125]. In contrast to the transfer of unsentenced prisoners under s.48, the powers of detention under s.47 are not parasitic on the patient's status as a prisoner once the transfer has taken place[126]. Therefore the expiry of a prisoner's sentence does not invalidate the authority to continue a MHA detention where the conditions for the latter continue to be met. Section 47(3) states that a transfer under s.47 shall have the same effect as a hospital order under s.37.

5.68 Prisoners transferred under restriction orders can be returned to prison by the Home Secretary if their mental state improves, or their condition is deemed untreatable or not requiring treatment[127]. The power to return a transferred prisoner falls away, with the restriction order itself, at the point of that prisoner's release date, from which time he or she is an unrestricted hospital order patient. It can be helpful at this point (i.e. upon the date of release from sentence) to regard the detention power for the purposes of administration as a 'notional s.37'. Where a prisoner is transferred under s.47 without a restriction order, there is an argument for administrative classification of that patient as a notional s.37 from admission (i.e. regardless of the release date), as there is no power to return the patient to prison and he is practically, but not theoretically, an ex-prisoner from the point of entry into the mental health system.

5.69 Administrators have objected that the administrative term 'notional s.37' has no statutory basis and 'administrative reclassification' is a legal fiction. We accept that this is the case, but these objections are in our view outweighed by the fact that it seems manifestly unfair, and potentially confusing, to continue to classify a patient who is in fact an ex-prisoner as a 'person serving sentences of imprisonment' (the title of s.47). It seems much better to recognise at the date of release from sentence, or perhaps at the point where the prison system relinquishes its claim on the patient, that his status has changed. It would also be useful to be able statistically to distinguish those patients whose status has changed from

---

[124] The term appears only once in Richard Jones' *Mental Health Act Manual*, ninth edition, at para 1-628, where it is not fully explained.

[125] The expiry of the sentence for these purposes is the actual release date at the end of the full sentence, taking into account any early release days awarded to the patient for good behaviour under the Crime Sentences Act 1997, s.11, but disregarding any other expectations that the prisoner might have for discretionary early release that might have been applied by the parole board or Home Secretary.

[126] In the case of transfers of unsentenced prisoners under s.48, the liability to detain under MHA powers remains parasitic on, for example, the remand order that put the prisoner into custody in the first place. In such cases, s.51(2) of the Act states that the powers of detention under the MHA fall when the court disposes of the case (although this does not prevent such a disposal from being a hospital order under s.37 or indeed the subsequent use of civil powers of detention).

[127] MHA 1983 s.50

being a prisoner (in most cases subject to return to prison) to being a hospital order patient. Needless to say, no such distinction is made in practice in current statistical presentations[128].

5.70   The draft Mental Health Bill 2004 proposals on prison transfers would make all sentenced prisoners (including fine defaulters such as *T* at Chapter 1.182 *et seq* below) who are transferred to hospital subject to restrictions, and all other prisoners liable to restrictions at the determination of the Home Secretary. Whether or not transferred prisoners of any kind are restricted patients, they would be liable to be returned to prison if they regain their health or if treatment fails or is discontinued for any other reason. The proposals would also make *all* transfer orders for sentenced prisoners expire with the sentence release date[129]. At this point patients would be liable to civil detention if the conditions were met. This is perhaps more rational than the current system, although for unrestricted patients the current system is perhaps better suited as an after-the-event diversionary system when a mentally disordered offender has been sent to prison because of missed diagnoses or lack of available health placements at time of sentence. Under the Mental Health Bill 2004 proposals no convicted prisoner is finally diverted from the penal system until their sentence expires, however inappropriate a return to prison would be in their case. In this sense the proposals of the 2004 Bill (in particular in relation to these powers conjoined with the potential expansion of hybrid orders as court disposals linking hospital directions to custodial sentences discussed at paragraph 5.89 *et seq* below) could blur the 'diversionary' element of mental health disposals. It is important that steps are taken in the implementation of any such proposals to preserve the policy and general principle of mental health disposals as a diversion from punitive criminal justice: a just society does not punish its members for being mentally disordered.

> **Recommendation 54:** Government should be alert to the potential for Mental Health Bill proposals discussed above to undermine the principle of diverting mentally disordered offenders from penal custody, and may wish to consider ways in which such consequences might be avoided.
>
> (see also recommendation 56 below)

---

[128] Our reading of Home Office Statistics (bulletin 16/04, table 16a) suggests that, in 2003, notional 37s must have accounted for some proportion - and probably quite a large proportion – of 127 patients whose restriction orders were lifted or who died, but who, if still living, remained in hospital. Proportionally, the resident population of sentenced prisoners overall is only about 1/5 that of patients subject to court orders, but it seems likely that the proportion of transferred prisoners among these 127 patients is greater than this. Courts rarely issue time-limited restriction orders under s.41, and so there is no formal mechanism to rescind them outside of MHRT proceedings. Although the Secretary of State may rescind restriction orders passed by the courts where s/he finds them no longer required for public protection (s.42(1)), we suggest that use of this power is likely to be rare. Of the 127 patients in the 2003 statistics, 97 had been in hospital for less than two years; 11 for 2-5 years; six for 5-10 years; 7 for 10-20 years; one for 20-30 years; and five for over 30 years.

[129] Draft Mental Health Bill 2004, clauses 135 to 139.

Prison transfers and preventive detention

5.71   In previous reports we have expressed concern at the transfer to hospital of prisoners near the end of their sentence[130]. There could be several reasons for late transfers. At Chapter 1.187 *et seq* above we discuss a case where difficulties in arranging the transfer led to it being effected on the day before a young offender was due to be released. In that case the judge suggested that the Home Secretary was under a duty to set the assessment mechanisms for potential transfer running once the prison service had reasonable grounds to believe that the prisoner requires treatment in a mental hospital. This may be an easier principle to apply in relation to acute illnesses than it is for the ranges of personality disorder and learning disability that is evident within the prison population. It may be that some late transfers (particularly of personality disordered patients) reflect a lack of urgency on the part of authorities to address a prisoner's mental disorder until such time as the release date is imminent. This, as well as the generally lower threshold for detention in hospital for people already deprived of their liberty through the criminal justice system (see paragraph 5.57 above) may give rise to the perception (particularly with the prisoner concerned) that the discovery of mental disorder requiring hospitalisation is rather too convenient for authorities who are unhappy at the prospect of a prisoner's release.

5.72   The Act requires that the nature or degree of the prisoner's mental disorder must justify treatment in hospital for the transfer to take place, and, if that disorder is mental impairment or psychopathic disorder, treatment must be justified against the criteria that it is likely to alleviate or prevent a deterioration of the condition. The treatability criteria can be interpreted fairly expansively. In 2002 the courts declared lawful the transfer to hospital of a personality disordered prisoner who had initially been found 'untreatable', on the grounds that treatment in hospital would manage the patient's environment to minimise the disorder's effects and seek to inculcate skills to enable the prisoner to cope with his disorder so that he might be gradually discharged through increasing leave arrangements[131].

5.73   The Home Secretary is not obliged to direct transfers when requested to do so. In practice, the responsibility for examining requests falls to the Home Office Mental Health Unit, which relies upon information provided to it upon standard prison service forms to determine the Secretary of State's response to any request for transfer. It is therefore very important that the information provided through such forms addresses the question of whether the legal criteria for transfer are met.

5.74   In this reporting period we were concerned to find that a prisoner had been transferred near the end of his sentence to High Security Hospital care on the strength of two prison service recommendations which did not, in our view, address the 'treatability' criterion even in terms established by the courts in 2002. It is possible that this was due to omission rather than deliberate choice. We corresponded with the Home Office Mental Health unit over our concerns but received no satisfactory answer as to how the Home Secretary had been able to determine that the statutory criteria for detention were met. Upon being informed that the

---

[130] See, for example, MHAC (1999) *Eighth Biennial Report*, Chapter 4.67.

[131] *South West London and St George's Mental Health NHS Trust v W* [2002] EWHC 1770 Admin

patient had appealed detention to the Mental Health Review Tribunal, we copied our correspondence with the Home Office to the MHRT with a request that it be disclosed to all parties. We understand that the patient subsequently withdrew his application to the MHRT on more than one occasion. At the time of writing he was resident in a medium-secure DSPD unit under leave arrangements from high security.

5.75   In our view this case exemplifies the dangers of mental health law being distorted by its use for public protection, especially when decisions regarding the use of that law are made by an administrative arm of the State whose focus is stated to be solely concerned with public protection rather than also with clinical matters[132]. We have no doubt that it was universally held that the prisoner concerned was a danger to the public, but the prospect that this danger should be contained by treatment under the Mental Health Act does not appear to have been mooted (including under a Multi-Agency Public Protection Plan for his discharge) until two months before the release date. Within days of the first psychiatric referee declining to act without further information as to the 'therapeutic rationale' for the referral, a Home Office official wrote that the prisoner 'is due for release on [here a date was given a month from the letter] and we are eager to get him transferred to a hospital under section 47/49 of the MHA before that date'. It is clear that there were pressures on administrators (whose primary function was deemed to be ensuring public protection) to provide a medical rationale for continued detention in this case, and that the rationale was read into the medical reports finally obtained. Such a system provides little protection against the misapplication of mental health law. In this particular case, it seems possible that a case for the prisoner's 'treatability' *could* have been made in the terms established by the 2002 judgment discussed above, but we are greatly concerned that the transfer appeared to be solicited and approved by the Home Office without it *actually* being made. We are also concerned that, if the prisoner did warrant removal to hospital for treatment of his mental disorder, this appears not to have been considered earlier in his prison sentence. We discuss the Home Office role in making decisions about clinical outcomes further at paragraphs 5.108 *et seq* below.

Remands to hospital

5.76   Under the 1983 Act an offender can be remanded to hospital for a report on his or her mental condition under s.35, or remanded for treatment under s.36. The remand powers may last up to twelve weeks. Remand for treatment is rarely used: an average of 22 remands of this type have been made in each of the last ten years[133]. The use of s.35 is shown at figure

---

[132]   See also paragraph 5.109 below. The claim that the Home Office function is 'solely' about public protection is made twice in Home Office Mental Health Unit (2005) *Guidance for Responsible Medical Officers; Leave of Absence for Patients Subject to Restrictions.* March 2005: introductory para, page 1; checklist of points, page 20.

[133]   Department of Health statistics show an unusually high number of uses (65) in 1993/4, but there is no notable decline in use overall (annually uses of c.30 are reported in the 1980s). Available DH returns for the last eleven years are:

1993/4	1994/5	1995/6	1996/7	1997/8	1998/9	1999/0	2000/1	2001/2	2002/3	2003/4
65	18	21	33	25	23	18	18	25	23	14

data source: Department of Health (1999, 2004) *In-patients formally detained in hospitals under the Mental Health Act 1983 and other legislation, England,* table 1.

144 below. In our last report we speculated that the apparent decline in the use of this powers could be an effect of the use of non-NHS facilities to receive patients[134], but the data set out below would appear to show that this is not the case.

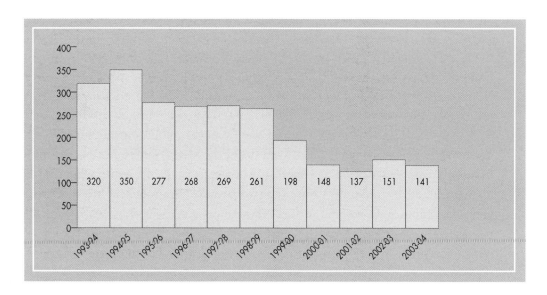

Fig 144: remands to hospital for assessment (s.35), NHS & Independent Hospitals, England 1993/4 – 2003/4[135]

5.77 The treatment provisions of Part IV of the Act do not apply to patients remanded under s.35 for assessment. This has led to the practice of 'dual detention', whereby a patient is detained under civil powers at the same time as being subject to assessment under remand powers. We discussed this in our last report[136], highlighting that Richard Jones has argued forcefully that this practice, which was declared lawful by 'a pragmatic decision of the Court of Appeal'[137] cannot have been the intention of Parliament when passing the 1983 Act, especially given the conflicting powers available to the Responsible Medical Officer under each detaining power. One example of such a conflict is that an RMO may grant leave to a patient detained under s.3 but not s.35. In practical terms this conflict is resolved by the RMO's power to grant leave under s.3 being effectively cancelled by the patient's remand status. If a patient requires leave for any reason, courts may therefore be asked to agree to modify the terms of their remand order, although it is not clear that they have a power to do so.

5.78 At paragraph 17.3 of the Mental Health Act Code of Practice it is suggested that, where a s.35 patient needs treatment, that patient should be referred back to the court as soon as possible with an assessment and an appropriate recommendation for disposal (which in most cases would probably be a hospital order under s.37), and that only in cases where there could be a delay in achieving this should concurrent detention under s.3 can be considered. The Code

[134] MHAC (2003) *Tenth Biennial Report: Placed Amongst Strangers.* Chapter 13.1

[135] Data source: as for Fig 142 above.

[136] MHAC (2003) *Tenth Biennial Report: Placed Amongst Strangers.* Chapter 13.1 - 13.4

[137] Jones, R (2004) *Mental Health Act Manual* ninth edition, para 1-483. The case in question is *R v North West London Mental Health Trust ex parte Stewart* [1997] 4 All E.R. 871, CA.

does not mention the possibility of using s.2 of the Act instead of s.3, although in circumstances where there is uncertainty over a patient's true diagnosis or prognosis the use of s.2 assessment powers may be the more appropriate course. The Code's guidance that the patient should be returned to court with a recommendation for further disposal is not always achievable. In one case brought to our attention in this reporting period, the patient requiring treatment had just had a remand order renewed, implying that the patient's assessment was not yet concluded to the point where a recommendation for detention under a hospital order could be made in good faith. The Code does not seem to countenance the possibility that a trial of certain treatments might be a prerequisite of an adequate assessment, although we expect that this is quite a common occurrence.

5.79   We welcome the draft Mental Health Bill 2004 proposal to provide courts with comprehensive powers to state, when remanding a patient for assessment, whether the clinician responsible for that patient may grant leave or administer treatment, or for the Tribunal to authorise treatment where the conditions for its use are met subsequent to a remand order being made[138]. Although the proposed law in this area is complex, it does at least remove the illogicality of the present legal position.

Returning patients on remand or interim orders to court

5.80   The Code of Practice guidance on returning patients held under ss.35, 36, or 38 to court states that the conveyance of the patient to court is a responsibility of the detaining hospital, but that once the patient is on court premises he or she will come under the supervision of police or prison officers there[139]. This assumption appears to have been rendered practically obsolete by the privatisation of court security services. Forensic clinicians report that police resources for conveyance are not usually available, and that court security staff claim that their contracts explicitly exclude responsibility for psychiatric patients. Nursing staff are therefore left with little option but to retain their supervisory role over the patient throughout court proceedings. We have heard of incidences where use of secure custody areas has been given only reluctantly by court security staff, and of refusals to provide meals to patients left in the care of nursing staff on court premises. Hospital nursing staff, whose authority to detain a patient who is technically a prisoner of the court is apparently unfounded, have therefore been left in sole charge of patients in secure areas of court (often using spare capacity that nominally reserved for female prisoners) and have on occasion been locked in with patients by court security staff, or else given keys to court secure areas by court security staff and left to manage by themselves. Nursing staff have similarly been expected to control patients in the court-room, for example by preventing patients from leaving the dock.

5.81   We are aware that these issues have been raised by West London Mental Health Trust managers with the Department of Health, Lord Chancellor's Department and Home Office but that no solution has been found. We urge Government to look again at this question.

---

[138] Draft Mental Health Bill 2004, clauses 91 *et seq.*

[139] Mental Health Act 1983 Code of Practice, Chapter 29.6

> **Recommendation 55:** Government should address the concerns of mental health services over court-based security provision with a view to ensuring that the court administration fulfils its legal duties towards the custody of defendants.

Hospital orders under section 37 of the Act.

5.82 Under s.37 of the Act a Court may impose a hospital order rather than a custodial sentence when convicting an offender for crimes punishable with imprisonment (provided that the offence does not carry a mandatory sentence).

5.83 Available data on the admission of patients to hospital suggests that, over the lifetime of the Act (until 2003/04) the courts have ordered over 18,500 patients to hospital using s.37. Unfortunately, the sources of this data show radical divergences when examined in any detail.

5.84 Figure 145 shows the variation between published Home Office and Department of Health statistics on the use of s.37. That the two authorities provide a similar total number of uses over the two decades would appear to be coincidence rather than indicative of any profound similarities between their data. The incompatibility of the figures cannot be solely a result of the fact that the Home Office collates by calendar year, whereas the Department of Health moved to financial years in 1997. The Department of Health data suggests that fewer court orders are made now than at any previous time during the two decades of the Act's implementation: this is contradicted by the Home Office data. Both sets of data suggest that there are proportionally more restriction orders now than in past years, although according to the Department of Health this is due to a marked fall in unrestricted orders, whereas the Home Office indicates a rise in the number of restricted orders made. Overall the Department of Health counted nearly a third more restriction orders than the Home Office seemed to be aware of [140].

5.85 Because of the Home Office's close involvement with administering restriction orders, which in part give a greater credibility to its claims for the sources of data on this aspect of the use of s.37, we have generally preferred their data in our analyses throughout this report[141]. We discuss the use of restriction orders in more detail at paragraph 5.99 below.

---

[140] Total uses of s.37 between 1983 and 2003 recorded by the Home Office and Dept. of Health are as follows:

	Home Office	Dept. of Health
unrestricted	14,585	11,782
restricted	3,975	6,239
total	18,560	18,538

[141] The Home Office collates information on unrestricted court orders from its database on court proceedings statistics, with restricted patient data being extracted from its own database used in managing casework. The data published is supplemented by and cross-checked against information from the Home Office copies of court orders, and from half-yearly returns from hospitals (Home Office (2004) *Statistics of Mentally Disordered Offenders* 2003. Bulletin 16/04, paras 10-11). However, see also paragraph 5.61 above.

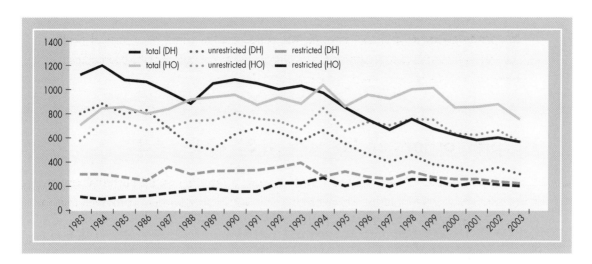

Fig 145: divergences in Home Office and Department of Health statistics on the use of MHA section 37, 1983 – 2003[142].

However, the source of data for the Home Office on *unrestricted* court orders may be more open to question, and we do not entirely discount the possibility that the Department of Health is correct in reflecting a steeper decline in unrestricted orders passed by the courts.

5.86   Details relating to the apparent decline in court orders under s.37 have been discussed in print by Bartlett and Sandland (using Home Office figures to 2001)[143]. They warn against investing apparent trends with too much significance, given that absolute numbers involved are small and represent less than 1% of all persons sentenced by the courts, and that global numbers of convictions move up and down from year to year. However, they did note apparent declining trends in hospital orders made between 1999 and 2001 for which the introduction of mandatory sentencing *could* have been a partial explanation. Non-restricted court orders subsequent to convictions for non-fatal violent offences reduced by a fifth between 1999 (227 orders) and 2001 (181 orders). Although Home Office statistics for 2002 show a possible reverse to 201 unrestricted orders in this category, provisional figures for 2003 show only 156 such orders. Non-restricted court orders subsequent to convictions for sexual offences have reduced from 50 in 1999 to a provisional figure of 39 in 2003.

---

[142]   Data source: Home Office *Statistics of Mentally Disordered Offenders* 1985 to 2004; Department of Health statistical bulletins *Inpatients formally detained under the Mental Health Act and other legislation*, 1985 to 2004.

[143]   Bartlett P and Sandland R (2003) *Mental Health Law Policy and Practice*, second edition, pp.290. For Home Office statistics on the offences of persons given unrestricted orders between 1992 and 2003, see Home Office *Statistics of Mentally Disordered Offenders* 2002, 2003, table 18.

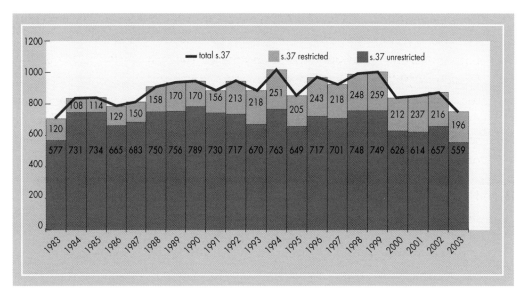

Fig 146: Home Office statistics on the use of MHA s.37, England and Wales, 1983 -2003[144]

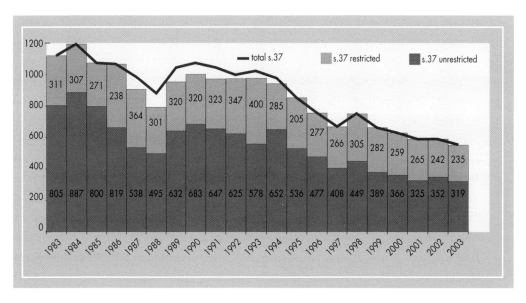

Fig 147: Department of Health statistics on the use of MHA s.37, England and Wales, 1983 -2003[145]

5.87   Bartlett and Sandland's analysis of data to 2001 also suggested that the use of hospital orders on summary convictions appeared to be in long-term decline (from 159 such orders in 1990 and 145 in 1991, to 82 in 2001)[146]. In 2002, 108 such court orders were made, but the provisional figure for 2003 is 84. According to Bartlett and Sandland, the use of hospital orders for summary convictions are potentially a cause for concern, given that patients are

[144] Data source: Home Office *Statistics of Mentally Disordered Offenders* 1985 - 2004

[145] Data source: Department of Health *Inpatients formally detained under the Mental Health Act and other legislation,* statistical bulletins 1985 – 2004. Section 37(4) was listed separately by DH statistics bulletins between the years of 1986 and 1995/6. We have shown these uses in the total only, and so the graph shows a higher number of total uses between these dates than apparently can be accounted for by restricted and unrestricted orders combined.

[146] Bartlett P and Sandland R (2003) *supra,* p. 291.

likely to remain in hospital for much longer than the six months maximum sentence available to a magistrates' court. We are wary, however, of the implied equivalence behind this concern of hospitalisation and imprisonment. The decline in the use of hospital orders for summary offence disposals does not seem to have resulted in a concomitant rise in the use of community-based court disposals: over the 1990s there has also been an overall decline in the number of psychiatric probation orders made by the courts, although there was a rise from 584 such orders in 1999 to 699 in 2001. In 2002 the number of probation orders fell again to 550 (see figure 165, page 423 below).

5.88   However the details of these figures may be interpreted, it seems incontrovertible that there has been some level of decline in the diversion of mentally disordered offenders at the point of sentencing. Given the overall rise in the prison population (see paragraph 5.63 above) we are not confident that this decline is the result of diversion at an earlier stage of the criminal justice process.

Hybrid Orders

5.89   Section 45A of the 1983 Act provides a power for a 'hospital and limitation direction', which is a hybrid order allowing a Crown Court to impose a prison sentence upon an offender suffering from psychopathic disorder with a direction that he be removed directly to hospital and treated there as if transferred from prison. It was introduced by the Crime Sentences Act 1997, based upon proposals of a 1986 Home Office/DHSS working group (given qualified support in the Reed Report of 1994[147]), which were revived in the 1996 White Paper *Protecting the Public*[148].

5.90   Writing nearly a decade ago in response to the White Paper, (where it was suggested that hybrid orders might extend to all categories of mentally disordered offender and not just the legal category of 'psychopathic disorder'), Nigel Walker noted that 'until now hospital orders have been not a sentence but an alternative. This may not last.'[149] Professor Nigel Eastman, writing at the same time, argued that 'an instrument which was proposed [by the Reed Committee] to overcome a clinical problem in relation to psychopaths' had changed its logical focus, from a concern with questions of 'treatability', which only apply to use of the Act for the detention of patients with psychopathic disorder or mental impairment, to a more general grounding on issues of legal culpability and public safety'[150]. The Government's suggestion that hybrid orders could provide 'a punitive element in the disposal … to reflect the offender's whole or partial responsibility'[151] was widely questioned

---

[147]   Department of Health and the Home Office (1994) *Report of the Working Group on Psychopathic Disorder* (the Reed Report). The Reed Committee's main focus was the problem of the 'treatability' requirement in mental health detention offering a potential 'way-out' of custodial care in hospital for dangerous offenders who could claim to be untreatable.

[148]   *Protecting the Public*, 1996, Cmnd 3190; see also Home Office (1996) *Mentally Disordered Offenders: Sentencing and Discharge Arrangements*.

[149]   Walker, N 'Hybrid Orders' *Journal of Forensic Psychiatry* Vol 7 No 3 December 1996 469-472.

[150]   Eastman, N 'Hybrid orders: a revolution' *Journal of Forensic Psychiatry* Vol 7 No 3 December 1996 481-494

[151]   Home Office (1996) *Mentally Disordered Offenders: Sentencing and Discharge Arrangements.* Para 1.6

on the grounds that it was purportedly the aim of mental health disposals to divert the mentally disordered from punitive sanctions, and that the hybrid orders required clinicians to become involved in determination of punitive measures, advising on questions of criminal responsibility which is not a clinical concept[152].

5.91 In the event, the Crime (Sentences) Act 1997 only extended the new hybrid order's reach to the detention of patients with psychopathic disorder and the Home Office guidance on its use made no specific reference to criminal 'responsibility', instead suggesting that the disposal was appropriate either where the other provisions of the 1997 Act would require an automatic life-sentence for a mentally disordered offender who required hospital treatment, or where it would be 'the most effective way to protect the public from further harm'[153]. It is arguable that this advice, whilst it avoids explicit mention of 'responsibility' or 'culpability', does not alter the fact that the policy of hybrid orders is grounded upon the policy decision that some mental health disposals must be backed up with a power of punitive detention to be exercised in circumstances when the requirement for therapeutic detention ends (whether due to its success or failure) before the patient's tariff expires. The very notion of that a mentally disordered offender could have a sentence 'tariff' rests upon the presumption that criminal responsibility, even if diminished by mental disorder, is not to go unpunished.

5.92 It should be a matter of concern to Government that this presumption (which we do not dismiss as necessarily misconstrued) must be applied to a legal framework whose concept of criminal responsibility is based upon a cognitive test established in the early-Victorian era. We discuss the legal concept of insanity and the 1843 *M'Naghten* rules that still govern that concept today at paragraph 5.22 *et seq* above.

5.93 Hybrid orders have not proved popular with the UK courts. Home Office figures suggest that the courts have exercised their power to impose hybrid orders in a dozen cases between 2000 and 2003, at a rate of three or four each year (with no recorded uses prior to 2000)[154]. The reason for their limited appeal may well be that sentencing judges find s.37 hospital orders to be quite adequate for any disposal where they are left with the discretion to impose them: it would be helpful in this respect to know whether the hybrid orders of the last five years all result from instances where recent law on sentencing[155] would have otherwise required the imprisonment of mentally disordered offenders. Home Office figures suggest

---

[152] See Bartlett, P & Sandland R (2003) *supra*, pp.307.

[153] Home Office Circular 52/1997 para 3

[154] Home Office *Statistics of Mentally Disordered Offenders* 2000 - 2003; table 4. Department of Health statistics only count eight admissions to hospital under hybrid orders between 1997/98 and 2003/04 (*Inpatients formally detained in hospitals under the MHA 1983 and other legislation, England, 1993-94 to 2003-04.* Bulletin 2004/22, table 1). In Scotland, where hybrid orders are not limited to offenders with psychopathic disorder, (s.59A of the Criminal Procedure (Scotland) Act 1995 as inserted by s.6 of the Crime and Punishment (Scotland) Act 1997), published data on their use also indicates that the take-up of the power has been limited (between 1998 and 2000, their were two such orders, neither involving a psychopathically disordered patient: see Scottish Executive Central Research Unit (2001) *Mentally Disordered Offenders and the Use of Hospital Directions and Interim Hospital Orders*, Crime & Criminal Justice Research Findings no.56).

[155] i.e. Crime (Sentences) Act 1997, s.2; Powers of Criminal Courts (Sentencing) Act 2000, s.82; or CJA 2003.

that between 20 and 34 offenders whose classification included psychopathic disorder were given court orders under s.37/41 in 2003, compared to four uses of s.45A in that year[156].

5.94   The Courts may not see any need to use a hybrid order where a hospital order can be made under s.37. The statutory criteria for the use of hybrid orders under s.45A are identical to that of hospital orders under s.37[157]. In *R v Birch*[158] it was stated that 'even where there is culpability, the right way to deal with dangerous and disordered persons' is a restricted hospital order under s.37. *Birch* also confirmed the necessity, in the sentencing of mentally disordered offenders who are found to require custodial disposals, of considering and rejecting making an order under s.37 before giving any prison sentence[159]. As a hybrid order is a prison sentence with a hospital order attached, it can only be used where the Court determines that s.37 is for some reason not an appropriate disposal[160].

5.95   At Chapter 1.208 *et seq* above we discuss the judiciary's concern at the limitation of this power to offenders whose diagnosis includes psychopathic disorder, which means that mandatory sentencing may preclude offenders whose diagnoses fall into other legal classifications from immediate diversion to hospital. In May 2003 the highest UK court recommended that the scope of hybrid orders be reconsidered in the light of this concern[161]. Government has not yet used the powers afforded to it under s.45A to widen the scope of the hybrid order through regulations[162], but it did include an equivalent to the hybrid order in the draft Mental Health Bill 2004 which eschews any specific classification of mental disorder[163].

5.96   The potential widening of hybrid orders to all classifications of mental disorder therefore raises again the question of what is the purpose of a combined court order and prison sentence. Depending upon the practical effects of any 'treatability' requirement under a new

---

[156]   Home Office *Statistics of Mentally Disordered Offenders* 2002, 2003; table 4. It is difficult to be certain as to the exact number of offenders who may have had psychopathic disorder in their classification at the time of sentencing, as the statistics are grouped into categories that include 'mental illness with other disorder', many (but not necessarily all) of whom will have been classified with psychopathic disorder. The lowest number in our range represents those positively identified in these statistics as having psychopathic disorder within their legal classification; the highest number is that total added to the category 'mental illness with other mental disorders'. In 2002 between 17 and 32 offenders with psychopathic disorder were given court orders under s.37/41, compared to three uses of s.45A. The number of mentally ill offenders made subject to s.37/41 court orders in 2002 was 185; in 2003 this was 163. Over the two years at least 15 learning disabled offenders (who did not have concurrent legal categorisation of psychopathic disorder or mental illness) were detained under s.37/41. We are not aware of available statistical data or research that would indicate how many mentally ill or learning disabled offenders (who may have been eligible for hospital orders) were given mandatory life sentences and imprisoned during this period because s.45A does not extend to their legal categorisation.

[157]   Indeed the patient must be deemed treatable at the point of sentencing for the hybrid order to be imposed; see on this point Bartlett, P & Sandland R (2003) *supra* p.306-7 and para 5.96 above.

[158]   *R v Birch* (1989) 11 Cr App R(S) 202 (CA),

[159]   Bartlett, P & Sandland R (2003) *supra*, p.308 (this requirement does not apply in respect of mandatory sentences where the defendant is criminally responsible and fit to be tried (*R v Drew* [2003] UKHL 259). See Chapter 1.215 *et seq* above).

[160]   MHA 1983 s.45A(1)(b)

[161]   *R v Drew* [2003] UKHL 259. See Chapter 1.215 *et seq* above.

[162]   MHA 1983 s.45A(10), (11)

[163]   Draft Mental Health Bill 2004, clause 130.

Act[164], it might be argued that the Government's fears that patients with psychopathic disorder might obtain inappropriate discharge from detention based upon the 1983 Act simply by demonstrating their resistance to any form of 'treatment' should extend to any use of the draft Bill's powers for psychiatric compulsion, regardless of diagnosis. It is notable in this respect that both the current and proposed hybrid orders establish a treatability requirement at the point of their imposition[165]. However, under the 1983 Act, where an offender's 'treatability' (i.e. whether detention in hospital rather than prison is appropriate) is unclear, an interim hospital order under s.38 can provide authority for up to a year's assessment and treatment in hospital (whatever the legal classification of mental disorder) before the court makes a final disposal (which could be a hospital order, a custodial sentence or neither). It has been argued that the powers of s.38 (which were themselves amended by the Crime (Sentences) Act 1997 to extend the maximum duration of detention from six months to a year) were in themselves adequate to address problems with questionable treatability in psychopathically disordered offenders[166], and it may be that interim orders are used by the courts for this purpose. The draft Bill did not reproduce an equivalent authority to this power, but only provided remand powers of much shorter maximum duration (16 weeks). Given that interim hospital orders appear to be used in relatively significant numbers by the courts, we are unsure of the evidence-base for the policy decision to abolish them in the next Act[167].

5.97   Alongside our specific concerns that the current legal concept of criminal responsibility is inadequate for the role it plays in decisions to use hybrid orders, there are some practical concerns that need to be considered, especially if the scope of hybrid orders is extended to patients suffering from all forms of mental disorder:

- We are concerned that hybrid orders, if they are to be used at all, must not become the normative disposal for any mentally disordered offender who a court views as criminally responsible to some degree. Public policy should continue to emphasise diversion from punitive sanction and a health care model for the treatment of mentally disordered offenders that provides a socially humane response to their needs while recognising the needs of public safety. The shift of perception of mentally disordered offenders from 'patients who have committed offences' to 'prisoner/patients' should not be undertaken lightly by any humane society[168].

- The imposition of punishment alongside medical intervention, even if punitive detention remains only a possibility at the point that medical intervention will cease,

---

[164] i.e., in the 2004 draft Bill, a condition of hospital orders (and also the equivalent of hybrid orders) is that 'medical treatment is available which is appropriate in the person's case'. See, for example, clauses 116(4),130(5).

[165] MHA 1983, s.45A(2)(c); Draft Mental Health Bill 2004, clause 130(5).

[166] Eastman N & Peay J. (1998) 'Sentencing Psychopaths: Is the "Hospital and Limitation Direction" an ill-considered hybrid?' *Criminal Law Review* 93-108.

[167] According to Department of Health Statistics (Bulletin 2004/22, table 1) up to 192 interim hospital orders were made by the courts over the financial year 2003/04. The Home Office publish no data on interim orders, and the Department of Health's data does not differentiate their use from a general category that also includes s.44 (detention whilst a patient's case is moved to a higher court for the purposes of passing a restriction order) and s.46 (detention of servicemen), although neither of these other sections are likely to have substantial usage. Over the last decade, detentions in hospital under ss.38, 44 or 46 are recorded to average about 160 a year (DH Bulletins 2004/22, 1999/25; table 1).

[168] Eastman, N (1996) 'Hybrid orders: a revolution' *Journal of Forensic Psychiatry* Vol 7 No 3, 481-494

may undermine treatment compliance and effectiveness, by downgrading the attention that a patient pays to their disorder as the cause of their violence, and instilling a sense of 'doing time'. This may make hybrid orders counter-productive in reducing their overall effectiveness as public protection measures for all but unlimited sentences[169]. Patients who do not want to confront their problems may be offered an 'escape route' out of hospital into the prison system[170], where powers of psychiatric coercion would fall away; or the system may create a disincentive towards recovery where a patient fears transfer to prison.

- Many mental illnesses are chronic or relapsing in nature, with continuing disability even in the absence of florid symptoms. Once 'positive' symptoms of mental illness have been treated in hospital, there will be a dilemma as to whether the patient should remain in hospital (even if the continuing 'negative' symptoms would not really justify continued hospitalisation), or be sent to complete their tariff in prison, where their treatment is likely to be sub-optimal and where, for want of continued powers to enforce medication, there may be a recurrence of positive symptoms and a relapse into illness. In this way, hybrid orders could result in clinicians being reluctant to recognise mentally ill patients' readiness to move from secure hospital beds, and have the unintended consequence of increasing the hospital stay of patients beyond that which is clinically necessary[171].

- It is possible that the Tribunal, faced with determining whether to allow a patient's appeal against detention in hospital under a hybrid order, would be similarly unable to justify a decision that hospital placement was no longer necessary in the knowledge that such a decision could only result in a patient being sent to prison, where appropriate treatment might not be available, or where the general regime might cause a relapse in the mental disorder[172], when it would otherwise recommend transfer to lesser security or even community-based treatment. Similar concerns could be raised with Tribunals hearing the cases of prisoners transferred under ss.47 or 48 under the current law (and therefore this may be more of a matter of concern if hybrid orders become a widely-used form of court order). In this reporting period we have expressed our grave concerns to the Joint Committee on Human Rights and others that the MHRT was placed in a similar position when reviewing the detention in Broadmoor Hospital of a patient transferred from prison under the Anti-Terrorism laws passed in 2001 (see paragraph 5.123 *et seq* below].

5.98   It may be that the apparent need for hybrid orders is less consequential upon the require-ments of any specific group of mentally disordered offenders than it is upon the tensions and confusions of mental health and sentencing law:

- Whilst it may be the case that 'untreatable' personality disordered offenders pose a genuine social policy problem, it may be argued that it is the attempt to address this problem in the context of mental health legislation designed to provide a framework for compulsory treatment that has imported notions of punishment into that framework and thrown up many of the dilemmas and concerns that we highlight above. The attempt to provide a framework for preventive detention of untreatable personality

---

[169] *ibid.*

[170] MHAC (1995) *Sixth Biennial Report* 1993-1995 p.72.

[171] Eastman, N (1996) 'Hybrid orders' *supra.*

[172] Walker, N (1996) 'Hybrid Orders' *Journal of Forensic Psychiatry* Vol 7 No 3, 469-472

disordered patients will continue to distort the conception and treatment of all mentally disordered offenders under the Act, and we endorse the suggestion of the Joint Committee on the draft Mental Health Bill that the solution to this is to have separate legislation to manage such individuals[173].

- Looked at in the context of the need to divert mentally disordered offenders from prison, the hybrid order is only required to mitigate otherwise inhumane results of mandatory sentencing policies. It would be preferable to address problems with sentencing law directly than to allow them to distort the priorities of mental health law.

Recommendation 56: Parliament should be alert to the potential for Mental Health Bill proposals discussed above to undermine the principle of diverting mentally disordered offenders from penal custody. We recommend that the policy aims of Government regarding preventive detention of dangerous people are pursued through criminal justice rather than mental health law, as suggested by the Joint Committee on the draft Mental Health Bill.

(see also Recommendation 54 above)

The rise of restriction orders

No longer is the offender regarded simply as a patient whose interests are paramount…

Mustill LJ on the effect of restriction orders in *R v Birch* (1989)[174]

5.99   Within a year of its creation in 1919, the Ministry of Health became responsible for most powers over lunacy and mental deficiency that had previously rested with the Home Office. This rearrangement of Government departments has been described as 'an event of considerable symbolic significance [that] gave administrative expression to the view that lunacy was now, as far as the State was concerned, a matter of health rather than of public order.'[175]

5.100   The Home Secretary did not relinquish his claim on all psychiatric patients. For more than two centuries the English law has given exclusive powers to the Secretary of State over aspects of the treatment of some mentally disordered offenders[176]. Under the Mental Health

---

[173] Joint Committee on the Draft Mental Health Bill (2005) *Draft Mental Health Bill.* Vol 1, p.5.

[174] *R v Birch* (1989) 11 Cr App R(S) 202 (CA), p.211.

[175] Busfield, Joan (1986) *Managing Madness.* London, Unwin Hyman, p.317. This account is based upon Jones K (1960) *Mental Health and Social Policy*, 1845 – 1959. London, Routledge & Kegan Paul, p.99.

[176] See Mylan, D (2002) 'Casenotes: The Home Secretary's Referral Powers following *IH*' in the *Journal of Mental Health Law*, December 2002, p.308-312. Statute law passed in response to *Hadfield*'s Case (1800) 27 Howell's St. Tr. included the Georgian 'Act for the Safe Custody of Insane Persons charged with Offences' 39 & 40 George III Chapter 94. Hadfield was found insane after trying to assassinate the King.

Acts, the Home Office has retained control over a group of patients who, either having been transferred from prison or committed to hospital as a part of a court order, are made subject to 'restrictions'. The Secretary of State alone may determine whether a restricted patient may be granted leave of absence[177]; transferred from one hospital to another[178]; or discharged by the doctor who is nominally in charge of treatment[179]; and alone has the authority to recall a restricted patient to hospital from conditional discharge, although such a recall does trigger a right to a Tribunal hearing[180]. Both the Tribunal and the Secretary of State may discharge a restricted patient. That the Tribunal has rights of discharge over patients at all is a consequence of the European Court decision that the 1959 Act breached Article 5 of the ECHR by reserving the power to discharge restricted patients to the Secretary of State[181].

5.101 Restricted patients are thus exceptions to the assumption made in 1919 that mental health law is primarily a health measure. The symbolism of restriction orders is quite different: the question of public order (or at least public safety) is a consideration in the treatment of restricted patients that takes priority over health issues in the use of formal powers[182]. This was set out clearly by Mustill LJ in the judgment of *R v Birch* (1989), quoted at the head of this section of our report. In a practice note issued by the Court of Appeal in 1967 it was stated even more baldly:

> … a restriction order enables the Secretary of State to exercise the function … of a central authority which pays special regard to the protection of the public in controlling the discharge of dangerous patients. Apart from a restriction order it is inevitable that the hospital's first concern is the welfare of the patient and this does result in some cases in a patient who is subject to a hospital order alone securing his discharge earlier than he would do if subject to a restriction order. The Secretary of State might well feel that although the patient was apparently no longer in need of medical treatment a further period in hospital under observation was advisable or was required to guard against the possibility of a further relapse into crime[183].

Indeed the Home Office describes its own role in the management of restricted patients as concerned solely with the protection of the public from serious harm[184], and the Government response to the Joint Committee on the draft Mental Health Bill stated that:

---

[177] MHA 1983 s.41(3)(c)(i)

[178] MHA 1983 s.41(3)(c)(ii)

[179] MHA 1983 s.41(3)(c)(iii)

[180] MHA 1983 ss.42(3), 75(1)(a)

[181] *X v United Kingdom (Detention of a Mental Patient)* (1982) 4 EHRR 188

[182] It is notable, for example, that the law allows for less than absolute discharge of restricted patients who are found by the Tribunal to be no longer suffering from mental disorder (*R v Merseyside Mental Health Review Tribunal ex parte K* [1990] 1 All ER 694); although in an unreported case (*R v Mental Health Review Tribunal ex parte Cooper*, 14 February 1990), Justice Rose held that conditional discharge should be preferred over absolute discharge solely for therapeutic reasons and not simply because of the danger posed by a patient to others (see Jones, R (2004) *Mental Health Act Manual*, ninth edition, 1-830).

[183] *R v Gardiner* [1967] 1 W.L.R.464; 1 All E.R. 895; 51 Cr.App.R 187, CA (Crim Div), quoted in Walker, N. & McCabe, S. (1973) *Crime and Insanity in England*, Volume Two, p.94. Edinburgh University Press.

[184] Home Office Mental Health Unit (2005) *Guidance for Responsible Medical Officers; Leave of Absence for Patients Subject to Restrictions.* March 2005: introductory para, page 1; checklist of points, page 20.

the purpose of the Secretary of State's functions in respect of restricted patients is to provide an exclusively risk-management perspective on the management of dangerous offenders diverted from prison[185].

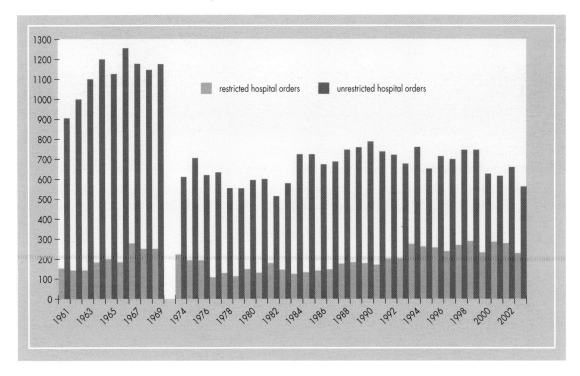

Fig 148: admissions of restricted / unrestricted patients subsequent to court orders under mental health acts and CPIA, England and Wales, 1974 – 2003[186]

5.102 The number of restriction orders made by the courts has increased over the lifetime of the 1983 Act (figure 148). The Court of Appeal's 1967 Practice Note following *Gardiner* urged restriction orders for 'all cases where it is thought the protection of the public is required' and for any committal to a High Security Hospital, and suggested that there should be compelling reasons explaining any decision not to issue a restriction order in cases of crimes of violence and more serious sexual offences, or where there is a history of mental disorder involving violent behaviour. This appears, from the available data, to have had an instant effect in increasing the percentage of restriction orders made by courts disposing of cases through use of the 1959 Act (figure 149). By the time of the implementation of the 1983 Act, restriction orders counted for about one in six court orders, but over the lifetime of the Act this proportion has risen to an average, over the last five years, of roughly one in three court orders including restrictions.

---

[185] *Government Response to the report of the Joint Committee on the draft Mental Health Bill 2004*, Cm 6624, response to recommendation 64 (p.32)

[186] Data source: 1961-69 from Walker, N. & McCabe, S. (1973) *supra* Table 6 (p96). 1970-76 from DHSS/Home Office (1978) *Review of the Mental Health Act 1959* (Cmnd 7320) Table 1.4, p 102; 1974-9 also published in *Reform of Mental Health Legislation* Cmnd 8405 Nov 1981, table 1.4. Otherwise Home Office *Statistics of Mentally Disordered Offenders*, 1985 – 2004. CPIA disposals in 'restricted' category only are included in data from 1974-2003. It is possible that this may exaggerate the proportion of restricted patients between 1974-2000 because there will have been a number of unrestricted CPIA disposals that will not show in the statistics. The research of Professor Mackay (see note 19 & 20 above) has shown 35 such unrestricted admissions between 1992 and 1996 subsequent to CPIA verdicts, which are not included in our data. We understand that data to be published by Professor Mackay may show an increase in the use of unrestricted hospital orders subsequent to CPIA disposals between 1997-2001.

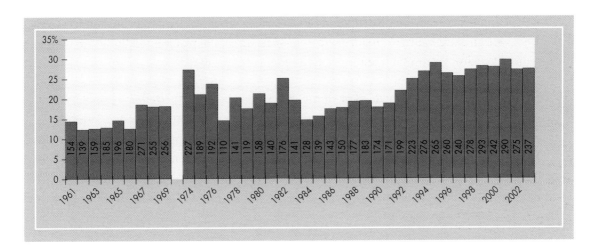

Fig 149: percentage of all hospital orders subject to restrictions, 1961-2003[187]

5.103 The data for resident populations of restricted patients in hospital (figure 150) shows a 40% rise since 1980. Although data limitations do not allow us to show for the whole period what proportion of this population is accounted for by transfers from prison (which should almost always involve restriction orders according to Home Office policy), we do have figures for the last fifteen years. Over this time an average of one in five restricted patients in hospital was a transferred prisoner, with the percentage of prisoners in the restricted hospital population peaking in 1995[188].

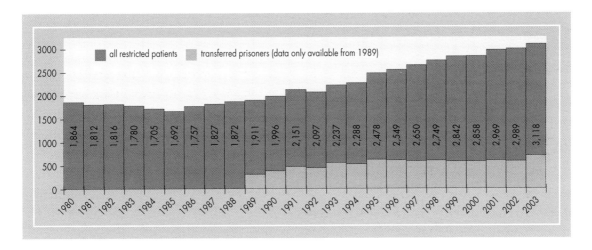

Fig 150: restricted patient population, England and Wales, 1980-2003 (showing proportion of transferred prisoners after 1989)[189]

---

[187] Data source: as for fig 148.

[188] Percentages of transferred prisoners in the restricted patient population in hospital 1989-2003:

1989	1990	1991	1992	1993	1994	1995	1996	1997	1998	1999	2000	2001	2002	2003
15%	17%	21%	20%	23%	22%	24%	22%	21%	21%	19%	19%	19%	18%	21%

Data source: as for fig 150 above. Although data in unavailable pre-1989, it should be noted that the 23% of transferred prisoners making up the 1993 restricted patient population would have been a significantly greater proportion than could have been possible in the first years of the Act's implementation. Government initiatives during the first decade of the Act caused a four-fold increase in the rate of transfer of convicted prisoners to hospital (from 70 patients in 1983 to 290 in 1993); and an almost five-fold increase in the rate of transfer of unconvicted prisoners (from 98 in 1983 to 486, or 47% of all restricted patient admissions, in 1993) (source: Home Office Bulletin *Statistics of Mentally Disordered Offenders* 01/95, para 6). Rates of transfer peaked in 1993-4 (see fig 136)

[189] data source: Home Office *Statistics of Mentally Disordered Offenders*, 1985 – 2004.

5.104   Restriction orders may be time-limited by courts at the sentencing stage, but rarely are: a 1997 study found that only about 5% of restriction orders have a limited duration, with a typical duration for time-limited restriction orders of three years[190].

5.105   Figure 151 below breaks down some of the data given above for the *resident* population of restricted patients to show the divisions by category of mental disorder. Whilst the usefulness of this data is severely compromised by the increasing proportion of unrecorded Mental Health Act categories in recent data, it does appear only to show a significant rise only for patients with mental illness. It is notable that the number of female patients with mental illness who are given restriction orders has almost doubled over the last fifteen years.

		1989	1990	1991	1992	1993	1994	1995	1996	1997	1998	1999	2000	2001	2002	2003	change
Mental illness	M	1,073	1,177	1,349	1,520	1,423	1,496	1,606	1,675	1,752	1,832	1,855	1,988	1,982	1,929	2,001	+ 86 %
	F	135	133	137	164	145	147	152	185	199	211	224	223	221	235	264	+ 96 %
Psy'path Disorder	M	345	337	334	336	339	326	346	350	356	343	350	348	343	337	347	+ 0.5 %
	F	92	88	91	83	80	80	79	77	73	71	78	76	72	79	86	- 6.5 %
Learning disability	M	189	178	171	169	128	138	144	153	157	164	182	198	200	192	190	+ 0.5 %
	F	19	19	21	20	14	12	14	14	15	13	16	16	16	19	19	0 %
Not known	M	21	30	38	39	129	127	125	116	126	125	136	139	145	173	182	+ 867 %
	F	0	2	2	2	18	17	16	16	16	17	16	15	23	25	29	+ 129 %
Total		**1,874**	**1,964**	**2,143**	**2,333**	**2,276**	**2,343**	**2,482**	**2,586**	**2,694**	**2,776**	**2,857**	**3,003**	**3,002**	**2,989**	**3,118**	**+ 166 %**

Fig 151: resident populations of restricted patients by category of mental disorder and patient gender, 1989 – 2003[191].

5.106   The rising use of restriction orders is not necessarily a reflection of a more cautious approach taken by the judiciary, although the final decision whether to impose restrictions does rest with the presiding judge in any particular case. There is some anecdotal evidence that increasingly doctors propose restriction orders so as to be relieved of an responsibility over the discharge of patients whom they consider to be dangerous. This is perhaps understandable, given the widespread perception amongst doctors that the culture of mental health enquiries is such that they are expected to not only predict but also take responsibility for the behaviour of any patient who is or has been in their care. In the case of *Ramadan*, the Royal London Hospital (St Clements) refused to take a s.37(3) patient unless he was made subject to a restriction order because in the view of clinicians he was 'very dangerous'[192]. Given that a restriction order's practical effect is simply to remove from such

---

[190]   Romilly,C. Parrott, J and Carney, P (1997) 'Limited Duration Restriction Orders: what are they for?' *Journal of Forensic Psychiatry* Vol 8 No 3 December 1997 562-572

[191]   Data from Home Office *Statistics of Mentally Disordered Offenders* 2003 and previous bulletins (generally table 8 in recent issues). In the above table 'mental illness' includes mental illness with other disorders; 'psychopathic disorder' includes mental impairment with psychopathic disorder; and 'learning disability' encompasses both mental impairment and severe mental impairment. Populations as at 31 December in each year.

[192]   *R v Thames Magistrates Court ex parte Ramadan* [1999] 1 Cr.App.R 386, para 4.

clinicians' discretion questions of the patient's leave, transfer or discharge from hospital, and to pass such responsibilities to the Home Office and/or (in the case of discharge) the Tribunal, it is difficult to see any other logic behind the hospital's position but that it did not want its clinicians to be held to account should the patient exhibit his dangerousness following any decision that they might make on 'security' matters.

The role of the Home Office

5.107 Whatever reason lies behind the rise in restriction orders, its result is that an increasing number of patients detained under Mental Health Act powers have their placement and certain aspects of their care regime ultimately determined by administrators acting on behalf of a politician rather than directly by a clinician. At paragraphs 5.123-31 we show an example, admittedly of rather unusual circumstances, which demonstrates why this has a potential to distort clinical priorities, even to the extent of providing counter-effective interventions in patients' mental health care and raising alarm in international human-rights organisations. We do not suggest, however, that our concerns regarding the placement of Anti-Terror Crime and Security Act detainees are in any way replicated across the whole spectrum of restricted patients. In many cases, the practical effect of a restriction order is rather obscure. Walker and McCabe suggested over thirty years ago that it was doubtful whether there was much point in a restriction order which specifies only that a patient must be detained in a particular hospital if that hospital is an 'ordinary' psychiatric facility, the security arrangements within which are beyond the control of the Home Office[193]. The increasing availability of more differentiated levels of secure provision (for example Medium Secure Units) since that time may have blunted this criticism, but it is the case that restriction orders are increasingly applied to patients who are not treated in high security (see figures 152-5 page 402/3 below), and in any event a restriction order is not required to place a patient at the level of secure provision that is clinically appropriate.

5.108 The Government's response to the report of the Joint Committee on the Draft Mental Health Bill 2004 claims that 'in law, the Home secretary is the primary avenue of discharge for restricted patients'[194]. In practice, as we show at figure 163, the Home Office now is instrumental in only a minority of decisions to conditionally discharge restricted patients (10% in 2003). From the passing of the 1983 Act, the Tribunal has been increasingly responsible for decisions to conditionally discharge patients under restrictions, and in 2003 was responsible for over half of all absolute discharges[195] (presumably in the face of Home Office representation that in its opinion such discharge is not yet appropriate[196]). If the Tribunal is now taking the bulk of the responsibility for the conditional discharge of restricted patients, and indeed overrules the Home Office in more than half of decisions to absolutely discharge

---

[193] Walker, N. & McCabe, S. (1973) *Crime and Insanity in England*, Volume Two, p.98.

[194] *The Government's response to the report of the Joint Committee on the Draft Mental Health Bill 2004.* Cm 6624 p.27.

[195] The Home Office has informed us that it was responsible in 2003 for 45 absolute discharges of patients who were already conditionally discharged. Home Office published data shows 96 absolute discharges in 2003.

[196] Were the Home Secretary not opposed to the conditional discharge of a restricted patient he or she would be under a logical, and presumably legal, obligation to grant such discharge him or herself rather than allowing the matter to go to the Tribunal.

patients, then the official role of the Home Secretary in determining leave, transfer or discharge of restricted patients may be argued to be an anachronism. We note that the Joint Committee on the Draft Mental Health Bill suggested that powers held exclusively by the Home Secretary under the current law (i.e. powers to approve leave or transfers) should be shared with the Tribunal under the proposals for a new Act[197]. We support this suggestion as being, in our view, necessary to allow the Tribunal to function properly in respect of its more active role in the management of patients' care-plans and the conditions of compulsion.

5.109 The current Home Office guidance on MHRT arrangements for restricted patients states that 'the MHRT has no statutory role to play in the pace of the patient's rehabilitation and as such have no statutory role in respect of matters such as transfer or community leave'[198]. We believe that it would be beneficial for the MHRT to have such a role, and indeed a number of the cases involving delays in moving restricted patients to clinically appropriate settings (see Chapter 1.131 *et seq* above) are in many professionals' view a good argument for giving the Tribunal wider powers. The Tribunal under the proposals of the draft Mental Health Bill 2004 would be given a statutory role in respect of matters such as the determination of whether compulsion is to take place in the community rather than in hospital, and we agree with the Joint Committee that this role should extend to 'restricted' patients, so that the judicial checks on deprivation of liberty for the treatment of mental disorder are unfettered and not beholden to political administration. It is notable from the Home Office's own guidance on its dealings with requests for leave of absence[199] that the Mental Health Unit, although primarily an administrative body that tasks itself solely with public protection (as we described at paragraph 5.101 above), is required nevertheless to weigh and judge clinical considerations in deciding whether or not to grant a doctor's request for a restricted patient's leave, and does so from information (including information about risks) supplied by the doctor seeking approval[200]. This arrangement may be a reassurance to some RMOs, whose ultimate responsibility is thus partially offset onto the Home Office's Mental Health Unit, but it is not rational. If decisions about the clinical management of patients are to be taken from the 'responsible' doctor it seems to us appropriate that they should then fall to a quasi-judicial rather than administrative body[201].

[197] Joint Committee on the Draft Mental Health Bill (2005) *Draft Mental Health Bill*. Vol 1. Para 277, rec 50. The MHAC fully endorses the submission of Dr Andrew Horne to the Committee on this matter (see *Draft Mental Health Bill*, Vol 3, p.1062-4).

[198] Home Office *MHRT Guidance* (October 2004, para 3.1); although we note that this guidance does allow that the Tribunal may make extra-statutory recommendations on such matters and that the Home Office undertakes to 'formally acknowledge' such recommendations (para 3.3).

[199] Home Office Mental Health Unit (2005) *Guidance for Responsible Medical Officers; Leave of Absence for Patients Subject to Restrictions.* March 2005, available from www.homeoffice.gov.uk. .

[200] *ibid.*,para 3.

[201] At the very least we would suggest that the Home Office's risk-assessment role should be informed by clinical perspectives, as with arrangements under the Scottish Office, where clinicians employed as psychiatric advisors to the Secretary of State are able to provide clinical expertise to decisions relating to essentially clinical matters, including risk assessment.

5.110 In response to consultation suggestions regarding the extension of the Tribunal role over restricted patients, the Government objected, rather oddly, that 'the Tribunal is not constituted to perform risk assessments, but to protect patients' rights'[202]. We do not see this distinction as tenable, especially in the structure proposed where a Tribunal is the gateway to compulsion. The Joint Committee chose to highlight against the Government response the submission of Lucy Scott-Moncrieff, who 'contended that the Home Office "had a shocking record of decision-making; it has no people working for it who are qualified to make risk-assessments, and yet it frequently and routinely rejects risk-assessments made by professionals and substitutes its own overestimation of risk" '[203]. The exclusively administrative make-up of the Home Office Mental Health Unit for England and Wales contrasts with long-standing arrangements in Scotland, where a clinician with forensic experience is employed as a 'psychiatric advisor' to provide clinical input into decision-making regarding restricted patients. We can see no reason why such input should not be a part of Home Office procedure for England and Wales.

5.111 The Government's own nascent policies on restriction orders undermine the justification for Home Office determination of conditions of compulsion in one further sense: the draft Bill of 2004 also suggested (to our considerable alarm) the creation of a 'civil' restriction order, where the Tribunal (rather than the Home Secretary) would reserve to itself decisions regarding discharge, leave or transfer in respect of unconvicted persons[204]. As such patients were likely to be defined in regulations as being at substantial risk of causing serious harm to other persons[205], it is difficult to see any public safety grounds for retaining the Home Secretary's role over similarly dangerous convicted persons. If, therefore, the role of the Home Secretary in determining the clinical settings of certain patients can still be justified, it must be because of their status as convicted offenders.

5.112 The simplest formulation of the Home Secretary's role, albeit not one that we expect to find favour with Government, is for the Home Office to play an advisory role only in decisions over leave, transfer or discharge of restricted patients, as was suggested by the Richardson Committee in 1999[206]. The Richardson Committee raised the possibility that, eventually, there may be a successful Article 5 challenge to the resting of powers relating to transfer and leave (which are essential precursors to discharge) in the hands of an executive arm of Government[207]. It also made the valuable but perhaps overlooked point that, under the current practical interpretation of the MHRT rules, it is expected that the Home Office will play an adversarial role in opposing applications to the MHRT for discharge[208]. This may lead the MHRT panel to attach less weight than they should to the information gathered

---

[202] Joint Committee on the Draft Mental Health Bill (2005) *Draft Mental Health Bill.* Vol 1, pages 93, 215.

[203] *ibid.*,page 92.

[204] Draft Mental Health Bill 2004 clauses 46(5),49(5)

[205] This formulation is used at clause 9(7) of the 2004 Bill to denote a special category of patients for whom compulsion will be applicable with special conditions.

[206] Department of Health (1999) *Review of the Mental Health Act* 1983; *Report of the Expert Committee.* November 1999; ('*Richardson Committee*') paras 15.17-23. See also Joint Committee on the Draft Mental Health Bill (2005) *Draft Mental Health Bill.* Vol 2, Ev 7 Q18-21 (Professor Genevra Richardson).

[207] *Richardson Committee,* para 15.21

[208] This impression is reinforced by the Home Office's *MHRT Guidance* issued in 2004.

through the Home Office's monitoring of an individual's case. It may also, as has been suggested by other observers, distort the presentation of the Home Office's knowledge about a patient[209]. It seems to us a sensible extension of the safeguards inherent in judicial processes to allow management of restricted patients through the Tribunal system under the next Mental Health Act. In our view it would be more appropriate for the Home Secretary to be an interested party to the Tribunal decision-making process, able to make representation at all stages of the Tribunal process, than for the Home Secretary to continue to share responsibilities for determining such matters as a rival authority to the judicial role of the Tribunal.

> **Recommendation 57:** the Review of the MHA 1983 should be taken as an opportunity to reconsider the role of the Home Secretary in decision-making concerning psychiatric detention and treatment.

The placement of restricted patients

5.113   Figures 152 to 155 below show the admissions and resident populations of restricted patients over the last 30 years. It is notable that there was at least a decade between the point at which the High Security Hospitals became the less-used destination for restricted patients compared to other psychiatric facilities, and the point at which restricted patients resident in facilities other than the high secure services outnumbered the restricted High Security Hospital population. In part, this is likely to be simply indicative of the relatively long periods that restricted patients spend in these facilities, so that changes in admissions are slow to be reflected in changes of population, although it may also reflect the rise in available medium secure unit places (including those in the independent sector) over the 1990s.

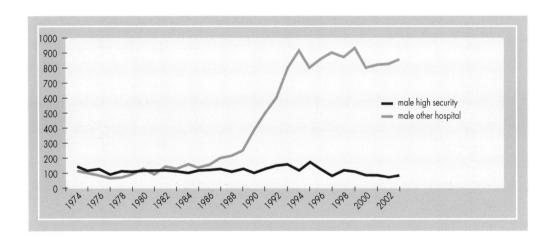

Fig 152: admissions of male restricted patients (court orders & prison transfers) to high security and other hospitals, 1974–2003.[210]

---

[209] See, paragraph 5.110 above: Ms Scott-Moncrieff has stated to the MHAC that she believes that the Home Office's knowledge about a patient is often presented to Tribunals with factors that may undermine the case for continued detention underemphasised of omitted.

[210] Data source for figs 152-5: Home Office *Statistics of Mentally Disordered Offenders* 1985 - 2003

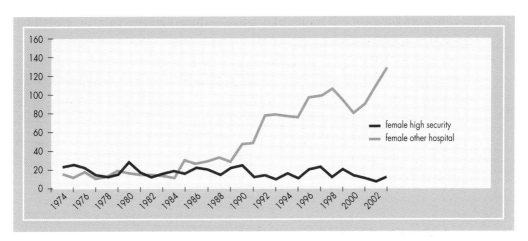

Fig 153: admissions of female restricted patients (court orders & prison transfers) to high security and other hospitals, 1974–2003

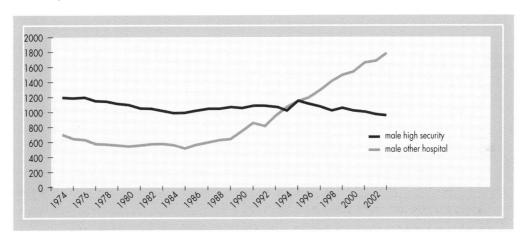

Fig 154: resident populations of male restricted patients in high security and other hospitals, 1974-2003

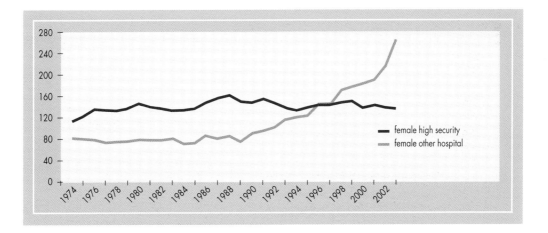

Fig 155: resident populations of female restricted patients in high security and other hospitals, 1974-2003

5.114 The general trend towards increased use of medium secure facilities rather than High Security Hospitals for the placement of restricted patients may be due not only to the rise in medium secure places available, but also to a changing profile in the type of index offence and clinical requirements of restricted patients. We provide some data on convictions in the next section of this report.

The convictions of mentally disordered offenders

5.115 Figure 156 below shows the proportions of restricted and unrestricted court orders under s.37, according to Home Office data, broken down by the offence for which the patient was convicted. We discuss some observations on the numbers of patients involved at paragraphs 5.82 *et seq* above.

		1995 %	1996 %	1997 %	1998 %	1999 %	2000 %	2001 %	2002 %	2003 %	average % 1995–2003
homicide	restricted	16.8	10.2	12.8	13.2	13	8.5	12.6	12.3	16.3	12.9
	unrestricted	0.8	2.0	1.7	1.2	0.8	2.8	3.3	2.9	3.9	2.2
other violence	restricted	37.9	30.2	40.3	35.7	35.2	34.6	29.3	30.9	29.1	34.6
	unrestricted	25.1	27.3	31.5	30.1	30.3	31.5	29.5	30.6	27.9	29.3
sexual offences	restricted	8.4	8.9	6.6	9.4	7.9	11.4	7.5	6.9	6.1	8.1
	unrestricted	6.9	6.3	6.0	6.0	6.7	6.4	6.8	5.3	7.0	6.4
burglary	restricted	3.0	4.9	2.8	3.0	1.6	2.4	2.5	1.5	1.5	2.6
	unrestricted	9.2	8.8	5.7	8.4	6.8	7.0	7.2	6.3	7.3	7.4
robbery	restricted	3.4	4.9	5.7	6.8	5.5	6.2	10.4	5.4	6.6	6.1
	unrestricted	4.9	5.7	4.1	5.6	5.0	5.8	7.0	5.9	7.5	5.7
theft/handling stolen goods	restricted	0.5	1.3	0.5	0.4	1.6	1.4	1.0	1.0	0.5	0.9
	unrestricted	8.2	10.3	8.1	7.2	9.7	8.0	5.5	5.6	5.4	7.6
fraud/forgery	restricted	-	0.4	-	-	-	-	-	-	-	0.0
	unrestricted	1.5	2.1	1.0	0.9	0.8	1.1	0.3	1.1	1.1	1.1
criminal damage (including arson)[211]	restricted	13.8 (10.8)	16 (10.7)	14.8 (10.9)	18.3 (12.8)	16.2 (13)	15.1 (12.3)	16.3 (15.1)	15.6 (12.7)	18.9 (15.8)	16.1 (12.7)
	unrestricted	15.3	13.1	16.4	17.2	18.2	14.4	16.1	14.3	16.6	15.7
other indictable or summary offences[212]	restricted	16.3	15.1	16.6	13.2	19.0	20.4	20.9	26.5	20.9	18.8
	unrestricted	28.0 (16.8)	24.4 (13.7)	25.4 (14.8)	23.3 (13.9)	21.6 (11.2)	23.9 (13.7)	24.3 13.4)	27.8 (16.4)	23.2 (15.0)	24.6 (14.3)
total number of hospital orders	restricted	203	225	211	235	253	211	239	204	196	220 (=100%)
	unrestricted	649	717	701	748	749	626	614	657	559	669 (=100%)

Fig 156 : percentages[213] of restricted and unrestricted s.37 court orders by offence 1995 – 2003[214]

---

[211] Totals for restricted patients' convictions for arson shown in brackets. Arson is not distinguished in the data available for unrestricted patients but is included in the total for that category.

[212] Totals for unrestricted patients' summary offences shown in brackets. Summary offences are not distinguished from indictable offences in the data available for restricted patients but are included in the total for that category.

[213] Figures for each offence calculated as percentages of the total court orders in each category (restricted, unrestricted): not as a percentage of all court orders. Therefore all restricted patients = 100%, and all unrestricted patients = 100%.

[214] Data source: HO Bulletins 20/96 - 16/04

5.116 For comparison, figure 157 below shows all admissions of restricted patients (other than those admitted subsequent to a court order under section 37) broken down by offence. This can only provide a rough comparison, and it should be noted that, unlike all the hospital orders in figure 156, a considerable proportion (possibly half) of the admissions listed in figure 157 may have been indicted on the offences categorised, but were not actually convicted of that offence[215].

	1995 %	1996 %	1997 %	1998 %	1999 %	2000 %	2001 %	2002 %	2003 %	average % 1995–2003
murder	10.5	7.9	8.9	7.7	7.3	8.2	8.9	7.6	9.7	8.5
other homicide	2.1	0.9	2.6	2	1.6	2.3	2.4	1.4	2	1.9
other violence	26.6	24.6	24.1	20.4	25.9	19.7	22.2	23.2	22.7	23.3
sexual offences	10.5	9	9.2	8.6	6.7	6.4	8	8.3	7.5	8.2
burglary	9	10.3	10.8	10.8	9.6	10.6	8.1	7.6	7.9	9.4
robbery	11.7	9.2	10.8	11.6	9.3	9.2	9.5	10.7	11.2	10.4
theft/handling stolen goods	2.1	3.2	2.4	1.6	2.7	1.1	2.1	1.9	2.4	2.2
fraud/forgery	0.5	0.6	0.3	0.5	0.5	0.3	0	0.6	0	0.4
arson	5.7	7.7	7.8	5.7	7.4	7.4	7.2	7.5	7.7	7.1
other criminal damage	4.6	6.4	5.4	7	7.3	6.4	6	7.6	4.8	6.2
other indictable and summary offences	16.6	20.3	18	24	21.6	28.5	25.5	24.9	24.1	22.6
Total number of hospital orders	801	847	877	853	861	752	749	799	883	825 (100%)

Fig 157: percentages of restricted patient admissions (other than s.37 hospital orders) by offence 1995-2003[216]

Reconvictions - hospital works?

'I feel good about my detention and medical treatment. The time out of the community has given me time to rest my brain and gather my thoughts, the medication is working to benefit my mental health. Since being in this hospital I have passed maths and English City & Guilds. Done woodwork, computer course, anger management, drug and alcohol misuse, a sign language course at college. I am at present doing art therapy and stress management, psychology.'

Richard Holmes, s.37/41 patient, Yorkshire

---

[215] It is not possible to distinguish remand prisoners from unsentenced prisoners in the transfer statistics available; but together these account for nearly two-thirds of all prison transfers during the nine years shown (i.e. 4,045 of 6,346 transfers). A much smaller proportion (e.g. less than 5% of restricted patient admissions during 2003 shown in fig. 157) result from findings under the Criminal Procedure Insanity Acts, which preclude conviction.

[216] Data source as for figure 156. Admissions in this table result from transfers into hospital of sentenced, unsentenced and untried prisoners; recalls from conditional discharge, disposals under the Criminal Procedure Insanity Acts, transfers from other jurisdictions and detention under section 45A. See note 215 above for data limitations.

5.117 There is a notable contrast between reconvictions for violent or sexual offences of restricted patients following release (usually on conditional discharge terms) and the recidivism of persons discharged from prison or sentenced to community punishments who match the restricted patients' criminal history and demographic characteristics. Such reconvictions are 10% less for restricted patients than for persons given punitive sentences (figure 158).

year of first discharge	total numbers of restricted patients first discharged[217]	number of persons reconvicted within two years of first release of sexual or violent offences[218]			
		reconvictions (number)	reconvictions (percentage)	expected % reconvictions[219]	% difference (actual-predicted)[220]
1986-1990	509 (470)[221]	6	1	11	-10
1987-1991	506 (467)	2	0	10	-10
1988-1992	566 (522)	2	0	11	-11
1989-1993	599 (547)	3	1	11	-10
1990-1994	608 (560)	4	1	11	-10
1991-1995	643 (585)	7	1	12	-11
1992-1996	680 (603)	10	2	12	-10
1993-1997	677 (594)	9	2	12	-10
1994-1998	695 (598)	9	2	11	-9
1995-1999	691 (573)	10	2	12	-10
1996-2000	732 (604)	10	2	11	-9
1997-2001	772 (639)	10	2	11	-9
1986-2001	1,1884 (1,659)	23	1	11	-10

Fig 158: restricted patients' actual and expected reconviction rates for violent and sexual offences[222]

Duties towards victims in relation to restricted patients

5.118 From July 2005, the diversion of a mentally disordered offender from the criminal justice system will no longer curtail duties towards victims of a sexual or violent index offence. Under the Domestic Violence, Crime and Victims Act 2004, local probation boards are

---

[217] Under s.66 of the Mental Health Act 1959 or ss.42 or 73 or the Mental Health Act 1983

[218] Violent and sexual offences are defined in appendix 3 of Criminal Statistics England and Wales 2002 as offences under the category of violence against the person and sexual offences. Briefly, these offences include homicide, endangering life, aggravated burglary, robbery, kidnapping, child abduction, wounding, cruelty or neglect of children, abandoning child under two years, concealment of birth, buggery, rape, indecent assault, incest, procuration, abduction, bigamy and gross indecency with children.

[219] The expected reconviction rate is the rate of reconviction that would be expected of discharged prisoners and those sentenced to community penalties who match the restricted patients on criminal history and demographic characteristics.

[220] The difference between the actual and predicted rates indicates whether the reconviction rate for restricted patients is above or below the level of reconviction expected of discharged prisoners and those sentenced to community penalties who match the restricted patients on criminal history or demographic factors.

[221] Figures in brackets represent number of patients matched against the Offenders Index and excludes those repatriated immediately on discharge.

[222] Data source: Home Office Bulletin 16/04, table 17a

required to identify whether a victim, or someone else acting for the victim (who might include the family of a victim who was killed or incapacitated by the offence), wishes to:

- make representations about whether a patient subject to a restriction order should be subject to any conditions if discharged from hospital, and if so, what conditions should be imposed; and

- receive information about any conditions to which the patient is to be subject in the event of his discharge.

Government has announced that it is considering ways in which victims of offences committed by unrestricted patients can be given information about the patient's management[223].

5.119   In practice, the provision of information and making representations on the victim's views will be done through a Victim Liaison Officer (VLO) of the probation board. The VLO will be under a duty to provide the above information to the victim if this is the victim's wish, and has discretion to provide 'such other information to the victim as the Board considers appropriate in all the circumstances of the case'[224]. Home Office guidance suggests that neither the statutory nor the discretionary element regarding information disclosure is intended to lead to the disclosure of any information covered by patient confidentiality[225]. Whilst this may be the case, it should be remembered that the requirement of medical confidentiality does not preclude disclosure of personal information without consent where this may be justified in the public interest on the grounds that failure to do so may expose the patient or others to risk of death or serious harm[226].

5.120   The statutory requirements regarding disclosure fall to the MHRT and Home Office as the bodies responsible for the patient's discharge and conditions of discharge. However, the Home Office guidance on the implementation of the law suggests that, where a victim indicates a wish to make representations or receive information about the patient, then the VLO will contact the patient's Responsible Medical Officer. The guidance suggests that 'it may be helpful for the [patient's care-team] to know the views of the victim of the offence' and that 'it is for the clinical team and the VLO to decide the level of contact between them e.g. whether or not the VLO should attend any meetings with the team about the case'[227].

5.121   There may indeed be circumstances, such as those outlined in the 2005 *O'Reilly* case (see Chapter 1. 36 *et seq* above) where the RMO wishes to contact a victim for information that may help with diagnosis or risk-assessment of the patient. It will be a help in such circumstances that the RMO will have a liaison point who should be able to ascertain the victim's views on being approached for information, although it is conceivable that attempts at an approach could be made in the face of reluctance on the part of the victim, as a justifiable infringement of their right to privacy.

---

[223] *The Government's response to the report of the Joint Committee on the Draft Mental Health Bill 2004.* Cm 6624 p.2

[224] Domestic Violence, Crime and Victims Act 2004 s.35(7)(c).

[225] Home Office Mental Health Unit (2005) *Duties to Victims under the Domestic Violence, Crime and Victims Act 2004: Guidance for Clinicians.* June 2005, para 8.

[226] General Medical Council *Confidentiality: Protecting and Providing Information.* April 2004, para 27. See also McHale, J (2000) 'Confidentiality and psychiatry: dilemmas of disclosure'. *Journal of Forensic Psychiatry* Vol 11 No.2 p255-259.

[227] *ibid.* paras 11, 12

5.122   We are very concerned at Government's supposition that any victim of a sexual or violent offence perpetrated by a mentally disordered patient should have an expectation of access and representation to that patient's care team. We expect clinicians and probation boards to ensure that any such expectations are exercised with due regard to the status of the offender as a patient rather than a prisoner. We do not foresee any situation where it would be appropriate for victims or their representatives to attend ward rounds and other clinical meetings, but it will be for all professionals involved to ensure that arrangements are not detrimental to the aims of hospital treatment (see also Chapter 4.124 *et seq* above).

Anti-terror detainees and the Mental Health Act

5.123   During this reporting period, four detainees under the Anti-Terrorism, Crime and Security Act 2001 (ATCSA) were transferred under the powers of the Mental Health Act 1983 from Belmarsh prison to high secure psychiatric facilities in Broadmoor Hospital. The care and treatment of these patients, whilst they remained subject to the 1983 Act, fell within the overview of the Mental Health Act Commission. We met with the patients in private and discussed their concerns and complaints, referring complaints to the hospital management for resolution through NHS procedures where appropriate. Shortly before the expiry of the ATCSA legislation in March 2005, three of the patients who remained in Broadmoor were released on bail (and concurrently released from the formal powers of the Mental Health Act). Following their release from detention under the 1983 Act, they were entitled to aftercare under s.117 of the Act, even when subject to control orders under the Prevention of Terrorism Act 2005. Whilst this report has been in preparation ten individuals – including at least one of the ex-Broadmoor patients – were retaken into prison custody. Those not granted bail by a subsequent Special Immigration Appeals Commission hearing remain under indefinite detention pending deportation arrangements. One has been returned to Broadmoor Hospital.

5.124   The case of one other transferred detainee, Mahmoud Abu Rideh, received considerable national publicity over the period. The Commission shared the concerns over the appropriateness of Mr Abu Rideh's placement in Broadmoor Hospital under ATCSA and the Mental Health Act that were also expressed by Mr Abu Rideh and his family; civil liberties organisations such as Amnesty International; some professionals from Broadmoor's clinical and managerial team, including his RMO; and (it was revealed in a report not published until June 2005) the Council of Europe's Committee for the Prevention of Torture and Inhuman or Degrading Treatment or Punishment (CPT). All of the above felt that the clinical requirements for Mr Abu Rideh's treatment would be better served in conditions of lesser security than Broadmoor Hospital. It is of great concern to us that detention in the high security environment may have been detrimental to Mr Abu Rideh's mental state[228].

5.125   The Secretary of State for the Home Department determined that Mr Abu Rideh should be transferred to Broadmoor Hospital in 2002. In exercising his powers relating to the transfer

---

[228] Mr Abu Rideh was granted refugee status (rescinded under ATCSA) in 1997. He had been diagnosed with post-traumatic stress disorder relating to detention and alleged torture overseas. It has been alleged that detention in conditions of high security and isolation at Belmarsh Prison have contributed to his mental deterioration by inducing flashbacks (Amnesty International (2002) *Rights Denied: the UK's Response to 11 September 2001.* September 2002, AI Index EUR 45/016/2002, page 15). The suggestion that detention in high security conditions was detrimental to Mr Abu Rideh's health was repeated by the Council of Europe's Committee for the Prevention of Torture (see above).

under the Mental Health Act 1983 of sentenced or unsentenced prisoners, and in determining appropriate levels of security in hospital accommodation for such transferred prisoners, the Home Secretary is entitled to consider issues unrelated to a patient's mental disorder or clinical needs – such as whether a patient requires high security provision for reasons unrelated to his illness[229]. The Home Office stated to the media that 'Broadmoor is an appropriate setting for Mr Abu Rideh, taking into account his clinical needs and the risk that he presents to the public' and that Mr Abu Rideh was 'detained in a High Security Hospital because he is a risk to national security'[230].

5.126   We wrote to the Home Office seeking reassurance as to the necessity of detention at this level of security on non-clinical grounds. We asked whether it was Home Office policy to insist on high security hospital accommodation for any hospital transfer under the 1983 Act of a person certified under Part 4 of ATCSA, or whether each case was considered individually. We received a response stating that each case was assessed on the basis of individual needs, and that the Home Secretary's initial assessment was reviewed regularly through the mechanisms of the Special Immigration Appeals Commission (SIAC) and Mental Health Review Tribunal (MHRT). We remained concerned, however, at whether the structures for formal review for detention under the Mental Health Act were hampered by restrictions on the availability of evidence and transparency of process that were inherent in the detention process under ATCSA[231]. We were not able to assuage our concerns as we were party neither to SIAC nor MHRT hearings in the case of Mr Abu Rideh, and our request to the MHRT for information on the Tribunal's ruling was declined. The Commission was clearly not entitled to examine the working of SIAC, and does not extend its monitoring to the functions of the MHRT (see Chapter 4.107 above). We did visit Mr Abu Rideh and monitored his care under the Act In hospital. In June 2004 we submitted our concerns over the automatic placement of ATCSA detainees in Broadmoor Hospital, and the degree to which the MHRT was

---

[229] Section 48 of the Mental Health Act 1983 allows the transfer of unsentenced prisoners to hospital at the Secretary of State's discretion, where the prisoner is suffering from mental illness or mental impairment of a nature or degree which makes it appropriate for him to be detained in a hospital for medical treatment and is in urgent need of such treatment. This threshold is considerably lower than that for detention in hospital under the civil powers of the 1983 Act, which also requires that treatment must be necessary for the health and safety of the patient or for the protection of others and that such treatment cannot be given unless the person is so detained.

[230] Quoted in Audrey Gillan 'Give me an injection and I will be dead', *The Guardian* 5/5/04

[231] In particular, we have in mind the criticisms of ATCSA Part 4 certification as a form of detention without charge or trial, without legal representation of choice and without disclosure of evidence to the accused. It seemed questionable to the MHAC whether the review mechanisms of the MHRT and SIAC could provide an opportunity for a fair challenge of decisions over the appropriate level of security provision. In part, this is simply because the patient and his legal adviser were not party to all of the evidence available to the judicial body, at least in the case of SIAC hearings. In the case of the MHRT, the judicial body itself could not be a party to all the evidence that was presented as justification of the patient's certification under Part 4 of ATCSA, and had no business in considering whether such certification is valid. We presumed that SIAC hearings regarding transferred prisoners do not adopt the evidential and procedural focus on clinical appropriateness of the MHRT. In theory, the two judicial bodies had discrete roles, with SIAC reviewing certification under ATCSA and the MHRT reviewing detention under the Mental Health Act 1983, but in reality it was not a simple matter to disentangle one legal mechanism, or the justification for its use, from the other, particularly when the justification for placement in high secure psychiatric provision was argued on non-clinical grounds.

fettered in considering that placement, to the Joint Committee on Human Rights' review of counter-terrorism powers[232].

5.127   It was revealed in June 2005 that the European Committee on the Prevention of Torture and Inhuman or Degrading Treatment or Punishment (CPT) had visited Mr Abu Rideh in March 2004 and had informed the UK Government that it believed his placement at Broadmoor Hospital to be clinically inappropriate. The CPT noted apparent serious deterioration of Mr Abu Rideh's condition and feared permanent damage. Following its visit the CPT requested his transfer as a matter of urgency to a different type of treatment facility[233].

5.128   The Government has categorically rejected the assertion of the CPT that the situation of ATCSA detainees, including that relating to the Mr Abu Rideh, 'could be considered as amounting to inhuman or degrading treatment' implying a breach of Article 3. The UK Government maintains that throughout their detention individuals received 'humane and decent treatment and the appropriate levels of medical and psychological care'[234]. We do not doubt that, with some exceptions in the case of staff members who were disciplined following substantiated complaints made by Mr Abu Rideh, the clinical and nursing staff at the hospital did indeed do their best to provide humane and decent care. We do question whether the placement should be described as having been an 'appropriate level' of care.

5.129   In the published response to the CPT, the Government stated that the Home Secretary's decision that a High Security Hospital placement was appropriate for Mr Abu Rideh 'was accepted by the MHRT ... an independent judicial body, which has powers under the Mental Health Act 1983 to discharge restricted patients'[235]. In our view this response is factually incorrect, for the following reasons:

(i)   The response does not make clear that the risk assessment upon which the Home Secretary justified a High Security Hospital placement was focussed upon his suspicion that Mr Abu Rideh was a 'terrorist' as broadly defined at s.21 of ATCSA[236], rather than upon his mental state and consequent need for particular levels of psychiatric care. In this sense, however, we concede Mr Abu Rideh was not treated differently to any other transferred prisoner, in that the security requirements for a patient's care need not be limited to clinical requirements alone, but must take account of wider security needs including those presented by the nature of the criminal charge or conviction against that patient.

---

[232] Joint Committee on Human Rights (2004) *Review of Counter Terrorism Powers.* Eighteenth Report of Session 2003-04. HL paper 158, HC 713, August 2004. pp. 63.

[233] Council of Europe (2005a) *Report to the Government of the United Kingdom on the visit to the United Kingdom carried out by the European Committee on the Prevention of Torture and Inhuman or Degrading Treatment or Punishment (CPT) from 14 to 19 March 2004.* CPT/Inf (2005)10. Strasbourg, 9 June 2005. Para 7.

[234] Council of Europe (2005b) *Response of the United Kingdom Government to the report of the European Committee on the Prevention of Torture and Inhuman or Degrading Treatment or Punishment (CPT) on its visit to the United Kingdom from 14 to 19 March 2004.* CPT/Inf (2005)11. Strasbourg, 9 June 2005. Para 15.

[235] Council of Europe (2005b) *supra* para 26.

[236] s.21 of ATCSA 2001 allowed the detention of suspects whom were believed by the Secretary of State to be a risk to national security, and were suspected by him either of (i) being involved in the planning or commission of terrorist acts, or (ii) of being a member of a terrorist group, or (iii) of having 'links with' a terrorist group. It would seem from the SIAC judgment of October 2003 that Mr Abu Rideh was detained under suspicion of 'having links' with terrorist groups, and that the main focus of such suspicion was his fundraising activities related to his charitable work.

(ii) However, Mr Abu Rideh *was* treated differently in comparison with other transferred prisoners (i.e. those detained under powers other than ATCSA) in that the allegations against him that would justify the level of security required for non-clinical aspects of his detention were neither revealed to the patient, his legal representative, nor the MHRT. Instead, the justification for high security care in Mr Abu Rideh's case was presented to the MHRT in the form of previous executive and judicial (SIAC) determinations over Mr Abu Rideh's certification as a suspected 'terrorist' within the broad meaning established under s.21 of ATSCA. More importantly, given the role that the Government has claimed for the MHRT in its response to the CPT report, the Secretary of State made representation to the MHRT arguing that the MHRT had 'neither jurisdiction, competence or expertise in relation to matters of national security and no remit to question the Secretary of State's belief over national security'[237]. The question of the appropriate level of security was therefore argued by the Secretary of State to be 'a matter for the Secretary of State and not the Tribunal' so that it was 'plainly inappropriate for the Tribunal in any way to comment upon the level of security which is appropriate for Mr Abu Rideh's detention'[238]. The solicitor acting for Mr Abu Rideh at his MHRT hearing has written that she was told on the day of the MHRT hearing by counsel for the Home Office that, if she attempted to argue that Mr Abu Rideh could safely be moved to a specialist nursing home which had been identified as potentially suitable for his care by his clinical team at Broadmoor Hospital, a Home Office witness would be called to give evidence that other allegations, including allegations of violent or potentially violent behaviour, 'might' have been made in closed session of previous SIAC hearings[239]. No information passed to Mr Abu Rideh and his representatives in connection with SIAC hearings had previously (including at the time of the SIAC hearings themselves) raised any allegations of violent behaviour, and the closed nature of the evidence prevented any questioning of whether such evidence existed and what it comprised of.

(iii) The Government response to the CPT report is disingenuous in implying that the MHRT's 'powers under the Mental Health Act 1983 to discharge restricted patients' were exercisable in relation to Mr Abu Rideh. The Home Secretary, having told the Tribunal that it was not appropriate for it to consider making any recommendations regarding transfer to lesser security hospitals, further argued to the Tribunal hearing that the question of whether Mr Abu Rideh should be discharged from hospital had to be approached 'by reference to the practical alternative': i.e. whether he should be returned to prison. The Tribunal duly accepted that 'the reality is that the Tribunal's decision could only result in the patient being returned to prison … or remaining in Broadmoor or some other secure hospital'[240].

5.130 We note that the CPT was 'not convinced' by the reply of the UK Government that Broadmoor Hospital was the most appropriate setting for Mr Abu Rideh in view of his clinical needs and

---

[237] Outline submission of the Secretary of State for the Home Department for Mr Abu Rideh's MHRT hearing of the 9 January 2004.

[238] *ibid.*

[239] *London Review of Books* 'Suspicion of Terrorism; Lucy Scott-Moncrieff on Mahmoud Abu Rideh, detained without trial'. 5 August 2004, p.22-24. the nursing home had been identified by the RMO in charge of Mr Rideh's treatment to provide him with appropriate treatment and care, and also meet the security requirements of the Home Office through preventing unsupervised access to telephones and providing escorts whenever he went out. Within three months of opposing such arrangements, the Home Office released Mr Abu Rideh on bail arrangements with little psychiatric support and an electronic tag as a security measure.

[240] Application of Mahmoud Abu Rideh, hearing 9 January 2004, Broadmoor Hospital. Reasons for the Tribunal's decision, para 12.

the risks he presents to the public[241]. The Committee concluded that the approach of the UK Government 'which appears to give little weight to therapeutic considerations – and thus to the patient's well-being – is not, in the opinion of the Committee, acceptable'[242].

5.131 The CPT recommended that UK authorities should take the necessary steps to ensure that Mr Abu Rideh, 'whose mental state has seriously deteriorated whilst in detention, benefits without further delay from the whole range of treatment required by his condition'[243]. Since all those detainees who were transferred to hospital under the Mental Health Act were entitled to appropriate aftercare upon their discharge, we are greatly disappointed at reports of poor provision and lack of support offered the men, exacerbated by the conditions of control orders attached to their release[244]. We are, of course, extremely concerned that men whose previous imprisonment led to serious mental disorder and transfer under the terms of the Mental Health Act were subsequently re-incarcerated on an indefinite basis whilst awaiting deportation.

The community treatment of mentally disordered offenders

5.132 A substantial proportion of formal arrangements involving mentally disordered offenders involve community-based supervision. Figure 159 below shows some figures from 2002, the latest year for which complete data is available.

	Number of times used in 2002	Outstanding cases as at 31/12/02
Psychiatric probation[245]	343	700[246]
Restricted patients conditionally discharged from hospital [247]	247	1,200[248]
Section 37 Guardianship[249]	26	6

Fig 159: community-based supervision of mentally disordered offenders.

5.133 The above data shows that the courts passed over 350 community-based orders for psychiatric supervision in 2002, usually with requirements that a patient resides in a specified place and receives psychiatric supervision with input from a social worker or probation

---

[241] Council of Europe (2005a), para 11.

[242] *ibid.*

[243] *ibid.*

[244] See, for example, Michael White and Vikram Dodd 'Teething troubles hit new terror act', *Guardian* 14/03/05; Audrey Gillan and Falsal al Yafai 'Control orders exposed', *Guardian*, 24/03/05.

[245] Home Office *Probation Statistics 2002* (published January 2004), table 5.3.

[246] This estimate based upon *Home Office Probation Statistics 2002*: the total number of outstanding probation orders in 2002 (116,859; table 5.3) against the total number starting probation service supervision (58,154; table 3.10). Probation orders can last up to three years: in 2002, the average length was 16 months, with 11% of community rehabilitation orders less than 1 year, 53% between 1 and 2 years, 33% between 2 and 3 years; and 2.5% the full three years (table 3.12). We have therefore estimated ongoing psychiatric probation orders to be about double the number of court orders for psychiatric probation over the year.

[247] Home Office *Statistics of Mentally Disordered Offenders* 2003 (published December 2004), table 16.

[248] See paragraph 5.137 below

[249] Department of Health *Guardianship under the Mental Health Act 2004* (published August 2004) table 1.

officer. Similar conditions would have been imposed upon the 250 restricted patients who were conditionally discharged from hospital into community supervision in that year. This is a significant proportion of all mental health disposals of offenders: by comparison, in 2002 the courts required under s.37 of the Act the hospitalisation of just 873 people.

5.134   In common with other 'criminal-justice' powers relating to the mentally disordered, these numbers are dwarfed by the use of formal psychiatric compulsion in civil cases. For example, the courts' use of Guardianship in 2002 amounted to less than 3% of all Mental Health Act Guardianship applications over the year[250].

> **Recommendation 58:** Research on mentally disordered offenders made subject to community-based orders for psychiatric supervision (whether under probation, guardianship or conditional discharge) could provide useful insight into the potential benefits and pitfalls of non-residential treatment orders under the Mental Health Bill proposals.

Conditional discharge

5.135   The Home Office or MHRT may conditionally discharge detained patient who is subject to a restriction order under ss.41 or 49. There are no statutory limitations to the conditions that may be attached to such discharges, and the power of the Home Secretary to recall a conditionally discharged patient to hospital is not linked to any breach in such conditions. There is no power to give treatment without consent, but a patient's compliance with treatment is usually a condition of discharge. Figure 160 below shows the gradual rise in use of conditional discharge over the last 30 years against the sharp increase in detentions of restricted patients.

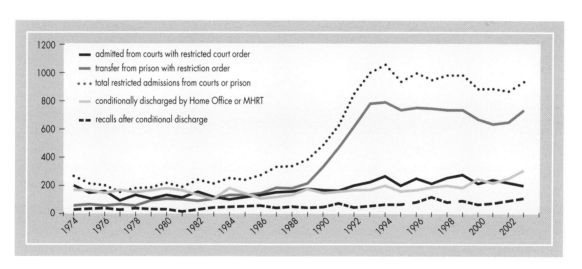

Fig 160: conditional discharge and recall against admissions of restricted patients, 1974 - 2003[251]

---

[250] *ibid.*

[251] Data sources: *Statistics of mentally disordered offenders, England and Wales.* Home Office Research & Statistics Directorate / National Statistics. 1974-5: 31/85, 1976-7: 28/88, 1978-9: 16/90, 1980: 29/91, 1981: 02/93, 1982: 04/94 (tables 3, 10), 1983: 01/95 (tables 3, 11), 1984: 20/95 (tables 3, 10), 1985: 20/96 (tables 3, 11), 1986: 20/97, 1987: 19/98, 1988: 7/00, 1989: 21/00, 1990: 22/01, 1991: 13/02, 1992: 14/03, 1993 - 2003: 16/04, (tables 3, 16).

5.136 Between 1994 and 2003 an average of approximately 200 patients were conditionally discharged from detention in hospital each year, against an average annual recall of about 80 conditionally discharged patients[252]. As can be seen from figures 160 and 161, the actual numbers of both conditional discharges and recalls have risen over this time, and are now at their highest level on record (295 conditional discharges and 118 recalls during 2003). It has been stated that recalls to hospital are always instigated by the supervising psychiatrist and not the Home Office[253]. We discuss the rise of restriction orders at paragraph 5.99 *et seq* above. The rate of successful appeal to the MHRT against conditions post-discharge[254] is not published.

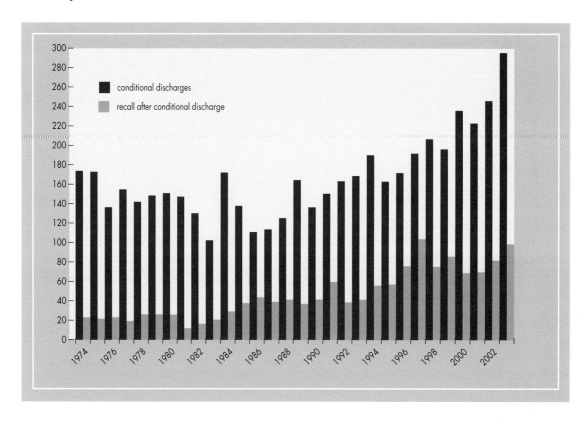

Fig 161: conditional discharges and recall to hospital of restricted patients, 1974 - 2003[255]

5.137 The number of conditionally discharged patients under active supervision in the community is estimated at 1,200 by the Home Office, with supervision undertaken by social services departments and the probation service, with the lead supervisor being chosen according to the needs of the patient, local knowledge among the agencies' staff [256] and of course service availability. The majority appear to be supervised by social workers: at the 31 December 2002, only 126 conditionally discharged patients were reported to be supervised by probation officers[257].

---

[252] Home Office *Statistics of Mentally Disordered Offenders* 2003, table 3

[253] Joint Committee on the Draft Mental Health Bill (2005) *Draft Mental Health Bill*. Vol 3. (Memorandum from Dr Andrew Horne, DM 308, para 2.3).

[254] MHA 1983 s.75

[255] Data sources: as for fig 160 above.

[256] Home Office *Notes for Social Supervisors*, 1997, para 12

[257] Home Office *Probation Statistics 2002*, table 5.3

5.138 Throughout the lifetime of the Act, as a result of a 1982 decision by the ECtHR, the Home Secretary has shared the power to discharge patients absolutely or subject to conditions with the Mental Health Review Tribunal (see paragraph 5.100 above). At figure 163 below we show that the MHRT has become, over the lifetime of the 1983 Act, the most frequent user of this power. We discuss the implications of this more broadly at paragraph 5.108 above. At figure 162 below, we show the periods spent in hospital before conditional discharges are granted.

period in hospital before conditional discharge	number of patients	percentage of patients
under 2 years	24	8.3
over 2 to 5 years	117	40.2
over 5 to 10 years	79	27.1
over 10 to 20 years	46	15.9
over 20 to 30 years	17	5.8
over 30 years	8	2.8
total	291	100

Fig 162: time spent in hospital prior to conditional discharge, 2003[258]

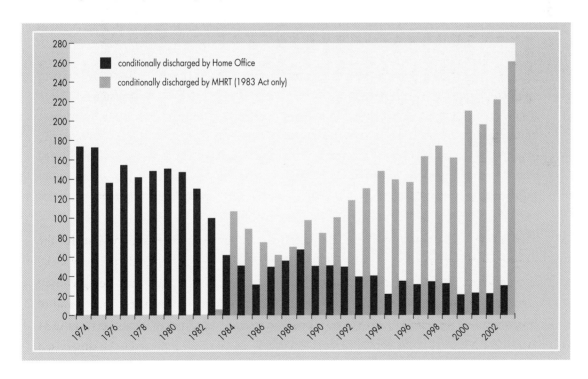

Fig 163: conditional discharge of restricted patients by deciding authority, 1974 - 2003[259]

---

[258] Data source: *Statistics of mentally disordered offenders, England and Wales.* National Statistics. Bulletin 16/04, table 16a. Total excludes 4 unsentenced or untried patients (all conditionally discharged after more than six months but without further data available). Period in hospital includes previous hospitalisations.

[259] Data sources: as for fig 160 above.

5.139 In this reporting period we have encountered conditionally discharged patients who are detained in hospital under the civil powers of s.3 of the Act. In two cases encountered in a London hospital we found little evidence that staff were aware of the patients' status (the conditions imposed upon the patient would be suspended but not cancelled by detention under civil powers) nor of contact having been made with the Home Office. Whilst we noted that the motivation in this example may have been to detain a patient using the least restrictive means appropriate, we were concerned that this could circumvent the risk-control mechanism of conditional discharge and the Home Office's supervisory function. We advised the hospital to ensure contact was made with the Home Office.

5.140 In its advice to supervising psychiatrists and social supervisors, Government indicates that it welcomes use of informal admission or civil detention to readmit a conditionally discharged patient in an urgent situation[260]. Where a supervising psychiatrist feels that such a patient's mental state or behaviour is putting the patient or others at immediate risk, then local action (including using powers under ss.2, 3 or 4 of the 1983 Act) should be taken, with the Home Office being informed without fail so that official recall to hospital can be considered[261]. The guidance for supervising psychiatrists suggested until recently that one broad criteria for recall was that 'it is generally inappropriate for a conditionally discharged patient to remain in hospital *for more than a short time* informally *or under civil powers of detention*'[262], but the revision of this guidance has altered this to suggest that

> if the use of civil powers is necessary to detain a patient or enable compulsory treatment to be given, immediate recall will almost invariably be appropriate to regularise the restricted patient's status under the Act[263]

The need for such regularity is not a specifically legal one. It was confirmed in *R v North West London Mental Health NHS Trust ex parte Stewart* [1997][264] that it was lawful to detain a conditionally discharged patient under s.3, and that Parts II and III of the 1983 Act are not mutually exclusive but may co-exist and operate independently of each other. The regularity required by the Home Office guidance is rather the reinstatement of the regime of control over a patient who is under its supervision and whose condition has deteriorated sufficiently to warrant civil detention. In this, however, the Government's guidance conflates civil detention criteria with such matters as may be indicative of an increase in 'the degree of danger which the particular patient might present' [265] leading to the need to recall. We trust that a degree of flexibility will be maintained in the operation of this policy.

---

[260] Home Office (1997) *Notes for the Guidance of Supervising Psychiatrists; Mental Health Act 1983 Supervision and After-Care of Conditionally Discharged Patients*, para 54

[261] *ibid.* para 50. See also *Notes for the Guidance of Social Supervisors; Mental Health Act 1983 Supervision and After-Care of Conditionally Discharged Patients*, para 69. These guidance notes were extant and available from Home office website as of October 2005, although contact information given for the Home Office and MHRT was no longer valid.

[262] *Notes for the Guidance of Supervising Psychiatrists*, para 52 (pre 2004 revision); 54 (revised version). Our emphasis.

[263] *ibid.* para 54, revised version.

[264] *R v North West London Mental Health NHS Trust ex parte Stewart* [1997] 4 All E.R. 871

[265] *Notes for the Guidance of Supervising Psychiatrists*

The role of Guardianship in the treatment of mentally disordered offenders

5.141 Guardianship Orders under s.37, like their civil equivalent, are designed to 'ensure that [an] offender receives care and protection rather than medical treatment'[266]. The Guardianship power enables the court to require the offender to:

- attend a specified place for medical treatment (but not to provide treatment in the face of a refusal of consent) or for occupation, education or training;
- to live at a specified place; and
- to ensure access is given to professionals and specified persons.

5.142 Guardianship is very little used in the criminal justice system, with Guardianship orders under s.37 accounting for an average of eleven court disposals each year over the last decade (figure 164 below); or just 3% of all Guardianship orders made under the Act overall. There is no evidence that, prior to the 1983 Act, Guardianship was used in the criminal justice system to any more significant extent[267]. This may because there is little to distinguish the powers available through Guardianship from those available under probation orders, which we discuss in the next section of this report.

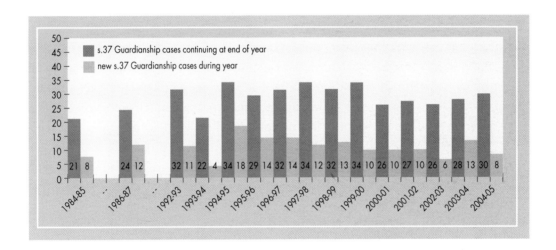

Fig 164: Guardianship as a court disposal, 1966 - 2004[268]

5.143 Under the proposals of the draft Mental Health Bill 2004, Guardianship powers would cease to exist altogether. Courts would have a disposal option of a non-residential treatment order in their place, although this has the potentially significant extra power of being able to authorise treatment without consent. In practice, however, it is unclear how significantly different such powers will prove to be. Although a patient who is expected to take

---

[266] Home Office Circular 66/90

[267] In 1968 it was stated that Guardianship Orders under s.60 of the Mental Health Act 1959 'have always been insignificant in numbers, averaging about 17 a year' (Walker, N. & McCabe, S. *Hospital Orders* in de Reuck, A.V.S. & Porter, R. [eds] (1968) *The Mentally Abnormal Offender*. London: J&A Churchill Ltd). Data from the 1970s suggests that this fell to between 5 and 10 uses per year during that decade (DHSS/Home Office (1978) *Review of the Mental Health Act 1959* (Cmnd 7320) Table 3, p.103).

[268] Data source: 1984-96 from Department of Health (2001) *Guardianship under the Mental Health Act 2000*. 1997-2004 from Department of Health (2004) *Guardianship under the Mental Health Act 2004*.

medication under current Guardianship powers cannot be forced to do so, defaulting on such treatment could instigate an admission to hospital if the conditions for detention (and subsequent deprivation of liberty) under civil powers are met. A patient required to comply with a non-residential treatment order under proposed powers would similarly need to be compulsorily admitted to a hospital or other healthcare environment for medication to be administered in the face of resistance, but such resistance itself would generally comprise the criteria for the deprivation of liberty that this admission would entail. To this extent, non-residential treatment orders involve an implied level of coercion that is not present in current Guardianship arrangements. For this reason we consider that probation will remain the nearest equivalent to current powers under s.37 Guardianship Orders under the legal framework proposed for the next Mental Health Act.

Psychiatric Probation

5.144   Probation has been an available option to courts for over a century, as a formal enactment of the ancient common law technique of binding-over to be of good behaviour[269]. Probation provides for an offender to remain at liberty but under the supervision of an officer of the court and liable, if not of good conduct, to be recalled for the court to consider further sentencing options. For just over half a century statute has allowed courts to require a probationer to undergo psychiatric treatment as a condition of his or her probation[270].

5.145   Treatment requirements may range from keeping psychotherapy or psychiatric clinic appointments to residence in hospital as an inpatient. As with all 'requirements' to undergo psychiatric treatment as conditions of probation, where a probationer is required to reside in hospital he or she does so technically as an informal patient (all probation orders require the consent of the probationer in principle)[271]. Although there are no formal sentencing guidelines or advice regarding the criteria for psychiatric probation, it can be generally assumed that psychiatric probation is usually considered appropriate in cases which would not warrant detention under Mental Health Act powers[272].

5.146   Courts have passed down probation orders with requirements for *residential* psychiatric treatment in an average of 54 cases each year for the last ten years of available data (1993

---

[269] Probation legislation may be dated from the Summary Jurisdiction Act 1879 and Probation of First Offenders Act 1887, although probation officers were not established until the Probation of Offenders Act 1907 or institutionalised until the Criminal Justice Act of 1925. Many subsequent Acts of Parliament (such as the Criminal Justice Acts between 1925 and 1993, the Powers of the Courts Act 1973 and the Crime and Disorder Act 1998) further developed probation practice, balancing (with different emphases at different times) the potentially competing aims of punishment and rehabilitation/treatment.

[270] The first explicit statutory power to require psychiatric treatment as a condition of probation was given by the Criminal Justice Act 1948, s.4. See Grünhut, Max (1963) *Probation and Mental Treatment.* London, Tavistock, pp5, and note 282 below.

[271] Research on attitudes of probationers (Mair, G. and May, C. (1997) *Offenders on Probation.* Home Office Research Study 167, pages 38 & 49) suggests that many are unsure whether their participation in certain activities whilst on probation was a condition of the order or on an entirely voluntary basis. It is common, of course, for probation officers to encourage clients to contact organisations or agencies other than those specified in any probation order requirement for help with their problems.

[272] See for example Gostin, L. O. (1977) *A Human Condition* Volume II, London, MIND, p195-7, and Walker, N. & McCabe, S. 'Hospital Orders' in de Reuck, A.V.S. & Porter, R. [eds] (1968) *The Mentally Abnormal Offender.* London: J&A Churchill Ltd, p.220.

–2002). Such residential orders amount to slightly less than one in ten of all probation orders over this time where psychiatric treatment is a requirement[273].

5.147 Probation with a requirement for psychiatric treatment is currently the second most common court disposal of cases where the court recognises the offender as suffering from a mental disorder warranting intervention (court orders under the Mental Health Act 1983 are used three times as frequently[274]). The extent of this use of probation has fluctuated over the period when the Mental Health Acts of 1959 and 1983 have been in force. For at least a decade prior to 1985, psychiatric probation seems to have been used more frequently as a court disposal than hospital orders under the Mental Health Acts. Figure 165 below compares the usage of psychiatric probation orders against court disposals under the two Mental Health Acts where we have available data.

5.148 In the mid-1980s psychiatric probation was described as showing an overall trend towards disuse[275]. This trend appears to have flattened out since that time, and the rate of probation disposals has remained relatively stable over the last ten years. A broader historical perspective (insofar as the limited availability of data allows) appears to show the following trends:

- *Non-residential psychiatric probation orders* gradually increased in number over the lifetime of the 1959 Act, then declined during the lifetime of the 1983 Act back to the levels similar to their original rate during the 1950s (see figure 166, page 424)[276]. Neither of these changes in usage can be confidently ascribed as an effect of the Mental Health Acts as alternative disposal mechanisms. Although the 1959 Act introduced Guardianship as an alternative non-residential court disposal to psychiatric probation, Guardianship orders by the courts do not appear to have averaged a frequency of more than 20 cases during the lifetime of either Mental Health Act (see figure 164). It is possible that treatment requirements that used to be classified as 'psychiatric' are no longer recognised as such (for example, since 1991 probation orders have been able to specify requirements for drug or alcohol treatment, and certain behavioural therapies (such as anger management etc) have been mainstreamed into wider probation activities).

- *Residential psychiatric probation orders* are now used much less than non-residential probation orders (see figure 166). Prior to the passing of the 1959 Act, residential orders were used about equally as often as non-residential orders, but they are now used in only one in ten probation orders that have a psychiatric treatment requirement.

---

[273] The average annual number of probation orders with requirement for psychiatric treatment over 1993 to 2002 was 578 (see fig 166, page 424).

[274] The average annual number of Mental Health Act Hospital Orders over 1993 to 2002 was 1,740 (fig 148, page 396), compared over the same period to an annual average of 578 probation orders with requirement for psychiatric treatment (fig 166, page 424).

[275] Gunn, J. & Taylor, P. [eds] (1993) *Forensic Psychiatry: Clinical Legal and Ethical Issues*. London, Butterworth Heinemann, p.784

[276] Although we should be cautious of assuming that this implies use of probation for the same reasons as pre-1959, or for the same groups of people. It is clear, for example, that probationary psychiatric treatment requirements were imposed upon persons convicted of homosexual acts or of attempted suicide: in 1953, 34 of the 636 probation orders resulted from homosexual offences involving adults ('where young men [aged] between 21 and 30 are strongly represented both in court cases generally and in the treatment group'), and 65 from prosecution of attempted suicides (Grünhut, Max (1963) *Probation and Mental Treatment*. London, Tavistock, pp.16).

When the 1959 Act came into force there was a slight fall in the frequency of psychiatric probation orders, which suggests that some cases which in the previous year would have received probation orders were instead given hospital orders under s.60 of the 1959 Act[277]. Although this dip in usage soon reversed, as both probation and hospital orders became more widely used in the 1960s, it remains likely that courts will consider making hospital orders under the Mental Health Act for any offender whose apparent requirement for psychiatric treatment warrants in-patient status. It does therefore seem likely that the rise in the use of MHA s.37 over the first decade of the 1983 Act may be linked to the fall in the use of probation requiring hospital residency.

5.149   There are a number of potential limitations of the probation as a vehicle for psychiatric compulsion:

- Perhaps most importantly, treatment requirements of probationers do not provide formal powers to provide treatment without consent. The probationer is therefore treated on an informal basis, and as such retains the right to refuse treatment. Failure to comply with the requirement of treatment – which might include leaving a hospital against medical advice, or failing to keep an outpatient appointment – can be regarded as a breach of probation, allowing the court to consider a different sentencing option or impose a further penalty. Courts are generally enabled to recognise refusals of treatment as reasonable if they are minded to do so: a refusal of consent is not an automatic breach of bail conditions[278].

- Probation orders extend for a maximum of three years (at the time of the 1959 Act's passing this was just one year[279]), after which time (if the probationer has not defaulted on requirements set) all control lapses.

- The medical criteria for deciding on a commitment to a psychiatric probation order are not, and never have been, very clear[280]. It is likely that psychiatric probation is generally used where detention under the Mental Health Act would be unjustifiable or unlawful, but there is nothing in the law to prevent it being used as an alternative to the Mental Health Act even where the conditions for detention under the latter are met. It is possible, given the likelihood that offenders considered for psychiatric probation are relatively 'low-risk', that the general lack of clarity dissuades courts from making specific conditions for psychiatric treatment where more general probationary conditions may appear to suffice. The possibility of requirements for psychiatric treatment is not mentioned in Government guidance for sentencers on community sentences[281].

---

[277] Walker, N. & McCabe, S. 'Hospital Orders' in de Reuck, A.V.S. & Porter, R. [eds] (1968) *The Mentally Abnormal Offender*. London: J&A Churchill Ltd. p.220

[278] *ibid.*, p.71

[279] Criminal Justice Act 1948

[280] Indeed the lack of clear definition of or criteria for 'psychiatric treatment' could be a factor in the apparent decline of psychiatric probation, and that apparent decline itself may simply be a reflection of changing terminology. Relatively recent legislation (i.e. the Criminal Justice Act 1991 and subsequent amendments) have increasingly made explicit powers to require treatment for drug and alcohol addiction, thus differentiating these requirements from 'psychiatric probation' where they once may have been classified. Similarly, it is not clear whether past definitions of 'psychiatric treatment' may have encompassed the sorts of 'offending behaviour programmes' (i.e. 'aggression replacement therapy'; 'integrated domestic abuse programme' etc) that are now no longer counted as such.

[281] See National Probation Service, *Information for Sentencers: A guide to the main community sentences for adults*, www.probation.homeoffice.gov.uk

- It is possible that resource limitations restrict medical recommendations for psychiatric treatment, given that such treatment is likely to take up out-patient places for which there are likely to be considerable pressure if not waiting-lists.

5.150   The MHAC has long been concerned at the hidden forms of coercion over informal patients (especially those who lack capacity to refuse treatment), and has raised the problem of *de facto* detention since its inception. Psychiatric probation orders (perhaps especially where these require residence in hospital) are a rather overt form of *de facto* detention or coercion of ostensibly 'informal' patients, with which the UK Government itself has not always been comfortable[282]. However, given the fact of the Court's involvement in the imposition of probation, probation does not share the inherent Article 5 problems relating to the absence of formal admission procedures for informal patients subject to *de facto* detention under the common law (see Chapters 1.1 and 3.3 *et seq* above). Furthermore, concern that probationers are thereby coerced into social treatment of unproven efficacy, or into medical treatment which may itself involve unpleasant side-effects, etc, must be balanced against the fact that to withhold the offer of probationary treatment on these grounds (i.e. that free choice is denied by the likelihood that the only other option may be prison) is to deprive potential patients of choice altogether[283]. The solution suggested by the authors of *Forensic Psychiatry* over a decade ago is not at all incompatible with the current Government agenda of patient empowerment and choice across all aspects of healthcare:

> the response to the risks of pressures must be impeccable practice in enhancing the choices and freedom of choice as far as possible.[284]

Such 'impeccable practice' in terms of probation would mean, for example, that:

> the roles and expectations of each participant in the probation contract should be very clear to each before an order is made, each potential client should be entitled to read all the probation and medical reports material to the decision, and to question the conclusions without prejudicing the support of the probation officer or psychiatrist.[285]

We hope, although we are no position to tell, that the influence of the Human Rights Act and the requirements of equality of arms before the law ensures that such impeccable practice, which mirrors the expectations for patient choice in other aspects of mental health services, applies to the courts' use of psychiatric probation.

---

[282] In 1932 the *Report of the Departmental Committee on Persistent Offenders* (Cmnd 4090) suggested that 'a certain number of offenders ['some cases of indecency and certain other sexual offences, magpie thefts and some minor peculations, as well as some cases of arson, violence and wilful damage to property'] might derive benefit from treatment while on probation' (paras 108, 117). But Home Office guidance (20 April 1934) stated that any demand for treatment by a probation order was incompatible with the voluntary character of the treatment of non-certified patients under the Mental Treatment Act 1930. Whilst the courts could not make psychiatric treatment a requirement of probation, it was however acceptable for the courts 'to take a lenient course' in suitable circumstances when arrangements had been made by friends or relatives for the offender to receive appropriate treatment. Enthusiasm for the psychological treatment of crime in the late 1930s put a stress on this restriction of court power, and on the eve of the war one London police court magistrate interpreted his powers under the 1907 Probation Act to extend to the setting of treatment requirements for a number of cases. Explicit powers were included in the Criminal Justice Bill of 1938, which led to their enactment in s.4 of the Criminal Justice Act 1948.

[283] Taylor & Gunn [eds] (1993) *supra* p.785

[284] *ibid.*

[285] *ibid.*

Psychiatric probation as a precursor of community treatment orders?

5.151 At paragraph 5.143 above, we suggest that probationary disposals with requirement of psychiatric treatment provide essentially similar powers of compulsion over patients as Guardianship under s.37 of the Mental Health Act, to the extent that the two disposals are probably interchangeable. Under the draft Mental Health Bill 2004 proposals, Guardianship would be abolished, although the courts would be enabled to give a non-residential treatment orders to patients falling within the scope of Mental Health Act powers. Given the very broad scope of the Bill as drafted in 2004, the power to make a non-residential treatment order would appear likely to be applicable to almost any conceivable case where Guardianship or psychiatric probation might be used in the current legal framework. We doubt, however, that psychiatric probation would even then fall into disuse. It may be that the conditions of psychiatric supervision of treatment are secondary in the court's reason for passing a probation order, in which case the Mental Health Act option may not be more attractive just because it is available. Also, we expect the conditions for compulsion under a future Mental Health Act to be tightened in light of the concerns of the Joint Committee on the draft Mental Health Bill[286], which may mean that psychiatric supervision remains used for persons who fall outside of the criteria for compulsion under Mental Health Act powers.

5.152 We are not aware that the potential overlap between probation and court-ordered non-residential treatment has been considered in any depth by Government. Without consideration of these issues it may be difficult to provide meaningful sentencing guidelines or protect against unintended consequences of changing legal structures (see recommendation 58, page 413 above).

---

[286] Joint Committee on the Draft Mental Health Bill (2005) *Draft Mental Health Bill*. Vol 1, chapter 3.

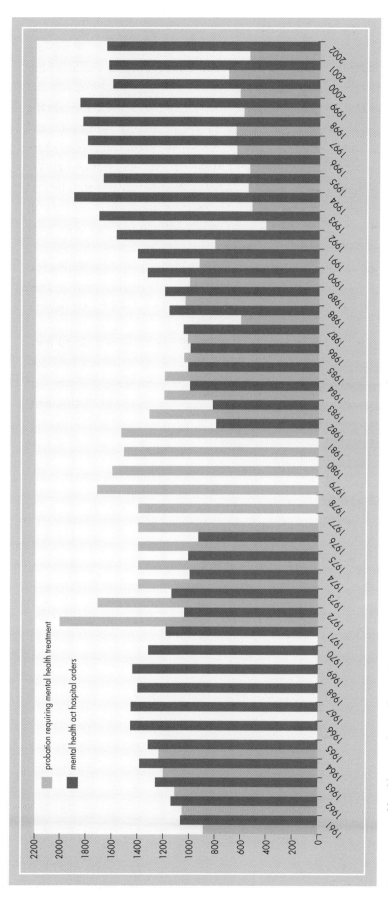

Fig 165: mental health court disposals – probation requiring mental health treatment and Mental Health Act hospital orders, 1961-2002 [287]

[287] Data sources (probation data unavailable for 1966 – 1971, MHA data unavailable for 1977 – 1981):

Psychiatric probation orders. 1961-65 from Walker, N. & McCabe, S. *Hospital Orders* in de Reuck, A.V.S. & Porter, R. [eds] (1968) *The Mentally Abnormal Offender*. London: J&A Churchill Ltd. p220, fig 1 (data read from graphic). 1972 – 1981 from Gunn, J. & Taylor, P. [eds] (1985) *Forensic Psychiatry: Clinical Legal and Ethical Issues*. London, Butterworth Heinemann, p784 (fig 19.1) (also read from graphic). 1982 – 1988 from Home Office (1992) *Probation Statistics England and Wales 1992* (table 2.7) (except for 1983 and 1984 totals, which were not published in official bulletins and are taken from Gunn and Taylor, *ibid* above). 1989 – 1991 from Home Office (1999) *Probation Statistics England and Wales 1999* (table 3.11). 1992 – 2002 from Home Office (2004) *Probation Statistics England and Wales 2002* (table 3.10).

Mental Health Act court orders. 1961-69 from Walker, N. & McCabe, S. (1973) *Crime and Insanity in England*, Volume Two. Edinburgh University Press. Table 6, p96. 1970-76 from DHSS/Home Office (1978) *Review of the Mental Health Act 1959* (Cmnd 7320) Table 1.4, p102. 1982 - 1991 from Home Office *Statistics of Mentally Disordered Offenders England and Wales 1992* (Bulletin 04/94), tables 6, 12. 1992 - 2002 from Home Office (2003) *Statistics of Mentally Disordered Offenders* England and Wales 2002 (Bulletin 14/03), tables 10, 18.

424

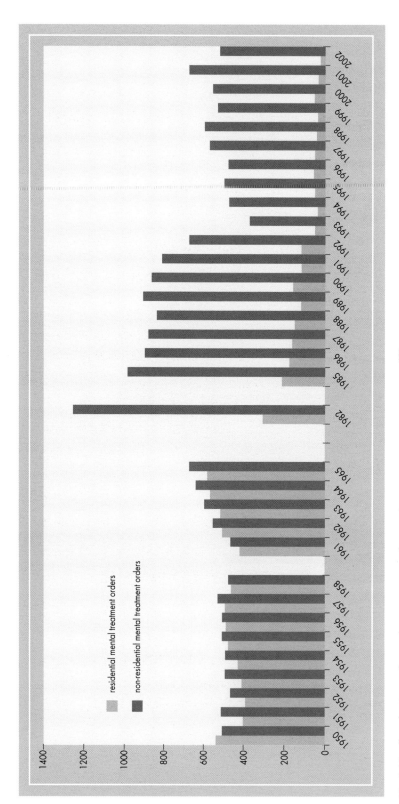

Fig 166: all probation orders with a requirement for psychiatric treatment, 1950-2002 [288]

288 Data sources as for figure 165 above, except 1950-58 from Grünhut, Max (1963) *Probation and Mental Treatment*. London, Tavistock. Table 1, p8. Post-1989 non-residential category includes 'mental treatment by/under qualified person', as well as 'non-residential mental treatment', but not other additional probation requirements (e.g. 'participate in specified activities'), as these are not described as having a mental treatment component (although in practice the distinction may be blurred).

Appendix A

Table of cases cited

Case reference   Paragraph in this report where cited

U.K. Cases

A Company (re) [1980] 1 CA 138.   1.103n

AR (by her litigation friend JT) v Bronglais Hospital and Pembrokeshire & Derwen
NHS Trust [2001] EWHC Admin 792.   1.32n

Attorney-General for Jersey v Dennis Peter Holley (Jersey) [2005] UKPC 23 (15 June 2005)
3 All ER 371.   5.47

Attorney-General v Great Eastern Railway Co (1880) 5 App Cas 473.   1.77n

Attorney-General v Neil Liam O'Driscoll, July 9 2003, JRC 117/2003 (Jersey). 5.17

Attorney-General v Jason Prior (Jersey).   5.22n, 5.47n

Attorney-General's Reference (no 34 of 1992) (1994) 15 Cr App R (s) 167.   5.41n

B v Croydon [1995] 2 WLR 294.   1.63n

C (adult refusal of treatment), Re [1994] 1 WLR 290.   3.38n

Dillon v O'Brien and David (1887) 16 cox C.C.245.   4.163

Director of Public Prosecutions v Pauline Zhao and John Zhao [2003] EWHC 1724. 1.84-6

E v Channel Four & Another [2005] EWHC 1144 (Fam).   3.29

Guardianship Order, Re McDougall or Muldoon [2005] ScotsSC 6.   1.13-9

Hadfield's Case (1800) 27 Howell's St. Tr.   5.100n

Lawal v Northern Spirit [2004] 1 All ER 187.   1.109n

M'Naghten's Case (1843) 10 C & F 200.   5.20-3, 5.92

MH v Secretary of State for Health & others [2005] UKHL 60.   1.87-93, 4.112-4

MP v Nottingham Healthcare NHS Trust [2003] EWHC 1782 (Admin).   1.165-6

Nadarajah v Secretary of State for the Home Department [2003] EWCA Civ 1768. 1.44n

Napier, Re Petition for Judicial Review [2004] ScotCS 100.   1.200-7

NHS Trust A v Mrs M [2001] Lloyds Rep. Med 27.   1.6n

Pickering v Liverpool Daily Post & Echo Newspapers plc [1991] 2 AC 370.   1.116n

Plymouth City Council v Her Majesty's Coroner for the County of Devon
(Plymouth & South West District) and the Secretary of State for Education and Skills
[2005] EWHC 1014 Admin.   1.225n

R (on the application of AL) v Secretary of State for the Home Department [2005]
EWCA Civ 02.   1.167-9

European Cases

US Cases

Appendix B

Mental Health Act Commission Members 2003 – 2005

Mr V Alexander

Dr A Ananthakopan*

Dr H Allen*

Mrs S Ali*

Mr S Armson

Mr M Atchia ~

Ms S Bailey*

Mr A Backer-Holst*

Mr R Backhouse ~

Ms H Bainbridge ~

Ms D Baldwin ~

Ms C Bamber*

Mr R Bamlett

Ms J Barnes ~

Mr A Barratt ~

Mr A Beaumont ~

Mrs G Beeching*

Dr a Sayal-Bennett*

Ms L Berry ~

Mr C Berry*

Ms K Berry*

Mr A Best*

Mr A Bevan

Ms L Bolter

Ms G Bodiaku-Bonsu ~

Ms A Bowden ~

Dr D Branford*

Mrs V Bramley*

Ms H Bramley ~

Ms S Brindle*

Mr R Brown

Mrs J Buckley ~

Mr B Burke

Mr P Callaghan ~

Mrs S Campbell W

Ms M Casewell*

Ms P Chadderton ~

Mrs B Chaffy*

Mr C Chambers ~

Ms P Chann*

Mr H Chapman*

Ms Noelle Chesworth

Ms E Cioffi ~

Mr F Cofie

Ms L Collins ~

Ms S Cookson ~

Mrs A Cooney*

Ms M Coombs ~

Mr B Commons ~

Ms A de la Cour ~

Ms S Cragg*

Mrs V Cranwell ~

Ms J Creek ~

Ms L Critchley ~

Ms J Croton

Mrs Ann Curno+ NED

Ms S Dare

Dr C Davies*w

Mr H Davies*w

Ms A Davison ~

Mr Barry Delaney+

Mrs S Desai*

Mr P De Ponte*

Mr M Dodds*w

Mrs M DosAnjos W

Ms K Doeser*

Mr R Dosoo

Mrs G Downham*

Mr K Dudleston ~

Mr A Drew

Mr R Earle*

Mr T Eaton

Mr N Errol ~

Mr W Evans ~ W

Mrs R Williams-Flew ~

Mr H Field

Mr M Follows

Mr M Foolchand W

Ms A Flower

Ms E Frost*

Mr S Gannon*

Ms M Garner*

Ms C Gilham*

Mr M Golightly*

Ms J Gossage

Ms P Gregory ~

Ms A Hall *w

Mrs P Douglas-Hall

Ms S Hallam*

Mr N Hamilton

Mr T Hanchen*

Miss C Harvey*

Mrs S Harvey*w

Mrs J Hassell*

Miss S Hayles

Ms K Herzberg

Ms P Heslop*

Mrs C Hewitt*

Mr D Hewitt*

Mr J Hewett ~

Mr D Hill*

Dr P Higson*w

Mr B Hoare*

Mr R Holdsworth ~

Mr D Holmes*

Mr W Horder*

Mr B Hormoz ~

Mrs B Howard*

Mr P Howes

Mr C Inyama*

Mr M Jamil*

Ms S Jarvis ~

Ms D Jenkins+

Mr R Jones W

Ms L Jones ~

Ms E Jones ~

Ms K Johnson ~

Dr O Junaid+*

Mr N Khan*

Mr S Klein*

Ms S Knight *

Dr S Knights*

Ms G Korgaonkar*

Ms A Lawrence*

Ms J Langan ~ W

Ms S Ledwith*

Mr P Lee*

Ms P Letts*

Ms H Lewis*

Mrs M Lloyd *w

Cannon F Longbottom

Ms E MacMin*

Ms M Madden*

Dr S Manjubhashini*

Mrs H Markson*

Miss L Marriot*

Mr Y Marsen-Luther

Mr L Marshall ~

Ms S Matthews

Mr C McCarthy*

Mr D McCarthy

Ms J McCallister*

Mr P McCormick*

Ms S McKeever*

Ms J McKenzie ~ W

Mr J McLean ~

Mrs S McMillan*

Miss N Mehta*

Mrs J Meredith

Ms L Messenger*

Ms L Metcalfe*

Mr A Milligan

Dr N Minton*

Mr P Moore*

Mr J Moran*

Ms G Morton ~

Mr P Moxley*

Mr M Murkin*w

Mr R Murphy*

Dr S Nagraj*

Ms M Napier

Mr M Naylor*

Ms A Navarro*

Ms M Nettle*

Mr I Newton*

Mr R Nichol*

Mr L Nicholas*

Mr J Nicholls ~

Mrs R Nicholson*

Mr N North

Mr M Ogley*

Ms J Oraka*

Dr R Parker*

Ms P Parma ~

Mrs J Patel*

Professor Kamlesh Patel OBE+

Mrs J Patterson*

Mr R Plumb*

Mrs S Plumb*

Ms L Pavincich*

Ms S Paxton ~ W

Mr T Peel*

Mr A Persaud*

Mr R Peters*

Mr J Price ~

Mr K Punamakuhzy ~

Ms V Rao ~

Mr S Ramrecha*

Mrs S Ramprogus*

Mrs L Relton ~

Dr G Roberts*

Ms H Roberts*

Mr R Robinson*

Ms C Robinson*

Ms N Sadique

Ms L Saunders*

Ms J Scudamore ~

Mr K Seacy*

Ms B Sensky*

Ms J Seres ~

Mrs D Shaw*

Mrs K Sheldon+

Mrs I Axt-Simmonds*

Ms C Smithson ~

Mr R Southern*

Mrs R Spafford*

Ms S Squires*w

Ms P Stafford*

Mr G Steele ~

Mrs P Stott*

Mr M Taylor*

Mr P Taylor*

Ms G Tipton*

Mrs H Thomas*w

Ms C Thompson ~

Mr P Thompson

Mr G Townsend*

Mrs C Trollope*

Ms J Turnbull*

Mrs M Turner*

Ms J Tweedie+

Mr P Veitch*

Dr G Wallen*

Mr J Walker*

Mr I Ward

Ms V Watson*

Ms K Whalley ~

Mr D Woodcock*

Mr M Wilce*

Mrs N Williams ~ W

Mr J Williams*

Dr A Williams ~ W

Mr B Williams*

Mr A Williamson ~

Mr B Windle*

Mr T Wishart*

Mr T Wrigglesworth*

Mrs M Wright*

Ms L Yearsley ~

Mr P Yeomans*

Key to symbols

Appendix C

Second Opinion Appointed Doctors 2003-2005

Dr M Abdurahman	Dr R Chitty	Dr T Fenton
Dr R T Abed	Dr J Christopher	Dr S Fernando
Dr P Abraham	Dr J Colgan	Dr M Forth
Dr D S Addala	Dr M Conway	Dr E Gallagher
Dr S W A A Ahmad	Dr M Courtney	Dr G R Gallimore
Dr M J Akhtar	Dr C A Cruickshank	Dr M George
Dr M Al-Bachari	Dr R Davenport	Dr S-E Goh
Dr M S Alexander	Dr I A Davidson	Dr M Goonatilleke
Dr M Alldrick	Dr C Davies	Dr G K Grewal
Dr S Ananthakopan	Dr M Davies	Dr J Grimshaw
Dr T Ananthanarayanan	Dr G H Dawson	Dr K C Gupta
Dr R P Arya	Dr K Day	Dr S Halstead
Dr D V Atapattu	Dr P B S Decalmer	Dr D M Hambidge
Dr G Bagley	Dr N Desai	Dr D C Hargreaves
Dr D Battin	Dr R Devine	Dr F Harrop
Dr K Balasubramaniam	Dr A Drummond	Dr G D Hayes
Dr C Berry	Dr G Dubourg	Dr M Hession
Dr J A O Besson	Dr K Dudleston	Dr P Hettiaratchy
Dr E Birchall	Dr D Dunleavy	Dr S Hettiaratchy
Dr R N Bloor	Dr J Dunlop	Dr R F Hill
Dr J Bolton	Dr A Easton	Dr G Hughes
Dr A C Briggs	Dr R Eastwood	Dr M Humphreys
Dr M F Bristow	Dr C M Edwards	Dr M Hussain
Dr A C Brown	Dr H Edwards	Dr K Hussain
Dr M Browne	Dr S Edwards	Dr G Ibrahimi
Dr A N Cade	Dr A El Komy	Dr S Iles
Dr W J Charles	Dr F J Eva	Dr W Jackson
Dr A Chaudhary	Dr G Feggetter	Dr J N Jain

Dr H James
Dr P Jefferys
Dr B John
Dr D Jones
Dr P A Jones
Dr S Joseph
Dr S H Kamlana
Dr S E Kanagaratnam
Dr G Kanakaratnam
Dr A Kellam
Dr J M Kellett
Dr L Kemp
Dr K Khan
Dr L Kremer
Dr N Lockhart
Dr M Loizou
Dr R P Londhe
Dr M R Lowe
Dr B Lowe
Dr E M Lucas
Dr G A M Luyombya
Dr S Malik
Dr H R Markar
Dr H Mathews
Dr J Mathews
Dr F McKenzie
Dr P S Meats
Dr G Mehta
Dr G Milner
Dr K Mosleh-Uddin
Dr N Muragananthan

Dr D Myers
Dr D W Nabi
Dr A C Nalpas
Dr G Nanayakkara
Dr C L Narayana
Dr T Nelson
Dr H Nissenbaum
Dr M O'Brien
Dr A E J Okoko
Dr R M Oliver
Dr S Olivieri
Dr S S Palia
Dr D Pariente
Dr J Parker
Dr A G Patel
Dr A Patel
Dr A Perini
Dr W B F Prothero
Dr E Quraishy
Dr D Rajapakse
Dr D Ramster
Dr B K Rao
Dr S Rastogi
Dr M A Razzaque
Dr J C Rigby
Dr G Roney
Dr M C Royston
Dr J Rucinski
Dr A Rugg
Dr C Ryan
Dr M Sabaratnam

Dr R Sagovsky
Dr G S Sarna
Dr A J Sheikh
Dr G Shetty
Dr N W H Silvester
Dr S B Singhal
Dr M J Smith
Dr A H M Soliman
Dr C Staley
Dr N Suleman
Dr R Symonds
Dr A W Talbot
Dr J E Tarry
Dr R Thavosothy
Dr R Thaya-Paran
Dr J Thomas
Dr R Toms
Dr H Verma
Dr N K Verma
Dr N A Wagner
Dr C M Wallbridge
Dr G Wallen
Dr A M Walsh
Dr D J Ward
Dr M Weller
Dr A M Whitehouse
Dr S Wood
Dr J Yermilli-Rao
Dr A Yonace
Dr E Yousif

Appendix D

MHAC Section 57 (Neurosurgery) Panel Members active 2003-2005

Mrs G Campbell
Dr E Chitty
Mr H Davis

Dr D Dunleavy
Dr P Jeffreys
Rev B Lillington

Mr A Milligan
Mrs M Morris
Prof F Oyebode

Appendix E

Mental Health Act Commission Publications

A full list of publications (including the Annual Report 2004/05; and responses to consultations etc) can be obtained from the MHAC secretariat or through the MHAC website. (www.mhac.org.uk)

Stationery Office publications of MHAC reports are available from the MHAC website or from TSO stockists:

Placed Amongst Strangers: the Tenth Biennial Report of the Mental Health Act Commission 2001-03 (2003) ISBN: 0-11-322652-7

Safeguarding children and adolescents detained under the Mental Health Act 1983 on adult psychiatric wards (2004) ISBN: 0-11-322685-3

Publications listed below are available from the MHAC website or direct from the Commission:

Patient information leaflets

Leaflets are available in English, Urdu, Bengali, Gujarati, Punjabi, French, German, Somali, Vietnamese, Cantonese, Mandarin, Tamil, Spanish, and Welsh.

Leaflet 1 - Information for detained patients about the Mental Health Act Commission

Leaflet 2 - Information for detained patients about consent to treatment - Medication

Leaflet 3 - Information for detained patients about consent to treatment - Electroconvulsive Therapy (ECT)

Leaflet 4 - Information for detained patients about how to make a complaint

Leaflet 5 - Information for patients about Neurosurgery for Mental Disorder (Psychosurgery) and the Mental Health Act Commission

Practice & guidance notes

Guidance for Commissioners on monitoring the use of seclusion

Mental Health Act Code of Practice - suggested annotations to reflect case law and other changes since publication

Voting and detained patients

Government statements on the European Court of Human Rights' judgement in HL v UK (the 'Bournewood case')

Guidance for Responsible Medical Officers following the PS case

Issues relating to children and minors detained under the Mental Health Act 1983

Guidance on the treatment of Anorexia Nervosa under the Mental Health Act 1983

Guidance on the administration of Clozapine and other treatments requiring blood tests under the provisions of the Mental Health Act

Use of the Mental Health Act 1983 in general hospitals without a psychiatric unit

General Practitioners and the Mental Health Act

Issues relating to the administration of the Mental Health Act in independent hospitals

Issues surrounding sections 17, 18 and 19 of the Mental Health Act

Nurses, the administration of medicine for mental disorder and the Mental Health Act 1983

Guidance for RMOs: R (on the application of Wooder) v Dr Feggetter and the Mental Health Act Commission

Guidance for SOADs: R (on the application of Wooder) v Dr Feggetter and the Mental Health Act Commission

Scrutinising and rectifying statutory forms for admission under the Mental Health Act

Guidance for Commissioners on consent to treatment

Taking a consistent approach to the use of CCTV in NHS and PVH mental health units

The House of Lords' Munjaz judgment (in preparation)

Copies of *MHAC Policy Briefings to Commissioners* (12 issues between 2002 and 2005) are also available from the MHAC website.

Appendix F

How to contact the Mental Health Act Commission

You can contact the Mental Health Act Commission at the following address:

Mental Health Act Commission
Maid Marion House
56 Hounds Gate
Nottingham
NG1 6BG

Tel: 0115 9437100
Fax: 0115 9437101
E-mail: Chief.executive@mhac.org.uk

Website: www.mhac.org.uk

Index

The numbers used in this index refer to paragraphs. The italic suffixes to paragraph numbers are as follows: *f* means figure; *n* means note; and *r* means recommendation. The figures and recommendations are given the number of the paragraph immediately preceding them. The notes are given the number of the paragraph in which the note number appears.

of MHRTs, 4.107; 5.126

of physical symptoms, 4.101, 101*f*

of section 61 reports, 4.58*r*

of section 136, 4.165

use of restraint, 4.219

on wards, 4.299, 299*f*, 299*r*

Multi-Agency Public Protection Arrangements, 4.149–50

murder/homicide, 5.26, 29, 33, 34, 35, 43–56, 48*f*, 49*f*, 53*f*

Nacro Mental Health Unit, 5.5–7, 7*f*

named professionals, 1.75–8

National Assistance Act 1948, 1.147

National Institute for Mental Health in England, 2.95; 4.100, 102*r*, 211

guidance, 4.140, 211*r*

National Patient Safety Agency, 4.305

National Service Framework for Mental Health, 2.95; 4.89

near-death cases, 1.230–2

nearest relatives, 1.25–34, 40, 88

negligence, 1.229

neurosurgery for mental disorder (NMD), 4.58, 78–82, 78*f*

NHS Security Management Service, 4.143, 144, 202, 212

NICE guidelines, 4.68–70, 211, 211*r*, 212, 216, 217*f*

nicotine withdrawal, 4.96

non-compliance, 3.39, 53, 60, 65; 4.16, 50 *see also* compliance with treatment

non-residential orders, 3.55–7, 59, 60, 66, 70, 71; 5.143, 151

notification, 4.220, 249–51, 279

notional s. 37, 5.66–70

nurses, 2.30–2

holding powers of, 4.25, 27

interactions with patients, 4.208, 209

responsibilities of, 4.46

statutory Form 13, 4.29, 29*r*

supervision of offenders, 5.80

training, 4.45

Nurses, Midwives and Health Visitors Act 1997, 4.29

obesity, 4.88

objectives, 3.86, 86*r*

observation, 4.300, 300*f*, 307

Obsessive Compulsive Disorder, 4.79, 83

offences, 5.115*f*, 116, 116*f see also* sexual offences; violent offences

offenders

dangerous, 5.36

mentally disordered, 1.208–21; 5.1, 3, 3*f*, 42, 44, 45, 115–16, 132–52, 141–3

right to vote of, 2.107

sexual, 5.39

supervision of, 5.3*f*, 39, 56, 80, 81, 81*r*, 137

violent, 5.39

officers, definition of, 1.106–7

Official Solicitor, 3.29

open verdicts, 4.282

outcomes

of MHRT hearings, 4.119, 119*f*

of second opinions, 4.67, 67*f*

overcrowding, 2.4, 11, 12, 25–9, 40

over-occupancy, 2.8, 10*f*

patients *see also* detained patients; informal patients

admissions, 2.17, 45; 5.113*f*, 116, 116*f*

age of, 4.66*f*

authority to obtain details, 1.35–40

basic needs of, 2.100

behaviour of, 4.202–78

from Black and minority ethnic groups, 2.40, 48, 50; 3.64, 66; 4.244, 283

'Bournewood', 1.9, 11

choice of professionals, 2.81

civil liberties and dignity of, 2.55

compliant, 1.1–19

control of, 3.6; 4.162, 213, 213*f*

death of, 1.227; 4.44, 44*f*, 300, 300*f*, 307, 307*f*, 312

elderly, 2.43; 4.219, 222

empowerment of, 3.47, 48; 4.91

gender of, 4.18–19, 18*f*, 64, 64*f*, 281, 281*f*, 301*f*, 302

inappropriately placed, 2.8

incapacitated, 1.1–19

interviews with, 4.255–60

involvement with care, 2.75, 76, 77

isolated, 4.260*f*

long-stay, 4.88, 92, 102

monitoring of, 3.75

out of area placements, 2.20–2, 40, 54

physical health of, 2.77

physically disabled, 4.105–6, 106*f*, 106*r*

protection of, 3.86; 4.254

re-detention of, 1.111–21

refusing consent, 1.45–51

representatives of, 1.7

responsibilities of, 3.47

responsibility for, 5.80

return to court, 5.80–1

return to prison, 1.190–2

risk to themselves, 3.14, 63; 4.14–15

sanitary facilities for, 1.202–5

section 2, 1.87–93

victims of crime, 4.148, 148*r*

views of, 4.278*f*

voluntary, 3.67–8; 4.4

women, 2.44–7

payment by results, 2.88–9

personal integrity, 1.69

personality disorders, 1.71

co-morbidity, 1.66

dangerous and severe (DSPD), 5.38